THE
WOOLLCOTT
READER

Also by Alexander Woollcott

WHILE ROME BURNS

THE WOOLLCOTT READER

BYPATHS IN THE REALMS OF GOLD

NEW YORK

THE VIKING PRESS

MCMXXXV

PUBLISHED DECEMBER 1935
SECOND PRINTING DECEMBER 1935
THIRD PRINTING DECEMBER 1935

THE WOOLLCOTT READER

ORIGINAL MATERIAL COPYRIGHT 1935 BY
ALEXANDER WOOLLCOTT

PRINTED IN U. S. A. BY QUINN & BODEN COMPANY, INC.

DISTRIBUTED IN CANADA BY THE MACMILLAN COMPANY
OF CANADA, LTD.

CONTENTS

CONTENTS

FOREWORD

BY ALEXANDER WOOLLCOTT

Assembled in this volume for you to have and to hold—not I hope too costly to have nor too unwieldy to hold—are certain of the minor masterpieces from the literature of my own day which have given me the deepest and most abiding satisfaction. Most of these works of my betters I have read not once but many times, and always with delight, and if they have anything further in common, it may be found in the tell-tale fact that, no matter how many copies I have acquired from time to time by purchase, inheritance, larceny, and other methods, there is never one left on my shelf when I am stricken suddenly in the night with a hunger to reread it. Thus for a quarter of a century I have been picking up stray copies of *A Doctor of the Old School,* which still seems to me the most moving and uplifting tale ever told in the English language. But I am so given to leaving it on boats and trains, or, as happens oftener, pressing it into the hands of some neighbor to whom I could wish to be more akin, that there is no copy left for me when I feel the need of it. It is nearly thirty years ago that I first read *My Little Boy,* and in that interval I must have bought at least fifty copies of that Danish beneficence. But the last one had wandered off on its eternal mission when first I began gathering material for this volume and, as it was out of print at the time, it took prodigies of emergency effort by several searching parties to find one for me in my moment of necessity. As for *Viva Mexico!* the enchanting book by that maddening underwriter, Mr. Charles Macomb Flandrau of St. Paul, it is in itself a traveling library which seemingly has a way of getting down off the shelf unaided and leaving the house while one's back is turned.

If you have read thus far in this preamble, you will have already detected in the editor's rolling eye the gleam of the proselytizer. It is quite true that, once in a blue moon, a book comes along which begets in me an impulse to fill a wheelbarrow with copies and trundle it from house to house until everyone in our street has one. Surely such an impulse is common enough to need no dissection. There comes to my mind a time some years ago when one of the great men of our country was giving me lodging for the night. During dinner a chance phrase revealed the fact that I had never read a certain novel by Henry James. This discovery brought to the face of my host a look of distress. Later, when I had said good-night and gone upstairs, I found that the book—it was *The Princess Casamassima*—had stealthily preceded me and was eying me with suspended judgment from beneath the lamp on my bedside table. If I did not let this pretty attention turn my head, it was because it was so clear that it was not I but the book our host was fond of. Here, I think, was no pity for, or even interest in, my poverty. He just couldn't bear having the book feel forgotten.

True, Thackeray said of *A Christmas Carol* that it came to every man and woman who read it as a personal kindness. But you can pass it on without the discomfiting fear of seeming to be a dear, kind soul. Probably you are acting from the purely selfish desire to keep those who make up your immediate world like-minded with yourself. One of the most exhilarating spectacles vouchsafed in the A.E.F. was the occasional meeting on a muddy road in France of two homesick doughboys from the same home town, and something of the satisfaction which was theirs is repeated whenever two people discover that they have both grown up happily in the same book. Certainly the rest of the world is forgotten when two indurated Dickensians strike hands in an English pub, and I think it is true of most of the works collected in this reader that they have it in them to create a fraternity out of those who enjoy them. I would grudgingly admit that a man might dismiss even *A Doctor of the Old School* as indifferent stuff without thereby implanting in me an unshakable conviction that he was also a secret practitioner of lycanthropy and given, in the dark of the moon, to draining the hearts of babes for the chalice of the Black Mass. But I *could* say this of him. He is one I would avoid on shipboard and I would look for new quarters in another street if ever he took the house next to mine. Occasions might arise when I would want to strangle him. At least we would not have enough in common to make good neighbors.

Now that this collection is ready to go forth, I find that the happy zeal with which I started to assemble it is tinged with a belated uneasiness. Once I was rebuked by the president of one of our universities because, through some published endorsement of mine, he had bought at Christmas time for his presumably cloistered niece one of the more ruffianly yarns of Master Dashiell Hammett. Did I really wish it believed, asked the outraged uncle, that so coarse a work represented my taste in literature? I was happy to be able to reply that it did, indeed. And, adding that so did *Alice in Wonderland, Emma,* and *The Early Life of Charles James Fox,* I left him to deplore me as incorrigibly miscellaneous. Now, I would be content enough to come up for judgment as one who thought highly of all the works in this volume and deeply loved some of them. It is true that its table of contents seldom duplicates the lists of books with which our best minds are constantly electing to be wrecked on some desert island—that putative retreat which must now be suffering from over-population.

In those lists (besides indisputable and nourishing essentials like *Pride and Prejudice, Wuthering Heights,* and *War and Peace*), I do often find austere works of such orthodox classicism as fills me with a mutinous suspicion that they have been included from a sense of duty and will be taken, if at all, medicinally. Indeed, when faced with certain of the monumental works of the world's literature, I am affected as was a *cuisinière* of my acquaintance by the State of California, to which brightly pigmented commonwealth she repaired late in life to make her home. To her former mistress in the darkling and rain-drenched East, she reported her arrival by sending a florid postcard on which she had scribbled this message: "It's very beautiful here I don't like it."

Mind you, even I would not pretend that any of the miniature masterpieces here presented (nor indeed all of them put together) is any match for such a glorious and filling work of genius as— let us say—*The Brothers Karamazov.* After all, the collection seeks merely the more modest and to me more congenial task of bringing together certain shorter flights of the imagination which have a way of getting out of print or are seldom found in the bookshops or for some other reason are hard to come upon. I suppose they are not of the full marketable length aimed at by the reprint publishers, who have a feeling, perhaps justified by bitter experience, that folks do like to get heft for their money.

Mrs. Winthrop Chanler once spoke of any anthology as being like a party. You are glad, she said, to come upon old friends of yours among the guests and filled with fury at finding present some few whom you dislike intensely. But as host at this party, I dread rather the reproaches of those who look about them in vain for some good friends of theirs. Before calling me to account, let them make sure that these friends were not invited. I am myself all too conscious of many vacant seats at this table. For instance, *A Lost Lady* by Willa Cather should certainly be here and so, of course, should *God and My Father* by Clarence Day and *An Habitation Enforced* by Rudyard Kipling. They are absent only because difficulties were encountered in obtaining what your radio announcer glibly refers to as "the permission of the copy-right-owners." I wanted to include *The Forest Lovers* by Maurice Hewlett because so many young people are growing up in the world without ever having heard of that glowing romance. But it proved to be too long. Of course a place above the salt belongs by every right to *Good-Bye, Mr. Chips,* but too many of you have read it too recently. Then, I wanted . . .

However, here is a five-inch shelf put into your hands by one who, having read less than some and more than most, has usually found his keenest enjoyment when striking off from the great highways. After all, there are bypaths in the realms of gold. This preface beckons you down some of them.

Bomoseen, Vermont
October 1935.

MARGARET OGILVY

by her son

J. M. BARRIE

TO THE MEMORY OF
MY SISTER JANE ANN

MARGARET OGILVY

HOW MY MOTHER GOT HER SOFT FACE

On the day I was born we bought six hair-bottomed chairs, and in our little house it was an event, the first great victory in a woman's long campaign; how they had been laboured for, the pound-note and the thirty threepenny bits they cost, what anxiety there was about the purchase, the show they made in possession of the west room, my father's unnatural coolness when he brought them in (but his face was white)—I so often heard the tale afterwards, and shared as boy and man in so many similar triumphs, that the coming of the chairs seems to be something I remember, as if I had jumped out of bed on that first day, and run ben to see how they looked. I am sure my mother's feet were ettling to be ben long before they could be trusted, and that the moment after she was left alone with me she was discovered barefooted in the west room, doctoring a scar (which she had been the first to detect) on one of the chairs, or sitting on them regally or withdrawing and re-opening the door suddenly to take the six by surprise. And then, I think, a shawl was flung over her (it is strange to me to think it was not I who ran after her with the shawl), and she was escorted sternly back to bed and reminded that she had promised not to budge, to which her reply was probably that she had been gone but an instant, and the implication that therefore she had not been gone at all. Thus was one little bit of her revealed to me at once: I wonder if I took note of it. Neighbours came in to see the boy and the chairs. I wonder if she deceived me when she affected to think that there were others like us, or whether I saw through her from the first, she was so easily seen through. When she seemed to agree with them

3

that it would be impossible to give me a college education, was I so easily taken in, or did I know already what ambitions burned behind that dear face? when they spoke of the chairs as the goal quickly reached, was I such a newcomer that her timid lips must say "They are but a beginning" before I heard the words? And when we were left together, did I laugh at the great things that were in her mind, or had she to whisper them to me first, and then did I put my arm round her and tell her that I would help? Thus it was for such a long time: it is strange to me to feel that it was not so from the beginning.

It is all guess-work for six years, and she whom I see in them is the woman who came suddenly into view when they were at an end. Her timid lips I have said, but they were not timid then, and when I knew her the timid lips had come. The soft face—they say the face was not so soft then. The shawl that was flung over her—we had not begun to hunt her with a shawl, nor to make our bodies a screen between her and the draughts, nor to creep into her room a score of times in the night to stand looking at her as she slept. We did not see her becoming little then, nor sharply turn our heads when she said wonderingly how small her arms had grown. In her happiest moments—and never was a happier woman—her mouth did not of a sudden begin to twitch, and tears to lie on the mute blue eyes in which I have read all I know and would ever care to write. For when you looked into my mother's eyes you knew, as if He had told you, why God sent her into the world—it was to open the minds of all who looked to beautiful thoughts. And that is the beginning and end of literature. Those eyes that I cannot see until I was six years old have guided me through life, and I pray God they may remain my only earthly judge to the last. They were never more my guide than when I helped to put her to earth, not whimpering because my mother had been taken away after seventy-six glorious years of life, but exulting in her even at the grave.

She had a son who was far away at school. I remember very little about him, only that he was a merry-faced boy who ran like a squirrel up a tree and shook the cherries into my lap. When he was thirteen and I was half his age the terrible news came, and I have been told the face of my mother was awful in its calmness as she set off to get between Death and her boy. We trooped with her down the brae to the wooden station, and I think I was envying her the journey in the mysterious wagons; I know we played around her, proud of our right to be there, but I do not recall it, I only speak from hearsay. Her ticket was taken, she had bidden us good-bye with that fighting face which I cannot see, and then my father came out of the telegraph-office and said huskily "He's gone!" Then we turned very quietly and went home again up the little brae. But I speak from hearsay no longer; I knew my mother for ever now.

That is how she got her soft face and her pathetic ways and her large charity, and why other mothers ran to her when they had lost a child. "Dinna greet, poor Janet," she would say to them, and they would answer, "Ah, Margaret, but you're greeting yoursel." Margaret Ogilvy had been her maiden name, and after the Scotch custom she was still Margaret Ogilvy to her old friends. Margaret Ogilvy I loved to name her. Often when I was a boy, "Margaret Ogilvy, are you there?" I would call up the stair.

She was always delicate from that hour, and for many months she was very ill. I have heard that the first thing she expressed a wish to see was the christening robe, and she looked long at it and then turned her face to the wall. That was what made me as a boy think of it always as the robe in which he was christened, but I knew later that we had all been christened in it, from the oldest of the family to the youngest, between whom stood twenty years. Hundreds of other children were christened in it also, such robes being then a rare possession, and the lending of ours among my mother's glories. It was carried carefully from house to house, as if it were itself a child; my mother made much of it, smoothed it out, petted it, smiled to it before putting it into the arms of those to whom it was being lent; she was in our pew to see it borne magnificently (something inside it now) down the aisle to the pulpit side, when a stir of expectancy went through the church and we kicked each other's feet beneath the book-board but were reverent in the face; and however the child might

behave, laughing brazenly or skirling to its mother's shame, and whatever the father as he held it up might do, look doited probably and
bow at the wrong time, the christening robe of long experience helped
them through. And when it was brought back to her she took it in
her arms as softly as if it might be asleep, and unconsciously pressed
it to her breast: there was never anything in the house that spoke to
her quite so eloquently as that little white robe; it was the one of her
children that always remained a baby. And she had not made it herself, which was the most wonderful thing about it to me, for she
seemed to have made all other things. All the clothes in the house were
of her making, and you don't know her in the least if you think they
were out of the fashion; she turned them and made them new again,
she beat them and made them new again, and then she coaxed them
into being new again just for the last time, she let them out and took
them in and put on new braid, and added a piece up the back, and
thus they passed from one member of the family to another until they
reached the youngest, and even when we were done with them they
reappeared as somthing else. In the fashion! I must come back to
this. Never was a woman with such an eye for it. She had no fashion-
plates; she did not need them. The minister's wife (a cloak), the
banker's daughters (the new sleeve)—they had but to pass our window once, and the scalp, so to speak, was in my mother's hands. Observe her rushing, scissors in hand, thread in mouth, to the drawers
where her daughters' Sabbath clothes were kept. Or go to church next
Sunday, and watch a certain family filing in, the boy lifting his legs
high to show off his new boots, but all the others demure, especially
the timid, unobservant-looking little woman in the rear of them. If you
were the minister's wife that day or the banker's daughters you would
have got a shock. But she bought the christening robe, and when I
used to ask why, she would beam and look conscious, and say she
wanted to be extravagant once. And she told me, still smiling, that the
more a woman was given to stitching and making things for herself,
the greater was her passionate desire now and again to rush to the
shops and "be foolish." The christening robe with its pathetic frills is
over half a century old now, and has begun to droop a little, like a

daisy whose time is past, but it is as fondly kept together as ever: I saw it in use again only the other day.

My mother lay in bed with the christening robe beside her, and I peeped in many times at the door and then went to the stair and sat on it and sobbed. I know not if it was that first day, or many days afterwards, that there came to me my sister, the daughter my mother loved the best, yes, more I am sure even than she loved me, whose great glory she has been since I was six years old. This sister, who was then passing out of her teens, came to me with a very anxious face and wringing her hands, and she told me to go ben to my mother and say to her that she still had another boy. I went ben excitedly, but the room was dark, and when I heard the door shut and no sound come from the bed I was afraid, and I stood still. I suppose I was breathing hard, or perhaps I was crying, for after a time I heard a listless voice that had never been listless before say, "Is that you?" I think the tone hurt me, for I made no answer, and then the voice said more anxiously, "Is that you?" again. I thought it was the dead boy she was speaking to, and I said in a little lonely voice, "No, it's no him, it's just me." Then I heard a cry, and my mother turned in bed, and though it was dark I knew that she was holding out her arms.

After that I sat a great deal in her bed trying to make her forget him, which was my crafty way of playing physician, and if I saw anyone out of doors do something that made the others laugh I immediately hastened to that dark room and did it before her. I suppose I was an odd little figure; I have been told that my anxiety to brighten her gave my face a strained look and put a tremor into the joke (I would stand on my head in the bed, my feet against the wall, and then cry excitedly, "Are you laughing, mother?")—and perhaps what made her laugh was something I was unconscious of, but she did laugh suddenly now and then, whereupon I screamed exultantly to that dear sister, who was ever in waiting, to come and see the sight, but by the time she came the soft face was wet again. Thus I was deprived of some of my glory, and I remember once only making her laugh before witnesses. I kept a record of her laughs on a piece of paper, a stroke for each, and it was my custom to show this proudly to the doctor every morning. There were five strokes the first time I slipped it into his hand, and when their meaning was explained to him, he laughed so boisterously that I cried, "I wish that was one of hers!" Then he was sympathetic, and asked me if my mother had seen the paper yet, and when I shook my head he said that if I showed it to her now and told her that these were her five laughs he thought I might win another. I had less confidence, but he was the mysterious man whom you ran for in the dead of night (you flung sand at his window to waken him, and if it was only toothache he extracted the tooth through the open window, but when it was something sterner he was with you in the dark square at once, like a man who slept in his topcoat), so I did as he bade me, and not only did she laugh then but again when I put the laugh down, so that though it was really one laugh with a tear in the middle I counted it as two.

It was doubtless that same sister who told me not to sulk when my mother lay thinking of him, but to try instead to get her to talk about him. I did not see how this could make her the merry mother she used to be, but I was told that if I could not do it nobody could, and this made me eager to begin. At first, they say, I was often jealous, stopping her fond memories with the cry, "Do you mind nothing about me?" but that did not last; its place was taken by an intense desire (again, I think, my sister must have breathed it into life) to become so like him that even my mother should not see the difference, and many and artful were the questions I put to that end. Then I practised in secret, but after a whole week had passed I was still rather like myself. He had such a cheery way of whistling, she had told me, it had always brightened her at her work to hear him whistling, and when he whistled he stood with his legs apart, and his hands in the pockets of his knickerbockers. I decided to trust to this, so one day after I had learned his whistle (every boy of enterprise invents a whistle of his own) from boys who had been his comrades, I secretly put on a suit of his clothes, dark grey they were, with little spots, and they fitted me many years afterwards, and thus disguised I slipped, unknown to the others, into my mother's room. Quaking, I doubt not, yet so pleased, I stood still until she saw me, and then—how it must have hurt her! "Listen!" I cried in a glow of triumph, and I stretched my legs wide apart and plunged my hands into the pockets of my knickerbockers, and began to whistle.

She lived twenty-nine years after his death, such active years until toward the end, that you never knew where she was unless you took hold of her, and though she was frail henceforth and ever growing frailer, her housekeeping again became famous, so that brides called as a matter of course to watch her ca'ming and sanding and stitching: there are old people still, one or two, to tell with wonder in their eyes how she could bake twenty-four bannocks in the hour, and not a chip in one of them. And how many she gave away, how much she gave away of all she had, and what pretty ways she had of giving it! Her face beamed and rippled with mirth as before, and her laugh, that I had tried so hard to force, came running home again. I have heard no such laugh as hers save from merry children; the laughter of most of us ages, and wears out with the body, but hers remained gleeful to the last, as if it were born afresh every morning. There was always something of the child in her, and her laugh was its voice, as eloquent of the past to me as was the christening robe to her. But I had not made her forget the bit of her that was dead; in those nine and twenty years he was not removed one day farther from her. Many a time she fell asleep speaking to him, and even while she slept her lips moved and she smiled as if he had come back to her, and when she woke he might vanish so suddenly that she started up bewildered and looked about her, and then said slowly, "My David's dead!" or perhaps he remained long enough to whisper why he must leave her now, and then she lay silent with filmy eyes. When I became a man and he was still a boy of thirteen, I wrote a little paper called "Dead this Twenty Years," which was about a similar tragedy in another woman's life, and it is the only thing I have written that she never spoke about, not even to that daughter she loved the best. No one ever spoke of it to her, or asked her if she had read it: one does not ask a mother if she knows that there is a little coffin in the house. She read many times the book in which it is printed, but when she came to that chapter she would put her hands to her heart or even over her ears.

WHAT SHE HAD BEEN

WHAT she had been, what I should be, these were the two great subjects between us in my boyhood, and while we discussed the one we were deciding the other, though neither of us knew it.

Before I reached my tenth year a giant entered my native place in the night, and we woke to find him in possession. He transformed it into a new town at a rate with which we boys only could keep up, for as fast as he built dams we made rafts to sail in them; he knocked down houses, and there we were crying, "Pilly!" among the ruins; he dug trenches, and we jumped them; we had to be dragged by the legs from beneath his engines; he sunk wells, and in we went. But though there were never circumstances to which boys could not adapt themselves in half an hour, older folk are slower in the uptake, and I am sure they stood and gaped at the changes so suddenly being worked in our midst, and scarce knew their way home now in the dark. Where had been formerly but the click of the shuttle was soon the roar of "power," handlooms were pushed into a corner as a room is cleared for a dance, every morning at half-past five the town was awakened with a yell, and from a chimney-stalk that rose high into our caller air the conqueror waved for evermore his flag of smoke. Another era had dawned, new customs, new fashions sprang into life, all as lusty as if they had been born at twenty-one; as quickly as two people may exchange seats, the daughter, till now but a knitter of stockings, became the breadwinner, he who had been the breadwinner sat down to the knitting of stockings: what had been yesterday a nest of weavers was today a town of girls.

I am not of those who would fling stones at the change; it is something, surely, that backs are no longer prematurely bent; you may no more look through dim panes of glass at the aged poor weaving tremulously for their little bit of ground in the cemetery. Rather are

their working years too few now, not because they will it so but because it is with youth that the power-looms must be fed. Well, this
teaches them to make provision, and they have the means as they
never had before. Not in batches are boys now sent to college, the half-
dozen a year have dwindled to one, doubtless because in these days
they can begin to draw wages as they step out of their fourteenth year.
Here assuredly there is loss, but all the losses would be but a pebble
in a sea of gain were it not for this, that with so many of the family,
young mothers among them, working in the factories, home life is
not so beautiful as it was. So much of what is great in Scotland has
sprung from the closeness of the family ties; it is there I sometimes
fear that my country is being struck. That we were all being reduced
to one dead level, that "character" abounds no more and life itself is
less interesting, such things I have read, but I do not believe them. I
have even seen them given as my reason for writing of a past time,
and in that at least there is no truth. In our little town, which is a
sample of many, life is as interesting, as pathetic, as joyous as ever it
was; no group of weavers was better to look at or think about than
the rivulet of winsome girls that overruns our streets every time the
sluice is raised, the comedy of summer evenings and winter firesides
is played with the old zest and every window-blind is the curtain
of a romance. Once the lights of a little town are lit, who could ever
hope to tell all its story, or the story of a single wynd in it? And
who looking at lighted windows needs to turn to books? The reason
my books deal with the past instead of with the life I myself have
known is simply this, that I soon grow tired of writing tales unless I
can see a little girl, of whom my mother has told me, wandering confidently through the pages. Such a grip has her memory of her girlhood
had upon me since I was a boy of six.

Those innumerable talks with her made her youth as vivid to me as
my own, and so much more quaint, for, to a child, the oddest of
things, and the most richly coloured picture-book, is that his mother
was once a child also, and the contrast between what she is and what
she was is perhaps the source of all humour. My mother's father, the
one hero of her life, died nine years before I was born, and I remember

this with bewilderment, so familiarly does the weather-beaten mason's figure rise before me from the old chair on which I was nursed and now write my books. On the surface he is as hard as the stone on which he chiselled, and his face is dyed red by its dust, he is rounded in the shoulders and a "hoast" hunts him ever; sooner or later that cough must carry him off, but until then it shall not keep him from the quarry, nor shall his chapped hands, as long as they can grasp the mell. It is a night of rain or snow, and my mother, the little girl in a pinafore who is already his housekeeper, has been many times to the door to look for him. At last he draws nigh, hoasting. Or I see him setting off to church, for he was a great "stoop" of the Auld Licht kirk, and his mouth is very firm now as if there were a case of discipline to face, but on his way home he is bowed with pity. Perhaps his little daughter who saw him so stern an hour ago does not understand why he wrestles so long in prayer tonight, or why when he rises from his knees he presses her to him with unwonted tenderness. Or he is in this chair repeating to her his favourite poem, "The Cameronian's Dream," and at the first lines so solemnly uttered,

"In a dream of the night I was wafted away,"

she screams with excitement, just as I screamed long afterwards when she repeated them in his voice to me. Or I watch, as from a window, while she sets off through the long parks to the distant place where he is at work, in her hand a flagon which contains his dinner. She is singing to herself and gleefully swinging the flagon, she jumps the burn and proudly measures the jump with her eye, but she never dallies unless she meets a baby, for she was so fond of babies that she must hug each one she met, but while she hugged them she also noted how their robes were cut, and afterwards made paper patterns, which she concealed jealously, and in the fullness of time her first robe for her eldest born was fashioned from one of these patterns, made when she was in her twelfth year.

She was eight when her mother's death made her mistress of the house and mother to her little brother, and from that time she scrubbed and mended and baked and sewed, and argued with the flesher about the quarter pound of beef and penny bone which provided dinner for two days (but if you think that this was poverty you don't know the meaning of the word), and she carried the water from the pump, and had her washing days and her ironings and a stocking always on the wire for odd moments, and gossiped like a matron with the other women, and humoured the men with a tolerant smile—all these things she did as a matter of course, leaping joyful from bed in the morning because there was so much to do, doing it as thoroughly and sedately as if the brides were already due for a lesson, and then rushing out in a fit of childishness to play dumps or palaulays with others of her age. I see her frocks lengthening, though they were never very short, and the games given reluctantly up. The horror of my boyhood was that I knew a time would come when I also must give up the games, and how it was to be done I saw not (this agony still returns to me in dreams, when I catch myself playing marbles, and look on with cold displeasure); I felt that I must continue playing in secret, and I took this shadow to her, when she told me her own experience, which convinced us both that we were very like each other inside. She had discovered that work is the best fun after all, and I learned it in time, but have my lapses, and so had she.

I know what was her favourite costume when she was at the age that they make heroines of: it was a pale blue with a pale blue bonnet, the white ribbons of which tied aggravatingly beneath the chin, and when questioned about this garb she never admitted that she looked pretty in it, but she did say, with blushes too, that blue was her colour, and then she might smile, as at some memory, and begin to tell us about a man who—but it ended there with another smile which was longer in departing. She never said, indeed she denied strenuously, that she had led the men a dance, but again the smile returned, and came between us and full belief. Yes, she had her little vanities; when she got the Mizpah ring she did carry that finger in such a way that the most reluctant must see. She was very particular about her gloves, and hid her boots so that no other should put them on, and then she forgot their hiding-place, and had suspicions of the one who found them. A good way of enraging her was to say that her last year's bonnet would do for this year without alteration, or that it would defy the face of clay to count the number of her shawls. In one of my books there is a mother who is setting off with her son for the town to which he had been called as minister, and she pauses on the threshold to ask him anxiously if he thinks her bonnet "sets" her. A reviewer said she acted thus, not because she cared how she looked, but for the sake of her son. This, I remember, amused my mother very much.

I have seen many weary on-dings of snow, but the one I seem to recollect best occurred nearly twenty years before I was born. It was at the time of my mother's marriage to one who proved a most loving as he was always a well-loved husband, a man I am very proud to be able to call my father. I know not for how many days the snow had been falling, but a day came when the people lost heart and would make no more gullies through it, and by next morning to do so was impossible, they could not fling the snow high enough. Its back was against every door when Sunday came, and none ventured out save a valiant few, who buffeted their way into my mother's home to discuss her predicament, for unless she was "cried" in the church that day she might not be married for another week, and how could she be cried with the minister a field away and the church buried to the waist? For hours they talked, and at last some men started for the church, which was several hundred yards distant. Three of them found a window, and forcing a passage through it, cried the pair, and that is how it came about that my father and mother were married on the first of March.

That would be the end, I suppose, if it were a story, but to my mother it was only another beginning, and not the last. I see her bending over the cradle of her first-born, college for him already in her eye (and my father not less ambitious), and anon it is a girl who is in the cradle, and then another girl—already a tragic figure to those who know the end. I wonder if any instinct told my mother that the great day of her life was when she bore this child; what I am sure of is that from the first the child followed her with the most wistful eyes and saw how she needed help and longed to rise and give it. For of physical strength my mother had never very much; it was her spirit that got through the work, and in those days she was often so ill that the sand rained on the doctor's window, and men ran to and fro with leeches, and "she is in life, we can say no more" was the information for those who came knocking at the door. "I am sorrow to say," her father writes in an old letter now before me, "that Margaret is in a state that she was never so bad before in this world. Till Wednesday night she was in as poor a condition as you could think of to be alive. However, after bleeding, leeching, etc., the Dr. says this morning that he is better hoped now, but at present we can say no more but only she is alive and in the hands of Him in whose hands all our lives are. I can give you no adequate view of what my feelings are, indeed they are a burden too heavy for me and I cannot describe them. I look on my right and left hand and find no comfort, and if it were not for the rock that is higher than I my spirit would utterly fail, but blessed be His name who can comfort those that are cast down. O for more faith in His supporting grace in this hour of trial."

Then she is "on the mend," she may "thole thro'" if they take great care of her, "which we will be forward to do." The fourth child dies when but a few weeks old, and the next at two years. She was her grandfather's companion, and thus he wrote of her death, this stern, self-educated Auld Licht with the chapped hands:

"I hope you received my last in which I spoke of Dear little Lydia being unwell. Now with deep sorrow I must tell you that yesterday I assisted in laying her dear remains in the lonely grave. She died at 7 o'clock on Wednesday evening, I suppose by the time you had got the letter. The Dr. did not think it was croup till late on Tuesday night, and all that Medical aid could prescribe was done, but the Dr. had no hope after he saw that the croup was confirmed, and hard indeed would the heart have been that would not have melted at seeing what the dear little creature suffered all Wednesday until the feeble frame was quite worn out. She was quite sensible till within 2 hours of her death, and then she sunk quite low till the vital spark fled, and all medicine that she got she took with the greatest readiness, as if apprehensive they would make her well. I cannot well describe my feelings on the occasion. I thought that the fountain head of my tears had now been dried up, but I have been mistaken, for I must confess that the briny rivulets descended fast on my furrowed cheeks, she was such a winning Child, and had such a regard for me and always came and told me all her little things, and as she was now speaking, some of her little prattle was very taking, and the lively images of these things intrude themselves more into my mind than they should do, but there is allowance for moderate grief on such occasions. But when I am telling you of my own grief and sorrow, I know not what to say of the bereaved Mother, she hath not met with anything in this world before that hath gone so near the quick with her. She had no handling of the last one as she was not able at the time, for she only had her once in her arms, and her affections had not time to be so fairly entwined around her. I am much afraid that she will not soon if ever get over this trial. Although she was weakly before, yet she was pretty well recovered, but this hath not only affected her mind but her body is so much affected that she is not well able to sit so long as her bed is making and hath scarcely tasted meat [i.e. food] since Monday might, and till some time is elapsed we cannot say how she may be. There is none that is not a parent themselves that can fully sympathize with one in such a state. David is much affected also, but it is not so well known on him, and the younger branches of the family are affected but it will be only momentary. But alas in all this vast ado, there is only the sorrow of the world which worketh death, O how gladdening would it be if we were in as great bitterness for sin as for the loss of a first-born. O how unfitted persons or families is for trials who knows not the divine art of casting all their cares upon the Lord, and what multitudes are there that when earthly comforts is taken away, may well say what have I more? all their delight is placed in some one thing or another in the world, and who can blame them for unwillingly parting with what they esteem their chief good. O that we were wise to lay up treasure for the time of need, for it is truly a solemn affair to enter the lists with the king of terrors. It is strange that the living lay the things so little to heart until they have to engage in that war where there is no discharge. O that my head were waters and mine eyes a fountain of tears that I might weep day and night for my own and others' stupidity in this great matter. O for grace to do every day work in its proper time and to live above the tempting cheating train of earthly things. The rest of the family are moderately well. I have been for some days worse than I have been for 8 months past, but I may soon get better, I am in the same way I have often been in before, but there is no security for it always being so, for I know that it cannot be far from the time when I will be one of those that once were. I have no other news to send you, and as little heart for them. I hope you will take the earliest opportunity of writing that you can, and be particular as regards Margaret, for she requires consolation."

He died exactly a week after writing this letter, but my mother was to live for another forty-four years. And joys of a kind never shared in by him were to come to her so abundantly, so long drawn out that, strange as it would have seemed to him to know it, her fuller life had scarce yet begun. And with the joys were to come their sweet, frightened comrades, pain and grief, again she was to be touched to the quick, again and again to be so ill that "she is in life, we can say no more," but still she had attendants very "forward" to help her, some of them unborn in her father's time.

She told me everything, and so my memories of our little red town are coloured by her memories. I knew it as it had been for generations, and suddenly I saw it change, and the transformation could not fail to strike a boy, for these first years are the most impressionable (nothing that happens after we are twelve matters very much); they are also the most vivid years when we look back, and more vivid the farther we have to look, until, at the end, what lies between bends like a hoop, and the extremes meet. But though the new town is to me a glass through which I look at the old, the people I see passing up and down these wynds, sitting, night-capped, on their barrow-shafts, hobbling in their blacks to church on Sunday, are less those I saw in my childhood than their fathers and mothers who did these things in the same way when my mother was young. I cannot picture the place without seeing her, as a little girl, come to the door of a certain house and beat her bass against the gav'le-end, or there is a wedding tonight, and the carriage with the white-eared horse is sent for a maiden in pale blue, whose bonnet-strings tie beneath the chin.

III

WHAT I SHOULD BE

MY mother was a great reader, and with ten minutes to spare before the starch was ready would begin the *Decline and Fall*—and finish it, too, that winter. Foreign words in the text annoyed her and made her bemoan her want of a classical education—she had only attended a Dame's school during some easy months—but she never passed the foreign words by until their meaning was explained to her, and when next she and they met it was as acquaintances, which I think was clever of her. One of her delights was to learn from me scraps of Horace, and then bring them into her conversation with "colleged men." I have come upon her in lonely places, such as the stair-head or the east room, muttering these quotations aloud to herself, and I well remember how she would say to the visitors, "Ay, ay, it's very true, Doctor, but as you know, 'Eheu fugaces, Postume, Postume, labuntur anni,'" or "Sal, Mr. so and so, my lassie is thriving well, but would it no be more to the point to say 'O mater, pulchra filia pulchrior'?" which astounded them very much if she managed to reach the end without being flung, but usually she had a fit of laughing in the middle, and so they found her out.

Biography and exploration were her favourite reading, for choice the biography of men who had been good to their mothers, and she liked the explorers to be alive so that she could shudder at the thought of their venturing forth again, but though she expressed a hope that they would have the sense to stay at home henceforth, she gleamed with admiration when they disappointed her. In later days I had a friend who was an African explorer, and she was in two minds about him; he was one of the most engrossing of mortals to her, she admired him prodigiously, pictured him at the head of his caravan, now attacked by savages, now by wild beasts, and adored him for the uneasy hours he gave her, but she was also afraid that he wanted to take me with him, and then she thought he should be put down by law. Explorers' mothers also interested her very much; the books might tell her nothing about them, but she could create them for herself and wring her hands in sympathy with them when they had got no news of him for six months. Yet there were times when she grudged him to them—as the day when he returned victorious. Then what was before her eyes was not the son coming marching home again but an old woman peering for him round the window curtain and trying not to look uplifted. The newspaper reports would be about the son, but my mother's comment was "She's a proud woman this night."

We read many books together when I was a boy, *Robinson Crusoe* being the first (and the second), and the *Arabian Nights* should have been the next, for we got it out of the library (a penny for three days), but on discovering that they were nights when we had paid for knights we sent that volume packing, and I have curled my lips at it ever since. *The Pilgrim's Progress* we had in the house (it was as common a possession as a dresser-head), and so enamoured of it was I that I turned our garden into sloughs of Despond, with pea-sticks to represent Christian on his travels and a buffet-stool for his burden, but when I dragged my mother out to see my handiwork she was scared, and I felt for days, with a certain elation, that I had been a dark character. Besides reading every book we could hire or borrow I also bought one now and again, and while buying (it was the occupation of weeks) I read, standing at the counter, most of the other books in the shop, which is perhaps the most exquisite way of reading. And I took in a magazine called *Sunshine,* the most delicious periodical, I am sure, of any day. It cost a halfpenny or a penny a month, and always, as I fondly remember, had a continued tale about the dearest girl, who sold water-cress, which is a dainty not grown and I suppose never seen in my native town. This romantic little creature took such hold of my imagination that I cannot eat water-cress even now without emotion. I lay in bed wondering what she would be up to in the next number; I have lost trout because when they nibbled my mind was wandering with her; my early life was embittered by her not arriving regularly on the first of the month. I know not whether it was owing to her loitering on the way one month to an extent flesh and blood could not bear, or because we had exhausted the penny library, but on a day I conceived a glorious idea, or it was put into my head by my mother, then desirous of making progress with her new clouty hearth-rug. The notion was nothing short of this, why should I not write the tales myself? I did write them—in the garret—but they by no means helped her to get on with her work, for when I finished a chapter I bounded downstairs to read it to her, and so short were the chapters, so ready was the pen, that I was back with new manuscript before another clout had been added to the rug. Authorship seemed, like her bannock-baking, to consist of running between two points. They were all tales of adventure (happiest is he who writes of adventure), no characters were allowed within if I knew their like in the flesh, the scene lay in unknown parts, desert islands, enchanted gardens, with knights (none of your nights) on black chargers, and round the first corner a lady selling water-cress.

At twelve or thereabout I put the literary calling to bed for a time, having gone to a school where cricket and football were more esteemed, but during the year before I went to the university, it woke up and I wrote great part of a three-volume novel. The publisher replied that the sum for which he would print it was a hundred and—however, that was not the important point (I had sixpence): where he stabbed us both was in writing that he considered me a "clever lady." I replied stiffly that I was a gentleman, and since then I have kept that manuscript concealed. I looked through it lately, and, oh, but it is dull. I defy anyone to read it.

The malignancy of publishers, however, could not turn me back. From the day on which I first tasted blood in the garret my mind was made up; there could be no hum-dreadful-drum profession for me; literature was my game. It was not highly thought of by those who wished me well. I remember being asked by two maiden ladies, about the time I left the university, what I was to be, and when I replied brazenly, "An author," they flung up their hands, and one exclaimed reproachfully, "And you an M.A.!" My mother's views at first were not dissimilar; for long she took mine jestingly as something I would grow out of, and afterwards they hurt her so that I tried to give them up. To be a minister—that she thought was among the fairest prospects, but she was a very ambitious woman, and sometimes she would add, half scared at her appetite, that there were ministers who had become professors, "but it was not canny to think of such things."

I had one person only on my side, an old tailor, one of the fullest men I have known, and quite the best talker. He was a bachelor (he told me all that is to be known about woman), a lean man, pallid of face, his legs drawn up when he walked as if he was ever carrying something in his lap; his walks were of the shortest, from the tea-pot on the hob to the board on which he stitched, from the board to the hob, and so to bed. He might have gone out had the idea struck him, but in the years I knew him, the last of his brave life, I think he was only in the open twice, when he "flitted"—changed his room for another hard by. I did not see him make these journeys, but I seem to see him now, and he is somewhat dizzy in the odd atmosphere; in one hand he carries a box-iron, he raises the other, wondering what this is on his head, it is a hat; a faint smell of singed cloth goes by with him. This man had heard of my set of photographs of the poets and asked for a sight of them, which led to our first meeting. I remember how he spread them out on his board, and after looking long at them, turned his gaze on me and said solemnly,

"What can I do to be for ever known,
And make the age to come my own?"

These lines of Cowley were new to me, but the sentiment was not new, and I marvelled how the old tailor could see through me so well. So it was strange to me to discover presently that he had not been thinking of me at all, but of his own young days, when that couplet sang in his head, and he, too, had thirsted to set off for Grub Street, but was afraid, and while he hesitated old age came, and then Death, and found him grasping a box-iron.

I hurried home with the mouthful, but neighbours had dropped in, and this was for her ears only, so I drew her to the stair, and said imperiously,

> "What can I do to be for ever known,
> And make the age to come my own?"

It was an odd request for which to draw her from a tea-table, and she must have been surprised, but I think she did not laugh, and in after years she would repeat the lines fondly, with a flush on her soft face. "That is the kind you would like to be yourself!" we would say in jest to her, and she would reply almost passionately, "No, but I would be windy of being his mother." It is possible that she could have been his mother had that other son lived, he might have managed it from sheer love of her, but for my part I can smile at one of those two figures on the stair now, having long given up the dream of being for ever known, and seeing myself more akin to my friend, the tailor, for as he was found at the end on his board, so I hope shall I be found at my handloom, doing honestly the work that suits me best. Who shall know so well as I that it is but a handloom compared to the great guns that reverberate through the age to come? But she who stood with me on the stair that day was a very simple woman, accustomed all her life to making the most of small things, and I weaved sufficiently well to please her, which has been my only steadfast ambition since I was a little boy.

Not less than mine became her desire that I should have my way— but, ah, the iron seats in that Park of horrible repute, and that bare room at the top of many flights of stairs! While I was away at college she drained all available libraries for books about those who go to London to live by the pen, and they all told the same shuddering tale. London, which she never saw, was to her a monster that licked up country youths as they stepped from the train; there were the garrets in which they sat abject, and the park seats where they passed the night. Those park seats were the monster's glaring eyes to her, and as

But there were times, she held, when Carlyle must have made his wife a glorious woman. "As when?" I might inquire.

"When she keeked in at his study door and said to herself, 'The whole world is ringing with his fame, and he is my man!'"

"And then," I might point out, "he would roar to her to shut the door."

"Pooh," said my mother, "a man's roar is neither here nor there." But her verdict as a whole was, "I would rather have been his mother than his wife."

So we have got her into her chair with the Carlyles, and all is well. Furthermore, "to mak siccar," my father has taken the opposite side of the fireplace and is deep in the latest five columns of Gladstone, who is his Carlyle. He is to see that she does not slip away fired by a conviction, which suddenly over-rides her pages, that the kitchen is going to rack and ruin for want of her, and she is to recall him to himself should he put his foot in the fire and keep it there, forgetful of all save his hero's eloquence. (We were a family who needed a deal of watching.) She is not interested in what Mr. Gladstone has to say; indeed she could never be brought to look upon politics as of serious concern for grown folk (a class in which she scarcely included man), and she gratefully gave up reading "leaders" the day I ceased to write them. But like want of reasonableness, a love for having the last word, want of humour and the like, politics were in her opinion a mannish attribute to be tolerated, and Gladstone was the name of the something which makes all our sex such queer characters. She had a profound faith in him as an aid to conversation, and if there were silent men in the company would give him to them to talk about, precisely as she divided a cake among children. And then, with a motherly smile, she would leave them to gorge on him. But in the idolizing of Gladstone she recognized, nevertheless, a certain inevitability, and would no more have tried to contend with it than to sweep a shadow off the floor. Gladstone was, and there was an end of it in her practical philosophy. Nor did she accept him coldly; like a true woman she sympathized with those who suffered severely, and they knew it and took counsel of her in the hour of need. I remember one ardent Glad-stonian who, as a general election drew near, was in sore straits indeed, for he disbelieved in Home Rule, and yet how could he vote against "Gladstone's man"? His distress was so real that it gave him a hang-dog appearance. He put his case gloomily before her, and until the day of the election she riddled him with sarcasm; I think he only went to her because he found a mournful enjoyment in seeing a false Glad-stonian tortured.

It was all such plain-sailing for him, she pointed out; he did not like this Home Rule, and therefore he must vote against it.

She put it pitiful clear, he replied with a groan.

But she was like another woman to him when he appeared before her on his way to the polling-booth.

"This is a watery Sabbath to you, I'm thinking," she said sympathetically, but without dropping her wires—for Home Rule or no Home Rule that stocking-foot must be turned before twelve o'clock.

A watery Sabbath means a doleful day, and "A watery Sabbath it is," he replied with feeling. A silence followed, broken only by the click of the wires. Now and again he would mutter, "Ay, well, I'll be going to vote—little did I think the day would come," and so on, but if he rose it was only to sit down again, and at last she crossed over to him and said softly (no sarcasm in her voice now), "Away with you, and vote for Gladstone's man!" He jumped up and made off without a word, but from the east window we watched him strutting down the brae. I laughed, but she said, "I'm no sure that it's a laughing matter," and afterwards, "I would have liked fine to be that Gladstone's mother."

It is nine o'clock now, a quarter past nine, half-past nine—all the same moment to me, for I am at a sentence that will not write. I know, though I can't hear, what my sister has gone upstairs to say to my mother:

"I was in at him at nine, and he said, 'In five minutes,' so I put the steak on the brander, but I've been in thrice since then, and every time he says, 'In five minutes,' and when I try to take the table cover off, he presses his elbows hard on it, and growls. His supper will be completely spoilt."

"Oh, that weary writing!"

"I can do no more, mother, so you must come down and stop him."

"I have no power over him," my mother says, but she rises smiling, and presently she is opening my door.

"In five minutes!" I cry, but when I see that it is she I rise and put my arm round her. "What a full basket!" she says, looking at the wastepaper basket which contains most of my work of the night, and with a dear gesture she lifts up a torn page and kisses it. "Poor thing," she says to it, "and you would have liked so fine to be printed!" and she puts her hand over my desk to prevent my writing more.

"In the last five minutes," I begin, "one can often do more than in the first hour."

"Many a time I've said it in my young days," she says slowly.

"And proved it, too!" cries a voice from the door, the voice of one who was prouder of her even than I; it is true, and yet almost unbelievable, that anyone could have been prouder of her than I.

"But those days are gone," my mother says solemnly, "gone to come back no more. You'll put by your work now, man, and have your supper, and then you'll come up and sit beside your mother for a whiley, for soon you'll be putting her away in the kirk-yard."

I hear such a little cry from near the door.

So my mother and I go up the stair together. "We have changed places," she says; "that was just how I used to help you up, but I'm the bairn now."

She brings out the Testament again; it was always lying within reach; it is the lock of hair she left me when she died. And when she has read for a long time she "gives me a look," as we say in the north, and I go out, to leave her alone with God. She had been but a child when her mother died, and so she fell early into the way of saying her prayers with no earthly listener. Often and often I have found her on her knees, but I always went softly away, closing the door. I never heard her pray, but I know very well how she prayed, and that, when that door was shut, there was not a day in God's sight between the worn woman and the little child.

V I

HER MAID OF ALL WORK

AND sometimes I was her maid of all work.

It is early morn, and my mother has come noiselessly into my room. I know it is she, though my eyes are shut, and I am only half awake. Perhaps I was dreaming of her, for I accept her presence without surprise, as if in the awakening I had but seen her go out at one door to come in at another. But she is speaking to herself.

"I'm sweer to waken him—I doubt he was working late—oh, that weary writing—no, I maunna waken him."

I start up. She is wringing her hands. "What is wrong?" I cry, but I know before she answers. My sister is down with one of the headaches against which even she cannot fight, and my mother, who bears physical pain as if it were a comrade, is most woe-begone when her daughter is the sufferer. "And she winna let me go down the stair to make a cup of tea for her," she groans.

"I will soon make the tea, mother."

"Will you?" she says eagerly. It is what she has come to me for, but "It is a pity to rouse you," she says.

"And I will take charge of the house today, and light the fires and wash the dishes——"

"Na, oh no; no, I couldna ask that of you, and you an author."

"It won't be the first time, mother, since I was an author."

"More like the fiftieth!" she says almost gleefully, so I have begun well, for to keep up her spirits is the great thing today.

Knock at the door. It is the baker. I take in the bread, looking so sternly at him that he dare not smile.

Knock at the door. It is the postman. (I hope he did not see that I had the lid of the kettle in my other hand.)

Furious knocking in a remote part. This means that the author is in the coal cellar.

Anon I carry two breakfasts upstairs in triumph. I enter the bed-room like no mere humdrum son, but after the manner of the Glasgow waiter. I must say more about him. He had been my mother's one waiter, the only man-servant she ever came in contact with, and they had met in a Glasgow hotel which she was eager to see, having heard of the monstrous things, and conceived them to resemble country inns with another twelve bedrooms. I remember how she beamed—yet tried to look as if it was quite an ordinary experience—when we alighted at the hotel door, but though she said nothing I soon read disappointment in her face. She knew how I was exulting in having her there, so would not say a word to damp me, but I craftily drew it out of her. No, she was very comfortable, and the house was grand beyond speech, but—but—where was he? he had not been very hearty. "He" was the landlord; she had expected him to receive us at the door and ask if we were in good health and how we had left the others, and then she would have asked him if his wife was well and how many children they had, after which we should all have sat down together to dinner. Two chambermaids came into her room and prepared it without a single word to her about her journey or on any other subject, and when they had gone, "They are two haughty misses," said my mother with spirit. But what she most resented was the waiter with his swagger black suit and short quick steps and the "towel" over his arm. Without so much as a "Welcome to Glasgow!" he showed us to our seats, not the smallest acknowledgment of our kindness in giving such munificent orders did we draw from him, he hovered around the table as if it would be unsafe to leave us with his knives and forks (he should have seen her knives and forks), when we spoke to each other he affected not to hear, we might laugh but this uppish fellow would not join in, we retired, crushed, and he had the final impudence to open the door for us. But though this hurt my mother at the time, the humour of our experiences filled her on reflection, and in her own house she would describe them with unction, sometimes to those who had been in many hotels, often to others who had been in none, and whoever were her listeners she made them laugh, though not always at the same thing.

So now when I enter the bedroom with the tray, on my arm is that badge of pride, the towel; and I approach with prim steps to inform Madam that breakfast is ready, and she puts on the society manner and addresses me as "Sir," and asks with cruel sarcasm for what purpose (except to boast) I carry the towel, and I say, "Is there anything more I can do for Madam?" and Madam replies that there is one more thing I can do, and that is, eat her breakfast for her. But of this I take no notice, for my object is to fire her with the spirit of the game, so that she eats unwittingly.

Now that I have washed up the breakfast things I should be at my writing, and I am anxious to be at it, as I have an idea in my head, which, if it is of any value, has almost certainly been put there by her. But dare I venture? I know that the house has not been properly set going yet, there are beds to make, the exterior of the teapot is fair, but suppose someone were to look inside? What a pity I knocked over the flour-barrel! Can I hope that for once my mother will forget to inquire into these matters? Is my sister willing to let disorder reign until to-morrow? I determine to risk it. Perhaps I have been at work for half-an-hour when I hear movements overhead. One or other of them is wondering why the house is so quiet. I rattle the tongs, but even this does not satisfy them, so back into the desk go my papers, and now what you hear is not the scrape of a pen but the rinsing of pots and pans, or I am making beds, and making them thoroughly, because after I am gone my mother will come (I know her) and look suspiciously beneath the coverlet.

The kitchen is now speckless, not an unwashed platter in sight, unless you look beneath the table. I feel that I have earned time for an hour's writing at last, and at it I go with vigour. One page, two pages, really I am making progress, when—was that a door opening? But I have my mother's light step on the brain, so I "yoke" again, and next moment she is beside me. She has not exactly left her room, she gives me to understand; but suddenly a conviction had come to her that I was writing without a warm mat at my feet. She carries one in her hands. Now that she is here she remains for a time, and though she is in the armchair by the fire, where she sits bolt upright (she loved to have cushions on the unused chairs, but detested putting her back against them), and I am bent low over my desk, I know that contentment and pity are struggling for possession of her face: contentment wins when she surveys her room, pity when she looks at me. Every article of furniture, from the chairs that came into the world with me and have worn so much better, though I was new and they were second-hand, to the mantel-border of fashionable design which she sewed in her seventieth year, having picked up the stitch in half a lesson, has its story of fight and attainment for her, hence her satisfaction; but she sighs at sight of her son, dipping and tearing, and chewing the loathly pen.

"Oh, that weary writing!"

In vain do I tell her that writing is as pleasant to me as ever was the prospect of a tremendous day's ironing to her; that (to some, though not to me) new chapters are as easy to turn out as new bannocks. No, she maintains, for one bannock is the marrows of another, while chapters—and then, perhaps, her eyes twinkle, and says she saucily, "But, sal, you may be right, for sometimes your bannocks are as alike as mine!"

Or I may be roused from my writing by her cry that I am making strange faces again. It is my contemptible weakness that if I say a character smiled vacuously, I must smile vacuously; if he frowns or leers, I frown or leer; if he is a coward or given to contortions, I cringe, or twist my legs until I have to stop writing to undo the knot. I bow with him, eat with him, and gnaw my moustache with him. If the character be a lady with an exquisite laugh, I suddenly terrify you by laughing exquisitely. One reads of the astounding versatility of an actor who is stout and lean on the same evening, but what is he to the novelist who is a dozen persons within the hour? Morally, I fear, we must deteriorate—but this is a subject I may wisely edge away from.

We always spoke to each other in broad Scotch (I think in it still), but now and again she would use a word that was new to me, or I might hear one of her contemporaries use it. Now is my opportunity to angle for its meaning. If I ask, boldly, what was that word she used just now, something like "bilbie" or "silvendy"? she blushes, and says she never said anything so common, or hoots, it is some auld-farrant word about which she can tell me nothing. But if in the course of conversation I remark casually, "Did he find bilbie?" or "Was that quite silvendy?" (though the sense of the question is vague to me) she falls into the trap, and the words explain themselves in her replies. Or maybe today she sees whither I am leading her, and such is her sensitiveness that she is quite hurt. The humour goes out of her face (to find bilbie in some more silvendy spot), and her reproachful eyes—but now I am on the arm of her chair, and we have made it up. Nevertheless, I shall get no more old-world Scotch out of her this forenoon, she weeds her talk determinedly, and it is as great a falling away as when the mutch gives place to the cap.

I am off for my afternoon walk, and she has promised to bar the door behind me and open it to none. When I return,—well, the door is still barred, but she is looking both furtive and elated. I should say that she is burning to tell me something, but cannot tell it without exposing herself. Has she opened the door, and if so, why? I don't ask, but I watch. It is she who is sly now:

"Have you been in the east room since you came in?" she asks with apparent indifference.

"No; why do you ask?"

"Oh, I just thought you might have looked in."

"Is there anything new there?"

"I dinna say there is, but—but just go and see."

"There can't be anything new if you kept the door barred," I say cleverly.

This crushes her for a moment; but her eagerness that I should see is greater than her fear. I set off for the east room, and she follows, affecting humility, but with triumph in her eye. How often those little scenes took place! I was never told of the new purchase, I was lured into its presence, and then she waited timidly for my start of surprise.

"Do you see it?" she says anxiously, and I see it, and hear it, for this time it is a bran-new wicker chair, of the kind that whisper to themselves for the first six months.

"A going-about body was selling them in a cart," my mother begins, and what followed presents itself to my eyes before she can utter another word. Ten minutes at the least did she stand at the door argy-bargying with that man. But it would be cruelty to scold a woman so uplifted.

"Fifteen shillings he wanted," she cries, "but what do you think I beat him down to?"

"Seven and sixpence?"

She claps her hands with delight. "Four shillings, as I'm a living woman!" she crows: never was a woman fonder of a bargain.

I gaze at the purchase with the amazement expected of me, and the chair itself crinkles and shudders to hear what it went for (or is it merely chuckling at her?). "And the man said it cost himself five shillings," my mother continues exultantly. You would have thought her the hardest person had not a knock on the wall summoned us about this time to my sister's side. Though in bed she has been listening, and this is what she has to say, in a voice that makes my mother very indignant, "You drive a bargain! I'm thinking ten shillings was nearer what you paid."

"Four shillings to a penny!" says my mother.

"I daresay," says my sister; "but after you paid him the money I heard you in the little bedroom press. What were you doing there?"

My mother winces. "I may have given him a present of an old top-coat," she falters. "He looked ill-happit. But that was after I made the bargain."

"Were there bairns in the cart?"

"There might have been a bit lassie in the cart."

"I thought as much. What did you give her? I heard you in the pantry."

"Four shillings was what I got that chair for," replies my mother firmly. If I don't interfere there will be a coldness between them for at least a minute. "There is blood on your finger," I say to my mother.

"So there is," she says, concealing her hand.

"Blood!" exclaims my sister anxiously, and then with a cry of triumph, "I warrant it's jelly. You gave that lassie one of the jelly cans!"

The Glasgow waiter brings up tea, and presently my sister is able to rise, and after a sharp fight I am expelled from the kitchen. The last thing I do as maid of all work is to lug upstairs the clothes-basket which has just arrived with the mangling. Now there is delicious linen for my mother to finger; there was always rapture on her face when the clothes-basket came in; it never failed to make her once more the active genius of the house. I may leave her now with her sheets and collars and napkins and fronts. Indeed, she probably orders me to go. A son is all very well, but suppose he were to tread on that counter-pane!

My sister is but and I am ben—I mean she is in the east end and I am in the west—tuts, tuts, let us get at the English of this by striving: she is in the kitchen and I am at my desk in the parlour. I hope I may not be disturbed, for tonight I must make my hero say "Darling," and it needs both privacy and concentration. In a word, let me admit (though I should like to beat about the bush) that I have sat down to a love-chapter. Too long has it been avoided, Albert has called Marion "dear" only as yet (between you and me these are not their real names), but though the public will probably read the word without blinking, it went off in my hands with a bang. They tell me—the Sassenach tell me—that in time I shall be able without a blush to make Albert say "darling," and even gather her up in his arms, but I begin to doubt it; the moment sees me as shy as ever; I still find it advisable to lock the door, and then—no witness save the dog—I "do" it dourly with my teeth clenched, while the dog retreats into the far corner and moans. The bolder Englishman (I am told) will write a love-chapter and then go out, quite coolly, to dinner, but such goings on are contrary to the Scotch nature; even the great novelists dared not. Conceive Mr. Stevenson left alone with a hero, a heroine, and a proposal impending (he does not know where to look). Sir Walter in the same circumstances gets out of the room by making his love-scenes take place between the end of one chapter and the beginning of the next, but he could afford to do anything, and the small fry must e'en to their task, moan the dog as he may. So I have yoked to mine when, enter my mother, looking wistful.

"I suppose you are terrible thrang," she says.

"Well, I am rather busy, but—what is it you want me to do?"

"It would be a shame to ask you."

"Still, ask me."

"I am so terrified they may be filed."

"You want me to——?"

"If you would just come up, and help me to fold the sheets!"

The sheets are folded and I return to Albert. I lock the door and at last I am bringing my hero forward nicely (my knee in the small of his back), when this startling question is shot by my sister through the keyhole:

"Where did you put the carrot-grater?"

It will all have to be done over again if I let Albert go for a moment, so, gripping him hard, I shout indignantly that I have not seen the carrot-grater.

"Then what did you grate the carrots on?" asks the voice, and the door-handle is shaken just as I shake Albert.

"On a broken cup," I reply with surprising readiness, and I get to work again but am less engrossed, for a conviction grows on me that I put the carrot-grater in the drawer of the sewing-machine.

I am wondering whether I should confess or brazen it out, when I hear my sister going hurriedly upstairs. I have a presentiment that she has gone to talk about me, and I basely open my door and listen.

"Just look at that, mother!"

"Is it a dish-cloth?"

"That's what it is now."

"Losh behears! it's one of the new table-napkins."

"That's what it was. He has been polishing the kitchen grate with it!"

(I remember!)

"Woe's me! That is what comes of his not letting me budge from this room. O, it is a watery Sabbath when men take to doing women's work!"

"It defies the face of clay, mother, to fathom what makes him so senseless."

"Oh, it's that weary writing."

"And the worst of it is he will talk tomorrow as if he had done wonders."

"That's the way with the whole clan-jamfray of them."

"Yes, but as usual you will humour him, mother."

"Oh, well, it pleases him, you see," says my mother, "and we can have our laugh when his door's shut."

"He is most terribly handless."

"He is all that, but, poor soul, he does his best."

V I I

R. L. S.

THESE familiar initials are, I suppose, the best beloved in recent literature, certainly they are the sweetest to me, but there was a time when my mother could not abide them. She said "That Stevenson man" with a sneer, and it was never easy to her to sneer. At thought of him her face would become almost hard, which seems incredible, and she would knit her lips and fold her arms, and reply with a stiff "oh" if you mentioned his aggravating name. In the novels we have a way of writing of our heroine, "she drew herself up haughtily," and when mine draw themselves up haughtily I see my mother thinking of Robert Louis Stevenson. He knew her opinion of him, and would write, "My ears tingled yesterday; I sair doubt she has been miscalling me again." But the more she miscalled him the more he delighted in her, and she was informed of this, and at once said "The scoundrel!" If you would know what was his unpardonable crime, it was this, he wrote better books than mine.

I remember the day she found it out, which was not, however, the day she admitted it. That day, when I should have been at my work, she came upon me in the kitchen, *The Master of Ballantrae* beside me, but I was not reading: my head lay heavy on the table and to her anxious eyes, I doubt not, I was the picture of woe. "Not writing!"

I echoed, no, I was not writing, I saw no use in ever trying to write again. And down, I suppose, went my head once more. She misunderstood, and thought the blow had fallen; I had awakened to the discovery, always dreaded by her, that I had written myself dry; I was no better than an empty ink-bottle. She wrung her hands, but indignation came to her with my explanation, which was that while R. L. S. was at it we others were only 'prentices cutting our fingers on his tools. "I could never thole his books," said my mother immediately, and indeed vindictively.

"You have not read any of them," I reminded her.

"And never will," said she with spirit.

And I have no doubt that she called him a dark character that very day. For weeks too, if not for months, she adhered to her determination not to read him, though I, having come to my senses and seen that there is a place for the 'prentice, was taking a pleasure, almost malicious, in putting *The Master of Ballantrae* in her way. I would place it on her table so that it said good-morning to her when she rose. She would frown, and carrying it downstairs, as if she had it in the tongs, replace it on its book-shelf. I would wrap it up in the cover she had made for the latest Carlyle: she would skin it contemptuously and again bring it down. I would hide her spectacles in it, and lay it on top of the clothes-basket and prop it up invitingly open against her tea-pot. And at last I got her, though I forget by which of many contrivances. What I recall vividly is a key-hole view, to which another member of the family invited me. Then I saw my mother wrapped up in *The Master of Ballantrae* and muttering the music to herself, nodding her head in approval, and taking a stealthy glance at the foot of each page before she began at the top. Nevertheless she had an ear for the door, for when I bounced in she had been too clever for me; there was no book to be seen, only an apron on her lap and she was gazing out at the window. Some such conversation as this followed:

"You have been sitting very quietly, mother."

"I always sit quietly, I never do anything, I'm just a finished stocking."

"Have you been reading?"

"Do I ever read at this time of day?"

"What is that in your lap?"

"Just my apron."

"Is that a book beneath the apron?"

"It might be a book."

"Let me see."

"Go away with you to your work."

But I lifted the apron. "Why, it's *The Master of Ballantrae!*" I exclaimed, shocked.

"So it is!" said my mother, equally surprised. But I looked sternly at her, and perhaps she blushed.

"Well, what do you think: not nearly equal to mine?" said I with humour.

"Nothing like them," she said determinedly.

"Not a bit," said I, though whether with a smile or a groan is immaterial; they would have meant the same thing. Should I put the book back on its shelf? I asked, and she replied that I could put it wherever I liked for all she cared, so long as I took it out of her sight (the implication was that it had stolen on to her lap while she was looking out at the window). My behaviour may seem small, but I gave her a last chance, for I said that some people found it a book there was no putting down until they reached the last page.

"I'm no that kind," replied my mother.

Nevertheless our old game with the haver of a thing, as she called it, was continued, with this difference, that it was now she who carried the book covertly upstairs, and I who replaced it on the shelf, and several times we caught each other in the act, but not a word said either of us; we were grown self-conscious. Much of the play no doubt I forget, but one incident I remember clearly. She had come down to sit beside me while I wrote, and sometimes, when I looked up, her eye was not on me, but on the shelf where *The Master of Ballantrae* stood inviting her. Mr. Stevenson's books are not for the shelf, they are for the hand; even when you lay them down, let it be on the table for the next comer. Being the most sociable that man has penned

in our time, they feel very lonely up there in a stately row. I think
their eye is on you the moment you enter the room, and so you are
drawn to look at them, and you take a volume down with the impulse that induces one to unchain the dog. And the result is not
dissimilar, for in another moment you two are at play. Is there any
other modern writer who gets round you in this way? Well, he had
given my mother the look which in the ball-room means, "Ask me
for this waltz," and she ettled to do it, but felt that her more dutiful
course was to sit out the dance with this other less entertaining partner.
I wrote on doggedly, but could hear the whispering.

"Am I to be a wall-flower?" asked James Durie reproachfully. (It
must have been leap-year.)

"Speak lower," replied my mother, with an uneasy look at me.

"Pooh!" said James contemptuously, "that kail-runtle!"

"I winna have him miscalled," said my mother, frowning.

"I am done with him," said James (wiping his cane with his cambric
handkerchief), and his sword clattered deliciously (I cannot think
this was accidental), which made my mother sigh. Like the man he
was, he followed up his advantage with a comparison that made me
dip viciously.

"A prettier sound that," said he, clanking his sword again, "than
the clack-clack of your young friend's shuttle."

"Whist!" cried my mother, who had seen me dip.

"Then give me your arm," said James, lowering his voice.

"I dare not," answered my mother. "He's so touchy about you."

"Come, come," he pressed her, "you are certain to do it sooner or
later, so why not now?"

"Wait till he has gone for his walk," said my mother; "and, forby
that, I'm ower old to dance with you."

"How old are you?" he inquired.

"You're gey an' pert!" cried my mother.

"Are you seventy?"

"Off and on," she admitted.

"Pooh," he said, "a mere girl!"

She replied instantly, "I'm no to be catched with chaff"; but she smiled and rose as if he had stretched out his hand and got her by the finger-tip.

After that they whispered so low (which they could do as they were now much nearer each other) that I could catch only one remark. It came from James, and seems to show the tenor of their whisperings, for his words were, "Easily enough, if you slip me beneath your shawl."

That is what she did, and furthermore she left the room guiltily, muttering something about redding up the drawers. I suppose I smiled wanly to myself, or conscience must have been nibbling at my mother, for in less than five minutes she was back, carrying her accomplice openly, and she thrust him with positive viciousness into the place where my Stevenson had lost a tooth (as the writer whom he most resembled would have said). And then like a good mother she took up one of her son's books and read it most determinedly. It had become a touching incident to me, and I remember how we there and then agreed upon a compromise: she was to read the enticing thing just to convince herself of its inferiority.

The Master of Ballantrae is not the best. Conceive the glory, which was my mother's, of knowing from a trustworthy source that there are at least three better awaiting you on the same shelf. She did not know Alan Breck yet, and he was as anxious to step down as Mr. Bally himself. John Silver was there, getting into his leg, so that she should not have to wait a moment, and roaring, "I'll lay to that!" when she told me consolingly that she could not thole pirate stories. Not to know these gentlemen, what is it like? It is like never having been in love. But they are in the house! That is like knowing that you will fall in love tomorrow morning. With one word, by drawing one mournful face, I could have got my mother to abjure the jam-shelf—nay, I might have managed it by merely saying that she had enjoyed *The Master of Ballantrae*. For you must remember that she only read it to persuade herself (and me) of its unworthiness, and that the reason she wanted to read the others was to get further proof. All this she made plain to me, eyeing me a little anxiously the while, and of course I accepted the explanation. Alan is the biggest child of them all, and I doubt not that she thought so, but curiously enough her views of him are among the things I have forgotten. But how enamoured she was of *Treasure Island,* and how faithful she tried to be to me all the time she was reading it! I had to put my hands over her eyes to let her know that I had entered the room, and even then she might try to read between my fingers, coming to herself presently, however, to say, "It's a haver of a book."

"Those pirate stories are so uninteresting," I would reply without fear, for she was too engrossed to see through me. "Do you think you will finish this one?"

"I may as well go on with it since I have begun it," my mother says, so slyly that my sister and I shake our heads at each other to imply, "Was there ever such a woman!"

"There are none of those one-legged scoundrels in my books," I say.

"Better without them," she replies promptly.

"I wonder, mother, what it is about the man that so infatuates the public?"

"He takes no hold of me," she insists. "I would a hantle rather read your books."

I offer obligingly to bring one of them to her, and now she looks at me suspiciously. "You surely believe I like yours best," she says with instant anxiety, and I soothe her by assurances, and retire advising her to read on, just to see if she can find out how he misleads the public. "Oh, I may take a look at it again by and by," she says indifferently, but nevertheless the probability is that as the door shuts the book opens, as if by some mechanical contrivance. I remember how she read *Treasure Island,* holding it close to the ribs of the fire (because she could not spare a moment to rise and light the gas), and how, when bed-time came, and we coaxed, remonstrated, scolded, she said quite fiercely, clinging to the book, "I dinna lay my head on a pillow this night till I see how that laddie got out of the barrel."

After this, I think, he was as bewitching as the laddie in the barrel to her— Was he not always a laddie in the barrel himself, climbing in for apples while we all stood around, like gamin, waiting for a bite? He was the spirit of boyhood tugging at the skirts of this old world

of ours and compelling it to come back and play. And I suppose my
mother felt this, as so many have felt it: like others she was a little
scared at first to find herself skipping again, with this masterful child
at the rope, but soon she gave him her hand and set off with him for
the meadow, not an apology between the two of them for the author
left behind. But never to the end did she admit (in words) that he
had a way with him which was beyond her son. "Silk and sacking,
that is what we are," she was informed, to which she would reply
obstinately, "Well, then, I prefer sacking."

"But if he had been your son?"

"But he is not."

"You wish he were?"

"I dinna deny but what I could have found room for him."

And still at times she would smear him with the name of black
(to his delight when he learned the reason). That was when some
podgy red-sealed blue-crossed letter arrived from Vailima, inviting me
to journey thither. (His directions were, "You take the boat at San
Francisco, and then my place is the second to the left.") Even London
seemed to her to carry me so far away that I often took a week to the
journey (the first six days in getting her used to the idea), and these
letters terrified her. It was not the finger of Jim Hawkins she now saw
beckoning me across the seas, it was John Silver, waving a crutch.
Seldom, I believe, did I read straight through one of these Vailima
letters; when in the middle I suddenly remembered who was upstairs and what she was probably doing, and I ran to her, three steps
at a jump, to find her, lips pursed, hands folded, a picture of gloom.

"I have a letter from——"

"So I have heard."

"Would you like to hear it?"

"No."

"Can you not abide him?"

"I canna thole him."

"Is he a black?"

"He is all that."

Well, Vailima was the one spot on earth I had any great craving to visit, but I think she always knew I would never leave her. Sometime, she said, she should like me to go, but not until she was laid away. "And how small I have grown this last winter. Look at my wrists. It canna be long now." No, I never thought of going, was never absent for a day from her without reluctance, and never walked so quickly as when I was going back. In the meantime that happened which put an end for ever to my scheme of travel. I shall never go up the Road of Loving Hearts now, on "a wonderful clear night of stars," to meet the man coming toward me on a horse. It is still a wonderful clear night of stars, but the road is empty. So I never saw the dear king of us all. But before he had written books he was in my part of the country with a fishing wand in his hand, and I like to think that I was the boy who met him that day by Queen Margaret's burn, where the rowans are, and busked a fly for him, and stood watching, while his lithe figure rose and fell as he cast and hinted back from the crystal waters of Noran-side.

VIII

A PANIC IN THE HOUSE

I was sitting at my desk in London when a telegram came announcing that my mother was again dangerously ill, and I seized my hat and hurried to the station. It is not a memory of one night only. A score of times, I am sure, I was called north thus suddenly, and reached our little town trembling, head out at railway-carriage window for a glance at a known face which would answer the question on mine. These illnesses came as regularly as the backend of the year, but were less regular in going, and through them all, by night and by day, I see my sister moving so unwearyingly, so lovingly, though with failing strength, that I bow my head in reverence for her. She was wearing herself done. The doctor advised us to engage a nurse, but the mere word frightened my mother, and we got between her and the door as if the woman was already on the stair. To have a strange woman in my mother's room—you who are used to them cannot conceive what it meant to us.

Then we must have a servant. This seemed only less horrible. My father turned up his sleeves and clutched the besom. I tossed aside my papers, and was ready to run the errands. He answered the door, I kept the fires going, he gave me a lesson in cooking, I showed him how to make beds, one of us wore an apron. It was not for long. I was led to my desk, the newspaper was put into my father's hand. "But a servant!" we cried, and would have fallen to again. "No servant comes into this house," said my sister quite fiercely, and, oh, but my mother was relieved to hear her. There were many such scenes, a year of them, I daresay, before we yielded.

I cannot say which of us felt it most. In London I was used to servants, and in moments of irritation would ring for them furiously, though doubtless my manner changed as they opened the door. I have even held my own with gentlemen in plush, giving one my hat, another my stick, and a third my coat, and all done with little more trouble than I should have expended in putting the three articles on the chair myself. But this bold deed, and other big things of the kind, I did that I might tell my mother of them afterwards, while I sat on the end of her bed, and her face beamed with astonishment and mirth.

From my earliest days I had seen servants. The manse had a servant, the bank had another; one of their uses was to pounce upon, and carry away in stately manner, certain naughty boys who played with me. The banker did not seem really great to me, but his servant—oh, yes. Her boots cheeped all the way down the church aisle; it was common report that she had flesh every day for her dinner; instead of meeting her lover at the pump she walked him into the country, and he returned with wild roses in his buttonhole, his hand up to hide them, and on his face the troubled look of those who know that if they take this lady they must give up drinking from the saucer for evermore. For the lovers were really common men until she gave them that glance over the shoulder which, I have noticed, is the fatal gift of servants.

According to legend we once had a servant—in my childhood I

could show the mark of it on my forehead, and even point her out to other boys, though she was now merely a wife with a house of her own. But even while I boasted I doubted. Reduced to life-size she may have been but a woman who came in to help. I shall say no more about her lest someone comes forward to prove that she went home at night.

Never shall I forget my first servant. I was eight or nine, in velveteen, diamond socks ("Cross your legs when they look at you," my mother had said, "and put your thumb in your pocket and leave the top of your handkerchief showing"), and I had travelled by rail to visit a relative. He had a servant, and as I was to be his guest she must be my servant also for the time being—you may be sure I had got my mother to put this plainly before me ere I set off. My relative met me at the station, but I wasted no time in hoping I found him well. I did not even cross my legs for him, so eager was I to hear whether she was still there. A sister greeted me at the door, but I chafed at having to be kissed; at once I made for the kitchen, where, I knew, they reside, and there she was, and I crossed my legs and put one thumb in my pocket, and the handkerchief was showing. Afterwards I stopped strangers on the highway with an offer to show her to them through the kitchen window, and I doubt not the first letter I ever wrote told my mother what they are like when they are so near that you can put your fingers into them.

But now when we could have servants for ourselves I shrank from the thought. It would not be the same house; we should have to dissemble; I saw myself speaking English the long day through. You only know the shell of a Scot until you have entered his home circle; in his office, in clubs, at social gatherings where you and he seem to be getting on so well he is really a house with all the shutters closed and the door locked. He is not opaque of set purpose, often it is against his will—it is certainly against mine, I try to keep my shutters open and my foot in the door but they will bang to. In many ways my mother was as reticent as myself, though her manners were as gracious as mine were rough (in vain, alas, all the honest oiling of them), and my sister was the most reserved of us all; you might at times see a light through one of my chinks: she was double-shuttered. Now, it seems to be a law of nature that we must show our true selves at some time, and as the Scot must do it at home, and squeeze a day into an hour, what follows is that there he is self-revealing in the superlative degree, the feelings so long dammed up overflow, and thus a Scotch family are probably better acquainted with each other, and more ignorant of the life outside their circle, than any other family in the world. And as knowledge is sympathy, the affection existing between them is almost painful in its intensity; they have not more to give than their neighbours, but it is bestowed upon a few instead of being distributed among many; they are reputed niggardly, but for family affection at least they pay in gold. In this, I believe, we shall find the true explanation why Scotch literature, since long before the days of Burns, has been so often inspired by the domestic hearth and has treated it with a passionate understanding.

Must a woman come into our house and discover that I was not such a dreary dog as I had the reputation of being? Was I to be seen at last with the veil of dourness lifted? My company voice is so low and unimpressive that my first remark is merely an intimation that I am about to speak (like the whirr of the clock before it strikes): must it be revealed that I had another voice, that there was one door I never opened without leaving my reserve on the mat? Ah, that room, must its secrets be disclosed? So joyous they were when my mother was well, no wonder we were merry. Again and again she had been given back to us; it was for the glorious today we thanked God; in our hearts we knew and in our prayers confessed that the fill of delight had been given us, whatever might befall. We had not to wait till all was over to know its value; my mother used to say, "We never understand how little we need in this world until we know the loss of it," and there can be few truer sayings, but during her last years we exulted daily in the possession of her as much as we can exult in her memory. No wonder, I say, that we were merry, but we liked to show it to God alone, and to Him only our agony during those many night-alarms, when lights flickered in the house and white faces were round my mother's bedside. Not for other eyes those long vigils when, night about, we sat watching, nor the awful nights when we stood together, teeth clenched—waiting—it must be now. And it was not then; her hand became cooler, her breathing more easy; she smiled to us. Once more I could work by snatches, and was glad, but what was the result to me compared to the joy of hearing that voice from the other room? There lay all the work I was ever proud of, the rest is but honest craftsmanship done to give her coal and food and softer pillows. My thousand letters that she so carefully preserved, always sleeping with the last beneath the sheet, where one was found when she died—they are the only writing of mine of which I shall ever boast. I would not there had been one less though I could have written an immortal book for it.

How my sister toiled—to prevent a stranger's getting any footing in the house! And how, with the same object, my mother strove to "do for herself" once more. She pretended that she was always well now, and concealed her ailments so craftily that we had to probe for them:

"I think you are not feeling well today?"

"I am perfectly well."

"Where is the pain?"

"I have no pain to speak of."

"Is it at your heart?"

"No."

"Is your breathing hurting you?"

"Not it."

"Do you feel those stounds in your head again?"

"No, no, I tell you there is nothing the matter with me."

"Have you a pain in your side?"

"Really, it's most provoking I canna put my hand to my side without your thinking I have a pain there."

"You have a pain in your side!"

"I might have a pain in my side."

"And you are trying to hide it! Is it very painful?"

"It's—it's no so bad but what I can bear it."

Which of these two gave in first I cannot tell, though to me fell the duty of persuading them, for whichever she was she rebelled as soon as the other showed signs of yielding, so that sometimes I had two converts in the week but never both on the same day. I would take them separately, and press the one to yield for the sake of the other, but they saw so easily through my artifice. My mother might go bravely to my sister and say, "I have been thinking it over, and I believe I would like a servant fine—once we got used to her."

"Did he tell you to say that?" asks my sister sharply.

"I say it of my own free will."

"He put you up to it, I am sure, and he told you not to let on that you did it to lighten my work."

"Maybe he did, but I think we should get one."

"Not for my sake," says my sister obstinately, and then my mother comes ben to me to say delightedly, "She winna listen to reason!"

But at last a servant was engaged; we might be said to be at the window, gloomily waiting for her now, and it was with such words as these that we sought to comfort each other and ourselves:

"She will go early to her bed."

"She needna often be seen upstairs."

"We'll set her to the walking every day."

"There will be a many errands for her to run. We'll tell her to take her time over them."

"Three times she shall go to the kirk every Sabbath, and we'll egg her on to attending the lectures in the hall."

"She is sure to have friends in the town. We'll let her visit them often."

"If she dares to come into your room, mother!"

"Mind this, every one of you, servant or no servant, I fold all the linen mysel."

"She shall not get cleaning out the east room."

"Nor putting my chest of drawers in order."

"Nor tidying up my manuscripts."

"I hope she's a reader, though. You could set her down with a book, and then close the door canny on her."

And so on. Was ever servant awaited so apprehensively? And then she came—at an anxious time, too, when her worth could be put to the proof at once—and from first to last she was a treasure. I know not what we should have done without her.

I X

MY HEROINE

WHEN it was known that I had begun another story my mother might ask what it was to be about this time.

"Fine we can guess who it is about," my sister would say pointedly.

"Maybe you can guess, but it is beyond me," says my mother, with the meekness of one who knows that she is a dull person.

My sister scorned her at such times. "What woman is in all his books?" she would demand.

"I'm sure I canna say," replies my mother determinedly. "I thought the women were different every time."

"Mother, I wonder you can be so audacious! Fine you know what woman I mean."

"How can I know? What woman is it? You should bear in mind that I hinna your cleverness." (They were constantly giving each other little knocks.)

"I won't give you the satisfaction of saying her name. But this I will say, it is high time he was keeping her out of his books."

And then as usual my mother would give herself away unconsciously. "That is what I tell him," she says chuckling, "and he tries to keep me out, but he canna; its more than he can do!"

On an evening after my mother had gone to bed, the first chapter would be brought upstairs, and I read, sitting at the foot of the bed, while my sister watched to make my mother behave herself, and my father cried "H'sh!" when there were interruptions. All would go well at the start, the reflections were accepted with a little nod of the head, the descriptions of scenery as ruts on the road that must be got over at a walking pace (my mother did not care for scenery, and that is why there is so little of it in my books). But now I am reading too quickly, a little apprehensively, because I know that the next paragraph begins with—let us say with, "Along this path came a woman": I had intended to rush on here in a loud bullying voice, but, "Along this path came a woman," I read, and stop. Did I hear a faint sound from the other end of the bed? Perhaps I did not; I may only have been listening for it, but I falter and look up. My sister and I look sternly at my mother. She bites her under-lip and clutches the bed with both hands, really she is doing her best for me, but first comes a smothered gurgling sound, then her hold on herself relaxes and she shakes with mirth.

"That's a way to behave!" cries my sister.

"I cannot help it," my mother gasps.

"And there's nothing to laugh at."

"It's that woman," my mother explains unnecessarily.

"Maybe she's not the woman you think her," I say, crushed.

"Maybe not," says my mother doubtfully. "What was her name?"

"Her name," I answer with triumph, "was not Margaret"; but this makes her ripple again. "I have so many names nowadays," she mutters.

"H'sh!" says my father, and the reading is resumed.

Perhaps the woman who came along the path was of tall and majestic figure, which should have shown my mother that I had contrived to start my train without her this time. But it did not.

"What are you laughing at now?" says my sister severely. "Do you not hear that she was a tall, majestic woman?"

"It's the first time I ever heard it said of her," replies my mother.

"But she is."

"Ke fy, havers!"

"The book says it."

"There will be a many queer things in the book. What was she wearing?"

I have not described her clothes. "That's a mistake," says my mother. "When I come upon a woman in a book, the first thing I want to know about her is whether she was good-looking, and the second, how she was put on."

The woman on the path was eighteen years of age, and of remarkable beauty.

"That settles you," says my sister.

"I was no beauty at eighteen," my mother admits, but here my father interferes unexpectedly. "There wasna your like in this countryside at eighteen," says he stoutly.

"Pooh!" says she, well-pleased.

"Were you plain, then?" we ask.

"Sal," she replies briskly, "I was far from plain."

"H'sh!"

Perhaps in the next chapter this lady (or another) appears in a carriage.

"I assure you we're mounting in the world," I hear my mother murmur, but I hurry on without looking up. The lady lives in a house where there are footmen—but the footmen have come on the scene too hurriedly. "This is more than I can stand," gasps my mother, and just as she is getting the better of a fit of laughter, "Footman, give me a drink of water," she cries, and this sets her off again. Often the readings had to end abruptly because her mirth brought on violent fits of coughing.

Sometimes I read to my sister alone, and she assured me that she could not see my mother among the women this time. This she said to humour me. Presently she would slip upstairs to announce triumphantly, "You are in again!"

Or in the small hours I might make a confidant of my father, and when I had finished reading he would say thoughtfully, "That lassie is very natural. Some of the ways you say she had—your mother had them just the same. Did you ever notice what an extraordinary woman your mother is?"

Then would I seek my mother for comfort. She was the more ready to give it because of her profound conviction that if I was found out—that is, if readers discovered how frequently and in how many guises she appeared in my books—the affair would become a public scandal.

"You see Jess is not really you," I begin inquiringly.

"Oh, no, she is another kind of woman altogether," my mother says, and then spoils the compliment by adding naïvely, "She had but two rooms and I have six."

I sigh.

"Without counting the pantry, and it's a great big pantry," she mutters.

This was not the sort of difference I could greatly plume myself upon, and honesty would force me to say, "As far as that goes, there was a time when you had but two rooms yourself——"

"That's long since," she breaks in. "I began with an up-the-stair, but I always had it in my mind—I never mentioned it, but there it was—to have the down-the-stair as well. Ay, and I've had it this many a year."

"Still, there is no denying that Jess had the same ambition."

"She had, but to her two-roomed house she had to stick to all her born days. Was that like me?"

"No, but she wanted——"

"She wanted, and I wanted, but I got and she didna. That's the difference betwixt her and me."

"If that is all the difference, it is little credit I can claim for having created her."

My mother sees that I need soothing. "That is far from being all the difference," she would say eagerly. "There's my silk, for instance. Though I say it mysel, there's not a better silk in the valley of Strathmore. Had Jess a silk of any kind—not to speak of a silk like that?"

"Well, she had no silk, but you remember how she got that cloak with beads."

"An eleven and a bit! Hoots, what was that to boast of! I tell you, every single yard of my silk cost——"

"Mother, that is the very way Jess spoke about her cloak!"

She lets this pass, perhaps without hearing it, for solicitude about her silk has hurried her to the wardrobe where it hangs.

"Ah, mother, I am afraid that was very like Jess!"

"How could it be like her when she didna even have a wardrobe? I tell you what, if there had been a real Jess and she had boasted to me about her cloak with beads, I would have said to her in a careless sort of voice, 'Step across with me, Jess, and I'll let you see something that is hanging in my wardrobe.' That would have lowered her pride!"

"I don't believe that is what you would have done, mother."

Then a sweeter expression would come into her face. "No," she would say reflectively, "it's not."

"What would you have done? I think I know."

"You canna know. But I'm thinking I would have called to mind that she was a poor woman, and ailing, and terrible windy about her cloak, and I would just have said it was a beauty and that I wished I had one like it."

"Yes, I am certain that is what you would have done. But oh, mother, that is just how Jess would have acted if some poorer woman than she had shown her a new shawl."

"Maybe, but though I hadna boasted about my silk I would have wanted to do it."

"Just as Jess would have been fidgeting to show off her eleven and a bit!"

It seems advisable to jump to another book; not to my first, because— well, as it was my first there would naturally be something of my mother in it, and not to the second, as it was my first novel and not much esteemed even in our family. (But the little touches of my mother in it are not so bad.) Let us try the story about the minister.

My mother's first remark is decidedly damping. "Many a time in my young days," she says, "I played about the Auld Licht manse, but I little thought I should live to be the mistress of it!"

"But Margaret is not you."

"N-no, oh, no. She had a very different life from mine. I never let on to a soul that she is me!"

"She was not meant to be you when I began. Mother, what a way you have of coming creeping in!"

"You should keep better watch on yourself."

"Perhaps if I had called Margaret by some other name——"

"I should have seen through her just the same. As soon as I heard she was the mother I began to laugh. In some ways, though, she's no so very like me. She was long in finding out about Babbie. I'se uphaud I should have been quicker."

"Babbie, you see, kept close to the garden-wall."

"It's not the wall up at the manse that would have hidden her from me."

"She came out in the dark."

"I'm thinking she would have found me looking for her with a candle."

"And Gavin was secretive."

"That would have put me on my mettle."

"She never suspected anything."

"I wonder at her."

But my new heroine is to be a child. What has madam to say to that?

A child! Yes, she has something to say even to that. "This beats all!" are the words.

"Come, come, mother, I see what you are thinking, but I assure you that this time——"

"Of course not," she said soothingly, "oh, no, she canna be me"; but anon her real thoughts are revealed by the artless remark, "I doubt, though, this is a tough job you have on hand—it is so long since I was a bairn."

We came very close to each other in those talks. "It is a queer thing," she would say softly, "that near everything you write is about this bit place. You little expected that when you began. I mind well the time when it never entered your head, any more than mine, that you could write a page about our squares and wynds. I wonder how it has come about?"

There was a time when I could not have answered that question, but that time had long passed. "I suppose, mother, it was because you were most at home in your own town, and there was never much pleasure to me in writing of people who could not have known you, nor of squares and wynds you never passed through, nor of a country- side where you never carried your father's dinner in a flagon. There is scarce a house in all my books where I have not seemed to see you a thousand times, bending over the fireplace or winding up the clock."

"And yet you used to be in such a quandary because you knew no- body you could make your women-folk out of! Do you mind that, and how we both laughed at the notion of your having to make them out of me?"

"I remember."

"And now you've gone back to my father's time. It's more than sixty years since I carried his dinner in a flagon through the long parks of Kinnordy."

"I often go into the long parks, mother, and sit on the stile at the edge of the wood till I fancy I see a little girl coming toward me with a flagon in her hand."

"Jumping the burn (I was once so proud of my jumps!) and swing- ing the flagon round so quick that what was inside hadna time to fall out. I used to wear a magenta frock and a white pinafore. Did I ever tell you that?"

"Mother, the little girl in my story wears a magenta frock and a white pinafore."

"You minded that! But I'm thinking it wasna a lassie in a pinafore you saw in the long parks of Kinnordy, it was just a gey done auld woman."

"It was a lassie in a pinafore, mother, when she was far away, but when she came near it was a gey done auld woman."

"And a fell ugly one!"

"The most beautiful one I shall ever see."

"I wonder to hear you say it. Look at my wrinkled auld face."

"It is the sweetest face in all the world."

"See how the rings drop off my poor wasted finger."

"There will always be someone nigh, mother, to put them on again."

"Ay, will there! Well I know it. Do you mind how when you were but a bairn you used to say, 'Wait till I'm a man, and you'll never have a reason for greeting again'?"

I remembered.

"You used to come running into the house to say, 'There's a proud dame going down the Marywellbrae in a cloak that is black on one side and white on the other; wait till I'm a man, and you'll have one the very same.' And when I lay on gey hard beds you said, 'When I'm a man you'll lie on feathers.' You saw nothing bonny, you never heard of my setting my heart on anything, but what you flung up your head and cried, 'Wait till I'm a man.' You fair shamed me before the neighbours, and yet I was windy, too. And now it has all come true like a dream. I can call to mind not one little thing I ettled for in my lusty days that hasna been put into my hands in my auld age; I sit here useless, surrounded by the gratification of all my wishes and all my ambitions, and at times I'm near terrified, for it's as if God had mista'en me for some other woman."

"Your hopes and ambitions were so simple," I would say, but she did not like that. "They werena that simple," she would answer, flushing.

I am reluctant to leave those happy days, but the end must be faced, and as I write I seem to see my mother growing smaller and her face more wistful, and still she lingers with us, as if God had said, "Child of mine, your time has come, be not afraid," and she was not afraid, but still she lingered, and He waited, smiling. I never read any of that last book to her; when it was finished she was too heavy with years to follow a story. To me this was as if my book must go out cold into the world (like all that may come after it from me), and my sister, who took more thought for others and less for herself than any other human being I have known, saw this, and by some means unfathomable to a man coaxed my mother into being once again the woman she had been. On a day but three weeks before she died my father and I were called softly upstairs. My mother was sitting bolt upright, as she loved to sit, in her old chair by the window, with a manuscript in her hands. But she was looking about her without much understanding. "Just to please him," my sister whispered, and then in a low, trembling voice my mother began to read. I looked at my sister. Tears of woe were stealing down her face. Soon the reading became very slow and stopped. After a pause, "There was something you were to say to him," my sister reminded her. "Luck," muttered a voice as from the dead, "luck." And then the old smile came running to her face like a lamp-lighter, and she said to me, "I am ower far gone to read, but I'm thinking I am in it again!" My father put her Testament in her hands, and it fell open—as it always does—at the Fourteenth of John. She made an effort to read but could not. Suddenly she stooped and kissed the broad page. "Will that do instead?" she asked.

x

ART THOU AFRAID HIS POWER SHALL FAIL?

FOR years I had been trying to prepare myself for my mother's death, trying to foresee how she would die, seeing myself when she was dead. Even then I knew it was a vain thing I did, but I am sure there was no morbidness in it. I hoped I should be with her at the end, not as the one she looked at last but as him from whom she would turn only to look upon her best-beloved, not my arm but my sister's should be round her when she died, not my hand but my sister's should close her eyes. I knew that I might reach her too late; I saw myself open a door where there was none to greet me, and go up the old stair into the old room. But what I did not foresee was that which happened. I little thought it could come about that I should climb the old stair, and pass the door beyond which my mother lay dead, and enter another room first, and go on my knees there.

My mother's favourite paraphrase is one known in our house as David's because it was the last he learned to repeat. It was also the last thing she read—

> Art thou afraid his power shall fail
> When comes thy evil day?

And can an all-creating arm
Grow weary or decay?

I heard her voice gain strength as she read it, I saw her timid face take courage, but when came my evil day, then at the dawning, alas for me, I was afraid.

In those last weeks, though we did not know it, my sister was dying on her feet. For many years she had been giving her life, a little bit at a time, for another year, another month, latterly for another day, to her mother, and now she was worn out. "I'll never leave you, mother."—"Fine I know you'll never leave me." I thought that cry so pathetic at the time, but I was not to know its full significance until it was only the echo of a cry. Looking at these two then it was to me as if my mother had set out for the new country, and my sister held her back. But I see with a clearer vision now. It is no longer the mother but the daughter who is in front, and she cries, "Mother, you are lingering so long at the end, I have ill waiting for you."

But she knew no more than we how it was to be; if she seemed weary when we met her on the stair, she was still the brightest, the most active figure in my mother's room; she never complained, save when she had to depart on that walk which separated them for half an hour. How reluctantly she put on her bonnet, how we had to press her to it, and how often, having gone as far as the door, she came back to stand by my mother's side. Sometimes as we watched from the window, I could not but laugh, and yet with a pain at my heart, to see her hasting doggedly onward, not an eye for right or left, nothing in her head but the return. There was always my father in the house, than whom never was a more devoted husband, and often there were others, one daughter in particular, but they scarce dared tend my mother—this one snatched the cup jealously from their hands. My mother liked it best from her. We all knew this. "I like them fine, but I canna do without you." My sister, so unselfish in all other things, had an unwearying passion for parading it before us. It was the rich reward of her life.

The others spoke among themselves of what must come soon, and they had tears to help them, but this daughter would not speak of it, and her tears were ever slow to come. I knew that night and day she was trying to get ready for a world without her mother in it, but she must remain dumb, none of us was so Scotch as she, she must bear her agony alone, a tragic solitary Scotchwoman. Even my mother, who spoke so calmly to us of the coming time, could not mention it to her. These two, the one in bed, and the other bending over her, could only look long at each other, until slowly the tears came to my sister's eyes, and then my mother would turn away her wet face. And still neither said a word, each knew so well what was in the other's thoughts, so eloquently they spoke in silence, "Mother, I am loath to let you go," and "Oh, my daughter, now that my time is near, I wish you werena quite so fond of me." But when the daughter had slipped away my mother would grip my hand and cry, "I leave her to you; you see how she has sown, it will depend on you how she is to reap." And I made promises, but I suppose neither of us saw that she had already reaped.

In the night my mother might waken and sit up in bed, confused by what she saw. While she slept, six decades or more had rolled back and she was again in her girlhood; suddenly recalled from it she was dizzy, as with the rush of the years. How had she come into this room? When she went to bed last night, after preparing her father's supper, there had been a dresser at the window: what had become of the salt-bucket, the meal-tub, the hams that should be hanging from the rafters? There were no rafters; it was a papered ceiling. She had often heard of open beds, but how came she to be lying in one? To fathom these things she would try to spring out of bed and be startled to find it a labour, as if she had been taken ill in the night. Hearing her move I might knock on the wall that separated us, this being a sign, pre-arranged between us, that I was near by, and so all was well, but sometimes the knocking seemed to belong to the past, and she would cry, "That is my father chapping at the door, I maun rise and let him in." She seemed to see him—and it was one much younger than herself that she saw—covered with snow, kicking clods of it from his boots, his hands swollen and chapped with sand and wet. Then I would hear—it was a common experience of the night—my sister soothing her lovingly, and turning up the light to show her where she was, helping her to the window to let her see that it was no night of snow, even humouring her by going downstairs, and opening the outer door, and calling into the darkness, "Is anybody there?" and if that was not sufficient, she would swaddle my mother in wraps and take her through the rooms of the house, lighting them one by one, pointing out familiar objects, and so guiding her slowly through the sixty-odd years she had jumped too quickly. And perhaps the end of it was that my mother came to my bedside and said wistfully, "Am I an auld woman?"

But with daylight, even during the last week in which I saw her, she would be up and doing, for though pitifully frail she no longer suffered from any ailment. She seemed so well comparatively that I, having still the remnants of an illness to shake off, was to take a holiday in Switzerland, and then return for her, when we were all to go to the much-loved manse of her much-loved brother in the west country. So she had many preparations on her mind, and the morning was the time when she had any strength to carry them out. To leave her house had always been a month's work for her, it must be left in such perfect order, every corner visited and cleaned out, every chest probed to the bottom, the linen lifted out, examined and put back lovingly as if to make it lie more easily in her absence, shelves had to be re-papered, a strenuous week devoted to the garret. Less exhaustively, but with much of the old exultation in her house, this was done for the last time, and then there was the bringing out of her own clothes, and the spreading of them upon the bed and the pleased fingering of them, and the consultations about which should be left behind. Ah, beautiful dream! I clung to it every morning; I would not look when my sister shook her head at it, but long before each day was done, I too knew that it could never be. It had come true many times, but never again. We two knew it, but when my mother, who must always be prepared so long beforehand, called for her trunk and band-boxes we brought them to her, and we stood silent, watching, while she packed.

The morning came when I was to go away. It had come a hundred times, when I was a boy, when I was an undergraduate, when I was a man, when she had seemed big and strong to me, when she was grown so little and it was I who put my arms round her. But always it was the same scene. I am not to write about it, of the parting and the turning back on the stair, and two people trying to smile, and the setting off again, and the cry that brought me back. Nor shall I say more of the silent figure in the background, always in the background, always near my mother. The last I saw of these two was from the gate. They were at the window which never passes from my eyes. I could not see my dear sister's face, for she was bending over my mother, pointing me out to her, and telling her to wave her hand and smile, because I liked it so. That action was an epitome of my sister's life.

I had been gone a fortnight when the telegram was put into my hands. I had got a letter from my sister, a few hours before, saying that all was well at home. The telegram said in five words that she had died suddenly the previous night. There was no mention of my mother, and I was three days' journey from home.

The news I got on reaching London was this: my mother did not understand that her daughter was dead, and they were waiting for me to tell her.

I need not have been such a coward. This is how these two died— for, after all, I was too late by twelve hours to see my mother alive.

Their last night was almost gleeful. In the old days that hour before my mother's gas was lowered had so often been the happiest that my pen steals back to it again and again as I write: it was the time when my mother lay smiling in bed and we were gathered round her like children at play, our reticence scattered on the floor or tossed in sport from hand to hand, the author become so boisterous that in the pauses they were holding him in check by force. Rather woeful had been some attempts latterly to renew those evenings, when my mother might be brought to the verge of them, as if some familiar echo called her, but where she was she did not clearly know, because the past was roaring in her ears like a great sea. But this night was the last gift to my sister. The joyousness of their voices drew the others in the house upstairs, where for more than an hour my mother was the centre of a merry party and so clear of mental eye that they, who were at first cautious, abandoned themselves to the sport, and whatever they said, by way of humorous rally, she instantly capped as of old, turning their darts against themselves until in self-defence they were three to one, and the three hard pressed. How my sister must have been rejoicing. Once again she could cry, "Was there ever such a woman!" They tell me that such a happiness was on the daughter's face that my mother commented on it, that having risen to go they sat down again, fascinated by the radiance of these two. And when eventually they went, the last words they heard were, "They are gone, you see, mother, but I am here, I will never leave you," and "Na, you winna leave me; fine I know that." For some time afterwards their voices could be heard from downstairs, but what they talked of is not known. And then came silence. Had I been at home I should have been in the room again several times, turning the handle of the door softly, releasing it so that it did not creak, and standing looking at them. It had been so a thousand times. But that night, would I have slipped out again, mind at rest, or should I have seen the change coming while they slept?

Let it be told in the fewest words. My sister awoke next morning with a headache. She had always been a martyr to headaches, but this one, like many another, seemed to be unusually severe. Nevertheless she rose and lit my mother's fire and brought up her breakfast, and then had to return to bed. She was not able to write her daily letter to me, saying how my mother was, and almost the last thing she did was to ask my father to write it, and not to let on that she was ill, as it would distress me. The doctor was called, but she rapidly became unconscious. In this state she was removed from my mother's bed to another. It was discovered that she was suffering from an internal disease. No one had guessed it. She herself never knew. Nothing could be done. In this unconsciousness she passed away, without knowing that she was leaving her mother. Had I known, when I heard of her death, that she had been saved that pain, surely I could have gone home more bravely with the words,

> Art thou afraid his power shall fail
> When comes thy evil day?

Ah, you would think so, I should have thought so, but I know myself now. When I reached London I did hear how my sister died, but still I was afraid. I saw myself in my mother's room telling her why the door of the next room was locked, and I was afraid. God had done so much, and yet I could not look confidently to Him for the little that was left to do. "O ye of little faith!" These are the words I seem to hear my mother saying to me now, and she looks at me so sorrowfully.

He did it very easily, and it has ceased to seem marvellous to me because it was so plainly His doing. My timid mother saw the one who was never to leave her carried unconscious from the room, and she did not break down. She who used to wring her hands if her daughter was gone for a moment never asked for her again, they were afraid to mention her name; an awe fell upon them. But I am sure they need not have been so anxious. There are mysteries in life and death, but this was not one of them. A child can understand what happened. God said that my sister must come first, but He put His hand on my mother's eyes at that moment and she was altered.

They told her that I was on my way home, and she said with a confident smile, "He will come as quick as trains can bring him." That is my reward, that is what I have got for my books. Everything I could do for her in this life I have done since I was a boy; I look back through the years and I cannot see the smallest thing left undone.

They were buried together on my mother's seventy-sixth birthday, though there had been three days between their deaths. On the last day, my mother insisted on rising from bed and going through the house. The arms that had so often helped her on that journey were now cold in death, but there were others only less loving, and she went slowly from room to room like one bidding good-bye, and in mine she said, "The beautiful rows upon rows of books, and he said every one of them was mine, all mine!" and in the east room, which was her greatest triumph, she said caressingly, "My nain bonny room!" All this time there seemed to be something that she wanted, but the one was dead who always knew what she wanted, and they produced many things at which she shook her head. They did not know then that she was dying, but they followed her through the house in some apprehension, and after she returned to bed they saw that she was becoming very weak. Once she said eagerly, "Is that you, David?" and again she thought she heard her father knocking the snow off his boots. Her desire for that which she could not name came back to her, and at last they saw that what she wanted was the old christening robe. It was brought to her, and she unfolded it with trembling, exultant hands, and when she had made sure that it was still of virgin fairness her old arms went round it adoringly, and upon her face there was the ineffable mysterious glow of motherhood. Suddenly she said, "Wha's bairn's dead? is a bairn of mine dead?" but those watching dared not speak, and then slowly as if with an effort of memory she repeated our names aloud in the order in which we were born. Only one, who should have come third among the ten, did she omit, the one in the next room, but at the end, after a pause, she said her name and repeated it again and again and again, lingering over it as if it were the most exquisite music and this her dying song. And yet it was a very commonplace name.

They knew now that she was dying. She told them to fold up the christening robe and almost sharply she watched them put it away, and then for some time she talked of the long lovely life that had been hers, and of Him to whom she owed it. She said good-bye to them all, and at last turned her face to the side where her best-beloved had lain, and for over an hour she prayed. They only caught the words now and again, and the last they heard were "God" and "love." I think God was smiling when He took her to Him, as He had so often smiled at her during those seventy-six years.

I saw her lying dead, and her face was beautiful and serene. But it was the other room I entered first, and it was by my sister's side that I fell upon my knees. The rounded completeness of a woman's life that was my mother's had not been for her. She would not have it at the price. "I'll never leave you, mother."—"Fine I know you'll never leave me." The fierce joy of loving too much, it is a terrible thing. My sister's mouth was firmly closed, as if she had got her way.

And now I am left without them, but I trust my memory will ever go back to those happy days, not to rush through them, but dallying here and there, even as my mother wanders through my books. And if I also live to a time when age must dim my mind and the past comes sweeping back like the shades of night over the bare road of the present it will not, I believe, be my youth I shall see but hers, not a boy clinging to his mother's skirt and crying, "Wait till I'm a man, and you'll lie on feathers," but a little girl in a magenta frock and a white pinafore, who comes toward me through the long parks, singing to herself, and carrying her father's dinner in a flagon.

AN AFTERWORD ON
"MARGARET OGILVY"

THIS unique and lovely biography, Barrie's portrait of his mother and the poor, proud Scottish home from which she watched him go forth to fame and fortune, was published when he was six-and-thirty. In the four decades which have since slipped by, he has done nothing better. It would usually and pardonably afflict any author to be told that, in a lifetime of putting words on paper, he had managed nothing better than something he wrote forty years before. But surely Margaret Ogilvy's son would not have you say otherwise.

If she was always proud and pleased and immoderately amused to discover herself, unsuccessfully disguised, as the heroine of each of his earlier stories, how she would have relished the mightier stories and the endearing plays which she did not live to read or see. For who was Grizel in *Sentimental Tommy* but the same little girl in a magenta frock and white pinafore who used to carry her father's dinner in a flagon? Who else was Wendy in *Peter Pan?* Who else on this earth could have served as the model for *The Old Lady Shows Her Medals?* And at the Haymarket when the Great War was raging, she would gleefully have recognized herself in every quirk and fancy which made up the dauntless heroine of *A Kiss for Cinderella.* This mothering youngster had such a way with the bobby, who had found her frozen and half-starved in the street, that he used to visit her in hospital and would sometimes write her from the police-station. "There are thirty-four policemen sitting in this room," he wrote her once, "but I'd rather have you, my dear." Cinderella sought counsel as to whether this was a love letter. If not it was at least a very near thing. Margaret Ogilvy would also have made a point of being in doubt.

On a May day in 1922 Barrie made the Rectorial address at St. Andrews University in Edinburgh. By that time he had become a crusty baronet full of years, an almost legendary figure, as cherished and sacrosanct an item in the British possessions as Magna Charta or the Kohinoor diamond. Courage was his theme that day and at one point he read to the boys a letter which he thought would hearten them. They heard him say:

I have the little filmy sheets here. I thought you might like to see the actual letter; it has been a long journey; it has been to the South Pole. It is a letter to me from Captain Scott of the Antarctic, and was written in the tent you know of, where it was found long afterwards with his body and those of some other very gallant gentlemen, his comrades. The writing is in pencil, still quite clear, though toward the end some of the words trail away as into the great silence that was waiting for them. It begins: "We are pegging out in a very comfortless spot. Hoping this letter may be found and sent to you, I write you a word of farewell. I want you to think well of me and my end." (After some private instructions too intimate to read, he goes on): "Good-bye—I am not at all afraid of the end, but sad to miss many a simple pleasure which I had planned for the future in our long marches. . . . We are in a desperate state—feet frozen, etc., no fuel, and a long way from food, but it would do your heart good to be in our tent, to hear our songs and our cheery conversation. . . . Later—" (It is here that the words become difficult)— "We are very near the end. . . . We did intend to finish ourselves when things proved like this, but we have decided to die naturally without."

I think it may uplift you all to stand for a moment by that tent and listen, as he says, to their songs and cheery conversation. When I think of Scott I remember the strange Alpine story of the youth who fell down a glacier and was lost, and of how a scientific companion, one of several who accompanied him, all young, computed that the body would again appear at a certain date and place many years afterwards. When that time came round some of the survivors returned to the glacier to see if the prediction would be fulfilled; all old men now; and the body reappeared as young as on the day he left them. So Scott and his comrades emerge out of the white immensities always young.

In the hushed audience that day—Galsworthy was there and Ellen Terry and Field-Marshal Haig—there must have been some who knew by rumor and more who guessed that that last letter written by Scott was sent to the good friend who had backed his expedition. And you who have lingered over this portrait of the little old woman with the soft face must know for sure that if Barrie stood behind Scott it was because Margaret Ogilvy would have wished him to—she who "liked the explorers to be alive so that she could shudder at the thought of their venturing forth again, but though she expressed a hope that they would have the sense to stay at home henceforth, she gleamed with admiration when they disappointed her." On that day when such a one would return victorious she grudged him to his mother. Then, what was before her eyes was not the son come marching home again but an old woman peering for him around the window-curtain and trying not to look uplifted. The newspaper reports would be about the son but Margaret Ogilvy's comment was: "She's a proud woman this night."

A. W.

THE DOLLY
DIALOGUES

by

ANTHONY HOPE

THESE ARE FOOLISH THINGS TO ALL THE WISE—
AND I LOVE WISDOM MORE THAN SHE LOVES ME

THE DOLLY DIALOGUES

I

A LIBERAL EDUCATION

"There's ingratitude for you!" Miss Dolly Foster exclaimed suddenly.

"Where?" I asked, rousing myself from meditation.

She pointed at a young man who had just passed where we sat. He was dressed very smartly, and was walking with a lady attired in the height of the fashion.

"I *made* that man," said Dolly, "and now he cuts me dead before the whole of the Row! It's atrocious. Why, but for me, do you suppose he'd be at this moment engaged to three thousand a year and—and the plainest girl in London?"

"Not that," I pleaded; "think of——"

"Well, very plain, anyhow. I was quite ready to bow to him. I almost did."

"In fact, you did?"

"I didn't. I declare I didn't."

"Oh, well, you didn't, then. It only looked like it."

"I met him," said Miss Dolly, "three years ago. At that time he was —oh, quite unpresentable. He was everything he shouldn't be. He was a teetotaler, you know, and he didn't smoke, and he was always going to concerts. Oh, and he wore his hair long, and his trousers short, and his hat on the back of his head. And his umbrella——"

"Where did he wear that?"

"He *carried* that, Mr. Carter. Don't be silly! Carried it unrolled, you know, and generally a paper parcel in the other hand; and he had spectacles too."

85

"He has certainly changed outwardly at least."

"Yes, I know; well, I did that. I took him in hand, and I just taught him, and now——!"

"Yes, I know that. But how did you teach him? Give him Saturday-evening lectures, or what?"

"Oh, every-evening lectures, and most-morning walks. And I taught him to dance, and I broke his wretched fiddle with my own hands!"

"What very arbitrary distinctions you draw!"

"I don't know what you mean. I do like a man to be smart, anyhow. Don't you, Mr. Carter? You're not so smart as you might be. Now, shall I take you in hand?" And she smiled upon me.

"Let's hear your method. What did you do to him?"

"To Phil Meadows? Oh, nothing. I just slipped in a remark here and there, whenever he talked nonsense. I used to speak just at the right time, you know."

"But how had your words such influence, Miss Foster?"

"Oh, well, you know, Mr. Carter, I made it a *condition* that he should do just what I wanted in little things like that. Did he think I was going to walk about with a man carrying a brown-paper parcel —as if we had been to the shop for a pound of tea?"

"Still, I don't see why he should alter all his——"

"Oh, you are stupid! Of course, he liked me, you know."

"Oh, did he? I see."

"You seem to think that very funny."

"Not that he did—but that, apparently, he doesn't."

"Well, you got out of that rather neatly—for you. No, he doesn't now. You see, he misunderstood my motive. He thought—well, I do believe he thought I cared for him, you know. Of course I didn't."

"Not a bit?"

"Just as a friend—and a pupil, you know. And when he'd had his hair cut and bought a frock-coat (fancy! he'd never had one!), he looked quite nice. He has nice eyes. Did you notice them?"

"Lord, no!"

"Well, you're so unobservant."

"Oh, not always. I've observed that your——"

' Please don't! It's no use, is it?"

I looked very unhappy. There is an understanding that I am very unhappy since Miss Foster's engagement to the Earl of Mickleham was announced.

"What was I saying before—before you—you know—oh, about Phil Meadows, of course. I did like him very much, you know, or I shouldn't have taken all that trouble. Why, his own mother thanked me!"

"I have no more to say," said I.

"But she wrote me a horrid letter afterward."

"You're so very elliptical."

"So very what, Mr. Carter?"

"You leave so much out, I mean. After what?"

"Why, after I sent him away. Didn't I tell you? Oh, we had the most awful scene. He *raved,* Mr. Carter. He called me the most horrid names, and——"

"Tore his hair?"

"It wasn't long enough to get hold of," she tittered. "But don't laugh. It was really dreadful. And so unjust! And then, next day, when I thought it was comfortably over, you know, he came back, and—and apologized, and called himself the most awful names, and—well, that was really worse."

"What did the fellow complain of?" I asked in wondering tones.

"Oh, he said I'd destroyed his faith in women, you know, and that I'd led him on, and that I was—well, he was very rude indeed. And he went on writing me letters like that for a whole year! It made me quite uncomfortable."

"But he didn't go back to short trousers and a fiddle, did he?" I asked anxiously.

"Oh, no. But he forgot all he owed me, and he told me that his heart was dead, and that he should never love anyone again."

"But he's going to marry that girl."

"Oh, he doesn't care about her," said Miss Dolly, reassuringly. "It's the money, you know. He hadn't a farthing of his own. Now he'll be set up for life."

"And it's all due to you!" said I, admiringly.

"Well, it is, really."

"I don't call her such a bad-looking girl, though." (I hadn't seen her face.)

"Mr. Carter! She's *hideous!*"

I dropped that subject.

"And now," said Miss Dolly again, "he cuts me dead!"

"It is the height of ingratitude. Why, to love you was a liberal education!"

"Yes, wasn't it? How nicely you put that! 'A liberal education'! I shall tell Archie." (Archie is Lord Mickleham.)

"What, about Phil Meadows?"

"Goodness me, no, Mr. Carter. Just what you said, you know."

"But why not tell Mickleham about Phil Meadows?" I urged. "It's all to your credit, you know."

"Yes, I know, but men are so foolish. You see, Archie thinks——"

"Of course he does."

"You might let me finish."

"Archie thinks you were never in love before."

"Yes, he does. Well, of course, I wasn't in love with Phil——"

"Not a little bit?"

"Oh, well——"

"Nor with anyone else?"

Miss Dolly prodded the path with her parasol.

"Nor with anyone else?" I asked again.

Miss Dolly looked for an instant in my direction.

"Nor with anyone else?" said I.

Miss Dolly looked straight in front of her.

"Nor with——" I began.

"Hullo, old chappie, where did you spring from?"

"Why, Archie!" cried Miss Dolly.

"Oh, how are you, Mickleham, old man? Take this seat; I'm just off—just off. Yes, I was, upon my honour—got to meet a man at the club. Good-bye, Miss Foster. Jove! I'm late!"

And as I went I heard Miss Dolly say, "I thought you were *never* coming, Archie, dear!" Well, she didn't think he was coming just then. No more did I.

II

CORDIAL RELATIONS

THE other day I paid a call on Miss Dolly Foster for the purpose of presenting to her my small offering on the occasion of her marriage to Lord Mickleham. It was a pretty little bit of jewellery—a pearl heart, broken (rubies played the part of blood) and held together by a gold pin, set with diamonds, the whole surmounted by an earl's coronet. I had taken some trouble about it, and I was grateful when Miss Dolly asked me to explain the symbolism.

"It is my heart," I observed. "The fracture is of your making: the pin——"

Here Miss Dolly interrupted; to tell the truth, I was not sorry, for I was fairly gravelled for the meaning of the pin.

"What nonsense, Mr. Carter!" said she; "but it's awfully pretty. Thanks, so very, very much. Aren't relations funny people?"

"If you wish to change the subject, pray do," said I. "I'll change anything except my affections."

"Look here," she pursued, holding out a bundle of letters. "Here are the congratulatory epistles from relations. Shall I read you a few?"

"It will be a most agreeable mode of passing the time," said I.

"This is from Aunt Georgiana—she's a widow—lives at Cheltenham. 'My dearest Dorothea——' "

"Who?"

"Dorothea's my name, Mr. Carter. It means the gift of Heaven, you know."

"Precisely. Pray proceed, Miss Dolly. I did not at first recognize you."

" 'My dearest Dorothea, I have heard the news of your engagement to Lord Mickleham with deep thankfulness. To obtain the love of an honest man is a great prize. I hope you will prove worthy of it. Marriage is a trial and an opportunity——' "

"Hear, hear!" said I. "A trial for the husband and——"

"Be quiet, Mr. Carter. 'A trial and an opportunity. It searches the heart and it affords a sphere of usefulness which—' So she goes on, you know. I don't see why I need be lectured just because I'm going to be married, do you, Mr. Carter?"

"Let's try another," said I. "Who's that on pink paper?"

"Oh, that's Georgy Vane. She's awful fun. 'Dear old Dolly,—So you've brought it off. Hearty congrats. I thought you were going to be silly and throw away—' There's nothing else there, Mr. Carter. Look here. Listen to this. It's from Uncle William. He's a clergyman, you know. 'My dear niece,—I have heard with great gratification of your engagement. Your aunt and I unite in all good wishes. I recollect Lord Mickleham's father when I held a curacy near Worcester. He was a regular attendant at church and a supporter of all good works in the diocese. If only his son takes after him' (fancy Archie!) 'you have secured a prize. I hope you have a proper sense of the responsibilities you are undertaking. Marriage affords no small opportunities; it also entails certain trials——' "

"Why, you're reading Aunt Georgiana again."

"Am I? No, it's Uncle William."

"Then let's try a fresh cast—unless you'll finish Georgy Vane's."

"Well, here's Cousin Susan's. She's an old maid, you know. It's very long. Here's a bit: 'Woman has it in her power to exercise a sacred influence. I have not the pleasure of knowing Lord Mickleham, but I hope, my dear, that you will use your power over him for good. It is useless for me to deny that when you stayed with me, I thought you were addicted to frivolity. Doubtless marriage will sober you. Try to make a good use of its lessons. I am sending you a biscuit tin'—and so on."

"A very proper letter," said I.

Miss Dolly indulged in a slight grimace, and took up another letter. "This," she said, "is from my sister-in-law, Mrs. Algernon Foster."

"A daughter of Lord Doldrums, wasn't she?"

"Yes. 'My dear Dorothea,—I have heard your news. I do hope it will turn out happily. I believe that any woman who *conscientiously* does her duty can find happiness in married life. Her husband and children occupy all her time and all her thoughts, and if she can look for a few of the *lighter* pleasures of life, she has at least the knowledge that she is of *use* in the world. Please accept the accompanying volumes' (it's Browning) 'as a small—' I say, Mr. Carter, do you think it's really like that?"

"There is still time to draw back," I observed.

"Oh, don't be silly. Here, this is my brother Tom's. 'Dear Dol,—I thought Mickleham rather an ass when I met him, but I dare say you know best. What's his place like? Does he take a moor? I thought I read that he kept a yacht. Does he? Give him my love and a kiss. Good luck, old girl.—Tom. *P.S.*—I'm glad it's not me, you know.'"

"A disgusting letter," I observed.

"Not at all," said Miss Dolly, dimpling. "It's just like dear old Tom. Listen to grandpapa's. 'My dear Granddaughter,—The alliance' (I rather like it's being called an alliance, Mr. Carter. It sounds like the Royal Family, doesn't it?) 'you are about to contract is in all respects a suitable one. I send you my blessing, and a small cheque to help toward your trousseau.—Yours affectionately, Jno. Wm. Foster.'"

"That," said I, "is the best up to now."

"Yes, it's 500," said she, smiling. "Here's old Lady M.'s."

"*Whose?*" I exclaimed.

"Archie's mother's, you know. 'My dear Dorothea (as I suppose I must call you now),—Archibald has informed us of his engagement, and I and the girls' (there are five girls, Mr. Carter) 'hasten to welcome his bride. I am sure Archie will make his wife very happy. He is rather particular (like his dear father), but he has a good heart, and is not fidgety about his meals. Of course we shall be *delighted* to move out of The Towers at once. I hope we shall see a great deal of you soon. Archie is full of your praises, and we thoroughly trust his taste. Archie—' It's all about Archie, you see."

"Naturally," said I.

"Well, I don't know. I suppose I count a little, too. Oh, look here.

Here's Cousin Fred's—but he's always so silly. I shan't read you his."

"Oh, just a bit of it," I pleaded.

"Well, here's one bit. 'I suppose I can't murder him, so I must wish him joy. All I can say is, Dolly, that he's the luckiest' (something I can't read—either fellow or—devil) 'I ever heard of. I wonder if you've forgotten that evening——'"

"Well, go on." For she stopped.

"Oh, there's nothing else."

"In fact, you have forgotten the evening?"

"Entirely," said Miss Dolly, tossing her head. "But he sends me a love of a bracelet. He can't possibly pay for it, poor boy."

"Young knave!" said I, severely. (I had paid for my pearl heart.)

"Then come a lot from girls. Oh, there's one from Maud Tottenham—she's a second cousin, you know—it's rather amusing. 'I used to know your *fiancé* slightly. He seemed very nice, but it's a long while ago, and I never saw much of him. I hope he is really fond of you, and that it is not a mere *fancy*. Since you love him so much, it would be a pity if he did not care deeply for you.'"

"Interpret, Miss Dolly," said I.

"She tried to catch him herself," said Miss Dolly.

"Ah, I see. Is that all?"

"The others aren't very interesting."

"Then let's finish Georgy Vane's."

"Really?" she asked, smiling.

"Yes. Really."

"Oh, if you don't mind, I don't," said she, laughing, and she hunted out the pink note and spread it before her. "Let me see. Where was I? Oh, here. 'I thought you were going to be silly and throw away your chances on some of the men who used to flirt with you. Archie Mickleham may not be a genius, but he's a good fellow and a swell and rich; he's not a pauper, like Phil Meadows, or a snob, like Charlie Dawson, or—' *shall* I go on, Mr. Carter? No, I won't. I didn't see what it was."

"Yes, you shall go on."

"Oh, no, I can't," and she folded up the letter.

"Then I will," and I'm ashamed to say I snatched the letter. Miss Dolly jumped to her feet. I fled behind the table. She ran round. I dodged.

" 'Or—' " I began to read.

"Stop!" cried she.

" 'Or a young spendthrift like that man—I forget his name—whom you used to go on with at such a pace at Monte Carlo last winter.' "

"Stop!" she cried, stamping her foot. I read on:

" 'No doubt he was charming, my dear, and no doubt anybody would have thought you meant it; but I never doubted you. Still, weren't you just a little——' "

"Stop!" she cried. "You must stop, Mr. Carter."

So then I stopped. I folded the letter and handed it back to her. Her cheeks flushed red as she took it.

"I thought you were a gentleman," said she, biting her lip.

"I was at Monte Carlo last winter myself," said I.

"Lord Mickleham," said the butler, throwing open the door.

III

RETRIBUTION

In future I am going to be careful what I do. I am also—and this is by no means less important—going to be very careful what Miss Dolly Foster does. Everybody knows (if I may quote her particular friend Nellie Phaeton) that dear Dolly means no harm, but she is "just a little harum-scarum." I thanked Miss Phaeton for the expression.

The fact is that "old Lady M." (here I quote Miss Dolly) sent for me the other day. I have not the honour of knowing the Countess, and I went in some trepidation. When I was ushered in, Lady Mickleham put up her "starers." (You know those abominations! *Pince-nez* with long torture—I mean tortoise—shell handles.)

"Mr.—er—Carter?" said she.

I bowed. I would have denied it if I could.

"My dears!" said Lady Mickleham.

Upon this five young ladies who had been sitting in five straight-backed chairs, doing five pieces of embroidery, rose, bowed, and filed out of the room. I felt very nervous. A pause followed. Then the Countess observed—and it seemed at first rather irrelevant:

"I've been reading an unpleasant story."

"In these days of French influence," I began apologetically (not that I write such stories, or indeed any stories, but Lady Mickleham invites an apologetic attitude), and my eye wandered to the table. I saw nothing worse (or better) than the morning paper there.

"Contained in a friend's letter," she continued, focusing the "starers" full on my face.

I did not know what to do, so I bowed again.

"It must have been as painful for her to write as for me to read," Lady Mickleham went on. "And that is saying much. Be seated, pray."

I bowed, and sat down in one of the straight-backed chairs. I also began, in my fright, to play with one of the pieces of embroidery.

"Is Lady Jane's work in your way?" (Lady Jane is named after Jane, the famous Countess, Lady-in-Waiting to Caroline of Anspach.)

I dropped the embroidery, and put my foot on my hat.

"I believe, Mr. Carter, that you are acquainted with Miss Dorothea Foster?"

"I have that pleasure," said I.

"Who is about to be married to my son, the Earl of Mickleham?"

"That, I believe, is so," said I. I was beginning to pull myself together.

"My son, Mr. Carter, is of a simple and trusting disposition. Perhaps I had better come to the point. I am informed by this letter that, in conversation with the writer the other day, Archibald mentioned, quite incidentally, some very startling facts. Those facts concern you, Mr. Carter."

"May I ask the name of the writer?"

"I do not think that is necessary," said she. "She is a lady in whom I have the utmost confidence."

"That is, of course, enough," said I.

"It appears, Mr. Carter—and you will excuse me if I speak plainly" —(I set my teeth) "that you have, in the first place, given to my son's bride a wedding present, which I can only describe as——"

"A pearl ornament," I interposed; "with a ruby or two, and——"

"A pearl heart," she corrected; "er—fractured, and that you explained that this absurd article represented your heart."

"Mere *badinage,*" said I.

"In execrably bad taste," said she.

I bowed.

"In fact, most offensive. But that is not the worst. From my son's further statements it appears that on one occasion, at least, he found you and Miss Foster engaged in what I can only call——"

I raised my hand in protest. The Countess took no notice.

"What I can only call *romping.*"

She shot this word at me with extraordinary violence, and when it was out she shuddered.

"Romping!" I cried.

"A thing not only atrociously vulgar at all times, but under the circumstances—need I say more? Mr. Carter, you were engaged in chasing my son's future bride round a table!"

"Pardon me, Lady Mickleham. Your son's future bride was engaged in chasing me round a table."

"It is the same thing," said Lady Mickleham.

"I should have thought there was a distinction," said I.

"None at all."

I fell back on a second line of defence.

"I didn't let her catch me, Lady Mickleham," I pleaded.

Lady Mickleham grew quite red. This made me feel more at my ease.

"No, sir. If you had——"

"Goodness knows!" I murmured, shaking my head.

"As it happened, however, my son entered in the middle of this disgraceful——"

"It was at the beginning," said I, with a regretful sigh.

Upon this—and I have really never been so pleased at anything in all my life—the Countess, the violence of her emotions penetrating to her very fingers, gripped the handle of her "starers" with such force that she broke it in two! She was a woman of the world, and in a moment she looked as if nothing had happened. With me it was different; and that I am not now on Lady Mickleham's visiting-list is due to (*inter alia et enormia*) the fact that I laughed! It was out before I could help it. In a second I was as grave as a mute. The mischief was done. The Countess rose. I imitated her example.

"You are amused?" said she, and her tones banished the last of my mirth. I stumbled on my hat, and it rolled to her feet.

"It is not probable," she observed, "that after Miss Foster's marriage you will meet her often. You will move in—er—somewhat different circles."

"I may catch a glimpse of her in her carriage from the top of my 'bus," said I.

"Your *milieu* and my son's——"

"I know his valet, though," said I.

Lady Mickleham rang the bell. I stooped for my hat. To tell the truth, I was rather afraid to expose myself in such a defenceless attitude, but the Countess preserved her self-control. The butler opened the door. I bowed, and left the Countess regarding me through the maimed "starers." Then I found the butler smiling. He probably knew the signs of the weather. I wouldn't be Lady Mickleham's butler if you made me a duke.

As I walked home through the Park I met Miss Dolly and Mickleham. They stopped. I walked on. Mickleham seized me by the coat-tails.

"Do you mean to cut us?" he cried.

"Yes," said I.

"Why, what the deuce—?" he began.

"I've seen your mother," said I. "I wish, Mickleham, that when you do happen to intrude as you did the other day, you wouldn't repeat what you see."

"Lord!" he cried. "She's not heard of that? I only told Aunt Cynthia."

I said something about Aunt Cynthia.

"Does—does she know it *all?*" asked Miss Dolly.

"More than all—much more."

"Didn't you smooth it over?" said Miss Dolly, reproachfully.

"On reflection," said I, "I don't know that I did—much." (I hadn't, you know.)

Suddenly Mickleham burst out laughing.

"What a game!" he exclaimed.

"That's all very well for you," said Dolly. "But do you happen to remember that we dine there tonight?"

Archie grew grave.

"I hope you'll enjoy yourselves," said I. "I always cling to the belief that the wicked are punished." And I looked at Miss Dolly.

"Never you mind, little woman," said Archie, drawing Miss Dolly's arm through his. "I'll see you through. After all, everybody knows that old Carter's an ass."

That piece of universal knowledge may help matters, but I do not quite see how. I walked on, for Miss Dolly had quite forgotten me, and was looking up at Archie Mickleham like—well, hang it, in the way they do, you know. So I just walked on.

I believe Miss Dolly has got a husband who is (let us say) good enough for her. And, for one reason and another, I am glad of it. And I also believe that she knows it. And I am—I suppose—glad of that too. Oh, yes, of course I am. Of course.

I V

THE PERVERSENESS OF IT

"I TELL you what, Mr. Carter," said Miss Nellie Phaeton, touching up Rhino with her whip, "love in a cottage is——"

"Lord forgive us, cinders, ashes, dust," I quoted.

We were spanking round the Park behind Ready and Rhino. Miss Phaeton's horses are very large; her groom is very small, and her courage is indomitable. I am no great hand at driving myself, and I am not always quite comfortable. Moreover, the stricter part of my acquaintance consider, I believe, that Miss Phaeton's attentions to me are somewhat pronounced, and that I ought not to drive with her in the Park.

"You're right," she went on. "What a girl wants is a good house and lots of cash, and some ridin' and a little huntin' and——"

"A few 'g's'!" I cried in shuddering entreaty. "If you love me, a 'g' or two."

"Well, I suppose so," said she. "You can't go ridin' without gees, can you?"

Apparently one could go driving without any, but I did not pursue the subject.

"It's only in stories that people are in love when they marry," observed Miss Phaeton, reflectively.

"Yes, and then it's generally with somebody else," said I.

"Oh, if you count *that!*" said she, hitting Ready rather viciously. We bounded forward, and I heard the little groom bumping on the back seat. I am always glad not to be a groom—it's a cup-and-ball sort of life, which must be very wearying.

"Were you ever in love?" she asked, just avoiding a brougham which contained the Duchess of Dexminster. (If, by the way, I have to run into anyone, I like it to be the Duchess: you get a much handsomer paragraph.)

"Yes," said I.

"Often?"

"Oh, not too often, and I always take great care, you know.

"What of?"

"That it shall be quite out of the question, you know. It's not at all difficult. I only have to avoid persons of moderate means."

"But aren't you a person of——?"

"Exactly. That's why. So I choose either a pauper—when it's impossible—or an heiress—when it's preposterous. See?"

"But don't you ever want to get—?" began Miss Phaeton.

"Let's talk about something else," said I.

"I believe you're humbuggin' me," said Miss Phaeton.

"I am offering a veiled apology," said I.

"Stuff!" said she. "You know you told Dolly Foster that I should make an excellent wife for a trainer."

Oh, these women! A man had better talk to a phonograph.

"Or anybody else," said I, politely.

Miss Phaeton whipped up her horses.

"Look out! There's the mounted policeman," I cried.

"No, he isn't. Are you afraid?" she retorted.

"I'm not fit to die," I pleaded.

"I don't care a pin for your opinion, you know," she continued (I had never supposed that she did); "but what did you mean by it?"

"I never said it."

"Oh!"

"All right—I never did."

"Then Dolly invented it?"

"Of course," said I, steadily.

"On your honour?"

"Oh, come, Miss Phaeton!"

"Would—would other people think so?" she asked, with a highly surprising touch of timidity.

"Nobody would," I said. "Only a snarling old wretch would say so, just because she thought it smart."

There was a long pause. Then Miss Phaeton asked me abruptly:

"You never met him, did you?"

"No."

A pause ensued. We passed the Duchess again, and scratched the nose of her poodle, which was looking out of the carriage window. Miss Phaeton flicked Rhino, and the groom behind went plop-plop on the seat.

"He lives in town, you know," remarked Miss Phaeton.

"They mostly do—and write about the country," said I.

"Why shouldn't they?" she asked fiercely.

"My dear Miss Phaeton, by all means let them," said I.

"He's awfully clever, you know," she continued; "but he wouldn't always talk. Sometimes he just sat and said nothin', or read a book."

A sudden intuition discovered Mr. Gay's feelings to me.

"You were talking about the run, or something, I suppose?"

"Yes, or the bag, you know."

As she spoke she pulled up Ready and Rhino. The little groom jumped down and stood under (not at) their heads. I leant back and surveyed the crowd sitting and walking. Miss Phaeton flicked a fly off Rhino's ear, put her whip in the socket, and leant back also.

"Then I suppose you didn't care much about him?" I asked.

"Oh, I liked him pretty well," she answered very carelessly.

At this moment, looking along the walk, I saw a man coming toward us. He was a handsome fellow, with just a touch of "softness" in his face. He was dressed in correct fashion, save that his hair was a trifle longer, his coat a trifle fuller, his hat a trifle larger, his tie a trifle looser than they were worn by most. He caught my attention, and I went on looking at him for a little while, till a slight movement of my companion's made me turn my head.

Miss Phaeton was sitting bolt upright: she fidgeted with the reins; she took her whip out of the socket and put it back again; and, to my amazement, her cheeks were very red.

Presently the man came opposite the carriage. Miss Phaeton bowed. He lifted his hat, smiled, and made as if to pass on. Miss Phaeton held out her hand. I could see a momentary gleam of surprise in his eye, as though he thought her cordiality more than he might have looked for—possibly even more than he cared about. But he stopped and shook hands.

"How are you, Mr. Gay?" she said, not introducing me.

"Still with your inseparables!" he said gaily, with a wave of his hand toward the horses. "I hope, Miss Phaeton, that in the next world your faithful steeds will be allowed to bear you company, or what will you do?"

"Oh, you think I care for nothin' but horses?" said she, petulantly, but she leant toward him, and gave me her shoulder.

"Oh, no," he laughed. "Dogs also, and I'm afraid one day it was ferrets, wasn't it?"

"Have—have you written any poetry lately?" she asked.

"How conscientious of you to inquire!" he exclaimed, his eyes twinkling. "Oh, yes, half a hundred things. Have you—killed—anything lately?"

I could swear she flushed again. Her voice trembled as she answered:

"No, not lately."

I caught sight of his face behind her back, and I thought I saw a trace of puzzle—nothing more. He held out his hand.

"Well, so glad to have seen you, Miss Phaeton," said he, "but I must run on. Good-bye."

"Good-bye, Mr. Gay," said she.

And, lifting his hat again, smiling again gaily, he was gone. For a moment or two I said nothing. Then I remarked:

"So that's your friend Gay, is it? He's not a bad-looking fellow."

"Yes, that's him," said she, and, as she spoke, she sank back in her seat for a moment. I did not look at her face. Then she sat up straight again and took the whip.

"Want to stay any longer?" she asked.

"No," said I.

The little groom sprang away, Rhino and Ready dashed ahead.

"Shall I drop you at the club?" she asked. "I'm goin' home."

"I'll get out here," said I.

We came to a stand again, and I got down.

"Good-bye," I said.

She nodded at me, but said nothing. A second later the carriage was tearing down the road, and the little groom hanging on for dear life.

Of course it's all nonsense. She's not the least suited to him; she'd make him miserable, and then be miserable herself. But it seems a little perverse, doesn't it? In fact, twice at least between the courses at dinner I caught myself being sorry for her. It is, when you think of it, so remarkably perverse.

v

A MATTER OF DUTY

LADY MICKLEHAM is back from her honeymoon. I mean young Lady Mickleham—Dolly Foster (well, of course I do. Fancy the Dowager on a honeymoon!). She signified the fact to me by ordering me to call on her at tea-time; she had, she said, something which she wished to consult me about *confidentially*. I went.

"I didn't know you were back," I observed.

"Oh, we've been back a fortnight, but we went down to The Towers. They were all there, Mr. Carter."

"All who?"

"All Archie's people. The Dowager said we must get really to know one another as soon as possible. I'm not sure I like really knowing people. It means that they say whatever they like to you, and don't get up out of your favourite chair when you come in."

"I agree," said I, "that a *soupçon* of unfamiliarity is not amiss."

"Of course it's nice to be one of the family," she continued.

"The cat is that," said I. "I would not give a fig for it."

"And the Dowager taught me the ways of the house."

"Ah, she taught me the way out of it."

"And showed me how to be most disagreeable to the servants."

"It is the first lesson of a housekeeper."

"And told me what Archie particularly liked, and how bad it was for him, poor boy."

"What should we do without our mothers? I do not, however, see how I can help in all this, Lady Mickleham."

"How funny that sounds!"

"Aren't you accustomed to your dignity yet?"

"I meant from *you*, Mr. Carter."

I smiled. That is Dolly's way. As Miss Phaeton says, she means no harm, and it is admirably conducive to the pleasure of a *tête-à-tête*.

"It wasn't that I wanted to ask you about," she continued, after she had indulged in a pensive sigh (with a dutifully bright smile and a glance at Archie's photograph to follow. Her behaviour always reminds me of a varied and well-assorted *menu*). "It was about something much more difficult. You won't tell Archie, will you?"

"This becomes interesting," I remarked, putting my hat down.

"You know, Mr. Carter, that before I was married—oh, how long ago it seems!"

"Not at all."

"Don't interrupt. That before I was married I had several—that is to say, several—well, several——"

"Start quite afresh," I suggested encouragingly.

"Well, then, several men were silly enough to think themselves—you know."

"No one better," I assented cheerfully.

"Oh, if you won't be sensible—! Well, you see, many of them are Archie's friends as well as mine; and, of course, they've been to call."

"It is but good manners," said I.

"One of them waited to be sent for, though."

"Leave that fellow out," said I.

"What I want to ask you is this—and I believe you're not silly, really, you know, except when you choose to be."

"Walk in the Row any afternoon," said I, "and you won't find ten wiser men."

"It's this. Ought I to tell Archie?"

"Good gracious! Here's a problem!"

"Of course," pursued Lady Mickleham, opening her fan, "it's in some ways more comfortable that he shouldn't know."

"For him?"

"Yes—and for me. But then it doesn't seem quite fair."

"To him?"

"Yes—and to me. Because if he came to know from anybody else, he might exaggerate the things, you know."

"Impossible!"

"Mr. Carter!"

"I—er—mean he knows you too well to do such a thing."

"Oh, I see. Thank you. Yes. What do you think?"

"What does the Dowager say?"

"I haven't mentioned it to the Dowager."

"But surely, on such a point, her experience——"

"She can't have any," said Lady Mickleham, decisively. "I believe in her husband, because I must. But nobody else! You're not giving me your opinion."

I reflected for a moment.

"Haven't we left out one point of view?" I ventured to suggest.

"I've thought it all over very carefully," said she; "both as it would affect me and as it would affect Archie."

"Quite so. Now suppose you think how it would affect them!"

"Who?"

"Why, the men."

Lady Mickleham put down her cup of tea.

"What a very curious idea!" she exclaimed.

"Give it time to sink in," said I, helping myself to another piece of toast.

She sat silent for a few moments—presumably to allow of the permeation I suggested. I finished my tea and leant back comfortably. Then I said:

"Let me take my own case. Shouldn't I feel rather awkward——?"

"Oh, it's no good taking your case," she interrupted.

"Why not mine as well as another?"

"Because I told him about you long ago."

I was not surprised. But I could not permit Lady Mickleham to laugh at me in the unconscionable manner in which she proceeded to laugh. I spread out my hands and observed blandly:

"Why not be guided—as to the others, I mean—by your husband's example?"

"Archie's example? What's that?"

"I don't know; but you do, I suppose."

"What do you mean, Mr. Carter?" she asked, sitting upright.

"Well, has he ever told you about Maggie Adeane?"

"I never heard of her."

"Or Lily Courtenay?"

"*That* girl!"

"Or Alice Layton?"

"The red-haired Layton?"

"Or Florence Cunliffe?"

"Who was she?"

"Or Millie Trehearne?"

"She squints, Mr. Carter."

"Or——"

"Stop, stop! What do you mean? What should he tell me?"

"Oh, I see he hasn't. Nor, I suppose, about Sylvia Fenton, or that little Delancy girl, or handsome Miss—what was her name?"

"Hold your tongue—and tell me what you mean."

"Lady Mickleham," said I, gravely, "if your husband has not thought fit to mention these ladies—and others whom I could name—to you, how could I presume——?"

"Do you mean to tell me that Archie——?"

"He'd only known you three years, you see."

"Then it was before——?"

"Some of them were before," said I.

Lady Mickleham drew a long breath.

"Archie will be in soon," said she.

I took my hat.

"It seems to me," I observed, "that what is sauce—that, I should say, husband and wife ought to stand on an equal footing in these matters. Since he has—no doubt for good reasons—not mentioned to you——"

"Alice Layton was a positive fright."

"She came last," said I. "Just before you, you know. However, as I was saying——"

"And that horrible Sylvia Fenton——"

"Oh, he couldn't have known you long then. As I was saying, I should, if I were you, treat him as he has treated you. In my case it seems to be too late."

"I'm sorry I told him that."

"Oh, pray don't mind, it's of no consequence. As to the others——"

"I should never have thought it of Archie!"

"One never knows," said I, with an apologetic smile. "I don't suppose he thinks it of you."

"I won't tell him a single word. He may find out if he likes. Who was the last girl you mentioned?"

"Is it any use trying to remember all their names?" I asked in a soothing tone. "No doubt he's forgotten them by now—just as you've forgotten the others."

"And the Dowager told me that he had never had an attachment before."

"Oh, if the Dowager said that! Of course, the Dowager would know!"

"Don't be so silly, for goodness' sake! Are you going?"

"Certainly I am. It might annoy Archie to find me here when he wants to talk to you."

"Well, I want to talk to him."

"Of course you won't repeat what I've——"

"I shall find out for myself," she said.

"Good-bye. I hope I've removed all your troubles?"

"Oh, yes, thank you. I know what to do now, Mr. Carter."

"Always send for me if you're in any trouble. I have some exp——"

"Good-bye, Mr. Carter."

"Good-bye, Lady Mickleham. And remember that Archie—like you——"

"Yes, yes; I know. Must you go?"

"I'm afraid I must. I've enjoyed our talk so——"

"There's Archie's step."

I left the room. On the stairs I met Archie. I shook hands sympathetically. I was sorry for Archie. But in great causes the individual cannot be considered. I had done my duty to my sex.

VI

MY LAST CHANCE

"Now mind," said Mrs. Hilary Musgrave, impressively, "this is the last time I shall take any trouble about you. She's a very nice girl, quite pretty, and she'll have a lot of money. You can be very pleasant when you like——"

"This unsolicited testimonial——"

"Which isn't often—and if you don't do it this time I wash my hands of you. Why, how old are you?"

"Hush, Mrs. Hilary."

"You must be nearly——"

"It's false—false—false!"

"Come along," said Mrs. Hilary; and she added, over her shoulder, "she has a slight north-country accent."

"It might have been Scotch," said I.

"She plays the piano a good deal."

"It might have been the fiddle," said I.

"She's very fond of Browning."

"It might have been Ibsen," said I.

Mrs. Hilary, seeing that I was determined to look on the bright side, smiled graciously on me and introduced me to the young lady. She was decidedly good-looking, fresh and sincere of aspect, with large inquiring eyes—eyes which I felt would demand a little too much of me at breakfast—but then a large tea-urn puts that all right.

"Miss Sophia Milton—Mr. Carter," said Mrs. Hilary, and left us.

Well, we tried the theatres first; but as she had only been to the Lyceum and I had only been to the Gaiety, we soon got to the end of that. Then we tried Art: she asked me what I thought of Degas: I evaded the question by criticizing a drawing of a horse in last week's *Punch*—which she hadn't seen. Upon this she started literature. She said *Some Qualms and a Shiver* was the book of the season. I put my money on *The Queen of the Quorn*. Dead stop again! And I saw Mrs. Hilary's eye upon me: there was wrath in her face. Something must be done.

A brilliant idea seized me. I had read that four-fifths of the culture of England were Conservative. I also was a Conservative. It was four to one on! I started politics. I could have whooped for joy when I elicited something particularly incisive about the ignorance of the masses.

"I do hope you agree with me," said Miss Milton. "The more one reads and thinks, the more one sees how fatally false a theory it is that the ignorant masses—people such as I have described—can ever rule a great Empire."

"The Empire wants gentlemen; that's what it wants," said I, nodding my head, and glancing triumphantly at Mrs. Hilary.

"Men and women," said she, "who are acquainted with the best that has been said and thought on all important subjects."

At the time I believed this observation to be original, but I have since been told that it was borrowed. I was delighted with it.

"Yes," said I, "and have got a stake in the country, you know, and know how to behave 'emselves in the House, don't you know?"

"What we have to do," pursued Miss Milton, "is to guide the voters. These poor rustics need to be informed——"

"Just so," I broke in. "They have to be told——"

"Of the real nature of the questions——"

"And which candidate to support."

"Or they must infallibly—" she exclaimed.

"Get their marching orders," I cried, in rapture. It was exactly what I always did on my small property.

"Oh, I didn't quite mean that," she said reproachfully.

"Oh, well, neither did I—quite," I responded adroitly. What was wrong with the girl now?

"But with the help of the League—" she went on.

"Do you belong?" I cried, more delighted than ever.

"Oh, yes!" said she. "I think it's a duty. I worked very hard at the last election. I spent days distributing packages of——"

Then I made, I'm sorry to say, a false step. I observed, interrupting:

"But it's ticklish work now, eh? Six months' 'hard' wouldn't be pleasant, would it?"

"What do you mean, Mr.—er—Carter?" she asked.

I was still blind. I believe I winked, and I'm sure I whispered, *"Tea."* Miss Milton drew herself up very straight.

"I do not *bribe,*" she said. "What I distribute is pamphlets."

Now I suppose that "pamphlets" and "blankets" don't really sound much alike, but I was agitated.

"Quite right," said I. "Poor old things! They can't afford proper fuel."

She rose to her feet.

"I was not joking," she said with horrible severity.

"Neither was I," I declared in humble apology. "Didn't you say 'blankets'?"

"Pamphlets."

"Oh!"

There was a long pause. I glanced at Mrs. Hilary. Things had not fallen out as happily as they might, but I did not mean to give up yet.

"I see you're right," I said, still humbly. "To descend to such means as I had in mind is——"

"To throw away our true weapons," said she, earnestly. (She sat down again—good sign.)

"What we really need—" I began.

"Is a reform of the upper classes," said she. "Let them give an example of duty, of self-denial, of frugality."

I was not to be caught out again.

"Just what I always say," I observed impressively.

"Let them put away their horse-racing, their betting, their luxurious living, their——"

"You're right, Miss Milton," said I.

"Let them set an example of morality."

"They should," I assented.

Miss Milton smiled.

"I thought we agreed really," said she.

"I'm sure we do," cried I; and I winked with my "off" eye at Mrs. Hilary as I sat down beside Miss Milton.

"Now I heard of a man the other day," said she, "who's nearly forty. He's got an estate in the country. He never goes there, except for a few days' shooting. He lives in town. He spends too much. He passes an absolutely vacant existence in a round of empty gaiety. He has by no means a good reputation. He dangles about, wasting his time and his money. Is that the sort of example——?"

"He's a traitor to his class," said I, warmly.

"If you want him, you must look on a race-course, or at a tailor's, or in some fashionable woman's boudoir. And his estate looks after itself. He's too selfish to marry, too idle to work, too silly to think."

I began to be sorry for this man, in spite of his peccadilloes.

"I wonder if I've met him," said I. "I'm occasionally in town, when I can get time to run up. What's his name?"

"I don't think I heard—or I've forgotten. But he's got the place next to a friend of mine in the country, and she told me all about him. She's exactly the opposite sort of person—or she wouldn't be my friend."

"I should think not, Miss Milton," said I, admiringly.

"Oh, I should like to meet that man, and tell him what I think of him!" said she. "Such men as he is do more harm than a dozen agitators. So contemptible, too!"

"It's revolting to think of," said I.

"I'm *so* glad you—" began Miss Milton, quite confidentially; I pulled my chair a trifle closer, and cast an apparently careless glance toward Mrs. Hilary. Suddenly I heard a voice behind me.

"Eh, what? Upon my honour it is! Why, Carter, my boy, how are you? Eh, what? Miss Milton, too, I declare! Well, now, what a pity Annie didn't come."

I disagreed. I hate Annie. But I was very glad to see my friend and neighbour, Robert Dinnerly. He's a sensible man—his wife's a little prig.

"Oh, Mr. Dinnerly," cried Miss Milton, "how funny that you should come just now! I was just trying to remember the name of a man

Mrs. Dinnerly told me about. I was telling Mr. Carter about him. You know him."

"Well, Miss Milton, perhaps I do. Describe him."

"I don't believe Annie ever told me his name, but she was talking about him at our house yesterday."

"But I wasn't there, Miss Milton."

"No," said Miss Milton, "but he's got the next place to yours in the country."

I positively leapt from my seat.

"Why, good gracious, Carter himself, you mean!" cried Dinnerly, laughing. "Well, that is a good 'un—ha-ha-ha!"

She turned a stony glare on me.

"Do you live next to Mr. Dinnerly in the country?" she asked.

I would have denied it if Dinnerly had not been there. As it was I blew my nose.

"I wonder," said Miss Milton, "what has become of Aunt Emily."

"Miss Milton," said I, "by a happy chance you have enjoyed a luxury. You have told the man what you think of him."

"Yes," said she; "and I have only to add that he is also a hypocrite."

Pleasant, wasn't it? Yet Mrs. Hilary says it was my fault! That's a woman all over!

VII

THE LITTLE WRETCH!

SEEING that little Johnny Tompkins was safely out of the country, under injunctions to make a new man of himself, and to keep that new man, when made, at the Antipodes, I could not see anything indiscreet in touching on the matter in the course of conversation with Mrs. Hilary Musgrave. In point of fact, I was curious to find out what she knew, and, supposing she knew, what she thought. So I mentioned little Johnny Tompkins.

"Oh, the little wretch!" cried Mrs. Hilary. "You know he came here two or three times? Anybody can impose on Hilary."

"Happy woman! I—I mean unhappy man, Mrs. Hilary."

"And how much was it he stole?"

"Hard on a thousand," said I. "For a time, you know, he was quite a man of fashion."

"Oh, I know. He came here in his own hansom, perfectly dressed, and——"

"Behaved all right, didn't he?"

"Yes. Of course there was a something."

"Or you wouldn't have been deceived!" said I, with a smile.

"I wasn't deceived," said Mrs. Hilary, an admirable flush appearing on her cheeks.

"That is to say, Hilary wouldn't."

"Oh, Hilary! Why didn't his employers prosecute him, Mr. Carter?"

"In the first place, he had that inestimable advantage in a career of dishonesty—respectable relations."

"Well, but still——"

"His widowed mother was a trump, you know."

"Do you mean a good woman?"

"Doubtless she was; but I meant a good card. However, there was another reason."

"I can't see any," declared Mrs. Hilary.

"I'm going to surprise you," said I. "Hilary interceded for him."

"Hilary?"

"You didn't know it? I thought not. Well, he did."

"Why, he always pretended to want him to be convicted."

"Cunning Hilary!" said I.

"He used to speak most strongly against him."

"That was his guile," said I.

"Oh, but why in the world—?" she began; then she paused, and went on again: "It was nothing to do with Hilary."

"Hilary went with me to see him, you know, while they had him under lock and key at the firm's offices."

"Did he? I never heard that."

"And he was much impressed with his bearing."

"Well, I suppose, Mr. Carter, that if he was really penitent——"

"Never saw a man less penitent," I interrupted. "He gloried in his crime; if I remember his exact expression, it was that the jam was jolly well worth the powder, and if they liked to send him to chokee, they could and be—and suffer accordingly, you know."

"And after that, Hilary——!"

"Oh, anybody can impose on Hilary, you know. Hilary only asked what 'the jam' was."

"It's a horrid expression, but I suppose it meant acting the part of a gentleman, didn't it?"

"Not entirely. According to what he told Hilary, Johnny was in love."

"Oh, and he stole for some wretched——?"

"Now, do be careful. What do you know about the lady?"

"The *lady!* I can imagine Johnny Tompkins' ideal!"

"So can I, if you come to that."

"And she must have known his money wasn't his own."

"Why must she?" I asked. "According to what he told Hilary, she didn't."

"I don't believe it," said Mrs. Hilary, with decision.

"Hilary believed it!"

"Oh, Hilary!"

"But then, Hilary knew the girl."

"Hilary knew——! You mean to say Hilary knew——?"

"No one better," said I, composedly.

Mrs. Hilary rose to her feet.

"Who was the creature?" she asked sharply.

"Come," I expostulated, "how would you like it, if your young man had taken to theft, and——"

"Oh, nonsense. Tell me her name, please, Mr. Carter."

"Johnny told Hilary that just to see her and talk to her and sit by her was 'worth all the money'—but, then, to be sure, it was somebody else's money—and that he'd do it again to get what he had got over again. Then, I'm sorry to say, he swore."

"And Hilary believed that stuff?"

"Hilary agreed with him," said I. "Hilary, you see, knows the lady."

"What's her name, Mr. Carter?"

"Didn't you notice his attentions to anyone?"

"I notice! You don't mean that I've seen her?"

"Certainly you have."

"Was she ever here?"

"Yes, Mrs. Hilary. Hilary takes care of that."

"I shall be angry in a minute, Mr. Carter. Oh, I'll have this out of Hilary!"

"I should."

"Who was she?"

"According to what he told Hilary, she was the most fascinating woman in the world. Hilary thought so too."

Mrs. Hilary began to walk up and down.

"Oh, so Hilary helped to let him go, because they both——?"

"Precisely," said I.

"And you dare to come and tell me?"

"Well, I thought you ought to know," said I. "Hilary's just as mad about her as Johnny—in fact, he said he'd be hanged if he wouldn't have done the same himself."

I have once seen Madame Ristori play Lady Macbeth. Her performance was recalled to me by the tones in which Mrs. Hilary asked:

"Who is this woman, if you please, Mr. Carter?"

"So Hilary got him off—gave him fifty pounds too."

"Glad to get him away, perhaps," she burst out, in angry scorn.

"Who knows?" said I. "Perhaps."

"Her name?" demanded Lady Macbeth—I mean Mrs. Hilary—again.

"I shan't tell you, unless you promise to say nothing to Hilary."

"To say nothing! Well, really——"

"Oh, all right!" and I took up my hat.

"But I can watch them, can't I?"

"As much as you like."

"Won't you tell me?"

"If you promise."

"Well, then, I promise."

"Look in the glass."

"What for?"

"To see your face, to be sure."

She started, blushed red, and moved a step toward me.

"You don't mean—?" she cried.

"Thou art the woman," said I.

"Oh, but he never said a word——"

"Johnny had his code," said I. "And in some ways it was better than some people's—in some, alas! worse."

"And Hilary?"

"Really you know better than I do whether I've told the truth about Hilary."

A pause ensued. Then Mrs. Hilary made three short remarks, which I give in their order:

(1) "The little wretch!"

(2) "Dear old Hilary!"

(3) "Poor little man!"

I took my hat. I knew that Hilary was due from the City in a few minutes. Mrs. Hilary sat down by the fire.

"How dare you torment me so?" she asked, but not in the least like Lady Macbeth.

"I must have my little amusements," said I.

"What an audacious little creature!" said Mrs. Hilary. "Fancy his daring!—Aren't you astounded?"

"Oh, yes, I am. But Hilary, you see——"

"It's nearly his time," said Mrs. Hilary.

I buttoned my left glove and held out my right hand.

"I've a good mind not to shake hands with you," she said. "Wasn't it absurd of Hilary?"

"Horribly."

"He ought to have been all the more angry."

"Of course he ought."

"The presumption of it!" And Mrs. Hilary smiled. I also smiled.

"That poor old mother of his," reflected Mrs. Hilary. "Where did you say she lived?"

"Hilary knows the address," said I.

"Silly little wretch!" mused Mrs. Hilary, still smiling.

"Good-bye," said I.

"Good-bye," said Mrs. Hilary.

I turned toward the door and had laid my hand on the knob, when Mrs. Hilary called softly:

"Mr. Carter."

"Yes," said I, turning.

"Do you know where the little wretch has gone?"

"Oh, yes," said I.

"I—I suppose you don't ever write to him?"

"Dear me, no," said I.

"But you—could?" suggested Mrs. Hilary.

"Of course," said I.

She jumped up and ran toward me. Her purse was in one hand, and a bit of paper fluttered in the other.

"Send him that—don't tell him," she whispered, and her voice had a little catch in it. "Poor little wretch!" said she.

As for me, I smiled cynically—quite cynically, you know: for it was very absurd.

"Please go," said Mrs. Hilary.

And I went.

Supposing it had been another woman! Well, I wonder!

VIII

AN EXPENSIVE PRIVILEGE

A RATHER uncomfortable thing happened the other day which threatened a schism in my acquaintance and put me in a decidedly awkward position. It was no other than this: Mrs. Hilary Musgrave had definitely informed me that she did not approve of Lady Mickleham.

The attitude is, no doubt, a conceivable one, but I was surprised that a woman of Mrs. Hilary's large sympathies should adopt it. Besides, Mrs. Hilary is quite good-looking herself.

The history of the affair is much as follows: I called on Mrs. Hilary to see whether I could do anything, and she told me all about it. It appears that Mrs. Hilary had a bad cold and a cousin up from the country about the same time (she was justly aggrieved at the double event), and, being unable to go to the Duchess of Dexminster's "squash," she asked Dolly Mickleham to chaperon little Miss Phyllis. Little Miss Phyllis, of course, knew no one there—the Duchess least of all (but then very few of us—yes, I was there—knew the Duchess, and the Duchess didn't know any of us; I saw her shake hands with a waiter myself, just to be on the safe side)—and an hour after the party began, she was discovered wandering about in a most desolate condition. Dolly had told her that she would be in a certain place; and when Miss Phyllis came Dolly was not there. The poor little lady wandered about for another hour, looking so lost that one was inclined to send for a policeman; and then she sat down on a seat by the wall, and in desperation asked her next-door neighbour if he knew Lady Mickleham by sight, and had he seen her lately. The next-door neighbour, by way of reply, called out to a quiet elderly gentleman who was sidling unobtrusively about, "Duke, are there any particularly snug corners in your house?" The Duke stopped, searched his memory, and said that at the end of the Red Corridor there was a passage; and that a few yards down the passage, if you turned very suddenly to the right, you would come on a little nook under the stairs. The little nook just held a settee, and the settee (the Duke thought) might just hold two people. The next-door neighbour thanked the Duke, and observed to Miss Phyllis:

"It will give me great pleasure to take you to Lady Mickleham." So they went, it being then, according to Miss Phyllis's sworn statement, precisely two hours and five minutes since Dolly had disappeared; and, pursuing the route indicated by the Duke, they found Lady Mickleham. And Lady Mickleham exclaimed, "Good gracious, my dear, I'd quite forgotten you! Have you had an ice? Do take her to have an ice, Sir John." (Sir John Berry was the next-door neighbour.) And with that Lady Mickleham is said to have resumed her conversation.

"Did you ever hear anything more atrocious?" concluded Mrs. Hilary. "I really cannot think what Lord Mickleham is doing."

"You surely mean, what Lady Mickleham——?"

"No, I don't," said Mrs. Hilary, with extraordinary decision. "Anything might have happened to the poor child."

"Oh, there were not many of the aristocracy present," said I, soothingly.

"But it's not that so much, as the thing itself. She's the most disgraceful flirt in London."

"How do you know she was flirting?" I inquired with a smile.

"How do I know?" echoed Mrs. Hilary.

"It is a very hasty conclusion," I persisted. "Sometimes I stay talking with you for an hour or more. Are you, therefore, flirting with me?"

"With *you!*" exclaimed Mrs. Hilary, with a little laugh.

"Absurd as the supposition is," I remarked, "it yet serves to point the argument. Lady Mickleham might have been talking with a friend just in the quiet, rational way in which we are talking now."

"I don't think that's likely," said Mrs. Hilary; and—well, I do not like to say that she sniffed—it would convey too strong an idea, but she did make an odd little sound something like a much etherealized sniff.

I smiled again, and more broadly. I was enjoying beforehand the little victory which I was to enjoy over Mrs. Hilary.

"Yet it happens to be true," said I.

Mrs. Hilary was magnificently contemptuous.

"Lord Mickleham told you so, I suppose?" she asked. "And I suppose Lady Mickleham told him—poor man!"

"Why do you call him 'poor man'?"

"Oh, never mind. Did he tell you?"

"Certainly not. The fact is, Mrs. Hilary—and really, you must excuse me for having kept you in the dark a little—it amused me so much to hear your suspicions."

Mrs. Hilary rose to her feet.

"Well, what are you going to say?" she asked. I laughed, as I answered:

"Why, I was the man with Lady Mickleham when your friend and Berry inter—when they arrived, you know."

Well, I should have thought—I should still think—that she would have been pleased—relieved, you know—to find her uncharitable opinion erroneous, and pleased to have it altered on the best authority. I'm sure that is how I should have felt. It was not, however, how Mrs. Hilary felt.

"I am deeply pained," she observed after a long pause; and then she held out her hand.

"I was sure you'd forgive my little deception," said I, grasping it. I thought still that she meant to bury all unkindness.

"I should never have thought it of you," she went on.

"I didn't know your friend was there at all," I pleaded; for by now I was alarmed.

"Oh, please don't shuffle like that," said Mrs. Hilary.

She continued to stand, and I rose to my feet. Mrs. Hilary held out her hand again.

"Do you mean that I'm to go?" said I.

"I hope we shall see you again some day," said Mrs. Hilary; the tone suggested that she was looking forward to some future existence, when my earthly sins should have been sufficiently purged. It reminded me for the moment of King Arthur and Queen Guinevere.

"But I protest," I began, "that my only object in telling you was to show you how absurd——"

"Is it any good talking about it now?" asked Mrs. Hilary. A discussion might possibly be fruitful in the dim futurity before mentioned—but not now—that was what she seemed to say.

"Lady Mickleham and I, on the occasion in question—" I began, with dignity.

"Pray spare me," quoth Mrs. Hilary, with much greater dignity.

I took my hat.

"Shall you be at home as usual on Thursday?" I asked.

"I have a great many people coming already," she remarked.

"I can take a hint," said I.

"I wish you'd take warning," said Mrs. Hilary.

"I will take my leave," said I; and I did, leaving Mrs. Hilary in a tragic attitude in the middle of the room. Never again shall I go out of my way to lull Mrs. Hilary's suspicions.

A day or two after this very trying interview, Lady Mickleham's victoria happened to stop opposite where I was seated in the Park. I went to pay my respects.

"Do you mean to leave me nothing in the world?" I asked, just by way of introducing the subject of Mrs. Hilary. "One of my best friends has turned me out of her house on your account."

"Oh, do tell me," said Dolly, dimpling all over her face.

So I told her; I made the story as long as I could for reasons connected with the dimples.

"What fun!" exclaimed Dolly. "I told you at the time that a young unmarried person like you ought to be more careful."

"I am just debating," I observed, "whether to sacrifice you."

"To sacrifice me, Mr. Carter?"

"Of course," I explained; "if I dropped you, Mrs. Hilary would let me come again."

"How charming that would be!" cried Dolly. "You would enjoy her nice serious conversation—all about Hilary!"

"She is apt," I conceded, "to touch on Hilary. But she is very picturesque."

"Oh, yes, she's handsome," said Dolly.

There was a pause. Then Dolly said, "Well?"

"Well?" said I in return.

"Is it good-bye?" asked Dolly, drawing down the corners of her mouth.

"It comes to this," I remarked. "Supposing I forgive you——"

"As if it was my fault!"

"And risk Mrs. Hilary's wrath—did you speak?"

"No; I laughed, Mr. Carter."

"What shall I get out of it?"

The sun was shining brightly: it shone on Dolly; she had raised her parasol, but she blinked a little beneath it. She was smiling slightly still, and one dimple stuck to its post—like a sentinel, ready to rouse the rest from their brief repose. Dolly lay back in the victoria, nestling luxuriously against the soft cushions. She turned her eyes for a moment on me.

"Why are you looking at me?" she asked.

"Because," said I, "there is nothing better to look at."

"Do you like doing it?" asked Dolly.

"It is a privilege," said I, politely.

"Well, then!" said Dolly.

"But," I ventured to observe, "it's rather an expensive one."

"Then you mustn't have it very often."

"And it is shared by so many people."

"Then," said Dolly, smiling indulgently, "you must have it—a little oftener. Home, Roberts, please."

I am not yet allowed at Mrs. Hilary Musgrave's.

IX

A VERY DULL AFFAIR

"To hear you talk," remarked Mrs. Hilary Musgrave—and, if anyone is surprised to find me at her house, I can only say that Hilary, when he asked me to take pot-luck, was quite ignorant of any ground of difference between his wife and myself, and that Mrs. Hilary could not very well eject me on my arrival in evening dress at ten minutes to eight—"to hear you talk one would think that there was no such thing as real love."

She paused. I smiled.

"Now," she continued, turning a fine, but scornful eye upon me, "I have never cared for any man in the world except my husband."

I smiled again. Poor Hilary looked very uncomfortable. With an apologetic air he began to stammer something about Parish Councils.

I was not to be diverted by any such manœuvre. It was impossible that he could really wish to talk on that subject.

"Would a person who had never eaten anything but beef make a boast of it?" I asked.

Hilary grinned covertly. Mrs. Hilary pulled the lamp nearer, and took up her embroidery.

"Do you always work the same pattern?" said I.

Hilary kicked me gently. Mrs. Hilary made no direct reply, but presently she began to talk.

"I was just about Phyllis's age"—(by the way, little Miss Phyllis was there)—"when I first saw Hilary. You remember, Hilary? At Bournemouth?"

"Oh—er—was it Bournemouth?" said Hilary, with much carelessness.

"I was on the pier," pursued Mrs. Hilary. "I had a red frock on, I remember, and one of those big hats they wore that year. Hilary wore——"

"Blue serge," I interpolated, encouragingly.

"Yes, blue serge," said she, fondly. "He had been yachting, and he was beautifully burnt. I was horribly burnt—wasn't I, Hilary?"

Hilary began to pat the dog.

"Then we got to know one another."

"Stop a minute," said I. "How did that happen?"

Mrs. Hilary blushed.

"Well, we were both always on the pier," she explained. "And—and somehow Hilary got to know father, and—and father introduced him to me."

"I'm glad it was no worse," said I. I was considering Miss Phyllis, who sat listening, open-eyed.

"And then, you know, father wasn't always there; and once or twice we met on the cliff. Do you remember that morning, Hilary?"

"What morning?" asked Hilary, patting the dog with immense assiduity.

"Why, the morning I had my white serge on. I'd been bathing, and my hair was down to dry, and you said I looked like a mermaid."

"Do mermaids wear white serge?" I asked; but nobody took the least notice of me—quite properly.

"And you told me such a lot about yourself; and then we found we were late for lunch."

"Yes," said Hilary, suddenly forgetting the dog, "and your mother gave me an awful glance."

"Yes, and then you told me that you were very poor, but that you couldn't help it; and you said you supposed I couldn't possibly——"

"Well, I didn't think——!"

"And I said you were a silly old thing; and then—" Mrs. Hilary stopped abruptly.

"How lovely!" remarked little Miss Phyllis, in a wistful voice.

"And do you remember," pursued Mrs. Hilary, laying down her embroidery and clasping her hands on her knees, "the morning you went to see father?"

"What a row there was!" said Hilary.

"And what an awful week it was after that! I was never so miserable in all my life. I cried till my eyes were quite red, and then I bathed them for an hour, and then I went to the pier, and you were there—and I mightn't speak to you!"

"I remember," said Hilary, nodding gently.

"And then, Hilary, father sent for me and told me it was no use; and I said I'd never marry anyone else. And father said, 'There, there, don't cry. We'll see what mother says.'"

"Your mother was a brick," said Hilary, poking the fire.

"And that night—they never told me anything about it, and I didn't even change my frock, but came down, looking horrible, just as I was, in an old black rag— Now, Hilary, don't say it was pretty!"

Hilary, unconvinced, shook his head.

"And when I walked into the drawing-room there was nobody there but just you; and we neither of us said anything for ever so long. And then father and mother came in and—do you remember after dinner, Hilary?"

"I remember," said Hilary.

There was a long pause. Mrs. Hilary was looking into the fire; little

Miss Phyllis's eyes were fixed, in rapt gaze, on the ceiling; Hilary was looking at his wife; I, thinking it safest, was regarding my own boots.

At last Miss Phyllis broke the silence.

"How perfectly lovely!" she said.

"Yes," said Mrs. Hilary. "And we were married three months afterward."

"Tenth of June," said Hilary, reflectively.

"And we had the most charming little rooms in the world! Do you remember those first rooms, dear? So tiny!"

"Not bad little rooms," said Hilary.

"How awfully lovely!" cried Miss Phyllis.

I felt that it was time to interfere.

"And is that all?" I asked.

"All? How do you mean?" said Mrs. Hilary, with a slight start.

"Well, I mean, did nothing else happen? Weren't there any complications? Weren't there any more troubles. or any more opposition, or any misunderstandings, or anything?"

"No," said Mrs. Hilary.

"You never quarrelled, or broke it off?"

"No."

"Nobody came between you?"

"No. It all went just perfectly. Why, of course it did."

"Hilary's people made themselves nasty, perhaps?" I suggested, with a ray of hope.

"They fell in love with her on the spot," said Hilary.

Then I rose and stood with my back to the fire.

"I do not know," I observed, "what Miss Phyllis thinks about it——"

"I think it was just perfect, Mr. Carter."

"But for my part, I can only say that I never heard of such a dull affair in all my life."

"*Dull!*" gasped Miss Phyllis.

"*Dull!*" murmured Mrs. Hilary.

"*Dull!*" chuckled Hilary.

"It was," said I, severely, "without a spark of interest from beginning to end. Such things happen by thousands. It's commonplaceness itself. I had some hopes when your father assumed a firm attitude, but——"

"Mother was such a dear," interrupted Mrs. Hilary.

"Just so. She gave away the whole situation. Then I did trust that Hilary would lose his place, or develop an old flame, or do something just a little interesting."

"It was a perfect time," said Mrs. Hilary.

"I wonder why in the world you told me about it," I pursued.

"I don't know why I did," said Mrs. Hilary, dreamily.

"The only possible excuse for an engagement like that," I observed, "is to be found in intense post-nuptial unhappiness."

Hilary rose, and advanced toward his wife.

"Your embroidery's falling on the floor," said he.

"Not a bit of it," said I.

"Yes, it is," he persisted; and he picked it up and gave it to her. Miss Phyllis smiled delightedly. Hilary had squeezed his wife's hand.

"Then we don't excuse it," said he.

I took out my watch. I was not finding much entertainment.

"Surely it's quite early, old man?" said Hilary.

"It's nearly eleven. We've spent half an hour on the thing," said I, peevishly, holding out my hand to my hostess.

"Oh, are you going? Good night, Mr. Carter."

I turned to Miss Phyllis.

"I hope you won't think all love affairs are like that," I said; but I saw her lips begin to shape into "lovely," and I hastily left the room.

Hilary came to help me on with my coat. He looked extremely apologetic, and very much ashamed of himself.

"Awfully sorry, old chap," said he, "that we bored you with our reminiscences. I know, of course, that they can't be very interesting to other people. Women are so confoundedly romantic."

"Don't try that on with me," said I, much disgusted. "You were just as bad yourself."

He laughed, as he leant against the door.

"She did look ripping in that white frock," he said, "with her hair——"

"Stop," said I, firmly. "She looked just like a lot of other girls."

"I'm hanged if she did!" said Hilary.

Then he glanced at me with a puzzled sort of expression.

"I say, old man, weren't you ever that way yourself?" he asked.

I hailed a hansom cab.

"Because if you were, you know, you'd understand how a fellow remembers every——"

"Good night," said I. "At least, I suppose you're not coming to the club?"

"Well, I think not," said Hilary. "Ta-ta, old fellow. Sorry we bored you. Of course, if a man has never——"

"Never!" I groaned. "A score of times!"

"Well, then, doesn't it——?"

"No," said I. "It's just that that makes stories like yours so infernally——"

"What?" asked Hilary; for I had paused to light a cigarette.

"Uninteresting," said I, getting into my cab.

X

STRANGE, BUT TRUE

The other day my young cousin George lunched with me. He is a cheery youth, and a member of the University of Oxford. He refreshes me very much, and I believe that I have the pleasure of affording him some matter for thought. On this occasion, however, he was extremely silent and depressed. I said little, but made an extremely good luncheon. Afterward we proceeded to take a stroll in the Park.

"Sam, old boy," said George, suddenly, "I'm the most miserable devil alive."

"I don't know what else you expect at your age," I observed, lighting a cigar. He walked on in silence for a few moments.

"I say, Sam, old boy, when you were young, were you ever—?" He paused, arranged his neckcloth (it was more like a bed-quilt—

oh, the fashion, of course, I know that), and blushed a fine crimson.

"Was I ever what, George?" I had the curiosity to ask.

"Oh, well, hard hit, you know—a girl, you know."

"In love, you mean, George? No, I never was."

"Never?"

"No. Are you?"

"Yes. Hang it!" Then he looked at me with a puzzled air and continued:

"I say, though, Sam, it's awfully funny you shouldn't have—don't you know what it's like, then?"

"How should I?" I inquired apologetically. "What is it like, George?"

George took my arm.

"It's just Hades," he informed me confidentially.

"Then," I remarked, "I have no reason to regret——"

"Still, you know," interrupted George, "it's not half bad."

"That appears to me to be a paradox," I observed.

"It's precious hard to explain it to you if you've never felt it," said George, in rather an injured tone. "But what I say is quite true."

"I shouldn't think of contradicting you, my dear fellow," I hastened to say.

"Let's sit down," said he, "and watch the people driving. We may see somebody—somebody we know, you know, Sam."

"So we may," said I, and we sat down.

"A fellow," pursued George, with knitted brows, "is all turned upside-down, don't you know?"

"How very peculiar!" I exclaimed.

"One moment he's the happiest dog in the world, and the next— well, the next, it's the deuce."

"But," I objected, "not surely without good reason for such a change?"

"Reason? Bosh! The least thing does it."

I flicked the ash from my cigar.

"It may," I remarked, "affect you in this extraordinary way, but surely it is not so with most people?"

"Perhaps not," George conceded. "Most people are cold-blooded asses."

"Very likely the explanation lies in that fact," said I.

"I didn't mean you, old chap," said George, with a penitence which showed that he had meant me.

"Oh, all right, all right," said I.

"But when a man's really far gone there's nothing else in the world but it."

"That seems to me not to be a healthy condition," said I.

"Healthy? Oh, you old idiot, Sam! Who's talking of health? Now, only last night I met her at a dance. I had five dances with her—talked to her half the evening, in fact. Well, you'd think that would last some time, wouldn't you?"

"I should certainly have supposed so," I assented.

"So it would with most chaps, I dare say, but with me—confound it, I feel as if I hadn't seen her for six months!"

"But, my dear George, that is surely rather absurd! As you tell me, you spent a long while with the young person——"

"The—young—person!"

"You've not told me her name, you see."

"No, and I shan't. I wonder if she'll be at the Musgraves' tonight!"

"You're sure," said I, soothingly, "to meet her somewhere in the course of the next few weeks."

George looked at me. Then he observed with a bitter laugh:

"It's pretty evident *you've* never had it. You're as bad as those chaps who write books."

"Well, but surely they often describe with sufficient warmth and—er—colour——"

"Oh, I dare say; but it's all wrong. At least, it's not what *I* feel. Then look at the girls in books! All *beasts!*"

George spoke with much vehemence; so that I was led to say:

"The lady you are preoccupied with is, I suppose, handsome?"

George turned swiftly round on me.

"Look here, can you hold your tongue, Sam?"

I nodded.

"Then I'm hanged if I won't point her out to you!"

"That's uncommon good of you, George," said I.

"Then you'll see," continued George. "But it's not only her looks, you know; she's the most——"

He stopped. Looking round to see why, I observed that his face was red; he clutched his walking-stick tightly in his left hand; his right hand was trembling, as if it wanted to jump up to his hat. "Here she comes! Look, look!" he whispered.

Directing my eyes toward the lines of carriages which rolled past us, I observed a girl in a victoria; by her side sat a portly lady of middle age. The girl was decidedly like the lady; a description of the lady would not, I imagine, be interesting. The girl blushed slightly and bowed. George and I lifted our hats. The victoria and its occupants were gone. George leant back with a sigh. After a moment he said:

"Well, that was her."

There was expectancy in his tone.

"She has an extremely prepossessing appearance," I observed.

"There isn't," said George, "a girl in London to touch her. Sam, old boy, I believe—I believe she likes me a bit."

"I'm sure she must, George," said I; and, indeed, I thought so.

"The governor's infernally unreasonable," said George, fretfully.

"Oh, you've mentioned it to him?"

"I sounded him. Oh, you may be sure he didn't see what I was up to. I put it quite generally. He talked rot about getting on in the world. Who wants to get on?"

"Who, indeed?" said I. "It is only changing what you are for something no better."

"And about waiting till I know my own mind. Isn't it enough to look at her?"

"Ample, in my opinion," said I.

George rose to his feet.

"They've gone to a party; they won't come round again," said he. "We may as well go, mayn't we?"

I was very comfortable; so I said timidly:

"We might see somebody else we know."

"Oh, somebody else be hanged! Who wants to see 'em?"

"I'm sure I don't," said I, hastily, as I rose from my armchair, which was at once snapped up.

We were about to return to the club, when I observed Lady Mickleham's barouche standing under the trees. I invited George to come and be introduced.

He displayed great indifference.

"She gives a good many parties," said I, "and perhaps——"

"By Jove! yes. I may as well," said George. "Glad you had the sense to think of that, old man."

So I took him up to Dolly and presented him. Dolly was very gracious: George is an eminently presentable boy. We fell into conversation.

"My cousin, Lady Mickleham," said I, "has been telling me——"

"Oh, shut up, Sam!" said George, not, however, appearing very angry.

"About a subject on which you can assist him more than I can, inasmuch as you are married. He is in love."

Dolly glanced at George.

"Oh, what fun!" said she.

"Fun!" cried George.

"I mean, how awfully interesting," said Dolly, suddenly transforming her expression.

"And he wanted to be introduced to you because you might ask her and him to——"

George became red, and began to stammer an apology.

"Oh, I don't believe him," said Dolly, kindly; "he always makes people uncomfortable if he can. What were you telling him, Mr. George?"

"It's no use telling him anything. He can't understand," said George.

"Is she very—?" asked Dolly, fixing doubtfully grave eyes on my young cousin.

"Sam's seen her," said he, in an access of shyness.

Dolly turned to me for an opinion, and I gave one.

"She is just," said I, "as charming as he thinks her."

Dolly leant over to my cousin, and whispered, "Tell me her name." And he whispered something back to Dolly.

"It's awfully kind of you, Lady Mickleham," he said.

"I am a kind old thing," said Dolly, all over dimples. "I can easily get to know them."

"Oh, you really are awfully kind, Lady Mickleham."

Dolly smiled upon him, waved her hand to me and drove off, crying: "Do try to make Mr. Carter understand!"

We were left alone. George wore a meditative smile. Presently he roused himself to say:

"She's really a very kind woman. She's so sympathetic. She's not like you. I expect she felt it once herself, you know."

"One can never tell," said I, carelessly. "Perhaps she did—once."

George fell to brooding again. I thought I would try an experiment.

"Not altogether bad-looking, either, is she?" I asked, lighting a cigarette.

George started.

"What! Oh, well, I don't know. I suppose some people might think so."

He paused, and added, with a bashful, knowing smile:

"You can hardly expect *me* to go into raptures about her, can you, old man?"

I turned my head away, but he caught me.

"Oh, you needn't smile in that infernally patronizing way," he cried angrily.

"Upon my word, George," said I, "I don't know that I need."

XI

THE VERY LATEST THING

"It's the very latest thing," said Lady Mickleham, standing by the table in the smoking-room, and holding an album in her hand.

"I wish it had been a little later still," said I, for I felt embarrassed.

"You promise, on your honour, to be absolutely sincere, you know, and then you write what you think of me. See what a lot of opinions I've got already," and she held up the thick album.

"It would be extremely interesting to read them," I observed.

"Oh! but they're quite confidential," said Dolly. "That's part of the fun."

"I don't appreciate that part," said I.

"Perhaps you will when you've written yours," suggested Lady Mickleham.

"Meanwhile, mayn't I see the Dowager's?"

"Well, I'll show you a little bit of the Dowager's. Look here: 'Our dear Dorothea is still perhaps just *a thought* wanting in seriousness, but the sense of her position is having a sobering effect.'"

"I hope not," I exclaimed apprehensively. "Whose is this?"

"Archie's."

"May I see a bit——?"

"Not a bit," said Dolly. "Archie's is—is rather foolish, Mr. Carter."

"So I suppose," said I.

"Dear boy!" said Dolly, reflectively.

"I hate sentiment," said I. "Here's a long one. Who wrote——?"

"Oh, you mustn't look at that—not at that, above all!"

"Why above all?" I asked with some severity.

Dolly smiled; then she observed in a soothing tone:

"Perhaps it won't be 'above all' when you've written yours, Mr. Carter."

"By the way," I said carelessly, "I suppose Archie sees all of them?"

"He has never asked to see them," answered Lady Mickleham.

The reply seemed satisfactory; of course, Archie had only to ask. I took a clean quill and prepared to write.

"You promise to be sincere, you know," Dolly reminded me.

I laid down my pen.

"Impossible!" said I, firmly.

"Oh, but why, Mr. Carter?"

"There would be an end of our friendship."

"Do you think as badly of me as all that?" asked Dolly, with a rueful air.

I leant back in my chair and looked at Dolly. She looked at me. She smiled. I may have smiled.

"Yes," said I.

"Then you needn't write it *quite* all down," said Dolly.

"I am obliged," said I, taking up my pen.

"You mustn't say what isn't true, but you needn't say everything that is—that might be—true," explained Dolly.

This, again, seemed satisfactory. I began to write, Dolly sitting opposite me with her elbows on the table, and watching me.

After ten minutes' steady work, which included several pauses for reflection, I threw down the pen, leant back in my chair, and lit a cigarette.

"Now read it," said Dolly, her chin in her hands and her eyes fixed on me.

"It is, on the whole," I observed, "complimentary."

"No, really?" said Dolly. "Yet you promised to be sincere."

"You would not have had me disagreeable?" I asked.

"That's a different thing," said Dolly. "Read it, please."

"Lady Mickleham," I read, "is usually accounted a person of considerable attractions. She is widely popular, and more than one woman has been known to like her."

"I don't quite understand that," interrupted Dolly.

"It is surely simple," said I; and I read on without delay: "She is kind even to her husband, and takes the utmost pains to conceal from her mother-in-law anything calculated to distress that lady."

"I suppose you mean that to be nice?" said Dolly.

"Of course," I answered; and I proceeded: "She never gives pain to anyone, except with the object of giving pleasure to somebody else, and her kindness is no less widely diffused than it is hearty and sincere."

"That really is nice," said Dolly, smiling.

"Thank you," said I, smiling also. "She is very charitable: she takes a pleasure in encouraging the shy and bashful——"

"How do *you* know that?" asked Dolly.

"While," I pursued, "suffering without impatience a considerable amount of self-assurance."

"You can't know whether I'm patient or not," remarked Dolly. "I'm polite."

"She thinks," I read on, "no evil of the most attractive of women, and has a smile for the most unattractive of men."

"You put that very nicely," said Dolly, nodding.

"The former may constantly be seen in her house—and the latter at least as often as many people would think desirable." (Here for some reason Dolly laughed.) "Her intellectual powers are not despicable."

"Thank you, Mr. Carter."

"She can say what she means on the occasions on which she wishes to do so, and she is, at other times, equally capable of meaning much more than she would be likely to say."

"How do you mean that, Mr. Carter, please?"

"It explains itself," said I, and I proceeded: "The fact of her receiving a remark with disapprobation does not necessarily mean that it causes her displeasure, nor must it be assumed that she did not expect a visitor, merely on the ground that she greets him with surprise."

Here I observed Lady Mickleham looking at me rather suspiciously.

"I don't think that's *quite* nice of you, Mr. Carter," she said pathetically.

"Lady Mickleham is, in short," I went on, coming to my peroration, "equally deserving of esteem and affection——"

"Esteem and affection! That sounds just right," said Dolly, approvingly.

"And those who have been admitted to the enjoyment of her friendship are unanimous in discouraging all others from seeking a similar privilege."

"I beg your pardon?" cried Lady Mickleham.

"Are unanimous," I repeated slowly and distinctly, "in discouraging all others from seeking a similar privilege."

Dolly looked at me, with her brow slightly puckered. I leant back, puffing at my cigarette. Presently—for there was quite a long pause—Dolly's lips curved.

"My mental powers are not despicable," she observed.

"I have said so," said I.

"I think I see," she remarked.

"Is there anything wrong?" I asked anxiously.

"N-no," said Dolly, "not exactly wrong. In fact, I rather think I like that last bit best. Still, don't you think——?"

She rose, came round the table, took up the pen, and put it back in my hand.

"What's this for?" I asked.

"To correct the mistake," said Dolly.

"Do you really think so?" said I.

"I'm afraid so," said Dolly.

I took the pen and made a certain alteration. Dolly took up the album.

"'Are unanimous,'" she read, "'in encouraging all others to seek a similar privilege.' Yes, you meant that, you know, Mr. Carter."

"I suppose I must have," said I, rather sulkily.

"The other was nonsense," urged Dolly.

"Oh, utter nonsense," said I.

"And you had to write the truth!"

"Yes, I had to write some of it."

"And nonsense can't be the truth, can it, Mr. Carter?"

"Of course it can't, Lady Mickleham."

"Where are you going, Mr. Carter?" she asked; for I rose from my chair.

"To have a quiet smoke," said I.

"Alone?" asked Dolly.

"Yes, alone," said I.

I walked toward the door. Dolly stood by the table fingering the album. I had almost reached the door; then I happened to look round.

"Mr. Carter!" said Dolly, as though a new idea had struck her.

"What is it, Lady Mickleham?"

"Well, you know, Mr. Carter, I—I shall try to forget that mistake of yours."

"You're very kind, Lady Mickleham."

"But," said Dolly, with a troubled smile, "I—I'm quite afraid I shan't succeed, Mr. Carter."

After all, the smoking-room is meant for smoking.

XII

AN UNCOUNTED HOUR

WE were standing, Lady Mickleham and I, at a door which led from the morning-room to the terrace at The Towers. I was on a visit to that historic pile (by Vanbrugh—out of the money accumulated by the third Earl—Paymaster to the Forces—*temp.* Queen Anne). The morning-room is a large room. Archie was somewhere in it. Lady Mickleham held a jar containing *pâté de foie gras;* from time to time she dug a piece out with a fork and flung the morsel to a big retriever which was sitting on the terrace. The morning was fine but cloudy. Lady Mickleham wore blue. The dog swallowed the *pâté* with greediness.

"It's so bad for him," sighed she; "but the dear likes it so much."

"How human the creatures are!" said I.

"Do you know," pursued Lady Mickleham, "that the Dowager says I'm extravagant. She thinks dogs ought not to be fed on *pâté de foie gras.*"

"Your extravagance," I observed, "is probably due to your having been brought up on a moderate income. I have felt the effect myself."

"Of course," said Dolly, "we are hit by the agricultural depression."

"The Carters also," I murmured, "are landed gentry."

"After all, I don't see much point in economy, do you, Mr. Carter?"

"Economy," I remarked, putting my hands in my pockets, "is going without something you do want in case you should, some day, want something which you probably won't want."

"Isn't that clever?" asked Dolly, in an apprehensive tone.

"Oh, dear, no," I answered reassuringly. "Anybody can do that—if they care to try, you know."

Dolly tossed a piece of *pâté* to the retriever.

"I have made a discovery lately," I observed.

"What are you two talking about?" called Archie.

"You're not meant to hear," said Dolly, without turning round.

"Yet if it's a discovery, he ought to hear it."

"He's made a good many lately," said Dolly.

She dug out the last bit of *pâté,* flung it to the dog, and handed the empty pot to me.

"Don't be so allegorical," I implored. "Besides, it's really not just to Archie. No doubt the dog is a nice one, but——"

"How foolish you are this morning! What's the discovery?"

"An entirely surprising one."

"Oh, but let me hear! It's nothing about Archie, is it?"

"No. I've told you all Archie's sins."

"Nor Mrs. Hilary? I wish it was Mrs. Hilary!"

"Shall we walk on the terrace?" I suggested.

"Oh, yes, let's," said Dolly, stepping out, and putting on a broad-brimmed, low-crowned hat, which she caught up from a chair hard by. "It isn't Mrs. Hilary?" she added, sitting down on a garden seat.

"No," said I, leaning on a sun-dial which stood by the seat.

"Well, what is it?"

"It is simple," said I, "and serious. It is not, therefore, like you, Lady Mickleham."

"It's like Mrs. Hilary," said Dolly.

"No; because it isn't pleasant. By the way, are you jealous of Mrs. Hilary?"

Dolly said nothing at all. She took off her hat, roughened her hair a little, and assumed an effective pose. Still, it is a fact (for what it is worth) that she doesn't care much about Mrs. Hilary.

"The discovery," I continued, "is that I'm growing middle-aged."

"You are middle-aged," said Dolly, spearing her hat with its long pin.

I was, very naturally, nettled at this.

"So will you be soon," I retorted.

"Not soon," said Dolly.

"Some day," I insisted.

After a pause of about half a minute, Dolly said, "I suppose so."

"You will become," I pursued, idly drawing patterns with my finger on the sun-dial, "wrinkled, rough, fat—and, perhaps, good."

"You're very disagreeable today," said Dolly.

She rose and stood by me.

"What do the mottoes mean?" she asked.

There were two: I will not say they contradicted one another, but they looked at life from different points of view.

"*Pereunt et imputantur,*" I read.

"Well, what's that, Mr. Carter?"

"A trite, but offensive, assertion," said I, lighting a cigarette.

"But what does it mean?" she asked, a pucker on her forehead.

"What does it matter?" said I. "Let's try the other."

"The other is longer."

"And better. *Horas non numero nisi serenas.*"

"And what's that?"

I translated literally. Dolly clapped her hands, and her face gleamed with smiles.

"I like that one!" she cried.

"Stop!" said I, imperatively. "You'll set it moving!"

"It's very sensible," said she.

"More freely rendered, it means, 'I live only when you——' "

"By Jove!" remarked Archie, coming up behind us, pipe in mouth, "there was a lot of rain last night. I've just measured it in the gauge."

"Some people measure everything," said I, with a displeased air. "It is a detestable habit."

"Archie, what does *Pereunt et imputantur* mean?"

"Eh? Oh, I see. Well, I say, Carter!—Oh, well, you know, I suppose it means you've got to pay for your fun, doesn't it?"

"Oh, is that all? I was afraid it was something horrid. Why did you frighten me, Mr. Carter?"

"I think it is rather horrid," said I.

"Why, it isn't even true," said Dolly, scornfully.

Now when I heard this ancient and respectable legend thus cavalierly challenged I fell to studying it again, and presently I exclaimed:

"Yes, you're right! If it said that, it wouldn't be true; but Archie translated wrong."

"Well, you have a shot," suggested Archie.

"The oysters are eaten and put down in the bill," said I. "And you will observe, Archie, that it does not say in whose bill."

"Ah!" said Dolly.

"Well, somebody's got to pay," persisted Archie.

"Oh, yes, somebody," laughed Dolly.

"Well, I don't know," said Archie. "I suppose the chap that has the fun——"

"It's not always a chap," observed Dolly.

"Well, then, the individual," amended Archie. "I suppose he'd have to pay."

"It doesn't say so," I remarked mildly. "And according to my small experience——"

"I'm quite sure your meaning is right, Mr. Carter," said Dolly, in an authoritative tone.

"As for the other motto, Archie," said I, "it merely means that a woman considers all hours wasted which she does not spend in the society of her husband."

"Oh, come, you don't gammon me," said Archie. "It means that the sun don't shine unless it's fine, you know."

Archie delivered this remarkable discovery in a tone of great self-satisfaction.

"Oh, you dear old thing!" said Dolly.

"Well, it does, you know," said he.

There was a pause. Archie kissed his wife (I am not complaining; he has, of course, a perfect right to kiss his wife) and strolled away toward the hothouses.

I lit another cigarette. Then Dolly, pointing to the stem of the dial, cried:

"Why, here's another inscription—oh, and in English!"

She was right. There was another—carelessly scratched on the old battered column—nearly effaced, for the characters had been but lightly marked—and yet not, as I conceived from the tenor of the words, very old.

"What is it?" asked Dolly, peering over my shoulder, as I bent down to read the letters, and shading her eyes with her hand. (Why didn't she put on her hat? We touch the Incomprehensible.)

"It is," said I, "a singularly poor, shallow, feeble, and undesirable little verse."

"Read it out," said Dolly.

So I read it. The silly fellow had written:

> "Life is Love, the poets tell us,
> In the little books they sell us;
> But pray, ma'am—what's of Life the Use,
> If Life be Love? For Love's the Deuce."

Dolly began to laugh gently, digging the pin again into her hat.

"I wonder," said she, "whether they used to come and sit by this old dial just as we did this morning!"

"I shouldn't be at all surprised," said I. "And another point occurs to me, Lady Mickleham."

"Oh, does it? What's that, Mr. Carter?"

"Do you think that anybody measured the rain-gauge?"

Dolly looked at me very gravely.

"I'm so sorry when you do that," said she, pathetically.

I smiled.

"I really am," said Dolly. "But you don't mean it, do you?"

"Certainly not," said I.

Dolly smiled.

"No more than he did!" said I, pointing to the sun-dial.

And then we both smiled.

"Will this hour count, Mr. Carter?" asked Dolly, as she turned away.

"That would be rather strict," said I.

XIII

A REMINISCENCE

"I KNOW exactly what your mother wants, Phyllis," observed Mrs. Hilary.

"It's just to teach them the ordinary things," said little Miss Phyllis.

"What are the ordinary things?" I ventured to ask.

"What all girls are taught, of course, Mr. Carter," said Mrs. Hilary. "I'll write about it at once." And she looked at me as if she thought that I might be about to go.

"It is a comprehensive curriculum," I remarked, crossing my legs, "if one may judge from the results. How old are your younger sisters, Miss Phyllis?"

"Fourteen and sixteen," she answered.

"It is a pity," said I, "that this didn't happen a little while back. I knew a governess who would have suited the place to a 't.'"

Mrs. Hilary smiled scornfully.

"We used to meet," I continued.

"Who used to meet?" asked Miss Phyllis.

"The governess and myself, to be sure," said I, "under the old apple-tree in the garden at the back of the house."

"What house, Mr. Carter?"

"My father's house, of course, Miss Phyllis. And——"

"Oh, but that must be ages ago!" cried she.

Mrs. Hilary rose, cast one glance at me, and turned to the writing-table. Her pen began to scratch almost immediately.

"And under the apple-tree," I pursued, "we had many pleasant conversations."

"What about?" asked Miss Phyllis.

"One thing and another," I returned. "The schoolroom windows looked out that way—a circumstance which made matters more comfortable for everybody."

"I should have thought—" began Miss Phyllis, smiling slightly, but keeping an apprehensive eye on Mrs. Hilary's back.

"Not at all," I interrupted. "My sisters saw us, you see. Well, of course they entertained an increased respect for me, which was all right, and a decreased respect for the governess, which was also all right. We met in the hour allotted to French lessons—by an undesigned but appropriate coincidence."

"I shall say about thirty-five, Phyllis," called Mrs. Hilary from the writing-table.

"Yes, Cousin Mary," called Miss Phyllis. "Did you meet often, Mr. Carter?"

"Every evening in the French hour," said I.

"She'll have got over any nonsense by then," called Mrs. Hilary. "They're often full of it."

"She had remarkably pretty hair," I continued; "very soft it was. Dear me! I was just twenty."

"How old was she?" asked Miss Phyllis.

"One's first love," said I, "is never any age. Everything went very well. Happiness was impossible. I was heart-broken, and the governess was far from happy. Ah, happy, happy times!"

"But you don't seem to have been happy," objected Miss Phyllis.

"Then came a terrible evening——"

"She ought to be a person of active habits," called Mrs. Hilary.

"I think so, yes, Cousin Mary. Oh, what happened, Mr. Carter?"

"And an early riser," added Mrs. Hilary.

"Yes, Cousin Mary. What *did* happen, Mr. Carter?"

"My mother came in during the French hour. I don't know whether you have observed, Miss Phyllis, how easy it is to slip into the habit of entering rooms when you had better remain outside. Now, even my friend Arch— However, that's neither here nor there. My mother, as I say, came in."

"Church of England, of course, Phyllis?" called Mrs. Hilary.

"Oh, of *course,* Cousin Mary," cried little Miss Phyllis.

"The sect makes no difference," I observed. "Well, my sisters, like good girls, began to repeat the irregular verbs. But it was no use. We were discovered. That night, Miss Phyllis, I nearly drowned myself."

"You must have been— Oh, how awful, Mr. Carter!"

"That is to say, I thought how effective it would be if I drowned myself. Ah, well, it couldn't last!"

"And the governess?"

"She left next morning."

There was a pause. Miss Phyllis looked sad and thoughtful: I smiled pensively and beat my cane against my leg.

"Have you ever seen her since?" asked Miss Phyllis.

"No."

"Shouldn't—shouldn't you like to, Mr. Carter?"

"Heaven forbid!" said I.

Suddenly Mrs. Hilary pushed back her chair, and turned round to us.

"Well, I declare," said she, "I must be growing stupid. Here have I been writing to the Agency, when I know of the very thing myself! The Polwheedles' governess is just leaving them; she's been there over fifteen years. Lady Polwheedle told me she was a treasure. I wonder if she'd go!"

"Is she what mamma wants?"

"My dear, you'll be most lucky to get her. I'll write at once and ask her to come to lunch tomorrow. I met her there. She's an admirable person."

Mrs. Hilary wheeled round again. I shook my head at Miss Phyllis.

"Poor children!" said I. "Manage a bit of fun for them sometimes."

Miss Phyllis assumed a staid and virtuous air.

"They must be properly brought up, Mr. Carter," said she.

"Is there a House Opposite?" I asked; and Miss Phyllis blushed.

Mrs. Hilary advanced, holding out a letter.

"You may as well post this for me," said she. "Oh, and would you like to come to lunch tomorrow?"

"To meet the Paragon?"

"No. She'll be there, of course; but you see it's Saturday, and Hilary will be here; and I thought you might take him off somewhere and leave Phyllis and me to have a quiet talk with her."

"That won't amuse her much," I ventured to remark.

"She's not coming to be *amused,*" said Mrs. Hilary, severely.

"All right; I'll come," said I, taking my hat.

"Here's the note for Miss Bannerman," said Mrs. Hilary.

That sort of thing never surprises me. I looked at the letter and read "Miss M. E. Bannerman." "M. E." stood for "Maud Elizabeth." I put my hat back on the table.

"What sort of a looking person is this Miss Bannerman?" I asked.

"Oh, a spare, upright woman—hair a little grey, and—I don't know how to describe it—her face looks a little weather-beaten. She wears glasses."

"Thank you," said I. "And what sort of a looking person am I?"

Mrs. Hilary looked scornful. Miss Phyllis opened her eyes.

"How old do I look, Miss Phyllis?" I asked.

Miss Phyllis scanned me from top to toe.

"I don't know," she said uncomfortably.

"Guess," said I, sternly.

"F-forty-three—oh, or forty-two?" she asked, with a timid upward glance.

"When you've done your nonsense—" began Mrs. Hilary; but I laid a hand on her arm.

"Should you call me fat?" I asked.

"Oh, no, not *fat,*" said Mrs. Hilary, with a smile, which she strove to render reassuring.

"I am undoubtedly bald," I observed.

"You're certainly bald," said Mrs. Hilary, with regretful candour.

I took my hat and remarked:

"A man has a right to think of himself, but I am not thinking mainly of myself. I shall not come to lunch."

"You said you would," cried Mrs. Hilary, indignantly.

I poised the letter in my hand, reading again, "Miss M(aud) E(liza-beth) Bannerman." Miss Phyllis looked at me curiously, Mrs. Hilary impatiently.

"Who knows," said I, "that I may not be a Romance—a Vanished Dream—a Green Memory—an Oasis? A person who has the fortune to be an Oasis, Miss Phyllis, should be very careful. I will not come to lunch."

"Do you mean that you used to know Miss Bannerman?" asked Mrs. Hilary, in her pleasant prosaic way.

It was a sin seventeen years old: it would hardly count against the blameless Miss Bannerman now.

"You may tell her when I'm gone," said I to Miss Phyllis.

Miss Phyllis whispered in Mrs. Hilary's ear.

"Another!" cried Mrs. Hilary, aghast.

"It was the very first," said I, defending myself.

Mrs. Hilary began to laugh. I smoothed my hat.

"Tell her," said I, "that I remembered her very well."

"I shall do no such thing," said Mrs. Hilary.

"And tell her," I continued, "that I am still handsome."

"I shan't say a word about you," said Mrs. Hilary.

"Ah, well, that will be better still," said I.

"She'll have forgotten your very name," remarked Mrs. Hilary.

I opened the door, but a thought struck me. I turned round and observed:

"I dare say her hair's just as soft as ever. Still—I'll lunch some other day."

X I V

ANCIENT HISTORY

"I've been hearing something about you, Mr. Carter," Dolly remarked, stroking the Persian kitten which she had bought to match her hair.

"I'm very weak. I shall like to hear it too." And I sat down.

Dolly kissed the kitten and went on. "About you and Dulcie Mildmay."

"That's very ancient history," said I, rather disgusted.

"You admit it is history, though?"

"History is what women have agreed to repeat, Lady Mickleham."

"Oh, if you're going to take it like that! I thought we were friends
—and——"

"There is no greater mark of friendship," I observed, "than a complete absence of interest in one's doings."

"An absence of interest?" smiled Dolly, retying the kitten's bow in
a meditative way.

"It makes the heart grow fonder (not, of course, that that's desirable). You notice, for example, that I don't ask where Archie is. It's
not my business; it's enough for me that he isn't here."

"You always were easily pleased," said Dolly, kindly.

"So with you and me. When we are together, we are——"

"Friends," said she, with a touch of firmness, as I thought.

"We are, as I was about to say, happy. When I'm away, what am I
to you? Nothing!"

"Well, I've an awful lot to do," murmured Dolly.

"And what are you to me?" I pursued. "A pleasing memory!"

"Thank you, Mr. Carter. But about Dulcie Mildmay?"

"Very well; only I wish you'd be a little more recent."

"You were in love with her, you know."

"I trust I'm always ready to learn," said I, resignedly.

"Oh, it's not as if I meant there was anything—anything there
oughtn't to be."

"Then indeed we would discuss it."

"It was long before she married."

"You must really forgive me then. She married in—'94. April 15th,
to be precise. I beg your pardon, Lady Mickleham?"

"I just smiled. You've such a splendid memory for dates."

"Uncle Joseph died last week and left me a legacy."

"It's really no use, Mr. Carter. Mrs. Hilary told me all about it."

"I never can conceal anything. It don't do, from Mrs. Hilary."

"You very nearly proposed to Dulcie, down the river one day. She
had great difficulty in stopping you."

"Preposterous! Is there ever any difficulty in stopping me?"

Dolly placed the kitten on her left shoulder, so that it could rub its
face against her ear. This action had all the effect of an observation.

"Though what you saw in her I can't think," she added.

"You should have asked me at the time," said I.

"Anyhow you were quite depressed for a month afterward—Mrs. Hilary said so."

"Occasionally," I remarked, "Mrs. Hilary does me justice. I should have been depressed only——"

"Only what?"

"Thankfulness supervened," said I.

"Then you did nearly——?"

"Oh, well, I was a little tempted, perhaps."

"You oughtn't to yield to temptation."

"Well, somebody must, or the thing becomes absurd," said I.

"I shall have to keep my eye on you, Mr. Carter."

"Well, I like having pretty things about me——"

"That's rather obvious," interrupted Dolly, scornfully.

"And so," I pursued, "I dare say I enjoyed myself with Dulcie Mildmay."

Dolly put the kitten down on the floor with quite a bump. I took my hat.

"Your story," said I, as I brushed my hat, "hasn't come to much, Lady Mickleham."

Dolly was not put out; nay, she picked up the kitten again and started rubbing its fur the wrong way.

"When you were a child, Mr. Carter—" she began.

"Dear, dear!" I murmured, stroking the crown of my head.

"Did you use to tell the truth?"

I put my hat back on the table. The conversation began to interest me.

"You may have noticed," said I, "that I am a man of method!"

"You do call regularly," Dolly agreed.

"I was the same at the B.C. sort of period you refer to. I had an invariable rule. I lied first."

"Yes, and then——?"

"Oh, they made a row. Then I told the truth, and was rewarded. If I'd told the truth the first time, you see, I should have got nothing. The thing would have degenerated into a matter of course, and I should have lost the benefit of confession."

"You got off, I suppose, by confessing?"

"I did. A halcyon period, Lady Mickleham. In later life one gets off by professing. Have you observed the difference?"

"Professing what?"

"An attachment to somebody else, to be sure. Weren't we talking of Dulcie Mildmay?"

"I asked you that question because Mrs. Hilary's little girl——"

"I am acquainted with that sad episode," I interposed. "Indeed, I took occasion to observe that I hoped it would make Mrs. Hilary more charitable to other people. As a matter of fact, it rather pleased me. Righteousness shouldn't run in families. It is all very well as a 'Sport,' but——"

"I don't see much sport in it," interrupted Dolly.

"I was speaking scientifically——"

"Then please don't." She paused and resumed in a thoughtful tone: "It reminded me of my first flirtation."

"This is indeed ancient history," I cried.

"Yes, I'm twenty-four."

In silent sympathy we stroked opposite ends of the Persian kitten.

"I didn't care one bit about him," Dolly assumed.

"Art for art's sake," said I, nodding approvingly.

"But there was nothing else to do and——"

"Are you busy this afternoon?"

"I was only sixteen and not very particular. I met him at the Wax-works——"

"Are they so called because they make parents angry?"

"There was a hospital close to, and by an unlucky chance our Vicar induced mamma to visit it. Well, we ran into mamma coming out, you see."

"What happened?" I asked.

"Oh, I said I'd met him when I was with papa at Kissingen. Don't make another pun, please."

"Did papa play up?"

"I hadn't time to see him first," said Dolly, sadly. "Mamma drove down and picked him up in the City."

"I detest a suspicious temperament like that," said I. "What did it come to?"

"No parties, and extra French for weeks," sighed Dolly. "Mamma said she wouldn't have minded if only I'd spoken the truth."

"If she really meant that," I remarked cautiously, "there was the basis of an understanding."

"Of course she didn't. That was just rubbing it in, you know."

We relapsed into a pensive silence. Dolly gave the kitten milk, I pulled its tail. We had become quite thoughtful.

"I always tell the truth now, except to the Dowager," said Dolly, presently.

"It doesn't do to be quixotic," I agreed. "Telling the truth to people who misunderstand you is really promoting falsehood, isn't it?"

"That's rather a good idea," said Dolly. "And if you——"

"Adapt?"

"Yes—why, then, they get it just right, don't they? You think of quite sensible things sometimes, Mr. Carter."

"Often when I'm not with you," said I.

"And I suppose you adapted in telling me about Dulcie Mildmay?"

"Do you know, I've a sort of idea that I confused her with somebody else."

"That's not very complimentary."

"Oh, I don't know. I remember the scene so well. It was in a backwater under a tree. There was a low bough over the water, and she——"

"Who?" asked Dolly, resuming exclusive possession of the kitten.

"Well, whoever it was—hung her hat on the bough. It was about eight o'clock, a very pleasant evening. I happen to recollect that the cushions were blue. And she wore blue. And I was blue, until— Did you say that she refused me?"

"Mrs. Hilary says she didn't let it come to that."

"Mrs. Hilary is right as usual. We got home at ten and— Your mother couldn't have meant what she said, I think."

"I don't see how mamma comes in," said Dolly, in a voice muffled by kitten fur.

"Because her mother minded considerably, although we spoke the truth."

"What did you do that for?" asked Dolly, reprovingly.

"Oh, because other people had seen us from a punt. So we just said that time had flown—not, perhaps, a particularly tactful thing to say. And that's the whole truth about Dulcie Mildmay."

I rose and took my hat again, as if I meant it this time too. Dolly rose too, and held out one hand to me; the other contained the kitten.

"What was the hat like?" asked Dolly.

"Just such a hat as you'd wear yourself," said I.

"I never wear hats like Dulcie Mildmay's."

"I told you there was a mistake somewhere," I observed triumphantly.

Dolly smiled; she looked up at me (well, I'm taller than she is, of course).

"Yes, I expect there is," said she. "But do you see any particular good in telling Mrs. Hilary so?"

"She wouldn't believe it."

"No—and——"

"It is, as you observe, so uncomplimentary to Mrs. Mildmay."

"And it's all such very Ancient History!"

I don't think anything more of interest occurred that afternoon—anyhow nothing more about Dulcie Mildmay.

XV

A FINE DAY

"I SEE nothing whatever to laugh at," said Mrs. Hilary, coldly, when I had finished.

"I did not ask you to laugh," I observed mildly. "I mentioned it merely as a typical case."

"It's not typical," she said, and took up her embroidery. But a moment later she added:

"Poor boy! I'm not surprised!"

"I'm not surprised either," I remarked. "It is, however, extremely deplorable."

"It's your own fault. Why did you introduce him?"

"A book," I observed, "might be written on the Injustice of the Just. How could I suppose that he would——?"

By the way, I may as well state what he—that is, my young cousin George—had done. Unless one is a genius, it is best to aim at being intelligible.

Well, he was in love; and with a view of providing him with another house at which he might be likely to meet the adored object, I presented him to my friend Lady Mickleham. That was on a Tuesday. A fortnight later, as I was sitting in Hyde Park (as I sometimes do), George came up and took the chair next to me. I gave him a cigarette, but made no remark. George beat his cane restlessly against the leg of his trousers.

"I've got to go up tomorrow," he remarked.

"Ah, well, Oxford is a delightful town," said I.

"D—d hole," observed George.

I was about to contest this opinion when a victoria drove by.

A girl sat in it, side by side with a portly lady.

"George, George!" I cried. "There she is— Look!"

George looked, raised his hat with sufficient politeness, and remarked to me:

"Hang it! one sees those people everywhere."

I am not easily surprised, but I confess I turned to George with an expression of wonder.

"A fortnight ago—" I began.

"Don't be an ass, Sam," said George, rather sharply. "She's not a bad girl, but—" He broke off and began to whistle.

There was a long pause. I lit a cigar, and looked at the people.

"I lunched at the Micklehams' today," said George, drawing a figure on the gravel with his cane. "Mickleham's not a bad fellow."

"One of the best fellows alive," I agreed.

"I wonder why she married him, though," mused George; and he added, with apparent irrelevance, "It's a dashed bore, going up." And then a smile spread over his face; a blush accompanied it, and proclaimed George's sense of delicious wickedness. I turned on him.

"Out with it!" said I.

"It's nothing. Don't be a fool," said George.

"Where did you get that rose?" I asked.

"This rose?" he repeated, fondling the blossom. "It was given to me."

Upon this I groaned—and I still consider that I had good reason for my action. It was the groan of a moralist.

"They've asked me to stay at The Towers next vac.," said George, glancing at me out of the corner of an immoral eye. Perhaps he thought it too immoral, for he added, "It's all *right,* Sam." I believe that I have as much self-control as most people, but at this point I chuckled.

"What the deuce are you laughing at?" asked George.

I made no answer, and he went on:

"You never told me what a—what she was like, Sam. Wanted to keep it to yourself, you old dog."

"George—George—George!" said I. "You go up tomorrow?"

"Yes, confound it!"

"And term lasts two months?"

"Yes—hang it!"

"All is well," said I, crossing my legs. "There is more virtue in two months than in Ten Commandments."

George regarded me with a dispassionate air.

"You're an awful ass sometimes," he observed critically, and he rose from his seat.

"Must you go?" said I.

"Yes—got a lot of things to do. Look here, Sam, don't go and talk about——"

"Talk about what?"

"Anything, you old idiot," said George, with a pleased smile, and he dug me in the ribs with his cane, and departed.

I sat on, admiring the simple elements which constitute the happiness of the young. Alas! with advancing years, Wrong loses half its flavour! To be improper ceases, by itself, to satisfy.

Immersed in these reflections, I failed to notice that a barouche had stopped opposite to me; and suddenly I found a footman addressing me.

"Beg your pardon, sir," he said. "Her ladyship wishes to speak to you."

"It is a blessed thing to be young, Martin," I observed.

"Yes, sir," said Martin. "It's a fine day, sir."

"But very short," said I. Martin is respectful, and said nothing—to me, at least. What he said to the coachman I don't know.

And then I went up to Dolly.

"Get in and drive round," suggested Dolly.

"I can't," said I. "I have a bad nose."

"What's the matter with your nose?" asked Dolly, smiling.

"The joint is injured," said I, getting into the barouche. And I added severely, "I suppose I'd better sit with my back to the horses?"

"Oh, no, you're not my husband," said Dolly. "Sit here"; and she made room by her, as she continued, "I rather like Mr. George."

"I'm ashamed of you," I observed. "Considering your age——"

"Mr. Carter!"

"Considering, I say, his age, your conduct is scandalous. I shall never introduce any nice boys to you again."

"Oh, please do," said Dolly, clasping her hands.

"You give them roses," said I, accusingly. "You make them false to their earliest loves——"

"She was a pudding-faced thing," observed Dolly.

I frowned. Dolly, by an accident, allowed the tip of her finger to touch my arm for an instant.

"He's a nice boy," said she. "How like he is to you, Mr. Carter!"

"I am a long way past that," said I. "I am thirty-six."

"If you mean to be disagreeable!" said she, turning away. "I beg your pardon for touching you, Mr. Carter."

"I did not notice it, Lady Mickleham."

"Would you like to get out?"

"It's miles from my club," said I, discontentedly.

"He's such fun," said Dolly, with a sudden smile. "He told Archie that I was the most charming woman in London! You've never done that!"

"He said the same about the pudding-faced girl," I observed.

There was a pause. Then Dolly asked:

"How is your nose?"

"The carriage-exercise is doing it good," said I.

"If," observed Dolly, "he is so silly now, what will he be at your age?"

"A wise man," said I.

"He suggested that I might write to him," bubbled Dolly.

Now when Dolly bubbles—an operation which includes a sudden turn toward me, a dancing of eyes, a dart of a small hand, a hurried rush of words, checked and confused by a speedier gust of gurgling sound—I am in the habit of ceasing to argue the question. Bubbling is not to be met by arguing. I could only say:

"He'll have forgotten by the end of the term."

"He'll remember two days later," retorted Dolly.

"Stop the carriage," said I. "I shall tell Mrs. Hilary all about it."

"I won't stop the carriage," said Dolly. "I'm going to take you home with me."

"I am at a premium today," I said sardonically.

"One must have something," said Dolly. "How is your nose now, Mr. Carter?"

I looked at Dolly. I had better not have done that.

"Would afternoon tea hurt it?" she inquired anxiously.

"It would do it good," said I, decisively.

And that is absolutely the whole story. And what in the world Mrs. Hilary found to disapprove of I don't know—especially as I didn't tell her half of it! But she did disapprove. However, she looks very well when she disapproves.

XVI

THE HOUSE OPPOSITE

WE were talking over the sad case of young Algy Groom; I was explaining to Mrs. Hilary exactly what had happened.

"His father gave him," said I, "a hundred pounds, to keep him for three months in Paris while he learnt French."

"And very liberal too," said Mrs. Hilary.

"It depends where you dine," said I. "However, that question did not arise, for Algy went to the Grand Prix the day after he arrived——"

"A *horse race?*" asked Mrs. Hilary, with great contempt.

"Certainly the competitors are horses," I rejoined. "And there he, most unfortunately, lost the whole sum, without learning any French to speak of."

"How disgusting!" exclaimed Mrs. Hilary, and little Miss Phyllis gasped in horror.

"Oh, well," said Hilary, with much bravery (as it struck me), "his father's very well off."

"That doesn't make it a bit better," declared his wife.

"There's no mortal sin in a little betting, my dear. Boys will be boys——"

"And even that," I interposed, "wouldn't matter if we could only prevent girls from being girls."

Mrs. Hilary, taking no notice whatever of me, pronounced sentence. "He grossly deceived his father," she said, and took up her embroidery.

"Most of us have grossly deceived our parents before now," said I. "We should all have to confess to something of the sort."

"I hope you're speaking for your own sex," observed Mrs. Hilary.

"Not more than yours," said I. "You used to meet Hilary on the pier when your father wasn't there—you told me so."

"Father had authorized my acquaintance with Hilary."

"I hate quibbles," said I.

There was a pause. Mrs. Hilary stitched: Hilary observed that the day was fine.

"Now," I pursued carelessly, "even Miss Phyllis here has been known to deceive her parents."

"Oh, let the poor child alone, anyhow," said Mrs. Hilary.

"Haven't you?" said I to Miss Phyllis.

I expected an indignant denial. So did Mrs. Hilary, for she remarked with a sympathetic air:

"Never mind his folly, Phyllis dear."

"Haven't you, Miss Phyllis?" said I.

Miss Phyllis grew very red. Fearing that I was causing her pain, I was about to observe on the prospects of a Dissolution when a shy smile spread over Miss Phyllis's face.

"Yes, once," said she, with a timid glance at Mrs. Hilary, who immediately laid down her embroidery.

"Out with it," I cried triumphantly. "Come along, Miss Phyllis. We won't tell, honour bright!"

Miss Phyllis looked again at Mrs. Hilary. Mrs. Hilary is human.

"Well, Phyllis dear," said she, "after all this time I shouldn't think it my duty——"

"It only happened last summer," said Miss Phyllis.

Mrs. Hilary looked rather put out.

"Still—" she began.

"We must have the story," said I.

Little Miss Phyllis put down the sock she had been knitting.

"I was very naughty," she remarked. "It was my last term at school."

"I know that age," said I to Hilary.

"My window looked out toward the street. You're sure you won't tell? Well, there was a house opposite——"

"And a young man in it," said I.

"How did you know that?" asked Miss Phyllis, blushing immensely.

"No girls' school can keep up its numbers without one," I explained.

"Well, there was, anyhow," said Miss Phyllis. "And I and two other girls went to a course of lectures at the Town Hall on literature or something of that kind. We used to have a shilling given us for our tickets."

"Precisely," said I. "A hundred pounds!"

"No, a shilling," corrected Miss Phyllis. "A hundred pounds! How absurd, Mr. Carter! Well, one day I—I——"

"You're sure you wish to go on, Phyllis?" asked Mrs. Hilary.

"You're afraid, Mrs. Hilary," said I, severely.

"Nonsense, Mr. Carter. I thought Phyllis might——"

"I don't mind going on," said Miss Phyllis, smiling. "One day I— I lost the other girls."

"The other girls are always easy to lose," I observed.

"And on the way there—oh, you know, he went to the lectures."

"The young dog," said I, nudging Hilary. "I should think he did!"

"On the way there it became rather—rather foggy."

"Blessings on it!" I cried; for little Miss Phyllis's demure but roguish expression delighted me.

"And he—he found me in the fog."

"What are you doing, Mr. Carter?" cried Mrs. Hilary, angrily.

"Nothing, nothing," said I. I believe I had winked at Hilary.

"And—and we couldn't find the Town Hall."

"Oh, Phyllis!" groaned Mrs. Hilary.

Little Miss Phyllis looked alarmed for a moment. Then she smiled.

"But we found the confectioner's," said she.

"The *Grand Prix,*" said I, pointing my forefinger at Hilary.

"He had no money at all," said Miss Phyllis.

"It's ideal!" said I.

"And—and we had tea on—on——"

"The shilling?" I cried in rapture.

"Yes," said little Miss Phyllis, "on the shilling. And he saw me home."

"Details, please," said I.

Little Miss Phyllis shook her head.

"And left me at the door."

"Was it still foggy?" I asked.

"Yes. Or he wouldn't have——"

"Now what did he——?"

"Come to the door, Mr. Carter," said Miss Phyllis, with obvious wariness. "Oh, it was such fun!"

"I'm sure it was."

"No, I mean when we were examined in the lectures. I bought the local paper, you know, and read it up, and I got top marks easily, and Miss Green wrote to mother to say how well I had done."

"It all ends most satisfactorily," I observed.

"Yes, didn't it?" said little Miss Phyllis.

Mrs. Hilary was grave again.

"And you never told your mother, Phyllis?" she asked.

"N-no, Cousin Mary," said Miss Phyllis.

I rose and stood with my back to the fire. Little Miss Phyllis took up her sock again, but a smile still played about the corners of her mouth.

"I wonder," said I, looking up at the ceiling, "what happened at the door." Then, as no one spoke, I added:

"Pooh! I know what happened at the door."

"I'm not going to tell you anything more," said Miss Phyllis.

"But I should like to hear it in your own——"

Miss Phyllis was gone! She had suddenly risen and run from the room.

"It did happen at the door," said I.

"Fancy Phyllis!" mused Mrs. Hilary.

"I hope," said I, "that it will be a lesson to you."

"I shall have to keep my eye on her," said Mrs. Hilary.

"You can't do it," said I, in easy confidence. I had no fear of little Miss Phyllis being done out of her recreations. "Meanwhile," I pursued, "the important thing is this: my parallel is obvious and complete."

"There's not the least likeness," said Mrs. Hilary, sharply.

"As a hundred pounds are to a shilling, so is the Grand Prix to the young man opposite," I observed, taking my hat, and holding out my hand to Mrs. Hilary.

"I am very angry with you," she said. "You've made the child think there was nothing wrong in it."

"Oh! nonsense," said I. "Look how she enjoyed telling it."

Then, not heeding Mrs. Hilary, I launched into an apostrophe.

"O Divine House Opposite!" I cried. "Charming House Opposite! What is a man's own dull uneventful home compared with that Glorious House Opposite! If only I might dwell for ever in the House Opposite!"

"I haven't the least notion what you mean," remarked Mrs. Hilary, stiffly. "I suppose it's something silly—or worse."

I looked at her in some puzzle.

"Have you no longing for the House Opposite?" I asked.

Mrs. Hilary looked at me. Her eyes ceased to be absolutely blank. She put her arm through Hilary's and answered gently:

"I don't want the House Opposite."

"Ah," said I, giving my hat a brush, "but maybe you remember the House—when it was Opposite?"

Mrs. Hilary, one arm still in Hilary's, gave me her hand.

She blushed and smiled.

"Well," said she, "it was your fault: so I won't scold Phyllis."

"No, don't, my dear," said Hilary, with a laugh.

As for me, I went downstairs, and, in absence of mind, bade my cabman drive to the House Opposite. But I have never got there.

XVII

A QUICK CHANGE

"WHY not go with Archie?" I asked, spreading out my hands.

"It will be dull enough, anyhow," said Dolly, fretfully. "Besides, it's awfully *bourgeois* to go to the theatre with one's husband."

"*Bourgeois*," I observed, "is an epithet which the riff-raff apply to what is respectable, and the aristocracy to what is decent."

"But it's not a nice thing to be, all the same," said Dolly, who is impervious to the most penetrating remark.

"You're in no danger of it," I hastened to assure her.

"How should you describe me, then?" she asked, leaning forward, with a smile.

"I should describe you, Lady Mickleham," I replied discreetly, "as being a little lower than the angels."

Dolly's smile was almost a laugh as she asked:

"How much lower, please, Mr. Carter?"

"Just by the depth of your dimples," said I, thoughtlessly.

Dolly became immensely grave.

"I thought," said she, "that we never mentioned them now, Mr. Carter."

"Did we ever?" I asked innocently.

"I seemed to remember once: do you recollect being in very low spirits one evening at Monte?"

"I remember being in very low water more than one evening there."

"Yes: you told me you were terribly hard up."

"There was an election in our division that year," I remarked, "and I remitted thirty per cent of my rents."

"You did—to M. Blanc," said Dolly. "Oh, and you were very dreary! You said you'd wasted your life and your time and your opportunities."

"Oh, you mustn't suppose I never have any proper feelings," said I, complacently.

"I think you were hardly yourself."

"Do be more charitable."

"And you said that your only chance was in gaining the affection of——"

"Surely I was not such an—so foolish?" I implored.

"Yes, you were. You were sitting close by me——"

"Oh, then, it doesn't count," said I, rallying a little.

"On a bench. You remember the bench?"

"No, I don't," said I, with a kind but firm smile.

"Not the bench?"

"No."

Dolly looked at me, then she asked in an insinuating tone:

"When did you forget it, Mr. Carter?"

"The day you were buried," I rejoined.

"I see. Well, you said then what you couldn't possibly have meant."

"I dare say. I often did."

"That they were——"

"That what were?"

"Why, the—the—what we're talking about."

"What we were—? Oh, to be sure, the—the blemishes?"

"Yes, the blemishes. You said they were the most——"

"Oh, well, it was a *façon de parler.*"

"I was afraid you weren't a bit sincere," said Dolly, humbly.

"Well, judge me by yourself," said I, with a candid air.

"But I said nothing!" cried Dolly.

"It was incomparably the most artistic thing to do," said I.

"I'm sometimes afraid you don't do me justice, Mr. Carter," remarked Dolly, with some pathos.

I did not care to enter upon that discussion, and a pause followed. Then Dolly, in a timid manner, asked me:

"Do you remember the dreadful thing that happened the same evening?"

"That chances to remain in my memory," I admitted.

"I've always thought it kind of you never to speak of it," said she.

"It is best forgotten," said I, smiling.

"We should have said the same about anybody," protested Dolly.

"Certainly. We were only trying to be smart," said I.

"And it was horribly unjust."

"I quite agree with you, Lady Mickleham."

"Besides, I didn't know anything about him then. He had only arrived that day, you see."

"Really we were not to blame," I urged.

"Oh, but doesn't it seem funny?"

"A strange whirligig, no doubt," I mused.

There was a pause. Then the faintest of smiles appeared on Dolly's face.

"He shouldn't have worn such clothes," she said, as though in self-defence. "Anybody would have looked absurd in them."

"It was all the clothes," I agreed. "Besides, when a man doesn't know a place, he always moons about and looks——"

"Yes. Rather awkward, doesn't he, Mr. Carter?"

"And the mere fact of his looking at you——"

"At us, please."

"Is nothing, although we made a grievance of it at the time."

"That was very absurd of you," said Dolly.

"It was certainly unreasonable of us," said I.

"We ought to have known he was a gentleman."

"But we scouted the idea of it," said I.

"It was a most curious mistake to make," said Dolly.

"Oh, well, it's all put right now," said I.

"Oh, Mr. Carter, do you remember mamma's face when we described him?"

"That was a terrible moment," said I, with a shudder.

"I said he was—ugly," whispered Dolly.

"And I said—something worse," murmured I.

"And mamma knew at once from our description that it was——"

"She saw it in a minute," said I.

"And then you went away."

"Well, I rather suppose I did," said I.

"Mamma is just a little like the Dowager sometimes," said Dolly.

"There is a touch now and then," I conceded.

"And when I was introduced to him the next day I absolutely blushed."

"I don't altogether wonder at that," I observed.

"But it wasn't as if he'd heard what we were saying."

"No; but he'd seen what we were doing."

"Well, what were we doing?" cried Dolly, defiantly.

"Conversing confidentially," said I.

"And a week later you went home!"

"Just one week later," said I.

There was a long pause.

"Well, you'll take me to the theatre?" asked Dolly, with something which, if I were so disposed, I might consider a sigh.

"I've seen the piece twice," said I.

"How tiresome of you! You've seen everything twice."

"I've seen some things much oftener," I observed.

"I'll get a nice girl for you to talk to, and I'll have a young man."

"I don't want my girl to be too *nice,*" I observed.

"She shall be pretty," said Dolly, generously.

"I don't mind if I do come with you," said I. "What becomes of Archie?"

"He's going to take his mother and sisters to the Albert Hall."

My face brightened.

"I am unreasonable," I admitted.

"Sometimes you are," said Dolly.

"I have much to be thankful for. Have you ever observed a small boy eat a penny ice?"

"Of course I have," said Dolly.

"What does he do when he's finished it?"

"Stops, I suppose."

"On the contrary," said I, "he licks the glass."

"Yes, he does," said Dolly, meditatively.

"It's not so bad—licking the glass," said I.

Dolly stood opposite me, smiling. At this moment Archie entered. He had been working at his lathe. He is very fond of making things which he doesn't want, and then giving them to people who have no use for them.

"How are you, old chap?" he began. "I've just finished an uncommon pretty——"

He stopped, paralysed by a cry from Dolly:

"Archie, what in the world are you wearing?"

I turned a startled gaze upon Archie.

"It's just an old suit I routed out," said he, apologetically.

I looked at Dolly; her eyes were close shut, and she gasped:

"My dear, dear boy, go and change it!"

"I don't see why it's not——"

"Go and change it, if you love me," besought Dolly.

"Oh, all right."

"You look hideous in it," she said, her eyes still shut.

Archie, who is very docile, withdrew. A guilty silence reigned for some moments. Then Dolly opened her eyes.

"It was the suit," she said, with a shudder. "Oh, how it all came back to me!"

"I could wish," I observed, taking my hat, "that it would all come back to me."

"I wonder if you mean that!"

"As much as I ever did," said I, earnestly.

"And that is——?"

"Quite enough."

"How tiresome you are!" she said, turning away with a smile.

Outside I met Archie in another suit.

"A quick change, eh, my boy?" said he.

"It took just a week," I remarked absently.

Archie stared.

XVIII

A SLIGHT MISTAKE

"I DON'T ask you for more than a guinea," said Mrs. Hilary, with a parade of forbearance.

"It would be the same," I replied politely, "if you asked me for a thousand"; with which I handed her half a crown. She held it in her open hand, regarding it scornfully.

"Yes," I continued, taking a seat, "I feel that pecuniary gifts——"

"Half a crown!"

"Are a poor substitute for personal service. May not I accompany you to the ceremony?"

"I dare say you spent as much as this on wine with your lunch!"

"I was in a mad mood today," I answered apologetically. "What are they taught at the school?"

"Above all, to be good girls," said Mrs. Hilary, earnestly. "What are you sneering at, Mr. Carter?"

"Nothing," said I, hastily; and I added with a sigh, "I suppose it's all right."

"I should like," said Mrs. Hilary, meditatively, "if I had not other duties, to dedicate my life to the service of girls."

"I should think twice about that, if I were you," said I, shaking my head.

"By the way, Mr. Carter, I don't know if I've ever spoken unkindly of Lady Mickleham. I hope not."

"Hope," said I, "is not yet taxed."

"If I have, I'm very sorry. She's been most kind in undertaking to give away the prizes today. There must be some good in her."

"Oh, don't be hasty!" I implored.

"I always *wanted* to think well of her."

"Ah! Now I never did."

"And Lord Mickleham is coming, too. He'll be most useful."

"That settles it," I exclaimed. "I may not be an earl, but I have a perfect right to be useful. I'll go too."

"I wonder if you'll behave properly," said Mrs. Hilary, doubtfully. I held out a half-sovereign, three half-crowns, and a shilling.

"Oh, well, you may come, since Hilary can't," said Mrs. Hilary.

"You mean he won't," I observed.

"He has always been prevented hitherto," said she, with dignity.

So I went, and it proved a most agreeable expedition. There were two hundred girls in blue frocks and white aprons (the girl three from the end of the fifth row was decidedly pretty)—a nice lot of prize books—the Micklehams (Dolly in demure black), ourselves, and the matron. All went well. Dolly gave away the prizes; Mrs. Hilary and Archie made little speeches. Then the matron came to me. I was sitting modestly at the back of the platform, a little distance behind the others.

"Mr. Musgrave," said the matron to me, "we're so glad to see you here at last. Won't you say a few words?"

"It would be a privilege," I responded cordially, "but unhappily I have a sore throat."

The matron (who was a most respectable woman) said, "Dear,

dear!" but did not press the point. Evidently, however, she liked me, for when we went to have a cup of tea, she got me in a corner and began to tell me all about the work. It was extremely interesting. Then the matron observed:

"And what an angel Mrs. Musgrave is!"

"Well, I should hardly call her that," said I, with a smile.

"Oh, you mustn't depreciate her—you, of all men!" cried the matron, with a somewhat ponderous archness. "Really I envy you her constant society."

"I assure you," said I, "I see very little of her."

"I beg your pardon?"

"I only go to the house about once a fortnight— Oh, it's not my fault. She won't have me there oftener."

"What do you mean? I beg your pardon. Perhaps I've touched on a painful——?"

"Not at all, not at all," said I, suavely. "It is very natural. I am neither young nor handsome, Mrs. Wiggins. I am not complaining."

The matron gazed at me.

"Only seeing her here," I pursued, "you have no idea of what she is at home. She has chosen to forbid me to come to her house——"

"Her house?"

"It happens to be more hers than mine," I explained. "To forbid me, I say, more than once to come to her house. No doubt she had her reasons."

"Nothing could justify it," said the matron, directing a wondering glance at Mrs. Hilary.

"Do not let us blame her," said I. "It is just an unfortunate accident. She is not as fond of me as I could wish, Mrs. Wiggins; and she is a great deal fonder than I could wish of——"

I broke off. Mrs. Hilary was walking toward us. I think she was pleased to see me getting on so well with the matron, for she was smiling pleasantly. The matron wore a bewildered expression.

"I suppose," said Mrs. Hilary, "that you'll drive back with the Micklehams?"

"Unless you want me," said I, keeping a watchful eye on the matron.

"Oh, I don't want you," said Mrs. Hilary, lightly.

"You won't be alone this evening?" I asked anxiously.

Mrs. Hilary stared a little.

"Oh, no!" she said. "We shall have our usual party."

"May I come one day next week?" I asked humbly.

Mrs. Hilary thought for a moment.

"I'm so busy next week; come the week after," said she, giving me her hand.

"That's very unkind," said I.

"Nonsense!" said Mrs. Hilary; and she added, "Mind you let me know when you're coming."

"I won't surprise you," I assured her, with a covert glance at the matron.

The excellent woman was quite red in the face, and could gasp out nothing but "Good-bye," as Mrs. Hilary affectionately pressed her hand.

At this moment Dolly came up. She was alone.

"Where's Archie?" I asked.

"He's run away; he's got to meet somebody. I knew you'd see me home. Mrs. Hilary didn't want you, of course?"

"Of course not," said I, plaintively.

"Besides, you'd rather come with me, wouldn't you?" pursued Dolly; and she added pleasantly to the matron, "Mrs. Hilary's so down on him, you know."

"I'd much rather come with you," said I.

"We'll have a cosy drive all to ourselves," said Dolly, "without husbands or wives or anything horrid. Isn't it nice to get rid of one's husband sometimes, Mrs. Wiggins?"

"I have the misfortune to be a widow, Lady Mickleham," said Mrs. Wiggins.

Dolly's eye rested upon her with an interested expression. I knew that she was about to ask Mrs. Wiggins whether she liked the condition of life, and I interposed hastily, with a sigh:

"But *you* can look back on a happy marriage, Mrs. Wiggins?"

"I did my best to make it so," said she, stiffly.

"You're right," said I. "Even in the face of unkindness we should strive——"

"My husband's not unkind," said Dolly.

"I didn't mean your husband," said I.

"What your poor wife would do if she cared a button for you, I don't know," observed Dolly.

"If I had a wife who cared for me, I should be a better man," said I, solemnly.

"But you'd probably be very dull," said Dolly. "And you wouldn't be allowed to drive with me."

"Perhaps it's all for the best," said I, brightening up. *"Good*-bye, Mrs. Wiggins."

Dolly walked on. Mrs. Wiggins held my hand for a moment.

"Young man," said she, sternly, "are you sure it's not your own fault?"

"I'm not at all sure, Mrs. Wiggins," said I. "But don't be distressed about it. It's of no consequence. I don't let it make me unhappy. Good-bye; so many thanks. Charming girls you have here—especially that one in the fifth—I mean, charming, all of them. Good-bye."

I hastened to the carriage. Mrs. Wiggins stood and watched. I got in and sat down by Dolly.

"Oh, Mrs. Wiggins," said Dolly, dimpling, "don't tell Mrs. Hilary that Archie wasn't with us, or we shall get into trouble." And she added to me, "Are you all right?"

"Rather!" said I, appreciatively; and we drove off, leaving Mrs. Wiggins on the doorstep.

A fortnight later I went to call on Mrs. Hilary. After some conversation she remarked:

"I'm going to the school again tomorrow."

"Really!" said I.

"And I'm so delighted—I've persuaded Hilary to come."

She paused, and then added:

"You really seemed interested last time."

"Oh, I was."

"Would you like to come again tomorrow?"

"No, I think not, thanks," said I, carelessly.

"That's just like you!" she said severely. "You never do any real good, because you never stick to anything."

"There are some things one can't stick to," said I.

"Oh, nonsense!" said Mrs. Hilary.

But there are—and I didn't go.

XIX

THE OTHER LADY

"By the merest chance," I observed meditatively, "I attended a reception last night."

"I went to three," said Lady Mickleham, selecting a sardine-sandwich with care.

"I might not have gone," I mused. "I might easily not have gone."

"I can't see what difference it would make if you hadn't," said she.

"I thought three times about going. It's a curious world."

"What happened? You may smoke, you know."

"I fell in love," said I, lighting a cigarette.

Lady Mickleham placed her feet on the fender—it was a chilly afternoon—and turned her face to me, shielding it from the fire with her handkerchief.

"Men of your age," she remarked, "have no business to be thinking of such things."

"I was not thinking of it," said I. "I was thinking of going home. Then I was introduced to her."

"And you stayed a little, I suppose?"

"I stayed two hours—or two minutes; I forget which"; and I added, nodding my head at Lady Mickleham, "There was something irresistible about me last night."

Lady Mickleham laughed.

"You seem very pleased with yourself," she said, reaching for a fan to replace the handkerchief.

"Yes, take care of your complexion," said I, approvingly. "She has a lovely complexion."

Lady Mickleham laid down the fan.

"I am very pleased with myself," I continued. "She was delighted with me."

"I suppose you talked nonsense to her."

"I have not the least idea what I talked to her. It was quite immaterial. The language of the eyes——"

"Oh, you might be a boy!"

"I was," said I, nodding again.

There was a long silence. Dolly looked at me; I looked at the fire. I did not, however, see the fire. I saw something quite different.

"She liked me very much," I observed, stretching my hands out toward the blaze.

"You absurd old man!" said Dolly. "Was she very charming?"

"She was perfect."

"How? Clever?"

I waved my hand impatiently.

"Pretty, Mr. Carter?"

"Why, of course; the prettiest creature I ever— But that goes without saying."

"It would have gone better without saying," remarked Dolly. "Considering——"

To have asked "Considering what?" would have been the acme of bad taste. I merely smiled, and waved my hand again.

"You're quite serious about it, aren't you?" said Dolly.

"I should think I was," said I, indignantly. "Not to be serious in such a matter is to waste it utterly."

"I'll come to the wedding," said Dolly.

"There won't be a wedding," said I. "There are Reasons."

"Oh! You're very unlucky, Mr. Carter."

"That," I observed, "is as it may be, Lady Mickleham."

"Were the Reasons at the reception?"

"They were. It made no difference."

"It's very curious," remarked Dolly, with a compassionate air, "that you always manage to admire people whom somebody else has married."

"It would be very curious," I rejoined, "if somebody had not married the people whom I admire. Last night, though, I made nothing of his sudden removal: my fancy rioted in accidental deaths for him."

"He won't die," said Dolly.

"I hate that sort of superstition," said I, irritably. "He's just as likely to die as any other man is."

"He certainly won't die," said Dolly.

"Well, I know he won't. Do let it alone," said I, much exasperated. It was probably only kindness, but Dolly suddenly turned her eyes away from me and fixed them on the fire; she took the fan up again and twirled it in her hand; a queer little smile bent her lips.

"I hope the poor man won't die," said Dolly, in a low voice.

"If he had died last night!" I cried longingly. Then, with a regretful shrug of my shoulders, I added, "Let him live now to the crack of doom!"

Somehow this restored my good humour. I rose and stood with my back to the fire, stretching myself and sighing luxuriously. Dolly leant back in her chair and laughed at me.

"Do you expect to be forgiven?" she asked.

"No, no," said I; "I had too good an excuse."

"I wish I'd been there—at the reception, I mean."

"I'm extremely glad you weren't, Lady Mickleham. As it was, I forgot all my troubles."

Dolly is not resentful; she did not mind the implied description. She leant back, smiling still. I sighed again, smiled at Dolly, and took my hat. Then I turned to the mirror over the mantelpiece, arranged my necktie, and gave my hair a touch.

"No one," I observed, "can afford to neglect the niceties of the toilet. Those dainty little curls on the forehead——"

"You've had none there for ten years," cried Lady Mickleham.

"I did not mean my forehead," said I.

Sighing once again, I held out my hand to Dolly.

"Are you doing anything this evening?" she asked.

"That depends on what I'm asked to do," said I, cautiously.

"Well, Archie's going to be at the House, and I thought you might take me to the Phaetons' party. It's quite a long drive—a horribly long drive, Mr. Carter."

I stood for a moment considering this proposal.

"I don't think," said I, "that it would be proper."

"Why, Archie suggested it! You're making an excuse. You know you are!" and Lady Mickleham looked very indignant. "As if," she added scornfully, "you cared about what was proper!"

I dropped into a chair, and said in a confidential tone, "I don't care a pin. It was a mere excuse. I don't want to come."

"You're very rude indeed. Many women would never speak to you again."

"They would," said I, "all do just as you will."

"And what's that, Mr. Carter?"

"Ask me again on the first opportunity."

"Why won't you come?" said Dolly, waiving this question.

I bent forward, holding my hat in my left hand, and sawing the air with my right forefinger.

"You fail to allow," said I, impressively, "for the rejuvenescence which recent events have produced in me. If I came with you this evening I should be quite capable—" I paused.

"Of anything dreadful?" asked Dolly.

"Of paying you pronounced attentions," said I, gravely.

"That," said Dolly, with equal gravity, "would be very regrettable. It would be unjust to me—and very insulting to her, Mr. Carter."

"It would be the finest testimonial to her," I cried.

"And you'll spend the evening thinking of her?" asked Dolly.

"I shall get through the evening," said I, "in the best way I can." And I smiled contentedly.

"What's her husband?" asked Dolly, suddenly.

"Her husband," I rejoined, "is nothing at all."

Dolly, receiving this answer, looked at me with a pathetic air.

"It's not quite fair," she observed. "Do you know what I'm thinking about, Mr. Carter?"

"Certainly I do, Lady Mickleham. You are thinking that you would like to meet me for the first time."

"Not at all. I was thinking that it would be amusing if you met me for the first time."

I said nothing. Dolly rose and walked to the window. She swung the tassel of the blind and it bumped against the window. The failing sun caught her ruddy brown hair. There were curls on her forehead, too.

"It's a grand world," said I. "And, after all, one can grow old very gradually."

"You're not really old," said Dolly, with the fleetest glance at me. A glance should not be over-long.

"Gradually and disgracefully," I murmured.

"If you met me for the first time—" said Dolly, swinging the tassel.

"By Heaven, it should be the last!" I cried, and I rose to my feet.

Dolly let the tassel go, and made me a very pretty curtsy.

"I am going to another party tonight," said I, nodding my head significantly.

"Ah!" said Dolly.

"And I shall again," I pursued, "spend my time with the prettiest woman in the room."

"Shall you?" asked Dolly, smiling.

"I am a very fortunate fellow," I observed. "And as for Mrs. Hilary, she may say what she likes."

"Oh, does Mrs. Hilary know the—Other Lady?"

I walked toward the door.

"There is," said I, laying my hand on the door, "no Other Lady."

"I shall get there about eleven," said Dolly.

XX

A LIFE SUBSCRIPTION

"I NEVER quite know," said Mrs. Hilary, taking up her embroidery, "what you mean when you talk about love."

"No more do I," I admitted, stroking the cat.

"If you mean that you dedicate to a woman your whole life——"

"And more than half your income."

Mrs. Hilary laid down the embroidery, and observed, as though she were concluding the discussion:

"The fact is, you don't know what real love is."

"I never met anyone who did," said I.

Mrs. Hilary opened her mouth.

"At least they could never tell me what it was," I added hastily.

Mrs. Hilary resumed the embroidery.

"Now the other day," I continued, "my friend Major Camperton married his cook."

"What for?" cried Mrs. Hilary.

"Because his wife was dead," said I.

"That's not a reason."

"You must admit that it's an excuse," I pleaded.

Mrs. Hilary, taking no notice of my apology, made a thoughtful stitch or two. Then she observed:

"I was never in love with any man except Hilary."

"You're always boasting of that: I suppose it was difficult?"

"But once I was awfully—but if I tell you, you'll talk about it."

"Upon my honour I won't."

"You will—to Lady Mickleham."

"Lady Mickleham takes no interest in you," said I.

"Well, once I was awfully tempted. It was before I knew Hilary."

"But after you knew me?" I suggested.

"Don't be absurd," said Mrs. Hilary. "He was very rich—rather handsome too."

"I have always persisted in maintaining that you were human," I observed complacently.

"I think," said she, gazing at me, "that you are the most *earthly* man I ever knew."

"Go on with the story," said I, taking the cat on my knee.

"And he was really very fond of me."

"Oh, so he said."

"But—well, I might have, if he hadn't."

"Oh, I understand; at least I hope so."

"I mean he wouldn't talk about anything else."

"I suppose he saw nothing else in you."

"That was what I felt. Good looks aren't everything."

"Were you good-looking?" I inquired.

Mrs. Hilary showed signs of being about to take up her embroidery.

"All right: Hilary isn't here," said I, in excuse.

"I hated it. I wanted to be—" She paused.

"What's in a word? Say 'esteemed.'"

"Yes—for something more than that."

"So you wouldn't have anything to say to him?"

"No. I was so glad—afterward."

"And what's become of him?"

"Oh, he's married."

"It's a just world. Now lots of those immoral writers would have rewarded him with perpetual bachelorhood."

Mrs. Hilary pushed her embroidery quite far off, and leant forward toward me.

"Aren't you *ever* going to marry?" she asked.

"Marriages are made in Heaven," said I. Mrs. Hilary nodded approvingly. "I thought of waiting till I got there," I added.

"Oh," said Mrs. Hilary. And she added, "I know a really charming girl."

"You cruel woman! Would you doom her to me?"

"You'd be all right," said Mrs. Hilary, "if you could be removed from——"

"Certain influences," I suggested hastily. "But for Hilary you also would be a pleasant woman."

"There's not the least comparison," said she, with a flush.

"There's always a comparison," I observed. "What are we talking about?"

Now Mrs. Hilary could not, as I well knew, answer this question.

"Well, I'm very sorry about it," she said.

"A romance," said I, "is a thing to be cherished."

"I can't think it's right," said Mrs. Hilary.

"To remember—to be proud of."

"I don't want to be hard about it," murmured Mrs. Hilary.

"To be taken——"

"Seriously? Yes, of course, or it's worse than——"

"To be taken," said I, "between meals."

Mrs. Hilary leapt to her feet.

"Or else you know," I added, "it would spoil dinner."

Mrs. Hilary was very angry; but she was also a little curious. The latter emotion was more powerful.

"I wonder," said she, "what you do really feel about——"

"What?"

"It," said Mrs. Hilary.

"Am I in the confessional?"

To my delight a smile lurked round Mrs. Hilary's lips.

"You think," she said, "that I don't understand it. Well, I do a little. She's been here."

"Has she, though? What was she doing here?"

"Oh, coaxing," said Mrs. Hilary. "She wanted a subscription from Hilary."

I was much interested.

"Were you present at the interview?" I asked.

"Yes," said Mrs. Hilary. "She got the subscription, Mr. Carter—a larger one than Hilary could afford."

"I have given her a larger one than I could afford."

The rare smile still twitched round Mrs. Hilary's mouth.

"What do you think Hilary did when she'd gone?" she asked.

"I should think he felt a fool," said I.

"He apologized," said Mrs. Hilary.

I laughed. Mrs. Hilary laughed reluctantly.

"Guileless creature!" I observed.

"Oh, you needn't do that!" she said, with a slight flush. "Shall I tell you what he did afterward?"

"Lord, I know that well enough!"

"I'm sure you don't."

"Gave you a new bonnet, of course."

I believe that Mrs. Hilary was annoyed; for she said quite sulkily:

"It was a bracelet."

"I told you so," I observed.

"He'd have given it me anyhow," she cried.

"Not he!" said I.

"He'd meant to, before," said she. "He said so."

I smiled; but I did not wish to make mischief, so I added, "The subscription was, of course, civility."

"That's all, of course. Still it is funny, isn't it?"

"Perhaps it is rather."

There was a pause.

"Do you care to meet that girl?" asked Mrs. Hilary.

"N-no," said I.

"I would give you one more chance," she said generously.

"Thank you. I'm still subscribing," I answered. "No bracelets for me."

"We laughed about it when she was gone. Hilary was amused at himself."

"I have experienced the feeling," I observed.

"I wonder if I ought to tell you what he called her?"

"Probably not. Go on."

"He said she was an insinuating little——"

"Why do you hesitate, Mrs. Hilary?"

"Devil," said Mrs. Hilary, almost under her breath.

"Ah!" said I, setting the cat down, and reaching for my hat.

"Yes, devil," said Mrs. Hilary, more courageously.

"And what did he say you were?" I asked.

"Oh, nothing," said Mrs. Hilary, blushing.

"Then you and Hilary are friends again?"

"I didn't mind in the least," declared Mrs. Hilary. "Only it's curious——"

I began to laugh. I enjoy a chance of laughing at Mrs. Hilary.

"We are all much indebted to her," said I; "some for a bracelet——"

"Nonsense!"

"Some for a momentary emotion——"

"He didn't feel even that."

"Some for a lifelong— Dear me, how late it grows! I must be off." And I held out my hand. As I did so, Hilary entered.

"By the way, Carter," said he, when he saw me, "what's that society Lady Mickleham collects for? She got something out of me. I hope it's not a fraud."

"I hope not," said I.

"Because I've given her a trifle."

"So have I," I remarked.

"A donation, you know."

"Oh, mine's a life subscription," said I.

"Oh, go away," said Mrs. Hilary, impatiently.

"Well, you've got nothing else to do with your money," said Hilary. "You've not got a wife and family."

"That is, of course," said I, "the explanation."

Then Mrs. Hilary drove me out. She'd have done it sooner only that in her heart she credits me with a tragedy.

XXI

WHAT MIGHT HAVE BEEN

UNFORTUNATELY it was Sunday; therefore the gardeners could not be ordered to shift the long row of flower-pots from the side of the terrace next the house, where Dolly had ordered them to be put, to the side remote from the house, where Dolly now wished them to stand. Yet Dolly could not think of living with the pots where they were till Monday. It would kill her, she said. So Archie left the cool shade of the great trees, where Dolly sat doing nothing, and Nellie Phaeton sat splicing the gig whip, and I lay in a deck-chair, with something iced beside me. Outside, the sun was broiling hot, and poor Archie mopped his brow at every weary journey across the broad terrace.

"It's a burnin' shame, Dolly," said Miss Phaeton. "I wouldn't do it if I were him."

"Oh, yes, you would, dear," said Dolly. "The pots looked atrocious on that side."

I took a long sip from my glass, and observed in a meditative tone:

"There, but for the grace of woman, goes Samuel Travers Carter."

Dolly's lazy lids half lifted. Miss Phaeton mumbled (her mouth was full of twine):

"What *do* you mean?"

"*Nemo omnibus horis sapit,*" said I, apologetically.

"I don't know what that means either."

"*Nemo*—everybody," I translated, "*sapit*—has been in love—*omnibus* —once—*horis*—at least."

"Oh, and you mean she wouldn't have you?" asked Nellie, with blunt directness.

"Not quite that," said I. "They——"

"They?" murmured Dolly, with half-lifted lids.

"*They,*" I pursued, "regretfully recognized my impossibility. Hence I am not carrying pots across a broad terrace under a hot sun."

"Why did they think you impossible?" asked Miss Phaeton, who takes much interest in this sort of question.

"A variety of reasons: for one I was too clever, for another too stupid; for others too good—or too bad; too serious—or too frivolous; too poor or——"

"Well, no one objected to your money, I suppose?" interrupted Nellie.

"Pardon me. I was about to say 'or not rich enough.'"

"But that's the same thing."

"The antithesis is certainly imperfect," I admitted.

"Mr. Gay," said Nellie, introducing the name with some timidity, "you know who I mean?—the poet—once said to me that man was essentially imperfect until he was married."

"It is true," I agreed. "And woman until she is dead."

"I don't think he meant it quite in that sense," said Nellie, rather puzzled.

"I don't think he meant it in any sense," murmured Dolly, a little unkindly.

We might have gone on talking in this idle way for ever so long had not Archie at this point dropped a large flower-pot and smashed it to bits. He stood looking at the bits for a moment, and then came toward us and sank into a chair.

"I'm off!" he announced.

"And half are on one side, and half on the other," said Dolly, regretfully.

A sudden impulse seized me. I got up, put on my straw hat, took off my coat, walked out into the sun, and began to move flower-pots across the broad terrace. I heard a laugh from Archie, a little cry from Dolly, and from Nellie Phaeton, "Goodness! what's he doin' that for?" I was not turned from my purpose. The luncheon bell rang. Miss Phaeton, whip and twine in hand, walked into the house. Archie followed her, saying as he passed that he hoped I shouldn't find it warm. I went on shifting the flower-pots. They were very heavy. I broke two, but I went on. Presently Dolly put up her parasol and came out from the shade to watch me. She stood there for a moment or two. Then she said:

"Well, do you think you'd like it, Mr. Carter?"

"Wait till I've finished," said I, waving my hand.

Another ten minutes saw the end of my task. Panting and hot, I sought the shade, and flung myself on to my deck-chair again. I also lit a cigarette.

"I think they looked better on the other side, after all," said Dolly, meditatively.

"Of course you do," said I, urbanely. "You needn't tell me that."

"Perhaps you'd like to move them back," she suggested.

"No," said I. "I've done enough to create the impression."

"And how did you like it?"

"It was," said I, "in its way a pleasant enough illusion." And I shrugged my shoulders, and blew a ring of smoke.

To my very considerable gratification, Dolly's tone manifested some annoyance as she asked:

"Why do you say 'in its way'?"

"Because, in spite of the momentary pleasure I gained from feeling myself a married man, I could not banish the idea that we should not permanently suit one another."

"Oh, you thought that?" said Dolly, smiling again.

"I must confess it," said I. "The fault, I know, would be mine."

"I'm sure of that," said Dolly.

"But the fact is that I can't exist in too high altitudes. The rarefaction of the moral atmosphere——"

"Please don't use all those long words."

"Well, then, to put it plainly," said I, with a pleasant smile, "I felt all the time that Mrs. Hilary would be too good for me."

It is not very often that it falls to my humble lot to startle Lady Mickleham out of her composure. But at this point she sat up quite straight in her chair; her cheeks flushed, and her eyelids ceased to droop in indolent *insouciance*.

"Mrs. Hilary!" she said. "What has Mrs. Hilary——?"

"I really thought you understood," said I, "the object of my experiment."

Dolly glanced at me. I believe that my expression was absolutely innocent—and I am, of course, sure that hers expressed mere surprise.

"I thought," she said, after a pause, "that you were thinking of Nellie Phaeton."

"Oh, I see," cried I, smiling. "A natural mistake, to be sure!"

"She thought so too," pursued Dolly, biting her lip.

"Did she, though?"

"And I'm sure she'd be quite annoyed if she thought you were thinking of Mrs. Hilary."

"As a matter of fact," I observed, "she didn't understand what I was doing at all."

Dolly leant back. The relics of a frown still dwelt on her brow; presently, however, she began to swing her hat on her forefinger, and she threw a look at me. I immediately looked up toward the branches above my head.

"We might as well go in to lunch," said Dolly.

"By all means," I acquiesced, with alacrity.

We went out into the sunshine, and came where the pots were. Suddenly Dolly said:

"Go back and sit down again, Mr. Carter."

"I want my lunch," I ventured to observe.

"Do as I tell you," said Dolly, stamping her foot; whereat, much intimidated, I went back, and stretched myself once more on the deck-chair.

Dolly approached a flower-pot. She stooped down, exerted her strength, lifted it, and carried it, not without effort, across the terrace. Again she did the like. I sat smoking and watching. She lifted a third pot, but dropped it half-way. Then, dusting her hands against one another, she came back slowly into the shade and sat down. I made no remark. Dolly glanced at me.

"Well?" she said.

"Woman—woman—woman!" said I, sadly.

"Must I carry some more?" asked Dolly, in a humble yet protesting tone.

"Mrs. Hilary," I began, "is an exceedingly attractive——"

Dolly rose with a sigh.

"Where are you going?" I asked.

"More pots," said Dolly, standing opposite me. "I must go on, you see."

"Till when, Lady Mickleham?"

"Till you tell the truth," said Dolly, and she suddenly burst into a little laugh.

"Woman—woman—woman!" said I again. "Let's go in to lunch."

"I'm going to carry the pots," said Dolly. "It's awfully hot, Mr. Carter—and look at my poor hands!"

She held them out to me.

"Lunch!" said I.

"Pots!" said Dolly, with infinite firmness.

The window of the dining-room opened and Archie put his head out.

"Come along, you two," he called. "Everything's getting cold."

Dolly turned an appealing glance on me.

"How obstinate you are!" she said. "You know perfectly well——"

I began to walk toward the house.

"I'm going in to lunch," said I.

"Ask them to keep some for me," said Dolly, and she turned up the sleeves of her gown till her wrists were free.

"It's most unfair," said I, indignantly.

"I don't care if it is," said Dolly, stooping down to lift a pot.

I watched her strain to lift it. She had chosen the largest and heaviest; she sighed delicately and delicately she panted. She also looked at her hands, and held them up for me to see the lines of brown on the pink. I put my hands in my pockets and said most sulkily, as I turned away toward the house:

"All right. It wasn't Mrs. Hilary, then."

Dolly rose up, seized me by the arm, and made me run to the house.

"Mr. Carter," she cried, "would stop for those wretched pots. He's moved all except two, but he's broken three. Isn't he stupid?"

"You are an old ass, Carter," said Archie.

"I believe you're right, Archie," said I.

XXII

A FATAL OBSTACLE

"What 1 can't make out," I observed (addressing myself to Lady Jane), "is why women don't fall in love with me. I'm all a man should be, and a reasonable number of things that he shouldn't."

Lady Jane always tries to be polite.

"Perhaps it's just that you don't find it out," she suggested after a moment's consideration.

"I shall adopt that view," said I, cordially. "It will add a spice to the most formal greeting."

"It'll make you do awfully silly things," remarked Dolly, with an air of experience.

Lady Jane was looking thoughtful. "Mamma says love comes with marriage," she went on presently.

"Yes, generally," I assented. "Not," I added, turning to Dolly, "that three in a brougham is really comfortable, you know."

"One has to invite him sometimes," Dolly murmured.

"Oh, but I'm sure mamma meant——"

"Mamma meant that you'd been flirting with the Curate, Jane."

"Dorothea dear!" gasped Lady Jane.

"The secret of love lies, I suppose, in unselfishness." (I threw out the suggestion in a tentative way.)

"That's what makes Archie such a good husband," said Dolly.

"It must, of course, exist on both sides, Lady Mickleham."

"Oh, no, that's tiresome. It's like getting through the door—nobody'll go first."

"True. You spend all your time trying to be allowed to do what you don't want to do; and the other party does the same."

"Mr. Shenton says that the power of sympathy is the real secret of it." Mr. Shenton, by the way, is the Curate.

I glanced at Dolly and shook my head; she nodded approvingly. Thus buttressed, I remarked deliberately:

"The power of sympathy has wrecked far more homes than it has— er—blessed. I would, on the whole, back it against the Victoria Cross."

"I think I could love a man just for being good," mused Lady Jane.

"Oh, you impossible kind of an old dear!" Dolly gurgled affectionately. "Besides, that's no use to poor Mr. Carter."

"I am not so very bad," said I. "Come now, we'll run through my vices and——"

"I think I forgot to water that fern," said Lady Jane, rather suddenly.

"There was once a governess—" I began, thinking to beguile Dolly's leisure with the story. Lady Jane had left us.

"I know about that. Mrs. Hilary told me."

"Then you're quite friends now?"

"Not particularly, but one must talk about something. There was another girl in love with you once, too."

"Why not have told me at the time? I should have enjoyed it."

"I mustn't tell you her name."

I did not speak for a moment.

"Well, then, it was Agatha Hornton."

"Agatha Martin that is?"

"I suppose she thought that, as you were hopeless" (Dolly was seeming a good deal amused at something), "she might as well marry Captain Martin."

"One can be unhappy without being absurd," said I, rather crossly. "Dear, dear! 'Having known me, to decline——'"

"Decline? I didn't say she absolutely asked you!"

"I wish you would read a little poetry sometimes. Your ignorance cramps my conversation. Was she very fond of me?"

"She thought you *handsome,*" said Dolly, conclusively.

"It was a *grande passion?*"

"Oh, no. She'd been very well brought up. But she just adored you."

"She was a nice girl—a thoroughly nice girl. I never thought much of Martin. Ugly fellow, too."

"She used to bore me awfully about you. You see, I was her great friend, and she knew she could trust me."

"Not to give her away?"

"Yes," said Dolly, gently caressing the Japanese pug that the Admiral Commanding on the Pacific Station has recently sent her.

"It's beautiful how you women stand by one another," I observed. "What was it that particularly attracted her in me?"

"I really cannot think," said Dolly; "any more than I can think what attracted— Oh, do you mind ringing the bell? It's Fushahima's tea-time."

"I wish she took it a minute later," said I, as I obeyed. "Martin was a very dull chap, you know."

"Something seems to have set you thinking of Captain Martin."

"I met them all coming back from church (they were coming back, I mean) a Sunday or two ago. Four, aren't there?"

"Five. Three girls and two boys."

"Getting big too, aren't they?"

"Fine children, Mr. Carter," observed Dolly, cheerfully.

"She was certainly a clever girl—in those days."

"Ah, in those days!" Dolly murmured with an indulgent smile—one that means you can go on if you like, but that you are obviously rather foolish.

"Idyllic happiness," said I, resuming my seat, "comes to very few of us, Lady Mickleham."

"Well, one marries, or something, you see."

"There is, of course, one's career."

"Archie's quite keen on being an Undersecretary."

"I may not understand, but I am willing to admire. Why didn't the girl encourage me? I expect that's all I wanted."

"Well, what do you mean by encouragement?" asked Dolly, pulling Fushahima's ears; she is always alive to the artistic value of the brute creation.

"What I mean by it is conveying, however delicately, that I was the only man in the world she ever did or ever could care for. Isn't that what you used to mean by it, Lady Mickleham?"

"You can take Fushahima, Pattern," said Dolly.

"Yes, my lady."

"Not too much cream in her milk."

"Very good, my lady."

"What were you saying, Mr. Carter?"

"I forget, my lady."

There was a moment's silence—sometimes there should be.

Then I took my tea and stood on the hearth-rug, drinking it.

"Solitude, I believe, has its consolations, when one looks at other people's families. Besides, it's surprising the number of little luxuries I get for nothing."

"For nothing?"

"Well, out of Mrs. Carter's dress-allowance. It's quite moderate—only four hundred a year—but it keeps a cab, and buys a little drawing, perhaps, and so on. It's a great comfort, I assure you."

Dolly began to laugh gently.

"She'd have exceeded it, and I never do more than anticipate it," I pursued.

"I've sometimes wondered at your extravagance."

"Ah, well, you understand it now."

"Did the allowance include frocks for the girls?"

"Pray curb your imagination, Lady Mickleham."

"You quite shuddered!"

"I had visions of short stiff frocks and long block stockings—like a family group at the Royal Academy—all legs and innocence, you know."

"Yes, and all named Carter!" sighed Dolly, with a commiserating air.

"You don't like the name?"

"Not much."

I looked at Dolly. I think we must have smiled.

"I might have known there was some such reason," said I.

"I do wonder what's become of Jane, and why they don't bring Fushahima back," said Dolly.

"It's always a comfort to get at the real reason of anything. Now if my name had been Vavasour—or——"

"I don't mind 'Mr. Carter' so much, but 'Mrs. Carter' sounds horrible," Dolly explained.

"Girls being, as we all know, in the habit of writing the competing names in conjunction with their own Christian names on the backs of envelopes and the fly-leaves of library books, in order to see how they look, I can well understand that if it came to a choice between Carter and——"

At this point, before I had fully developed my remark, Lady Jane came back. She sometimes does by accident what the Dowager would do on purpose. Heredity, I imagine.

"I've been thinking about it," said Lady Jane, "and I'm quite sure it's goodness of heart."

"A fatal obstacle!" I said, shaking my head despondently.

"Another!" murmured Dolly, with a lift of her brows.

"Shining through, you know, Mr. Carter," added Lady Jane.

"I really don't see the use of continuing the conversation."

"You must encourage him, Dorothea," said Lady Jane, with a smile.

Dolly laughed; I won't swear she didn't blush just a trifle.

"Oh, I've given up trying to do that long ago, Jane dear," said she.

"She used to succeed far too well, you know. Oh, but pray allow me to hand you a cup of tea."

I went away soon afterward. I had to pay a call—on the Martins.

XXIII

THE CURATE'S BUMP

"WHAT is the harm," I asked at lunch, "in being fat?" and I looked round the table.

I had led up to this subject because something which fell from Mrs. Hilary Musgrave the other day led me to suppose that I might appear to be growing stouter than I used to be.

"It doesn't matter in a man," said Nellie Phaeton.

"That," I observed, "is merely part of the favourite pretence of your sex."

"And what's that, Mr. Carter?" asked Dolly.

"That you're indifferent to a pleasing appearance in man. It won't go down."

"It would if you ate less," said Dolly, wilfully misunderstanding me.

"Napoleon was fat," remarked Archie; he is studying history.

"Mamma is rather fat," said Lady Jane, breaking a long silence; her tone seemed to imply that it was a graceful concession on the Dowager's part.

"I shouldn't say you ever had much of a figure," observed Dolly, gazing at me dispassionately.

"Mamma," resumed Lady Jane, with an amiable desire to give me useful information, "drinks nothing but lemonade. I make it hot for her and——"

"I should like to do that," said I, longingly.

"It's the simplest thing in the world," cried Lady Jane. "You can do it for yourself. You just take——"

"A pretty girl," I murmured absently. "I—I beg your pardon, Lady Jane. You see, Miss Phaeton is opposite and my thoughts wandered."

"It's no use talkin' sensibly where you are," said Miss Nellie, very severely, and she rose from the table.

"Won't anyone have any rice pudding?" asked Archie, appealingly.

"If I were a camel I would," said I.

"Why a camel, Mr. Carter?" asked Lady Jane.

"A camel, Lady Jane, is so constructed that it could keep one exclusively for rice pudding."

"One what, Mr. Carter?"

I strolled to the window, where Dolly stood looking out.

"Dear Jane!" said Dolly. "She never sees anything."

"I wish there were more like her," said I, cordially. "She doesn't inherit it from her mother, though."

"No, the Dowager sees a great deal more than there is there," laughed Dolly, glancing at me.

"But fortunately," said I, "not all there is in other places."

"Mamma says—" we heard Lady Jane remarking at the table. We strolled out into the garden.

"Now, isn't that provoking?" cried Dolly. "They haven't rolled the tennis lawn, and the people will be here directly."

"Shall I ask Archie to ask somebody to get somebody?"

"They've all gone to dinner, I expect. Suppose you roll it, Mr. Carter. It'll be so good for you. Exercise is what you want."

"Exercise is, no doubt, what I need," said I, doubtfully eyeing the roller.

"It's the same thing," said Dolly.

"It's an Eternal Antithesis," said I, taking off my coat.

I began to roll. Dolly stood watching me for a moment. Then she went indoors. I went on rolling. Presently, raising my eyes from my task, I found the Curate looking on; he was in flannels and carried a racket.

"Although," I observed to the Curate, "I have convinced my reason that there is no harm in being fat, yet, sooner than be fat, I roll. Can you explain that?"

"Reason is not everything," said the Curate.

"Your cloth obliges you to that," said I, suspiciously.

"I'm in flannels today," enjoined the Curate, with a smile.

I liked that. I loosed my hold of the roller and took the Curate's arm. We began to walk up and down.

"There is also," said I, "romance!"

"There's little enough of that for most of us," said the Curate.

"There has been too much for some of us," I returned. "But the lawn is smooth where the roller has been. The bumps—the pleasant bumps —are gone."

"They spoilt the game," observed the Curate.

"They made the game," said I, frowning a little.

There was silence for a minute. Then the Curate asked:

"Is Lady Jane going to play today?"

"I seemed like Fate with that roller," said I. "Or like Time."

The Curate smiled absently.

"Or like Morality," I pursued.

The Curate smiled indulgently; he was in flannels, good man.

"As to Lady Jane," said I, recollecting myself, "I don't know."

"It's of no consequence," murmured the Curate.

At once I knew that it was of consequence—to the Curate. But my thoughts drifted in another direction, and, when I emerged from the reverie, I saw Lady Jane and the Curate strolling together on the lawn, and Lady Mickleham approaching me in a white gown; she carried a red parasol.

"Archie and Nellie will be out directly," said she, "and then you can begin."

"They can," said I, putting on my coat and lighting a cigarette.

"Look at that poor dear man with Jane!" exclaimed Dolly. "Now should you have thought that Jane was the sort of person to——?"

"Everybody," said I, "is the sort of person—if the other person is."

"Of course he knows it's hopeless. The Dowager wouldn't hear of it."

"Really? And she hears of so many things!"

Dolly, after a contemptuous glance, began to inspect the lawn. I retired into the shade and sat down. Lady Jane and the Curate strolled a little farther off. Presently I was roused by an accusing cry from Dolly.

"She's found a bump," said I to myself, shaking my head.

"You can never do things properly," said Dolly, walking up to me.

"I certainly can't do many things in the way I should prefer," I admitted.

"You've left a great bump in the middle of the court."

My eyes strayed from Dolly to Lady Jane and the Curate, and thence back to Dolly.

"It's not my bump," said I; "it's the Curate's."

"You're getting into the habit," remarked Dolly, "of being unintelligible. I'm sure there's nothing clever in it. I met a man the other day who said he never understood what you meant."

"You'd understand if you'd stayed; why did you go away?"

"To change," answered Dolly.

I was pleased.

"It's an old trick of yours," said I.

"What did you mean by the bump being the Curate's?" asked Dolly, returning to the point.

I entered into an explanation. There was plenty of time; the Curate and Lady Jane were strolling, the click of billiard balls through the open windows accounted for Nellie and Archie.

"I see," said Dolly. "Poor man! Do you think he'd like it left?"

I walked leisurely toward the roller, Dolly following me.

"If it were my bump," said I, laying hold of the roller, and looking at Lady Mickleham.

Lady Mickleham smiled—under protest. It is a good enough variety of smile.

"If it were my bump," said I, "I should reduce it—so—and so again," and twice I passed the roller gently over the bump.

"It's awfully small now," said Dolly; and her voice sounded regretful.

"It's not so large as it was," said I, cheerfully.

Dolly let down her parasol with a jerk.

"You're horribly disagreeable today," she said. I leant on the handle of the roller and smiled.

"You're very rude and—and——"

"Nobody," said I, "likes to be told that he has no figure."

"You are an Apollo, Mr. Carter," said Dolly.

That was handsome enough.

"I would let it alone, if it were my bump," said I. "Hang these rollers!"

"It is your bump," said Dolly.

As she spoke Archie came out of the billiard-room. Lady Jane and the Curate hastened to join us. Archie inspected the lawn.

"Why, it's been rolled!" he cried.

"I rolled it," said I, proudly.

"Jove!" said Archie. "Hullo, though, old chap, you haven't been over here."

He had found the bump.

"I have been over there," said I, "oftener than anywhere else."

"Give me the——"

"Now, Archie, do begin to play," said Dolly, suddenly.

"Oh, well, one doesn't hurt," said Archie.

"It won't hurt much," said the Curate; upon which I smiled at Lady Jane.

"What is it, Mr. Carter?" she asked.

"He's so right, you know," said I.

X X I V

ONE WAY IN

I HAD a very curious dream the other night. In fact, I dreamt that I was dead. I passed through a green baize door and found myself in a small square room. Opposite me was another door, inscribed "Elysian Fields," and in front of it, at a large table with a raised ledge, sat

Rhadamanthus. As I entered, I saw a graceful figure vanish through the door opposite.

"It's no use trying to deceive me," I observed. "That was Mrs. Hilary, I think; if you don't mind, I'll join her."

"I'm afraid I must trouble you to take a seat for a few moments, Mr. Carter," said Rhadamanthus, "while I run over your little account."

"Any formalities which are usual," I murmured politely, as I sat down.

Rhadamanthus turned over the leaves of a large book.

"Carter—Samuel Travers, isn't it?" he asked.

"Yes. For goodness' sake don't confuse me with Vincent Carter. He only paid five shillings in the pound."

"Your case presents some peculiar features, Mr. Carter," said Rhadamanthus. "I hope I am not censorious, but—well, that fine at Bow Street?"

"I was a mere boy," said I, with some warmth, "and my solicitor grossly mismanaged the case."

"Well, well!" said he, soothingly. "But haven't you spent a great deal of time at Monte Carlo?"

"A man must be somewhere," said I.

Rhadamanthus scratched his nose.

"I should have wasted the money anyhow," I added.

"I suppose you would," he conceded. "But what of this *caveat* lodged by the Dowager Lady Mickleham? That's rather serious, you know; isn't it now—joking apart?"

"I am disappointed," I remarked, "to find a man of your experience paying any attention to such an ill-natured old woman."

"We have our rules," he replied, "and I'm afraid, Mr. Carter, that until that *caveat* is removed——"

"You don't mean that?"

"Really, I'm afraid so."

"Then I may as well go back," said I, taking my hat.

At this moment there was a knock at the door.

"Although I can't oblige you with an order of admission," said Rhadamanthus, very civilly, "perhaps it would amuse you to listen to a case or two. There's no hurry, you know. You've got lots of time before you."

"It will be an extremely interesting experience," said I, sitting down again.

The door opened, and, as I expected (I don't know why, but it happens like that in dreams), Dolly Mickleham came in. She did not seem to see me. She bowed to Rhadamanthus, smiled, and took a chair immediately opposite the table.

"Mickleham—Dorothea—Countess of—" she said.

"Formerly, I think, Dolly Foster?" asked Rhadamanthus.

"I don't see what that's got to do with it," said Dolly.

"The account runs on," he explained, and began to consult his big book. Dolly leant back in her chair, slowly peeling off her gloves. Rhadamanthus shut the book with a bang.

"It's not the least use," he said decisively. "It wouldn't be kind to pretend that it was, Lady Mickleham."

"Dear, dear!" said Dolly. "What's the matter?"

"Half the women in London have petitioned against you."

"Have they really?" cried Dolly, to all appearance rather delighted. "What do they say, Mr. Rhadamanthus? Is it in that book? Let me look." And she held out her hand.

"The book's too heavy for you to hold," said he.

"I'll come round," said Dolly. So she went round and leant over his shoulder and read the book.

"What's that scent you've got on?" asked Rhadamanthus.

"Bouquet du diable," said she. (I had never heard of the perfume before.) "Isn't it sweet?"

"I haven't smelt it since I was a boy," sighed Rhadamanthus.

"Poor old thing!" said Dolly. "I'm not going to read all this, you know." And, with a somewhat contemptuous smile, she walked back to her chair. "They ought to be ashamed of themselves," she added, as she sat down. "It's just because I'm not a fright."

"Aren't you a fright?" asked Rhadamanthus. "Where are my spectacles?"

He put them on and looked at Dolly.

"I must go in, you know," said Dolly, smiling at Rhadamanthus. "My husband has gone in!"

"I shouldn't have thought you'd consider that conclusive," said he, with a touch of satire in his tone.

"Don't be horrid," said Dolly, pouting.

There was a pause. Rhadamanthus examined Dolly through his spectacles.

"This is a very painful duty," said he, at last. "I have sat here for a great many years, and I have seldom had a more painful duty."

"It's very absurd of you," said Dolly.

"I can't help it, though," said he.

"Do you really mean that I'm not to go in?"

"I do, indeed," said Rhadamanthus.

Dolly rose. She leant her arms on the raised ledge which ran along the table, and she leant her chin on her hands.

"Really?" she said.

"Really," said he, looking the other way.

A sudden change came over Dolly's face. Her dimples vanished: her eyes grew pathetic and began to shine rather than to sparkle: her lip quivered just a little.

"You're very unkind," she said in an extremely low tone. "I had no idea you would be so unkind."

Rhadamanthus seemed very uncomfortable.

"Don't do that," he said quite sharply, fidgeting with the blotting-paper.

Dolly began to move slowly round the table. Rhadamanthus sat still. When she was standing close by him, she put her hand lightly on his arm and said:

"Please do, Mr. Rhadamanthus."

"It's as much as my place is worth," he grumbled.

Dolly's eyes shone still, but the faintest little smile began to play about her mouth.

"Some day," she said (with total inappropriateness, now I come to think of it, though it did not strike me so at the time), "you'll be glad to remember having done a kind thing. When you're old—because you are not really old now—you will say, 'I'm glad I didn't send poor Dolly Mickleham away crying.'"

Rhadamanthus uttered an inarticulate sound—half impatience, half, I fancy, something else.

"We are none of us perfect, I dare say. If I asked your wife——"

"I haven't got a wife," said Rhadamanthus.

"That's why you're so hard-hearted," said Dolly. "A man who's got a wife is never hard on other women."

There was another pause. Then Rhadamanthus, looking straight at the blotting-paper, said:

"Oh, well, don't bother me. Be off with you"; and as he spoke, the door behind him opened.

Dolly's face broke out into sudden sunshine. Her eyes danced, her dimples capered over her chin.

"Oh, you old dear!" she cried; and, stooping swiftly, she kissed Rhadamanthus. "You're horribly bristly!" she laughed; and then, before he could move, she ran through the door.

I rose from my seat, taking my hat and stick in my hand. I felt, as you may suppose, that I had been there long enough. When I moved, Rhadamanthus looked up, and with an attempt at unconsciousness observed:

"We will proceed with your case now, if you please, Mr. Carter."

I looked him full in the face. Rhadamanthus blushed. I pursued my way toward the door.

"Stop!" he said, in a blustering tone. "You can't go there, you know."

I smiled significantly.

"Isn't it rather too late for that sort of thing?" I asked. "You seem to forget that I have been here for the last quarter of an hour."

"I didn't know she was going to do it," he protested.

"Oh, of course," said I, "that will be your story. Mine, however, I shall tell in my own way."

Rhadamanthus blushed again. Evidently he felt that he was in a delicate position. We were standing thus, facing one another, when the door began to open again, and Dolly put her head out.

"Oh, it's you, is it?" she said. "I thought I heard your voice. Come along and help me to find Archie."

"This gentleman says I'm not to come in," said I.

"Oh, what nonsense! Now, you really mustn't be silly, Mr. Rhadamanthus—or I shall have to— Mr. Carter, you weren't there, were you?"

"I was—and a more interesting piece of scandal it has seldom been——"

"Hush! I didn't do anything. Now, you know I didn't, Mr. Carter!"

"No," said I, "you didn't. But Rhadamanthus, taking you unawares——"

"Oh, be off with you—both of you!" cried Rhadamanthus.

"That's sensible," said Dolly. "Because, you know, there really isn't any harm in poor Mr. Carter."

Rhadamanthus vanished. Dolly and I went inside.

"I suppose everything will be very different here," said Dolly, and I think she sighed.

Whether it were or not I don't know, for just then I awoke, and found myself saying aloud, in answer to the dream-voice and the dream-face (which had not gone altogether with the dream):

"Not everything"—a speech that, I agree, I ought not to have made, even though it were only in a dream.

AN AFTERWORD ON "THE DOLLY DIALOGUES"

TO those heroic explorers whose job it is, each day in your newspaper, to report on some work that has just made its first appearance, there must occur from time to time the souring thought that their younger readers might better ignore them and spend the long winter evenings among some of yesterday's successes, already gathering dust on neglected shelves in the library around the corner. Thus, in the still unabated freshet of biography stimulated in our time by the late Lytton Strachey, at least one work each year is hailed as a joy forever by those who have never had time to find out that none of them will bear a moment's comparison with the elder Trevelyan's *Early Life of Charles James Fox.* In the same sense it would be no prodigious feat in prophecy to forecast that none of the exquisite banter scheduled to find its way into print in 1936 will be as airy, as nonchalant, and as effortless as these forgotten dialogues which, for a dozen years past, I have been able to find only on the second-hand counters.

Anthony Hope Hawkins who, unlike the susceptible 'Liza, did not fawncy 'Awkins for his other nime and wrote, therefore, under the name of Anthony Hope, is still remembered as the author of *The Prisoner of Zenda* and *Rupert of Hentzau,* two lustrous tales wherewith he set a fashion in romance. His discovery of Ruritania led to other kingdoms more inkstained adventurers than you could shake a stick at, other kingdoms just as vague in their geography and just as ripe for high emprise. Indeed, their vogue lent a glamor to the Balkans which Shaw's *Arms and the Man* sought vainly to dispel.

Yet the piece of writing by Anthony Hope most likely to survive is none of these. It will outlive the rest because it was written in bronze. I refer to the single sentence: "His Foe was Folly & his Weapon Wit." You will find this graven on the Thames wall in London, just across the way from the Embankment Gardens and not far from the Savoy. It is the inscription on the memorial to the late W. S. Gilbert.

                                                              A. W.

THE
HAPPY JOURNEY
TO TRENTON
AND CAMDEN

by

THORNTON WILDER

THE HAPPY JOURNEY TO
TRENTON AND CAMDEN

*No scenery is required for this play. Perhaps a few dusty flats may be
seen leaning against the brick wall at the back of the stage.*

The five members of the Kirby family and the Stage Manager *compose the cast.*

*The Stage Manager not only moves forward and withdraws the few
properties that are required, but he reads from a typescript the lines
of all the minor characters. He reads them clearly, but with little
attempt at characterization, scarcely troubling himself to alter his
voice, even when he responds in the person of a child or a woman.*

As the curtain rises the Stage Manager *is leaning lazily against the
proscenium pillar at the audience's left. He is smoking.*

Arthur *is playing marbles in the center of the stage.*

Caroline *is at the remote back right talking to some girls who are
invisible to us.*

Ma Kirby *is anxiously putting on her hat before an imaginary mirror.*

MA. Where's your pa? Why isn't he here? I declare we'll never get
started.

ARTHUR. Ma, where's my hat? I guess I don't go if I can't find my
hat.

MA. Go out into the hall and see if it isn't there. Where's Caroline
gone to now, the plagued child?

ARTHUR. She's out waitin' in the street talkin' to the Jones girls.—
I just looked in the hall a thousand times, ma, and it isn't there. (*He
spits for good luck before a difficult shot and mutters:*) Come on,
baby.

Ma. Go and look again, I say. Look carefully.

Arthur *rises, runs to the right, turns around swiftly, returns to his game, flinging himself on the floor with a terrible impact and starts shooting an aggie.*

Arthur. No, ma, it's not there.

Ma (*serenely*). Well, you don't leave Newark without that hat, make up your mind to that. I don't go no journeys with a hoodlum.

Arthur. Aw, ma!

Ma *comes down to the footlights and talks toward the audience as through a window.*

Ma. Oh, Mrs. Schwartz!

The Stage Manager (*consulting his script*). Here I am, Mrs. Kirby. Are you going yet?

Ma. I guess we're going in just a minute. How's the baby?

The Stage Manager. She's all right now. We slapped her on the back and she spat it up.

Ma. Isn't that fine!—Well now, if you'll be good enough to give the cat a saucer of milk in the morning and the evening, Mrs. Schwartz, I'll be ever so grateful to you.—Oh, good afternoon, Mrs. Hobmeyer!

The Stage Manager. Good afternoon, Mrs. Kirby, I hear you're going away.

Ma (*modest*). Oh, just for three days, Mrs. Hobmeyer, to see my married daughter, Beulah, in Camden. Elmer's got his vacation week from the laundry early this year, and he's just the best driver in the world.

Caroline *comes "into the house" and stands by her mother.*

The Stage Manager. Is the whole family going?

Ma. Yes, all four of us that's here. The change ought to be good for the children. My married daughter was downright sick a while ago——

The Stage Manager. Tchk—Tchk—Tchk! Yes. I remember you tellin' us.

Ma. And I just want to go down and see the child. I ain't seen her since then. I just won't rest easy in my mind without I see her. (*To Caroline*) Can't you say good afternoon to Mrs. Hobmeyer?

CAROLINE (*blushes and lowers her eyes and says woodenly*). Good afternoon, Mrs. Hobmeyer.

THE STAGE MANAGER. Good afternoon, dear.—Well, I'll wait and beat these rugs after you're gone, because I don't want to choke you. I hope you have a good time and find everything all right.

MA. Thank you, Mrs. Hobmeyer, I hope I will.—Well, I guess that milk for the cat is all, Mrs. Schwartz, if you're sure you don't mind. If anything should come up, the key to the back door is hanging by the ice box.

ARTHUR AND CAROLINE. Ma! Not so loud. Everybody can hear yuh.

MA. Stop pullin' my dress, children. (*In a loud whisper*) The key to the back door I'll leave hangin' by the ice box and I'll leave the screen door unhooked.

THE STAGE MANAGER. Now have a good trip, dear, and give my love to Loolie.

MA. I will, and thank you a thousand times.
She returns "into the room."
What can be keeping your pa?

ARTHUR. I can't find my hat, ma.
Enter Elmer *holding a hat.*

ELMER. Here's Arthur's hat. He musta left it in the car Sunday.

MA. That's a mercy. Now we can start.—Caroline Kirby, what you done to your cheeks?

CAROLINE (*defiant-abashed*). Nothin'.

MA. If you've put anything on 'em, I'll slap you.

CAROLINE. No, ma, of course I haven't. (*Hanging her head*) I just rubbed'm to make'm red. All the girls do that at High School when they're goin' places.

MA. Such silliness I never saw. Elmer, what kep' you?

ELMER (*always even-voiced and always looking out a little anxiously through his spectacles*). I just went to the garage and had Charlie give a last look at it, Kate.

MA. I'm glad you did. I wouldn't like to have no breakdown miles from anywhere. Now we can start. Arthur, put those marbles away.

Anybody'd think you didn't want to go on a journey to look at yuh.

They go out through the "hall," take the short steps that denote going downstairs, and find themselves in the street.

ELMER. Here, you boys, you keep away from that car.

MA. Those Sullivan boys put their heads into everything.

The Stage Manager has moved forward four chairs and a low platform. This is the automobile. It is in the center of the stage and faces the audience. The platform slightly raises the two chairs in the rear. Pa's hands hold an imaginary steering wheel and continually shift gears. Caroline sits beside him. Arthur is behind him and Ma behind Caroline.

CAROLINE (*self-consciously*). Good-by, Mildred. Good-by, Helen.

THE STAGE MANAGER. Good-by, Caroline. Good-by, Mrs. Kirby. I hope y'have a good time.

MA. Good-by, girls.

THE STAGE MANAGER. Good-by, Kate. The car looks fine.

MA (*looking upward toward a window*). Oh, good-by, Emma! (*Modestly*) We think it's the best little Chevrolet in the world.—Oh, good-by, Mrs. Adler!

THE STAGE MANAGER. What, are you going away, Mrs. Kirby?

MA. Just for three days, Mrs. Adler, to see my married daughter in Camden.

THE STAGE MANAGER. Have a good time.

Now Ma, Caroline and the Stage Manager break out into a tremendous chorus of good-bys. The whole street is saying good-by. Arthur takes out his pea shooter and lets fly happily into the air. There is a lurch or two and they are off.

ARTHUR (*in sudden fright*). Pa! Pa! Don't go by the school. Mr. Biedenbach might see us!

MA. I don't care if he does see us. I guess I can take my children out of school for one day without having to hide down back streets about it.

Elmer *nods to a passerby.*

Ma *asks without sharpness:*

Who was that you spoke to, Elmer?

ELMER. That was the fellow who arranges our banquets down to the Lodge, Kate.

MA. Is he the one who had to buy four hundred steaks? (Pa *nods*.) I declare, I'm glad I'm not him.

ELMER. The air's getting better already. Take deep breaths, children.
They inhale noisily.

ARTHUR. Gee, it's almost open fields already. *"Weber and Heilbroner Suits for Well-Dressed Men."* Ma, can I have one of them some day?

MA. If you graduate with good marks perhaps your father'll let you have one for graduation.

CAROLINE (*whining*). Oh, pa! do we have to wait while that whole funeral goes by?
Pa takes off his hat.
Ma cranes forward with absorbed curiosity.

MA. Take off your hat, Arthur. Look at your father.—Why, Elmer, I do believe that's a lodge-brother of yours. See the banner? I suppose this is the Elizabeth branch.
Elmer nods. Ma sighs: Tchk—tchk—tchk. They all lean forward and watch the funeral in silence, growing momentarily more solemnized. After a pause, Ma continues almost dreamily:
Well, we haven't forgotten the one that we went on, have we? We haven't forgotten our good Harold. He gave his life for his country, we mustn't forget that. (*She passes her finger from the corner of her eye across her cheek. There is another pause.*) Well, we'll all hold up the traffic for a few minutes some day.

THE CHILDREN (*very uncomfortable*). Ma!

MA (*without self-pity*). Well, I'm "ready," children. I hope everybody in this car is "ready." (*She puts her hand on Pa's shoulder.*) And I pray to go first, Elmer. Yes. (*Pa touches her hand.*)

THE CHILDREN. Ma, everybody's looking at you. Everybody's laughing at you.

MA. Oh, hold your tongues! I don't care what a lot of silly people in Elizabeth, New Jersey, think of me.—Now we can go on. That's the last.

There is another lurch and the car goes on.

CAROLINE. *"Fit-Rite Suspenders. The Working Man's Choice."* Pa, why do they spell Rite that way?

ELMER. So that it'll make you stop and ask about it, Missy.

CAROLINE. Papa, you're teasing me.—Ma, why do they say *"Three Hundred Rooms Three Hundred Baths"*?

ARTHUR. *"Mueller's Spaghetti: The Family's Favorite Dish."* Ma, why don't you ever have spaghetti?

MA. Go along, you'd never eat it.

ARTHUR. Ma, I like it now.

CAROLINE (*with gesture*). Yum-yum. It looks wonderful up there. Ma, make some when we get home?

MA (*dryly*). "The management is always happy to receive suggestions. We aim to please."

The whole family finds this exquisitely funny. The children scream with laughter. Even Elmer *smiles.* Ma *remains modest.*

ELMER. Well, I guess no one's complaining, Kate. Everybody knows you're a good cook.

MA. I don't know whether I'm a good cook or not, but I know I've had practice. At least I've cooked three meals a day for twenty-five years.

ARTHUR. Aw, ma, you went out to eat once in a while.

MA. Yes. That made it a leap year.

This joke is no less successful than its predecessor. When the laughter dies down, Caroline *turns around in an ecstasy of well-being and kneeling on the cushions says:*

CAROLINE. Ma, I love going out in the country like this. Let's do it often, ma.

MA. Goodness, smell that air will you! It's got the whole ocean in it.—Elmer, drive careful over that bridge. This must be New Brunswick we're coming to.

ARTHUR (*jealous of his mother's successes*). Ma, when is the next comfort station?

MA (*unruffled*). You don't want one. You just said that to be awful.

CAROLINE (*shrilly*). Yes, he did, ma. He's terrible. He says that kind of thing right out in school and I want to sink through the floor, ma. He's terrible.

MA. Oh, don't get so excited about nothing, Miss Proper! I guess we're all yewman-beings in this car, at least as far as I know. And, Arthur, you try and be a gentleman.—Elmer, don't run over that collie dog. (*She follows the dog with her eyes.*) Looked kinda peakèd to me. Needs a good honest bowl of leavings. Pretty dog, too. (*Her eyes fall on a billboard.*) That's a pretty advertisement for Chesterfield cigarettes, isn't it? Looks like Beulah, a little.

ARTHUR. Ma?

MA. Yes.

ARTHUR (*"route" rhymes with "out"*). Can't I take a paper route with the Newark *Daily Post?*

MA. No, you cannot. No, sir. I hear they make the paper boys get up at four-thirty in the morning. No son of mine is going to get up at four-thirty every morning, not if it's to make a million dollars. Your *Saturday Evening Post* route on Thursday mornings is enough.

ARTHUR. Aw, ma.

MA. No, sir. No son of mine is going to get up at four-thirty and miss the sleep God meant him to have.

ARTHUR (*sullenly*). Hhm! Ma's always talking about God. I guess she got a letter from him this morning.

Ma *rises, outraged.*

MA. Elmer, stop that automobile this minute. I don't go another step with anybody that says things like that. Arthur, you get out of this car. Elmer, you give him another dollar bill. He can go back to Newark, by himself. I don't want him.

ARTHUR. What did I say? There wasn't anything terrible about that.

ELMER. I didn't hear what he said, Kate.

MA. God has done a lot of things for me and I won't have him made fun of by anybody. Go away. Go away from me.

CAROLINE. Aw, ma—don't spoil the ride.

MA. No.

ELMER. We might as well go on, Kate, since we've got started. I'll talk to the boy tonight.

MA (*slowly conceding*). All right, if you say so, Elmer. But I won't sit beside him. Caroline, you come, and sit by me.

ARTHUR (*frightened*). Aw, ma, that wasn't so terrible.

MA. I don't want to talk about it. I hope your father washes your mouth out with soap and water.—Where'd we all be if I started talking about God like that, I'd like to know! We'd be in the speak-easies and night-clubs and places like that, that's where we'd be.—All right, Elmer, you can go on now.

CAROLINE. What did he say, ma? I didn't hear what he said.

MA. I don't want to talk about it.

They drive on in silence for a moment, the shocked silence after a scandal.

ELMER. I'm going to stop and give the car a little water, I guess.

MA. All right, Elmer. You know best.

ELMER (*to a garage hand*). Could I have a little water in the radiator —to make sure?

THE STAGE MANAGER (*in this scene alone he lays aside his script and enters into a rôle seriously*). You sure can. (*He punches the tires.*) Air all right? Do you need any oil or gas?

ELMER. No, I think not. I just got fixed up in Newark.

MA. We're on the right road for Camden, are we?

THE STAGE MANAGER. Yes, keep straight ahead. You can't miss it. You'll be in Trenton in a few minutes.

He carefully pours some water into the hood.

Camden's a great town, lady, believe me.

MA. My daughter likes it fine,—my married daughter.

THE STAGE MANAGER. Ye'? It's a great burg all right. I guess I think so because I was born near there.

MA. Well, well. Your folks still live there?

THE STAGE MANAGER. No, my old man sold the farm and they built a factory on it. So the folks moved to Philadelphia.

MA. My married daughter Beulah lives there because her husband works in the telephone company.—Stop pokin' me, Caroline!—We're all going down to see her for a few days.

THE STAGE MANAGER. Ye'?

MA. She's been sick, you see, and I just felt I had to go and see her. My husband and my boy are going to stay at the Y.M.C.A. I hear they've got a dormitory on the top floor that's real clean and comfortable. Had you ever been there?

THE STAGE MANAGER. No. I'm Knights of Columbus myself.

MA. Oh.

THE STAGE MANAGER. I used to play basketball at the Y though. It looked all right to me.

He has been standing with one foot on the rung of Ma's *chair. They have taken a great fancy to one another. He reluctantly shakes himself out of it and pretends to examine the car again, whistling.*

Well, I guess you're all set now, lady. I hope you have a good trip; you can't miss it.

EVERYBODY. Thanks. Thanks a lot. Good luck to you.

Jolts and lurches.

MA (*with a sigh*). The world's full of nice people.—That's what I call a nice young man.

CAROLINE (*earnestly*). Ma, you oughtn't to tell'm all everything about yourself.

MA. Well, Caroline, you do your way and I'll do mine.—He looked kinda thin to me. I'd like to feed him up for a few days. His mother lives in Philadelphia and I expect he eats at those dreadful Greek places.

CAROLINE. I'm hungry. Pa, there's a hot dog stand. K'n I have one?

ELMER. We'll all have one, eh, Kate? We had such an early lunch.

MA. Just as you think best, Elmer.

ELMER. Arthur, here's half a dollar.—Run over and see what they have. Not too much mustard either.

Arthur *descends from the car and goes off stage right.*

Ma *and* Caroline *get out and walk a bit.*

MA. What's that flower over there?—I'll take some of those to Beulah.

CAROLINE. It's just a weed, ma.

MA. I like it.—My, look at the sky, wouldya! I'm glad I was born in New Jersey. I've always said it was the best state in the Union. Every state has something no other state has got.

They stroll about humming.

Presently Arthur returns with his hands full of imaginary hot dogs which he distributes. He is still very much cast down by the recent scandal. He finally approaches his mother and says falteringly:

ARTHUR. Ma, I'm sorry. I'm sorry for what I said.

He bursts into tears and puts his forehead against her elbow.

MA. There. There. We all say wicked things at times. I know you didn't mean it like it sounded.

He weeps still more violently than before.

Why, now, now! I forgive you, Arthur, and tonight before you go to bed you . . . (*She whispers.*) You're a good boy at heart, Arthur, and we all know it.

Caroline *starts to cry too.*

Ma *is suddenly joyously alive and happy.*

Sakes alive, it's too nice a day for us all to be cryin'. Come now, get in. You go up in front with your father, Caroline. Ma wants to sit with her beau. I never saw such children. Your hot dogs are all getting wet. Now chew them fine, everybody.—All right, Elmer, forward march.—Caroline, whatever are you doing?

CAROLINE. I'm spitting out the leather, ma.

MA. Then say: Excuse me.

CAROLINE. Excuse me, please.

MA. What's this place? Arthur, did you see the post office?

ARTHUR. It said Lawrenceville.

MA. Hhn. School kinda. Nice. I wonder what that big yellow house set back was.—Now it's beginning to be Trenton.

CAROLINE. Papa, it was near here that George Washington crossed the Delaware. It was near Trenton, mamma. He was first in war and first in peace, and first in the hearts of his countrymen.

MA (*surveying the passing world, serene and didactic*). Well, the thing I liked about him best was that he never told a lie.

The children are duly cast down.

There is a pause.

There's a sunset for you. There's nothing like a good sunset.

ARTHUR. There's an Ohio license in front of us. Ma, have you ever been to Ohio?

MA. No.

A dreamy silence descends upon them.

Caroline *sits closer to her father.*

Ma *puts her arm around* Arthur.

ARTHUR. Ma, what a lotta people there are in the world, ma. There must be thousands and thousands in the United States. Ma, how many are there?

MA. I don't know. Ask your father.

ARTHUR. Pa, how many are there?

ELMER. There are a hundred and twenty-six million, Kate.

MA (*giving a pressure about* Arthur's *shoulder*). And they all like to drive out in the evening with their children beside'm.

Another pause.

Why doesn't somebody sing something? Arthur, you're always singing something; what's the matter with you?

ARTHUR. All right. What'll we sing? (*He sketches:*)
"In the Blue-Ridge Mountains of Virginia,
  On the trail of the lonesome pine . . ."
No, I don't like that any more. Let's do:
"I been workin' on de railroad
  All de liblong day.
I been workin' on de railroad
Just to pass de time away."

Caroline *joins in at once.*

Finally even Ma *is singing.*

Even Pa *is singing.*

Ma *suddenly jumps up with a wild cry:*

MA. Elmer, that signpost said Camden, I saw it.

ELMER. All right, Kate, if you're sure.

Much shifting of gears, backing and jolting.

MA. Yes, there it is, Camden—five miles. Dear old Beulah.—Now, children, you be good and quiet during dinner. She's just got out of bed after a big sorta operation, and we must all move around kinda quiet. First you drop me and Caroline at the door and just say hello, and then you men-folk go over to the Y.M.C.A. and come back for dinner in about an hour.

CAROLINE (*shutting her eyes and pressing her fists passionately against her nose*). I see the first star. Everybody make a wish.

Star light, star bright,
First star I seen tonight.
I wish I may, I wish I might
Have the wish I wish tonight.

(*then solemnly*) Pins. Mamma, you say "needles."

　　She interlocks little fingers with her mother.

MA. Needles.

CAROLINE. Shakespeare. Ma, you say "Longfellow."

MA. Longfellow.

CAROLINE. Now it's a secret and I can't tell it to anybody. Ma, you make a wish.

MA (*with almost grim humor*). No, I can make wishes without waiting for no star. And I can tell my wishes right out loud too. Do you want to hear them?

CAROLINE (*resignedly*). No, ma, we know'm already. We've heard'm. (*She hangs her head affectedly on her left shoulder and says with un-malicious mimicry:*) You want me to be a good girl and you want Arthur to be honest-in-word-and-deed.

MA (*majestically*). Yes. So mind yourself.

ELMER. Caroline, take out that letter from Beulah in my coat pocket by you and read aloud the places I marked with red pencil.

CAROLINE (*working*). "*A few blocks after you pass the two big oil tanks on your left . . .*"

EVERYBODY (*pointing backward*). There they are!

CAROLINE. "*. . . you come to a corner where there's an A and P store on the left and a firehouse kitty-corner to it . . .*"

　　They all jubilantly identify these landmarks.

"... turn right, go two blocks, and our house is Weyerhauser St. Number 471."

MA. It's an even nicer street than they used to live in. And right handy to an A and P.

CAROLINE (*whispering*). Ma, it's better than our street. It's richer than our street.—Ma, isn't Beulah richer than we are?

MA (*looking at her with a firm and glassy eye*). Mind yourself, missy. I don't want to hear anybody talking about rich or not rich when I'm around. If people aren't nice I don't care how rich they are. I live in the best street in the world because my husband and children live there.

She glares impressively at Caroline *a moment to let this lesson sink in, then looks up, sees* Beulah, *and waves.*

There's Beulah standing on the steps lookin' for us.

Beulah *has appeared and is waving.*

They all call out: Hello, Beulah—Hello.

Presently they are all getting out of the car. Beulah *kisses her father long and affectionately.*

BEULAH. Hello, papa. Good old papa. You look tired, pa.—Hello, mamma.—Lookit how Arthur and Caroline are growing!

MA. They are bursting all their clothes!—Yes, your pa needs a rest. Thank Heaven, his vacation has come just now. We'll feed him up and let him sleep late. Pa has a present for you, Loolie. He would go and buy it.

BEULAH. Why, pa, you're terrible to go and buy anything for me. Isn't he terrible?

MA. Well, it's a secret. You can open it at dinner.

ELMER. Where's Horace, Loolie?

BEULAH. He was kep' over a little at the office. He'll be here any minute. He's crazy to see you all.

MA. All right. You men go over to the Y and come back in about an hour.

BEULAH (*as her father returns to the wheel, stands out in the street beside him*). Go straight along, pa, you can't miss it. It just stares at yuh. (*She puts her arm around his neck and rubs her nose against his temple.*) Crazy old pa, goin' buyin' things! It's me that ought to be buyin' things for you, pa.

ELMER. Oh, no! There's only one Loolie in the world.

BEULAH (*whispering, as her eyes fill with tears*). Are you glad I'm still alive, pa?

She kisses him abruptly and goes back to the house steps.

The Stage Manager *removes the automobile with the help of* Elmer *and* Arthur *who go off waving their good-bys.*

Well, come on upstairs, ma, and take off your things.

Caroline, there's a surprise for you in the back yard.

CAROLINE. Rabbits?

BEULAH. No.

CAROLINE. Chickens?

BEULAH. No. Go and see.

Caroline *runs off stage.*

Beulah *and* Ma *gradually go upstairs.*

There are two new puppies. You be thinking over whether you can keep one in Newark.

MA. I guess we can. It's a nice house, Beulah. You just got a *lovely* home.

BEULAH. When I got back from the hospital, Horace had moved everything into it, and there wasn't anything for me to do.

MA. It's lovely.

The Stage Manager *pushes out a bed from the left. Its foot is toward the right.* Beulah *sits on it, testing the springs.*

BEULAH. I think you'll find the bed comfortable, ma.

MA (*taking off her hat*). Oh, I could sleep on a heapa shoes, Loolie! I don't have no trouble sleepin'. (*She sits down beside her.*) Now let me look at my girl. Well, well, when I last saw you, you didn't know me. You kep' saying *When's mamma comin'? When's mamma comin'?* But the doctor sent me away.

BEULAH (*puts her head on her mother's shoulder and weeps*). It was awful, mamma. It was awful. She didn't even live a few minutes, mamma. It was awful.

MA (*looking far away*). God thought best, dear. God thought best.

We don't understand why. We just go on, honey, doin' our business.

Then almost abruptly—passing the back of her hand across her cheek.

Well, now, what are we giving the men to eat tonight?

BEULAH. There's a chicken in the oven.

MA. What time didya put it in?

BEULAH (*restraining her*). Aw, ma, don't go yet. I like to sit here with you this way. You always get the fidgets when we try and pet yuh, mamma.

MA (*ruefully, laughing*). Yes, it's kinda foolish. I'm just an old Newark bag-a-bones. (*She glances at the backs of her hands.*)

BEULAH (*indignantly*). Why, ma, you're good-lookin'! We always said you were good-lookin'.—And besides, you're the best ma we could ever have.

MA (*uncomfortable*). Well, I hope you like me. There's nothin' like being liked by your family.—Now I'm going downstairs to look at the chicken. You stretch out here for a minute and shut your eyes. —Have you got everything laid in for breakfast before the shops close?

BEULAH. Oh, you know! Ham and eggs.

They both laugh.

MA. I declare I never could understand what men see in ham and eggs. I think they're horrible.—What time did you put the chicken in?

BEULAH. Five o'clock.

MA. Well, now, you shut your eyes for ten minutes.

Beulah *stretches out and shuts her eyes.*

Ma *descends the stairs absent-mindedly singing:*

"There were ninety and nine that safely lay

In the shelter of the fold,

But one was out on the hills away,

Far off from the gates of gold. . . ."

And the curtain falls.

AN AFTERWORD ON "THE HAPPY JOURNEY TO TRENTON AND CAMDEN"

THE foregoing godsend to Little Theaters is the last item in a modest volume by Thornton Wilder called *The Long Christmas Dinner and Other Plays*. It is included here not only for its own sweet sake but just because it *is* a one-act play. It will eventually dawn on the persistent reader of this anthology that its editor has a belligerent regard for the shorter flights of the imagination. Just as Quintus Horatius Flaccus turns in his Sabine grave (while our own F.P.A. froths at the mouth) whenever woolly-witted reviewers speak slightingly of "light verse" and "humorous verse," as if the worth of poetry dwindled in proportion to its humor and lightness, so others of us—perhaps for reasons as tell-tale—are filled with a kind of benevolent rage whenever certain masterpieces of brevity are, because of this very virtue, overlooked or even dismissed as negligible.

It might be controversially enjoyable to linger here for a bootless debate on the question whether the traditionally venerated *Paradise Lost* was a greater poem than—to take a random example—that nameless quatrain sung by some long forgotten minstrel:

> O western wind, when wilt thou blow
> That the small rain down can rain?
> Christ, that my love were in my arms
> And I in my bed again.

Or, for that matter, whether any longer speech ever said as much as Mr. Lincoln once managed to say in two hundred and seventy-two words and considerably less than three minutes on a haunted battlefield in Pennsylvania. This, however, is not a parlor-game but a footnote and should, I suppose, be sternly limited to the subject of one-act plays. Even that limitation permits me to submit *The Happy Journey to Trenton and Camden* as a finer, wiser, and more beautiful play than—let us say—its contemporary, *Strange Interlude,* a glum and windy work which, by its sheer length, filled with pious awe all the reviewers, pedagogues, and drama-clubs of its little day. One is driven to wonder why it is that the pundits who meet every year to select the American play on which the Pulitzer Prize should be bestowed always start with the tacit assumption that that dubious guerdon can go only to a play which keeps the audience occupied from dinner-time until at least 11 p.m. I do not happen to recall the name of the opus thus rewarded for the season in which Edna St. Vincent Millay's *Aria da Capo* was first produced, but I feel reasonably sure that the latter was the better play and I would be willing to hazard a small wager that it was not even considered by the judges.

Of recent years our playwrights have been growing audibly restive in the box wherein they were cabin'd, cribb'd, and confined by the late Henrik Ibsen. Here Wilder has invented for his own use a device which sets himself, the players, and the audience free. In this respect his play is inspired in its ingenuity. But here as always the thing said remains more important than the way of saying it, and Wilder will have failed with you if you go away from his theater thinking of his technique rather than of that mother's work-worn hands.

Thornton Niven Wilder was abstractedly engaged in training Lawrenceville boys to say enough French passwords to get them through the carelessly guarded portals of Princeton when he was released by the still puzzling prosperity of a beautiful novel, which one would have thought of as addressed to a gratifying but fastidious and unprofitable minority. That novel was *The Bridge of San Luis Rey*. The fantastic contrast in form and substance between that book and *Heaven's My Destination*—it was as though the same author had written *Marius the Epicurean* and *Huckleberry Finn*—gives some clue to the variety of the long shelf he will leave behind him if he lives out the years promised him by Holy Writ. It will be a longer shelf if he once succeeds in resisting for any considerable time his strongest temptation. Strange mixture that he is of poet, prophet, humming-bird, and gadfly, Professor Wilder has a passion for teaching and, like a drunkard to his bottle, keeps scurrying back to his classroom at the University of Chicago.

A. W.

A DOCTOR
OF THE
OLD SCHOOL

by

IAN MACLAREN

A DOCTOR OF THE OLD SCHOOL

I

A GENERAL PRACTITIONER

DRUMTOCHTY was accustomed to break every law of health, except wholesome food and fresh air, and yet had reduced the Psalmist's farthest limit to an average life-rate. Our men made no difference in their clothes for summer or winter, Drumsheugh and one or two of the larger farmers condescending to a topcoat on Sabbath, as a penalty of their position, and without regard to temperature. They wore their blacks at a funeral, refusing to cover them with anything, out of respect to the deceased, and standing longest in the kirkyard when the north wind was blowing across a hundred miles of snow. If the rain was pouring at the Junction, then Drumtochty stood two minutes longer through sheer native dourness till each man had a cascade from the tail of his coat, and hazarded the suggestion, half-way to Kildrummie, that it had been "a bit scrowie," a "scrowie" being as far short of a "shoor" as a "shoor" fell below "weet."

This sustained defiance of the elements provoked occasional judgments in the shape of a "hoast" (cough), and the head of the house was then exhorted by his women folk to "change his feet" if he had happened to walk through a burn on his way home, and was pestered generally with sanitary precautions. It is right to add that the gudeman treated such advice with contempt, regarding it as suitable for the effeminacy of towns, but not seriously intended for Drumtochty. Sandy Stewart "napped" stones on the road in his shirt sleeves, wet or fair, summer and winter, till he was persuaded to retire from

223

active duty at eighty-five, and he spent ten years more in regretting his hastiness and criticizing his successor. The ordinary course of life, with fine air and contented minds, was to do a full share of work till seventy, and then to look after "orra" jobs well into the eighties, and to "slip awa" within sight of ninety. Persons above ninety were understood to be acquitting themselves with credit, and assumed airs of authority, brushing aside the opinions of seventy as immature, and confirming their conclusions with illustrations drawn from the end of last century.

When Hillocks' brother so far forgot himself as to "slip awa" at sixty, that worthy man was scandalized, and offered laboured explanations at the "beerial."

"It's an awfu' business ony wy ye look at it, an' a sair trial tae us a'. A' never heard tell o' sic a thing in oor family afore, an' it's no easy accoontin' for't.

"The gudewife was sayin' he wes never the same sin' a weet nicht he lost himsel on the muir and slept below a bush; but that's neither here nor there. A'm thinkin' he sappit his constitution thae twa years he wes grieve aboot England. That wes thirty years syne, but ye're never the same aifter thae foreign climates."

Drumtochty listened patiently to Hillocks' apologia, but was not satisfied.

"It's clean havers aboot the muir. Losh keep's, we've a' sleepit oot and never been a hair the waur.

"A' admit that England micht hae dune the job; it's no cannie stravagin' yon wy frae place tae place, but Drums never complained tae me as if he hed been nippit in the Sooth."

The parish had, in fact, lost confidence in Drums after his wayward experiment with a potato-digging machine, which turned out a lamentable failure, and his premature departure confirmed our vague impression of his character.

"He's awa noo," Drumsheugh summed up, after opinion had time to form; "an' there were waur fouk than Drums, but there's nae doot he wes a wee flichty."

When illness had the audacity to attack a Drumtochty man, it was described as a "whup," and was treated by the men with a fine negligence. Hillocks was sitting in the Post Office one afternoon when I looked in for my letters, and the right side of his face was blazing red. His subject of discourse was the prospects of the turnip "breer," but he casually explained that he was waiting for medical advice.

"The gudewife is keepin' up a ding-dong frae mornin' till nicht aboot ma face, and a'm fair deaved (deafened), so a'm watchin' for MacLure tae get a bottle as he comes wast: yon's him noo."

The doctor made his diagnosis from horseback on sight, and stated the result with that admirable clearness which endeared him to Drumtochty.

"Confoond ye, Hillocks, what are ye ploiterin' aboot here for in the weet wi' a face like a boiled beet? Div ye no ken that ye've a titch o' the rose (erysipelas), and ocht tae be in the hoose? Gae hame wi' ye afore a' leave the bit, and send a haflin for some medicine. Ye donnerd idiot, are ye ettlin tae follow Drums afore yir time?" And the medical attendant of Drumtochty continued his invective till Hillocks started, and still pursued his retreating figure with medical directions of a simple and practical character.

"A'm watchin', an' peety ye if ye pit aff time. Keep yir bed the mornin', and dinna show yir face in the fields till a' see ye. A'll gie ye a cry on Monday—sic an auld fule—but there's no ane o' them tae mind anither in the hale pairish."

Hillocks' wife informed the kirkyaird that the doctor "gied the gudeman an awfu' clearin'," and that Hillocks "wes keepin' the hoose," which meant that the patient had tea breakfast, and at that time was wandering about the farm buildings in an easy undress with his head in a plaid.

It was impossible for a doctor to earn even the most modest competence from a people of such scandalous health, and so MacLure had annexed neighbouring parishes. His house—little more than a cottage—stood on the roadside among the pines towards the head of our Glen, and from this base of operations he dominated the wild glen that broke the wall of the Grampians above Drumtochty—where the snow drifts were twelve feet deep in winter, and the only way of passage at times was the channel of the river—and the moorland district westwards till he came to the Dunleith sphere of influence, where there were four doctors and a hydropathic. Drumtochty in its length, which was eight miles, and its breadth, which was four, lay in his hand; besides a glen behind, unknown to the world, which in the night time he visited at the risk of life, for the way thereto was across the big moor with its peat holes and treacherous bogs. And he held the land eastwards towards Muirtown so far as Geordie, the Drumtochty post, travelled every day, and could carry word that the doctor was wanted. He did his best for the need of every man, woman, and child in this wild, straggling district, year in, year out, in the snow and in the heat, in the dark and in the light, without rest, and without holiday for forty years.

One horse could not do the work of this man, but we liked best to see him on his old white mare, who died the week after her master, and the passing of the two did our hearts good. It was not that he rode beautifully, for he broke every canon of art, flying with his arms, stooping till he seemed to be speaking into Jess's ears, and rising in the saddle beyond all necessity. But he could ride faster, stay longer in the saddle, and had a firmer grip with his knees than anyone I ever met, and it was all for mercy's sake. When the reapers in harvest time saw a figure whirling past in a cloud of dust, or the family at the foot of Glen Urtach, gathered round the fire on a winter's night, heard the rattle of a horse's hoofs on the road, or the shepherds, out after the sheep, traced a black speck moving across the snow to the upper glen, they knew it was the doctor, and, without being conscious of it, wished him God speed.

Before and behind his saddle were strapped the instruments and medicines the doctor might want, for he never knew what was before him. There were no specialists in Drumtochty, so this man had to do everything as best he could, and as quickly. He was chest doctor and doctor for every other organ as well; he was accoucheur and surgeon; he was oculist and aurist; he was dentist and chloroformist, besides being chemist and druggist. It was often told how he was far up Glen Urtach when the feeders of the threshing mill caught young Burnbrae, and how he only stopped to change horses at his house, and galloped all the way to Burnbrae, and flung himself off his horse and amputated the arm, and saved the lad's life.

"You wud hae thocht that every meenut was an hour," said Jamie Soutar, who had been at the threshing, "an' a'll never forget the puir lad lying as white as deith on the floor o' the loft, wi' his head on a sheaf, an' Burnbrae haudin' the bandage ticht an' prayin' a' the while, and the mither greetin' in the corner.

" 'Will he never come?' she cries, an' a' heard the soond o' the horse's feet on the road a mile awa in the frosty air.

" 'The Lord be praised!' said Burnbrae, and a' slippit doon the ladder as the doctor came skelpin' intae the close, the foam fleein' frae his horse's mooth.

" 'Whar is he?' wes a' that passed his lips, an' in five meenuts he hed him on the feedin' board, and wes at his wark—sic wark, neeburs—but he did it weel. An' ae thing a' thocht rael thochtfu' o' him: he first sent aff the laddie's mither tae get a bed ready.

" 'Noo that's feenished, and his constitution 'ill dae the rest,' and he carried the lad doon the ladder in his airms like a bairn, and laid him in his bed, and waits aside him till he wes sleepin', and then says he: 'Burnbrae, yir a gey lad never tae say "Collie, will ye lick?" for a' hevna tasted meat for saxteen hoors.'

"It was michty tae see him come intae the yaird that day, neeburs; the verra look o' him wes victory."

Jamie's cynicism slipped off in the enthusiasm of this reminiscence, and he expressed the feeling of Drumtochty. No one sent for Mac-Lure save in great straits, and the sight of him put courage in sinking hearts. But this was not by the grace of his appearance, or the advantage of a good bedside manner. A tall, gaunt, loosely made man, without an ounce of superfluous flesh on his body, his face burned a dark brick colour by constant exposure to the weather, red hair and beard turning grey, honest blue eyes that looked you ever in the face, huge hands with wrist bones like the shank of a ham, and a voice that hurled his salutations across two fields, he suggested the moor rather than the drawing-room. But what a clever hand it was in an operation, as delicate as a woman's, and what a kindly voice it was in the humble room where the shepherd's wife was weeping by her man's bedside. He was "ill pitten thegither" to begin with, but many of his physical defects were the penalties of his work, and endeared him to the Glen. That ugly scar that cut into his right eyebrow and gave him such a sinister expression, was got one night Jess slipped on the ice and laid him insensible eight miles from home. His limp marked the big snowstorm in the fifties, when his horse missed the road in Glen Urtach, and they rolled together in a drift. MacLure escaped with a broken leg and the fracture of three ribs, but he never walked like other men again. He could not swing himself into the saddle without making two attempts and holding Jess's mane. Neither can you "warstle" through the peat bogs and snow drifts for forty winters without a touch of rheumatism. But they were honourable scars, and for such risks of life men get the Victoria Cross in other fields. MacLure got nothing but the secret affection of the Glen, which knew that none had ever done one-tenth as much for it as this ungainly, twisted, battered figure, and I have seen a Drumtochty face soften at the sight of MacLure limping to his horse.

Mr. Hopps earned the ill-will of the Glen for ever by criticizing the doctor's dress, but indeed it would have filled any townsman with amazement. Black he wore once a year, on Sacrament Sunday, and, if possible, at a funeral; topcoat or waterproof never. His jacket and waistcoat were rough homespun of Glen Urtach wool, which threw off the wet like a duck's back, and below he was clad in shepherd's tartan trousers, which disappeared into unpolished riding boots. His shirt was grey flannel, and he was uncertain about a collar, but certain as to a tie which he never had, his beard doing instead, and his hat was soft felt of four colours and seven different shapes. His point of distinction in dress was the trousers, and they were the subject of unending speculation.

"Some threep that he's worn thae eedentical pair the last twenty year, an' a' mind masel him gettin' a tear ahint, when he was crossin' oor palin', and the mend's still veesible.

"Ithers declare 'at he's got a wab o' claith, and hes a new pair made in Muirtown aince in the twa year maybe, and keeps them in the garden till the new look wears aff.

"For ma ain pairt," Soutar used to declare, "a' canna mak up my mind, but there's ae thing sure, the Glen wud not like tae see him withoot them: it wud be a shock tae confidence. There's no muckle o' the check left, but ye can aye tell it, and when ye see thae breeks comin' in ye ken that if human pooer can save yir bairn's life it 'ill be dune."

The confidence of the Glen—and tributary states—was unbounded, and rested partly on long experience of the doctor's resources, and partly on his hereditary connexion.

"His father was here afore him," Mrs. Macfadyen used to explain; "atween them they've hed the countryside for weel on tae a century; if MacLure disna understand oor constitution, wha dis, a' wud like tae ask?"

For Drumtochty had its own constitution and a special throat disease, as became a parish which was quite self-contained between the woods and the hills, and not dependent on the lowlands either for its diseases or its doctors.

"He's a skilly man, Doctor MacLure," continued my friend Mrs. Macfadyen, whose judgment on sermons or anything else was seldom at fault; "an' a kind-hearted, though o' coorse he hes his faults like us a', an' he disna tribble the Kirk often.

"He aye can tell what's wrang wi a body, an' maistly he can put ye richt, and there's nae new-fangled wys wi' him: a blister for the ootside an' Epsom salts for the inside dis his wark, an' they say there's no an herb on the hills he disna ken.

"If we're tae dee, we're tae dee; an' if we're tae live, we're tae live," concluded Elspeth, with sound Calvinistic logic; "but a'll say this for the doctor, that whether yir tae live or dee, he can aye keep up a shairp meisture on the skin.

"But he's no verra ceevil gin ye bring him when there's naethin' wrang," and Mrs. Macfadyen's face reflected another of Mr. Hopps' misadventures of which Hillocks held the copyright.

"Hopps' laddie ate grosarts (gooseberries) till they hed to sit up a'

nicht wi' him, an' naethin' wud do but they maun hae the doctor an'
he writes 'immediately' on a slip o' paper.

"Weel, MacLure had been awa a' nicht wi' a shepherd's wife Dunleith wy, and he comes here withoot drawin' bridle, mud up tae the
een.

" 'What's a dae here, Hillocks?" he cries; 'it's no an accident, is't?'
and when he got aff his horse he cud hardly stand wi' stiffness and
tire.

" 'It's nane o' us, doctor; it's Hopps' laddie; he's been eatin' ower
mony berries.'

"If he didna turn on me like a tiger.

" 'Div ye mean tae say——'

" 'Weesht, weesht,' an' I tried tae quiet him, for Hopps wes comin'
oot.

" 'Well, doctor,' begins he, as brisk as a magpie, 'you're here at last;
there's no hurry with you Scotchmen. My boy has been sick all night,
and I've never had one wink of sleep. You might have come a little
quicker, that's all I've got to say.'

" 'We've mair tae dae in Drumtochty than attend tae every bairn
that hes a sair stomach,' and a' saw MacLure wes roosed.

" 'I'm astonished to hear you speak. Our doctor at home always
says to Mrs. 'Opps, "Look on me as a family friend, Mrs. 'Opps, and
send for me though it be only a headache." '

" 'He'd be mair sparin' o' his offers if he hed four and twenty mile
tae look aifter. There's naethin' wrang wi' yir laddie but greed. Gie
him a gude dose o' castor oil and stop his meat for a day, an he 'ill
be a' richt the morn.'

" 'He 'ill not take castor oil, doctor. We have given up those barbarous medicines.'

" 'Whatna kind o' medicines hae ye noo in the Sooth?'

" 'Well, you see, Doctor MacLure, we're homœopathists, and I've my
little chest here,' and oot Hopps comes wi' his boxy.

" 'Let's see't,' an' MacLure sits doon and taks oot the bit bottles,
and he reads the names wi' a lauch every time.

" 'Belladonna; did ye ever hear the like? Aconite; it cowes a'. Nux

Vomica. What next? Weel, ma mannie,' he says tae Hopps, 'it's a fine ploy, and ye 'ill better gang on wi' the Nux till it's dune, and gie him ony ither o' the sweeties he fancies.

"'Noo, Hillocks, a' maun be aff tae see Drumsheugh's grieve, for he's doon wi' the fever, and it's tae be a teuch fecht. A' hinna time tae wait for dinner; gie me some cheese an' cake in ma haund, and Jess 'ill tak a pail o' meal an' water.

"'Fee; a'm no wantin' yir fees, man; wi' that boxy ye dinna need a doctor; na, na, gie yir siller tae some puir body, Maister Hopps,' an' he was doon the road as hard as he cud lick."

His fees were pretty much what the folk chose to give him, and he collected them once a year at Kildrummie fair.

"Weel, doctor, what am a' awin' ye for the wife and bairn? Ye 'ill need three notes for that nicht ye stayed in the hoose an' a' the veesits."

"Havers," MacLure would answer, "prices are low, a'm hearing; gie's thirty shillings."

"No, a'll no, or the wife 'ill tak ma ears off," and it was settled for two pounds.

Lord Kilspindie gave him a free house and fields, and one way or other, Drumsheugh told me, the doctor might get in about £150 a year, out of which he had to pay his old housekeeper's wages and a boy's, and keep two horses, besides the cost of instruments and books, which he bought through a friend in Edinburgh with much judgment.

There was only one man who ever complained of the doctor's charges, and that was the new farmer of Milton, who was so good that he was above both churches, and held a meeting in his barn. (It was Milton the Glen supposed at first to be a Mormon, but I can't go into that now.) He offered MacLure a pound less than he asked, and two tracts, whereupon MacLure expressed his opinion of Milton, both from a theological and social standpoint, with such vigour and frankness that an attentive audience of Drumtochty men could hardly contain themselves.

Jamie Soutar was selling his pig at the time, and missed the meeting, but he hastened to condole with Milton, who was complaining everywhere of the doctor's language.

"Ye did richt tae resist him; it 'ill maybe roose the Glen tae mak a stand; he fair hauds them in bondage.

"Thirty shillings for twal veesits, and him no mair than seeven mile awa, an' a'm telt there werena mair than four at nicht.

"Ye 'ill hae the sympathy o' the Glen, for a'body kens yir as free wi' yir siller as yir tracts.

"Wes't 'Beware o' gude warks' ye offered him? Man, ye chose it weel, for he's been colleckin' sae mony thae forty years, a'm feared for him.

"A've often thocht oor doctor's little better than the Gude Samaritan, an' the Pharisees didna think muckle o' his chance aither in this warld or that which is tae come."

II

THROUGH THE FLOOD

Doctor MacLure did not lead a solemn procession from the sick bed to the dining-room, and give his opinion from the hearthrug with an air of wisdom bordering on the supernatural, because neither the Drumtochty houses nor his manners were on that large scale. He was accustomed to deliver himself in the yard, and to conclude his directions with one foot in the stirrup; but when he left the room where the life of Annie Mitchell was ebbing slowly away, our doctor said not one word, and at the sight of his face her husband's heart was troubled.

He was a dull man, Tammas, who could not read the meaning of a sign, and laboured under a perpetual disability of speech; but love was eyes to him that day, and a mouth.

"Is't as bad as yir lookin', doctor? tell's the truth; wull Annie no come through?" and Tammas looked MacLure straight in the face, who never flinched his duty or said smooth things.

"A' wud gie onything tae say Annie hes a chance, but a' daurna; a' doot yir gaein' tae lose her, Tammas."

MacLure was in the saddle, and as he gave his judgment, he laid his hand on Tammas's shoulder with one of the rare caresses that pass between men.

"It's a sair business, but ye 'ill play the man and no vex Annie; she 'ill dae her best, a'll warrant."

"An' a'll dae mine," and Tammas gave MacLure's hand a grip that would have crushed the bones of a weakling. Drumtochty felt in such moments the brotherliness of this rough-looking man, and loved him.

Tammas hid his face in Jess's mane, who looked round with sorrow in her beautiful eyes, for she had seen many tragedies, and in this silent sympathy the stricken man drank his cup, drop by drop.

"A' wesna prepared for this, for a' aye thocht she wud live the langest. . . . She's younger than me by ten years, and never wes ill. . . . We've been mairit twal year laist Martinmas, but it's juist like a year the day. . . . A' wes never worthy o' her, the bonniest, snoddest (neatest), kindliest lass in the Glen. . . . A' never cud mak oot hoo she ever lookit at me, 'at hesna hed ae word tae say aboot her till it's ower late. . . . She didna cuist up tae me that a' wesna worthy o' her, no her, but aye she said, 'Yir ma ain gudeman, and nane cud be kinder tae me.' . . . An' a' wes minded tae be kind, but a' see noo mony little trokes a' micht hae dune for her, and noo the time is bye. . . . Naebody kens hoo patient she wes wi' me, and aye made the best o' me, an' never pit me tae shame afore the fouk. . . . An' we never hed ae cross word, no ane in twal year. . . . We were mair nor man and wife, we were sweethearts a' the time. . . . Oh, ma bonnie lass, what 'ill the bairnies an' me dae withoot ye, Annie?"

The winter night was falling fast, the snow lay deep upon the ground, and the merciless north wind moaned through the close as Tammas wrestled with his sorrow dry-eyed, for tears were denied Drumtochty men. Neither the doctor nor Jess moved hand or foot, but their hearts were with their fellow creature, and at length the doctor made a sign to Marget Howe, who had come out in search of Tammas, and now stood by his side.

"Dinna mourn tae the brakin' o' yir hert, Tammas," she said, "as if Annie an' you hed never luved. Neither death nor time can pairt them that luve; there's naethin' in a' the warld sae strong as luve. If Annie gaes frae the sicht o' yir een she 'ill come the nearer tae yir hert. She wants tae see ye, and tae hear ye say that ye 'ill never forget her nicht nor day till ye meet in the land where there's nae pairtin'. Oh, a' ken what a'm sayin', for it's five year noo sin George gied awa, an' he's mair wi' me noo than when he wes in Edinboro' and I wes in Drumtochty."

"Thank ye kindly, Marget; thae are gude words and true, an' ye hev the richt tae say them; but a' canna dae without seein' Annie comin' tae meet me in the gloamin', an' gaein' in an' oot the hoose, an' hearin' her ca' me by ma name, an' a'll no con tell her that a' luve her when there's nae Annie in the hoose.

"Can naethin' be dune, doctor? Ye savit Flora Cammil, and young Burnbrae, an' yon shepherd's wife Dunleith wy, an' we were a' sae prood o' ye, an' pleased tae think that ye hed keepit deith frae anither hame. Can ye no think o' somethin' tae help Annie, and gie her back tae her man and bairnies?" and Tammas searched the doctor's face in the cold, weird light.

"There's nae pooer in heaven or airth like luve," Marget said to me afterwards; "it maks the weak strong and the dumb tae speak. Oor herts were as water afore Tammas's words, an' a' saw the doctor shake in his saddle. A' never kent till that meenut hoo he hed a share in a'body's grief, an' carried the heaviest wecht o' a' the Glen. A' peetied him wi' Tammas lookin' at him sae wistfully, as if he hed the keys o' life an' deith in his hands. But he wes honest, and wudna hold oot a false houp tae deceive a sore hert or win escape for himsel."

"Ye needna plead wi' me, Tammas, to dae the best a' can for yir wife. Man, a' kent her lang afore ye ever luved her; a' brocht her intae the warld, and a' saw her through the fever when she wes a bit lassikie; a' closed her mither's een, and it wes me hed tae tell her she wes an orphan, an' nae man wes better pleased when she got a gude husband, and a' helpit her wi' her fower bairns. A've naither wife nor bairns o' ma own, an' a' coont a' the fouk o' the Glen ma family. Div ye think a' wudna save Annie if I cud? If there wes a man in Muirtown 'at cud dae mir for her, a'd have him this verra nicht, but a' the doctors in Perthshire are helpless for this tribble.

"Tammas, ma puir fallow, if it could avail, a' tell ye a' wud lay doon this auld worn-oot ruckle o' a body o' mine juist tae see ye baith sittin' at the fireside, an' the bairns roond ye, couthy an' canty again; but it's no tae be, Tammas, it's no tae be."

"When a' lookit at the doctor's face," Marget said, "a' thocht him the winsomest man a' ever saw. He wes transfigured that nicht, for a'm judging there's nae transfiguration like luve."

"It's God's wull an' maun be borne, but it's a sair wull for me, an' a'm no ungratefu' tae you, doctor, for a' ye've dune and what ye said the nicht," and Tammas went back to sit with Annie for the last time.

Jess picked her way through the deep snow to the main road, with a skill that came of long experience, and the doctor held converse with her according to his wont.

"Eh, Jess wumman, yon wes the hardest wark a' hae tae face, and a' wud raither hae ta'en ma chance o' anither row in a Glen Urtach drift than tell Tammas Mitchell his wife wes deein'.

"A' said she cudna be cured, and it wes true, for there's juist ae man in the land fit for't, and they micht as weel try tae get the mune oot o' heaven. Sae a' said naethin' tae vex Tammas's hert, for it's heavy eneuch withoot regrets.

"But it's hard, Jess, that money wull buy life after a', an' if Annie wes a duchess her man wudna lose her; but bein' only a puir cottar's wife, she maun dee afore the week's oot.

"Gin we hed him the morn there's little doot she wud be saved, for he hesna lost mair than five per cent o' his cases, and they 'ill be puir toon's craturs, no strappin' women like Annie.

"It's oot o' the question, Jess, sae hurry up, lass, for we've hed a heavy day. But it wud be the grandest thing that was ever dune in the Glen in oor time if it could be managed by hook or crook.

"We 'ill gang and see Drumsheugh, Jess; he's anither man sin' Geordie Hoo's deith, and he wes aye kinder than fouk kent"; and the doctor passed at a gallop through the village, whose lights shone across the white frost-bound road.

"Come in by, doctor; a' heard ye on the road; ye 'ill hae been at Tammas Mitchell's; hoo's the gudewife? a' doot she's sober."

"Annie's deein', Drumsheugh, an' Tammas is like tae brak his hert."

"That's no lichtsome, doctor, no lichtsome ava, for a' dinna ken ony man in Drumtochty sae bund up in his wife as Tammas, and there's no a bonnier wumman o' her age crosses oor kirk door than Annie, nor a cleverer at her wark. Man, ye 'ill need tae pit yir brains in steep. Is she clean beyond ye?"

"Beyond me and every ither in the land but ane, and it wud cost a hundred guineas tae bring him tae Drumtochty."

"Certes, he's no blate; it's a fell chairge for a short day's work; but hundred or no hundred we 'ill hae him, an' no let Annie gang, and her no half her years."

"Are ye meanin' it, Drumsheugh?" and MacLure turned white below the tan.

"William MacLure," said Drumsheugh, in one of the few confidences that ever broke the Drumtochty reserve, "a'm a lonely man, wi' naebody o' ma ain blude tae care for me livin', or tae lift me intae ma coffin when a'm deid.

"A' fecht awa at Muirtown market for an extra pund on a beast, or a shillin' on the quarter o' barley, an' what's the gude o't? Burnbrae gaes aff tae get a goon for his wife or a buke for his college laddie, an' Lachlan Campbell 'ill no leave the place noo withoot a ribbon for Flora.

"Ilka man in the Kildrummie train has some bit fairin' in his pooch for the fouk at hame that he's bocht wi' the siller he won.

"But there's naebody tae be lookin' oot for me, an' comin' doon the road tae meet me, and daffin' (joking) wi' me aboot their fairing, or feeling ma pockets. Ou ay, a've seen it a' at ither hooses, though they tried tae hide it frae me for fear a' wud lauch at them. Me lauch, wi' ma cauld, empty hame!"

"Yir the only man kens, Weelum, that I aince luved the noblest wumman in the Glen or onywhere, an' a' luve her still, but wi' anither luve noo.

"She hed given her hert tae anither, or a've thocht a' micht hae won her, though nae man be worthy o' sic a gift. Ma hert turned tae bitterness, but that passed awa beside the brier bush whar George Hoo lay yon sad simmer time. Some day a'll tell ye ma story, Weelum, for you an' me are auld freends, and will be till we dee."

MacLure felt beneath the table for Drumsheugh's hand, but neither man looked at the other.

"Weel, a' we can dae noo, Weelum, gin we haena mickle brichtness in oor ain hames, is tae keep the licht frae gaein' oot in anither hoose. Write the telegram, man, and Sandy 'ill send it aff frae Kildrummie this verra nicht, and ye 'ill hae yir man the morn."

"Yir the man a' coonted ye, Drumsheugh, but ye 'ill grant me ae favour. Ye 'ill lat me pay the half, bit by bit—a' ken yir wullin' tae dae't a',—but a' haena mony pleesures, an' a' wud like tae hae ma ain share in savin' Annie's life."

Next morning a figure received Sir George on the Kildrummie platform, whom that famous surgeon took for a gillie, but who introduced himself as "MacLure of Drumtochty." It seemed as if the East had come to meet the West when these two stood together, the one in travelling furs, handsome and distinguished, with his strong, cultured face and carriage of authority, a characteristic type of his profession; and the other more marvellously dressed than ever, for Drumsheugh's topcoat had been forced upon him for the occasion, his face and neck one redness with the bitter cold; rough and ungainly, yet not without some signs of power in his eye and voice, the most heroic type of his noble profession. MacLure compassed the precious arrival with observances till he was securely seated in Drumsheugh's dogcart—a vehicle that lent itself to history—with two full-sized plaids added to his equipment—Drumsheugh and Hillocks had both been requisitioned—and MacLure wrapped another plaid round a leather case, which was placed below the seat with such reverence as might be given to the Queen's regalia. Peter attended their departure full of interest, and as soon as they were in the fir woods MacLure explained that it would be an eventful journey.

"It's a' richt in here, for the wind disna get at the snaw, but the drifts are deep in the Glen, and th' 'ill be some engineerin' afore we get tae oor destination."

Four times they left the road and took their way over fields, twice they forced a passage through a slap in a dyke, thrice they used gaps in the paling which MacLure had made on his downward journey.

"A' seleckit the road this mornin', an' a' ken the depth tae an inch; we 'ill get through this steadin' here tae the main road, but oor worst job 'ill be crossin' the Tochty.

"Ye see the bridge hes been shakin' wi' this winter's flood, and we daurna venture on it, sae we hev tae ford, and the snaw's been melting up Urtach way. There's nae doot the water's gey big, and it's threatenin' tae rise, but we 'ill win through wi' a warstle.

"It micht be safer tae lift the instruments oot o' reach o' the water; wud ye mind haddin' them on yir knee till we're ower, an' keep firm in yir seat in case we come on a stane in the bed o' the river?"

By this time they had come to the edge, and it was not a cheering sight. The Tochty had spread out over the meadows, and while they waited they could see it cover another two inches on the trunk of a tree. There are summer floods, when the water is brown and flecked with foam, but this was a winter flood, which is black and sullen, and runs in the centre with a strong, fierce, silent current. Upon the opposite side Hillocks stood to give directions by word and hand, as the ford was on his land, and none knew the Tochty better in all its ways.

They passed through the shallow water without mishap, save when the wheel struck a hidden stone or fell suddenly into a rut; but when they neared the body of the river MacLure halted, to give Jess a minute's breathing.

"It 'ill tak ye a' yir time, lass, an' a' wud rather be on yir back; but ye never failed me yet, and a wumman's life is hangin' on the crossin'."

With the first plunge into the bed of the stream the water rose to the axles, and then it crept up to the shafts, so that the surgeon could feel it lapping in about his feet, while the dogcart began to quiver, and it seemed as if it were to be carried away. Sir George was as brave as most men, but he had never forded a Highland river in flood, and the mass of black water racing past beneath, before, behind him, affected his imagination and shook his nerves. He rose from his seat and ordered MacLure to turn back, declaring that he would be condemned utterly and eternally if he allowed himself to be drowned for any person.

"Sit doon," thundered MacLure; "condemned ye will be suner or later gin ye shirk yir duty, but through the water ye gang the day."

Both men spoke much more strongly and shortly, but this is what they intended to say, and it was MacLure that prevailed.

Jess trailed her feet along the ground with cunning art, and held her shoulder against the stream; MacLure leant forward in his seat, a rein in each hand, and his eyes fixed on Hillocks, who was now standing up to the waist in the water, shouting directions and cheering on horse and driver.

"Haud tae the richt, doctor; there's a hole yonder. Keep oot o't for ony sake. That's it; yir daein' fine. Steady, man, steady. Yir at the deepest; sit heavy in yir seats. Up the channel noo, and ye'll be oot o' the swirl. Weel dune, Jess, weel dune, auld mare! Mak straicht for me, doctor, an' a'll gie ye the road oot. Ma word, ye've dune yir best, baith o' ye this mornin'," cried Hillocks, splashing up to the dogcart, now in the shallows.

"Sall, it wes titch an' go for a meenut in the middle; a Hielan' ford is a kittle (hazardous) road in the snaw time, but ye're safe noo.

"Gude luck tae ye up at Westerton, sir; nane but a richt-hearted man wud hae riskit the Tochty in flood. Ye're boond tae succeed aifter sic a graund beginnin'," for it had spread already that a famous surgeon had come to do his best for Annie, Tammas Mitchell's wife.

Two hours later MacLure came out from Annie's room and laid hold of Tammas, a heap of speechless misery by the kitchen fire, and carried him off to the barn, and spread some corn on the threshing floor and thrust a flail into his hands.

"Noo we've tae begin, an' we 'ill no be dune for an hoor, and ye've tae lay on withoot stoppin' till a' come for ye, an' a'll shut the door tae haud in the noise, an' keep yir dog beside ye, for there maunna be a cheep aboot the hoose for Annie's sake."

"A'll dae onything ye want me, but if—if——"

"A'll come for ye, Tammas, gin there be danger; but what are ye feared for wi' the Queen's ain surgeon here?"

Fifty minutes did the flail rise and fall, save twice, when Tammas crept to the door and listened, the dog lifting his head and whining.

It seemed twelve hours instead of one when the door swung back, and MacLure filled the doorway, preceded by a great burst of light, for the sun had arisen on the snow.

His face was as tidings of great joy, and Elspeth told me that there was nothing like it to be seen that afternoon for glory, save the sun itself in the heavens.

"A' never saw the marrow o't, Tammas, an' a'll never see the like again; it's a' ower, man, withoot a hitch frae beginnin' tae end, and she's fa'in' asleep as fine as ye like."

"Dis he think Annie . . . 'ill live?"

"Of coorse he dis, and be aboot the hoose inside a month; that's the gude a' bein' a clean-bluided, weel-livin'——

"Preserve ye, man, what's wrang wi' ye? it's a mercy a' keppit ye, or we wud hev hed anither job for Sir George.

"Ye're a' richt noo; sit doon on the strae. A'll come back in a whilie, an' ye' 'ill see Annie juist for a meenut, but ye maunna say a word."

Marget took him in and let him kneel by Annie's bedside.

He said nothing then or afterwards, for speech came only once in his lifetime to Tammas, but Annie whispered, "Ma ain dear man."

When the doctor placed the precious bag beside Sir George in our solitary first next morning, he laid a cheque beside it and was about to leave.

"No, no," said the great man. "Mrs. Macfadyen and I were on the gossip last night, and I know the whole story about you and your friend.

"You have some right to call me a coward, but I'll never let you count me a mean, miserly rascal," and the cheque with Drumsheugh's painful writing fell in fifty pieces on the floor.

As the train began to move, a voice from the first called so that all in the station heard.

"Give's another shake of your hand, MacLure; I'm proud to have met you; you are an honour to our profession. Mind the antiseptic dressings."

It was market day, but only Jamie Soutar and Hillocks had ventured down.

"Did ye hear yon, Hillocks? hoo dae ye feel? A'll no deny a'm lifted."

Halfway to the Junction Hillocks had recovered, and began to grasp the situation.

"Tell's what he said. A' wud like to hae it exact for Drumsheugh."

"Thae's the eedentical words, an' they're true; there's no a man in Drumtochty disna ken that, except ane."

"An' wha's that, Jamie?"

"It's Weelum MacLure himsel. Man, a've often girned that he sud fecht awa for us a', and maybe dee before he kent that he hed githered mair luve than ony man in the Glen.

"'A'm prood tae hae met ye,' says Sir George, an' him the greatest doctor in the land. 'Yir an honour tae oor profession.'"

"Hillocks, a' wudna hae missed it for twenty notes," said James Soutar, cynic-in-ordinary to the parish of Drumtochty.

III

A FIGHT WITH DEATH

WHEN Drumsheugh's grieve was brought to the gates of death by fever, caught, as was supposed, on an adventurous visit to Glasgow, the London doctor at Lord Kilspindie's shooting lodge looked in on his way from the moor, and declared it impossible for Saunders to live through the night.

"I give him six hours, more or less; it is only a question of time," said the oracle, buttoning his gloves and getting into the brake; "tell your parish doctor that I was sorry not to have met him."

Bell heard this verdict from behind the door, and gave way utterly, but Drumsheugh declined to accept it as final, and devoted himself to consolation.

"Dinna greet like that, Bell wumman, sae lang as Saunders is still livin'; a'll never give up houp, for ma pairt, till oor ain man says the word.

"A' the doctors in the land dinna ken as muckle aboot us as Weelum MacLure, an' he's ill tae beat when he's tryin' tae save a man's life."

MacLure, on his coming, would say nothing, either weal or woe, till he had examined Saunders. Suddenly his face turned into iron before their eyes, and he looked like one encountering a merciless foe. For there was a feud between MacLure and a certain mighty power which had lasted for forty years in Drumtochty.

"The London doctor said that Saunders wud sough awa afore mornin', did he? Weel, he's an authority on fevers an' sic like diseases, an' ought tae ken.

"It's may be presumptuous o' me tae differ frae him, and it wudna be verra respectfu' o' Saunders tae live aifter this opeenion. But Saunders wes aye thraun an' ill tae drive, an' he's as like as no tae gang his ain gait.

"A'm no meanin' tae reflect on sae clever a man, but he didna ken the seetuation. He can read fevers like a buik, but he never cam across sic a thing as the Drumtochty constitution a' his days.

"Ye see, when onybody gets as low as puir Saunders here, it's juist a hand to hand wrastle atween the fever and his constitution, an' of coorse, if he hed been a shilpit, stuntit, feckless effeegy o' a cratur, fed on tea an' made dishes and pushioned wi' bad air, Saunders wud hae nae chance; he wes boond tae gae oot like the snuff o' a candle.

"But Saunders hes been fillin' his lungs for five and thirty year wi' strong Drumtochty air, an' eatin' naethin' but kirny aitmeal, and drinkin' naethin' but fresh milk frae the coo, an' followin' the ploo through the new-turned, sweet-smellin' earth, an' swingin' the scythe in haytime and harvest, till the legs an' airms o' him were iron, an' his chest wes like the cuttin' o' an oak tree.

"He's a waesome sicht the nicht, but Saunders wes a buirdly man aince, and wull never lat his life be taken lichtly frae him. Na, na, he hesna sinned against Nature, and Nature 'ill stand by him noo in his oor o' distress.

"A' daurna say yea, Bell, muckle as a' wud like, for this is an evil disease, cunnin' an' treacherous as the deevil himsel, but a' winna say nay, sae keep yir hert frae despair.

"It wull be a sair fecht, but it 'ill be settled one wy or anither by sax o'clock the morn's morn. Nae man can prophecee hoo it 'ill end, but ae thing is certain, a'll no see deith tak a Drumtochty man afore his time if a' can help it.

"Noo, Bell ma wumman, yir near deid wi' tire, an' nae wonder. Ye've dune a' ye cud for yir man, an' ye 'ill lippen (trust) him the nicht tae Drumsheugh an' me; we 'ill no fail him or you.

"Lie doon an' rest, an' if it be the wull o' the Almichty a'll wauken ye in the mornin' tae see a livin' conscious man, an' if it be itherwise a'll come for ye the suner, Bell," and the big red hand went out to the anxious wife. "A' gie ye ma word."

Bell leant over the bed, and at the sight of Saunders' face a superstitious dread seized her.

"See, doctor, the shadow of deith is on him that never lifts. A've seen it afore, on ma father an' mither. A' canna leave him, a' canna leave him."

"It's hoverin', Bell, but it hesna fallen; please God it never wull. Gang but and get some sleep, for it's time we were at oor work.

"The doctors in the toons hae nurses an' a' kinds o' handy apparatus," said MacLure to Drumsheugh when Bell had gone, "but you an' me 'ill need tae be nurse the nicht, an' use sic things as we hev.

"It 'ill be a lang nicht and anxious wark, but a' wud raither hae ye, auld freend, wi' me than ony man in the Glen. Ye're no feared tae gie a hand?"

"Me feared? No likely. Man, Saunders cam tae me a haflin, and hes been on Drumsheugh for twenty years, an' though he be a dour chiel, he's a faithfu' servant as ever lived. It's waesome tae see him lyin' there moanin' like some dumb animal frae mornin' tae nicht, an' no able tae answer his ain wife when she speaks.

"Div ye think, Weelum, he hes a chance?"

"That he hes, at ony rate, and it 'ill no be your blame or mine if he hesna mair."

While he was speaking, MacLure took off his coat and waistcoat and hung them on the back of the door. Then he rolled up the sleeves of his shirt and laid bare two arms that were nothing but bone and muscle.

"It gar'd ma very blood rin faster tae the end of ma fingers juist tae look at him," Drumsheugh expatiated afterwards to Hillocks, "for a' saw noo that there was tae be a stand-up fecht atween him an' deith for Saunders, and when a' thocht o' Bell an' her bairns, a' kent wha wud win.

"'Aff wi' yir coat, Drumsheugh,' said MacLure; 'ye 'ill need tae bend yir back the nicht; gither a' the pails in the hoose and fill them at the spring, an' a'll come doon tae help ye wi' the carryin'.'"

It was a wonderful ascent up the steep pathway from the spring to the cottage on its little knoll, the two men in single file, bareheaded, silent, solemn, each with a pail of water in either hand, MacLure limping painfully in front, Drumsheugh blowing behind; and when they laid down their burden in the sick room, where the bits of furniture had been put to a side and a large tub held the centre, Drumsheugh looked curiously at the doctor.

"No, a'm no daft; ye needna be feared; but yir tae get yir first lesson in medicine the nicht, an' if we win the battle ye can set up for yersel in the Glen.

"There's twa dangers—that Saunders' strength fails, an' that the force o' the fever grows; and we have juist twa weapons.

"Yon milk on the drawers' head an' the bottle of whisky is tae keep up the strength, and this cool caller water is tae keep doon the fever.

"We 'ill cast oot the fever by the virtue o' the earth an' the water."

"Div ye mean tae pit Saunders in the tub?"

"Ye hiv it noo, Drumsheugh, and that's hoo a' need yir help."

"Man, Hillocks," Drumsheugh used to moralize, as often as he remembered that critical night, "it wes humblin' tae see hoo low sickness can bring a pooerfu' man, an' ocht tae keep us frae pride.

"A month syne there wesna a stronger man in the Glen than Saunders, an' noo he wes juist a bundle o' skin and bone, that naither saw nor heard, nor moved nor felt, that kent naethin' that was dune tae him.

"Hillocks, a' wudna hae wished ony man tae hev seen Saunders—for it wull never pass frae before ma een as long as a' live—but a' wish a' the Glen hed stude by MacLure kneelin' on the floor wi' his sleeves up tae his oxters and waitin' on Saunders.

"Yon big man wes as pitifu' an' gentle as a wumman, and when he laid the puir fallow in his bed again, he happit him ower as a mither dis her bairn."

Thrice it was done, Drumsheugh ever bringing up colder water from the spring, and twice MacLure was silent; but after the third time there was a gleam in his eye.

"We're haudin' oor ain; we're no bein' maistered, at ony rate; mair a' canna say for three oors.

"We 'ill no need the water again, Drumsheugh; gae oot and tak a breath o' air; a'm on gaird masel."

It was the hour before daybreak, and Drumsheugh wandered through fields he had trodden since childhood. The cattle lay sleeping in the pastures; their shadowy forms, with a patch of whiteness here and there, having a weird suggestion of death. He heard the burn running over the stones; fifty years ago he had made a dam that lasted till winter. The hooting of an owl made him start; one had frightened him as a boy so that he ran home to his mother—she died thirty years ago. The smell of ripe corn filled the air; it would soon be cut and garnered. He could see the dim outlines of his house, all dark and cold; no one he loved was beneath the roof. The lighted window in Saunders' cottage told where a man hung between life and death, but love was in that home. The futility of life arose before this lonely man, and overcame his heart with an indescribable sadness.

What a vanity was all human labour, what a mystery all human life.

But while he stood, a subtle change came over the night, and the air trembled round him as if one had whispered. Drumsheugh lifted his head and looked eastwards. A faint grey stole over the distant horizon, and suddenly a cloud reddened before his eyes. The sun was not in sight, but was rising, and sending forerunners before his face. The cattle began to stir, a blackbird burst into song, and before Drumsheugh crossed the threshold of Saunders' house, the first ray of the sun had broken on a peak of the Grampians.

MacLure left the bedside, and as the light of the candle fell on the doctor's face, Drumsheugh could see that it was going well with Saunders.

"He's nae waur; an' it's half six noo; it's ower sune tae say mair, but a'm houpin' for the best. Sit doon and take a sleep, for ye're needin' 't, Drumsheugh, an', man, ye hae worked for it."

As he dozed off, the last thing Drumsheugh saw was the doctor sitting erect in his chair, a clenched fist resting on the bed, and his eyes already bright with the vision of victory.

He awoke with a start to find the room flooded with the morning sunshine, and every trace of last night's work removed.

The doctor was bending over the bed, and speaking to Saunders.

"It's me, Saunders, Doctor MacLure, ye ken; dinna try tae speak or move; juist let this drap o' milk slip ower—ye 'ill be needin' yir breakfast, lad—and gang tae sleep again."

Five minutes, and Saunders had fallen into a deep, healthy sleep, all tossing and moaning come to an end. Then MacLure stepped softly across the floor, picked up his coat and waistcoat, and went out at the door.

Drumsheugh arose and followed him without a word. They passed through the little garden, sparkling with dew, and beside the byre, where Hawkie rattled her chain, impatient for Bell's coming, and by Saunders' little strip of corn ready for the scythe, till they reached an open field. There they came to a halt, and Doctor MacLure for once allowed himself to go.

His coat he flung east and his waistcoat west, as far as he could hurl them, and it was plain he would have shouted had he been a complete mile from Saunders' room. Any less distance was useless for adequate expression. He struck Drumsheugh a mighty blow that well-nigh levelled that substantial man in the dust, and then the doctor of Drumtochty issued his bulletin.

"Saunders wesna tae live through the nicht, but he's livin' this meenut, an' like to live.

"He's got by the warst clean and fair, and wi' him that's as good as cure.

"It 'ill be a graund waukenin' for Bell; she 'ill no be a weedow yet, nor the bairnies fatherless.

"There's nae use glowerin' at me, Drumsheugh, for a body's daft at a time, an' a' canna contain masel, and a'm no gaein' tae try."

Then it dawned upon Drumsheugh that the doctor was attempting the Highland fling.

"He's ill made tae begin wi'," Drumsheugh explained in the kirk-yard next Sabbath, "and ye ken he's been terrible mishannelled by accidents, sae ye may think what like it wes, but, as sure as deith, o' a' the Hielan' flings a' ever saw yon wes the bonniest.

"A' hevna shaken ma ain legs for thirty years, but a' confess tae a turn masel. Ye may lauch an' ye like, neeburs, but the thocht o' Bell an' the news that wes waitin' her got the better o' me."

Drumtochty did not laugh. Drumtochty looked as if it could have done quite otherwise for joy.

"A' wud hae made a third gin a' hed been there," announced Hillocks, aggressively.

"Come on, Drumsheugh," said Jamie Soutar, "gie's the end o't; it wes a michty mornin'."

"'We're twa auld fules,' says MacLure tae me, and he gaithers up his claithes. 'It wud set us better tae be tellin' Bell.'

"She wes sleepin' on the top o' her bed wrapped in a plaid, fair worn oot wi' three weeks' nursin' o' Saunders, but at the first touch she was oot upon the floor.

"'Is Saunders deein', doctor?' she cries. 'Ye promised tae wauken me; dinna tell me it's a' ower.'

" 'There's nae deein' aboot him, Bell; ye're no tae lose yir man this time, sae far as a' can see. Come ben an' jidge for yersel.'

"Bell lookit at Saunders, and the tears of joy fell on the bed like rain.

" 'The shadow's lifted,' she said; 'he's come back frae the mooth o' the tomb.

" 'A' prayed last nicht that the Lord wud leave Saunders till the laddies cud dae for themselves, an' thae words came intae ma mind, "Weepin' may endure for a nicht, but joy cometh in the mornin'." "

" 'The Lord heard ma prayer, and joy hes come in the mornin',' an' she gripped the doctor's hand.

" 'Ye've been the instrument, Doctor MacLure. Ye wudna gie him up, and ye did what nae ither cud for him, an' a've ma man the day, and the bairns hae their father.'

"An' afore MacLure kent what she was daein', Bell lifted his hand to her lips an' kissed it."

"Did she, though?" cried Jamie. "Wha wud hae thocht there wes as muckle spunk in Bell?"

"MacLure, of coorse, was clean scandalized," continued Drumsheugh, "an' pooed awa his hand as if it hed been burned.

"Nae man can thole that kind o' fraikin', and a' never heard o' sic a thing in the parish, but we maun excuse Bell, neeburs; it wes an occasion by ordinar," and Drumsheugh made Bell's apology to Drumtochty for such an excess of feeling.

"A' see naethin' tae excuse," insisted Jamie, who was in great fettle that Sabbath; "the doctor hes never been burdened wi' fees, and a'm judgin' he coonted a wumman's gratitude that he saved frae weedowhood the best he ever got."

"A' gaed up tae the Manse last nicht," concluded Drumsheugh, "and telt the minister hoo the doctor focht aucht oors for Saunders' life, an' won, and ye never saw a man sae carried. He walkit up and doon the room a' the time, and every other meenut he blew his nose like a trumpet.

" 'I've a cold in my head tonight, Drumsheugh,' says he; 'never mind me.' "

"A've hed the same masel in sic circumstances; they come on sudden," said Jamie.

"A' wager there 'ill be a new bit in the laist prayer the day, an' somethin' worth hearin'."

And the fathers went into kirk in great expectation.

"We beseech Thee for such as be sick, that Thy hand may be on them for good, and that Thou wouldst restore them again to health and strength," was the familiar petition of every Sabbath.

The congregation waited in a silence that might be heard, and were not disappointed that morning, for the minister continued:

"Especially we tender Thee hearty thanks that Thou didst spare Thy servant who was brought down into the dust of death, and hast given him back to his wife and children, and unto that end didst wonderfully bless the skill of him who goes out and in amongst us, the beloved physician of this parish and adjacent districts."

"Didna a' tell ye, neeburs?" said Jamie, as they stood at the kirkyard gate before dispersing; "there's no a man in the coonty cud hae dune it better. 'Beloved physician,' an' his 'skill,' tae, an' bringing in 'adjacent districts'; that's Glen Urtach; it wes handsome, and the doctor earned it, ay, every word.

"It's an awfu' peety he didna hear yon; but dear knows whar he is the day, maist likely up——"

Jamie stopped suddenly at the sound of a horse's feet, and there, coming down the avenue of beech trees that made a long vista from the kirk gate, they saw the doctor and Jess.

One thought flashed through the minds of the fathers of the commonwealth.

It ought to be done as he passed, and it would be done if it were not Sabbath. Of course it was out of the question on Sabbath.

The doctor is now distinctly visible, riding after his fashion.

There was never such a chance, if it were only Saturday; and each man reads his own regret in his neighbour's face.

The doctor is nearing them rapidly; they can imagine the shepherd's tartan.

Sabbath or no Sabbath, the Glen cannot let him pass without some tribute of their pride.

Jess has recognized friends, and the doctor is drawing rein.

"It hes tae be dune," said Jamie desperately, "say what ye like." Then they all looked towards him, and Jamie led.

"Hurrah," swinging his Sabbath hat in the air, "hurrah," and once more, "hurrah," Whinnie Knowe, Drumsheugh, and Hillocks joining lustily, but Tammas Mitchell carrying all before him, for he had found at last an expression for his feelings that rendered speech unnecessary.

It was a solitary experience for horse and rider, and Jess bolted without delay. But the sound followed and surrounded them, and as they passed the corner of the kirkyard, a figure waved his college cap over the wall and gave a cheer on his own account.

"God bless you, doctor, and well done."

"If it isna the minister," cried Drumsheugh, "in his goon an' bans; tae think o' that; but a' respeck him for it."

Then Drumtochty became self-conscious, and went home in confusion of face and unbroken silence, except Jamie Soutar, who faced his neighbours at the parting of the ways without shame.

"A' wud dae it a' ower again if a' hed the chance; he got naethin' but his due."

It was two miles before Jess composed her mind, and the doctor and she could discuss it quietly together.

"A' can hardly believe ma ears, Jess, an' the Sabbath tae; their verra jidgment hes gane frae the fouk o' Drumtochty.

"They've heard about Saunders, a'm thinkin', wumman, and they're pleased we brocht him roond; he's fairly on the mend, ye ken, noo.

"A' never expeckit the like o' this, though, and it wes juist a wee thingie mair than a' cud hae stude.

"Ye hev yir share in't tae, lass; we've hed mony a hard nicht and day thegither, an' yon wes oor reward. No mony men in this warld 'ill ever get a better, for it cam frae the hert o' honest fouk."

I V

THE DOCTOR'S LAST JOURNEY

DRUMTOCHTY had a vivid recollection of the winter when Dr. Mac-Lure was laid up for two months with a broken leg, and the Glen was dependent on the dubious ministrations of the Kildrummie doctor. Mrs. Macfadyen also pretended to recall a "whup" of some kind or other he had in the fifties, but this was considered to be rather a pyrotechnic display of Elspeth's superior memory than a serious statement of fact. MacLure could not have ridden through the snow of forty winters without suffering, yet no one ever heard him complain, and he never pled illness to any messenger by night or day.

"It took me," said Jamie Soutar to Milton afterwards, "the feck o' ten meenuts tae howk him an' Jess oot ae snawy nicht when Drums turned bad sudden, and if he didna try to excuse himself for no hearing me at aince wi' some story aboot juist comin' in frae Glen Urtach, and no bein' in his bed for the laist twa nichts.

"He wes that carefu' o' himsel an' lazy that if it hedna been for the siller, a've often thocht, Milton, he wud never hae dune a handstroke o' wark in the Glen.

"What scunnered me wes the wy the bairns were ta'en in wi' him. Man, a've seen him tak a wee laddie on his knee that his ain mither cudna quiet, an' lilt 'Sing a song o' saxpence' till the bit mannie wud be lauchin' like a gude ane, an' pooin' the doctor's beard.

"As for the weemen, he fair cuist a glamour ower them; they're daein' naethin' noo but speak aboot this body and the ither he cured, an' hoo he aye hed a couthy word for sick fouk. Weemen hae nae discernment, Milton; tae hear them speak ye wud think MacLure hed been a releegious man like yersel, although, as ye said, he wes little mair than a Gallio.

"Bell Baxter was haverin' awa in the shop tae sic an extent aboot the wy MacLure brocht roond Saunders when he hed the fever that a' gied oot at the door, a' wes that disgusted, an' a'm telt when Tammas Mitchell heard the news in the smiddy he wes juist on the greeting.

"The smith said that he wes thinkin' o' Annie's tribble, but ony wy a' ca' it rael bairnly. It's no like Drumtochty; ye're setting an example, Milton, wi' yir composure. But a' mind ye took the doctor's meesure as sune as ye cam intae the pairish."

It is the penalty of a cynic that he must have some relief for his secret grief, and Milton began to weary of life in Jamie's hands during those days.

Drumtochty was not observant in the matter of health, but they had grown sensitive about Dr. MacLure, and remarked in the kirkyard all summer that he was failing.

"He wes aye spare," said Hillocks, "an' he's been sair twisted for the laist twenty year, but a' never mind him booed till the year. An' he's gaein' intae sma' buke (bulk), an' a' dinna like that, neeburs.

"The Glen wudna dae weel withoot Weelum MacLure, an' he's no as young as he wes. Man, Drumsheugh, ye micht wile him aff tae the saut water atween the neeps and the hairst. He's been workin' forty year for a holiday, an' it's aboot due."

Drumsheugh was full of tact, and met MacLure quite by accident on the road.

"Saunders 'ill no need me till the shearing begins," he explained to the doctor, "an' a'm gaein' tae Brochty for a turn o' the hot baths; they're fine for the rheumatics.

"Wull ye no come wi' me for auld lang syne? it's lonesome for a solitary man, an' it wud dae ye gude."

"Na, na, Drumsheugh," said MacLure, who understood perfectly, "a've dune a' thae years withoot a break, an' a'm laith (unwilling) tae be takin' holidays at the tail end.

"A'll no be mony months wi' ye a' thegither noo, an' a'm wanting tae spend a' the time a' hev in the Glen. Ye see yersel that a'll sune be getting ma lang rest, an' a'll no deny that a'm wearyin' for it."

As autumn passed into winter, the Glen noticed that the doctor's hair had turned grey, and that his manner had lost all its roughness.

A feeling of secret gratitude filled their hearts, and they united in a conspiracy of attention. Annie Mitchell knitted a huge comforter in red and white, which the doctor wore in misery for one whole day, out of respect for Annie, and then hung in his sitting-room as a wall ornament. Hillocks used to intercept him with hot drinks, and one drifting day compelled him to shelter till the storm abated. Flora Campbell brought a wonderful compound of honey and whisky, much tasted in Auchindarroch, for his cough, and the mother of young Burnbrae filled his cupboard with black jam, as a healing measure. Jamie Soutar seemed to have an endless series of jobs in the doctor's direction, and looked in "juist tae rest himsel" in the kitchen.

MacLure had been slowly taking in the situation, and at last he unburdened himself one night to Jamie.

"What ails the fouk, think ye? for they're aye lecturin' me noo tae tak care o' the weet and tae wrap masel up, an' there's no a week but they're sendin' bit presents tae the hoose, till a'm fair ashamed."

"Oo, a'll explain that in a meenut," answered Jamie, "for a' ken the Glen weel. Ye see they're juist tryin' the Scripture plan o' heapin' coals o' fire on yer head.

"Here ye've been negleckin' the fouk in seeckness an' lettin' them dee afore their freends' eyes withoot a fecht, an' refusin' tae gang tae a puir wumman in her tribble, an' frichtenin' the bairns—no, a'm no dune—and scourgin' us wi' fees, and livin' yersel on the fat o' the land.

"Ye've been carryin' on this trade ever sin yir father dee'd, and the Glen didna notis. But ma word, they've fund ye oot at laist, an' they're gaein' tae mak ye suffer for a' yir ill usage. Div ye understand noo?" said Jamie, savagely.

For a while MacLure was silent, and then he only said:

"It's little a' did for the puir bodies; but ye hev a gude hert, Jamie, a rael good hert."

It was a bitter December Sabbath, and the fathers were settling the affairs of the parish ankle deep in snow, when MacLure's old housekeeper told Drumsheugh that the doctor was not able to rise, and wished to see him in the afternoon.

"Ay, ay," said Hillocks, shaking his head, and that day Drumsheugh omitted four pews with the ladle, while Jamie was so vicious on the way home that none could endure him.

Janet had lit a fire in the unused grate, and hung a plaid by the window to break the power of the cruel north wind, but the bare room with its half-a-dozen bits of furniture and a worn strip of carpet, and the outlook upon the snow drifted up to the second pane of the window and the black firs laden with their icy burden, sent a chill to Drumsheugh's heart.

The doctor had weakened sadly, and could hardly lift his head, but his face lit up at the sight of his visitor, and the big hand, which was now quite refined in its whiteness, came out from the bed-clothes with the old warm grip.

"Come in by, man, and sit doon; it's an awfu' day tae bring ye sae far, but a' kent ye wudna grudge the traivel.

"A' wesna sure till last nicht, an' then a' felt it wudna be lang, an' a' took a wearyin' this mornin' tae see ye.

"We've been freends sin' we were laddies at the auld schule in the firs, an' a' wud like ye tae be wi' me at the end. Ye 'ill stay the nicht, Paitrick, for auld lang syne."

Drumsheugh was much shaken, and the sound of the Christian name, which he had not heard since his mother's death, gave him a "grue" (shiver), as if one had spoken from the other world.

"It's maist awfu' tae hear ye speakin' aboot deein', Weelum; a' canna bear it. We 'ill hae the Muirtown doctor up, an' ye 'ill be aboot again in nae time.

"Ye hevna ony sair tribble; ye're juist trachled wi' hard wark an' needin' a rest. Dinna say ye're gaein' tae leave us, Weelum; we canna dae withoot ye in Drumtochty;" and Drumsheugh looked wistfully for some word of hope.

"Na, na, Paitrick, naethin' can be dune, an' it's ower late tae send for ony doctor. There's a knock that canna be mista'en, an' a' heard it last nicht. A've focht deith for ither fouk mair than forty year, but ma ain time hes come at laist.

"A've nae tribble worth mentionin'—a bit titch o' bronchitis—an' a've hed a graund constitution; but a'm fair worn oot, Paitrick; that's ma complaint, an' it's past curin'."

Drumsheugh went over to the fireplace, and for a while did nothing but break up the smouldering peats, whose smoke powerfully affected his nose and eyes.

"When ye're ready, Paitrick, there's twa or three little trokes a' wud like ye tae look aifter, an' a'll tell ye aboot them as lang's ma head's clear.

"A' didna keep buiks, as ye ken, for a' aye hed a guid memory, so naebody 'ill be harried for money aifter ma deith, and ye 'ill hae nae accoonts tae collect.

"But the fouk are honest in Drumtochty, and they 'ill be offerin' ye siller, an' a'll gie ye ma mind aboot it. Gin it be a puir body, tell her tae keep it and get a bit plaidie wi' the money, and she 'ill maybe think o' her auld doctor at a time. Gin it be a bien (well-to-do) man, tak half of what he offers, for a Drumtochty man wud scorn to be mean in sic circumstances; and if onybody needs a doctor an' canna pay for him, see he's no left tae dee when a'm oot o' the road."

"Nae fear o' that as lang as a'm livin', Weelum; that hundred's still tae the fore, ye ken, an' a'll tak care it's weel spent.

"Yon wes the best job we ever did thegither, an' dookin' Saunders; ye 'ill no forget that nicht, Weelum"—a gleam came into the doctor's eyes—"tae say naethin' o' the Hielan' fling."

The remembrance of that great victory came upon Drumsheugh, and tried his fortitude.

"What 'ill become o's when ye're no here tae gie a hand in time o' need? we 'ill tak ill wi' a stranger that disna ken ane o's frae anither."

"It's a' for the best, Paitrick, an' ye 'ill see that in a whilie. A've kent fine that ma day wes ower, an' that ye sud hae a younger man.

"A' did what a' cud tae keep up wi' the new medicine, but a' hed little time for readin', an' nane for traivellin'.

"A'm the last o' the auld schule, an' a' ken as weel as onybody thet a' wesna sae dainty an' fine-mannered as the town doctors. Ye took me as a' wes, an' naebody ever cuist up tae me that a' wes a plain man. Na, na; ye've been rael kind an' conseederate a' thae years."

"Weelum, gin ye cairry on sic nonsense ony langer," interrupted Drumsheugh, huskily, "a'll leave the hoose; a' canna stand it."

"It's the truth, Paitrick, but we 'ill gae on wi' our wark, for a'm failin' fast.

"Gie Janet ony sticks of furniture she needs tae furnish a hoose, and sell a' thing else tae pay the wricht (undertaker) an' bedrel (grave-digger). If the new doctor be a young laddie and no verra rich, ye micht let him hae the buiks an' instruments; it 'ill aye be a help.

"But a' wudna like ye tae sell Jess, for she's been a faithfu' servant, an' a freend tae. There's a note or twa in that drawer a' savit, an' if ye kent ony man that wud gie her a bite o' grass and a sta' in his stable till she followed her maister——"

"Confoond ye, Weelum," broke out Drumsheugh; "it's doonricht cruel o' ye to speak like this tae me. Whar wud Jess gang but tae Drumsheugh? she 'ill hae her run o' heck an' manger sae lang as she lives; the Glen wudna like tae see anither man on Jess, and nae man 'ill ever touch the auld mare."

"Dinna mind me, Paitrick, for a' expeckit this; but ye ken we're no verra gleg wi' oor tongues in Drumtochty, an' dinna tell a' that's in oor herts.

"Weel, that's a' that a' mind, an' the rest a' leave tae yersel. A've neither kith nor kin tae bury me, sae you an' the neeburs 'ill need tae lat me doon; but gin Tammas Mitchell or Saunders be stannin' near and lookin' as if they wud like a cord, gie't tae them, Paitrick. They're baith dour chiels, and haena muckle tae say, but Tammas hes a graund hert, and there's waur fouk in the Glen than Saunders.

"A'm gettin' drowsy, an' a'll no be able tae follow ye sune, a' doot; wud ye read a bit tae me afore a' fa' ower?

"Ye 'ill find ma mither's Bible on the drawers' heid, but ye 'ill need tae come close tae the bed, for a'm no hearin' or seein' sae weel as a' wes when ye cam."

Drumsheugh put on his spectacles and searched for a comfortable Scripture, while the light of the lamp fell on his shaking hands and the doctor's face, where the shadow was now settling.

"Ma mither aye wantit this read tae her when she wes sober

(weak)," and Drumsheugh began, "In My Father's house are many mansions," but MacLure stopped him.

"It's a bonnie word, an' yir mither wes a sanct; but it's no for the like o' me. It's ower gude; a' daurna tak it.

"Shut the buik an' let it open itsel, an' ye 'ill get a bit a've been readin' every nicht the laist month."

Then Drumsheugh found the Parable wherein the Master tells us what God thinks of a Pharisee and of a penitent sinner, till he came to the words: "And the publican, standing afar off, would not lift up so much as his eyes to heaven, but smote upon his breast, saying, God be merciful to me a sinner."

"That micht hae been written for me, Paitrick, or ony ither auld sinner that hes feenished his life, an' hes naethin' tae say for himsel.

"It wesna easy for me tae get tae kirk, but a' cud hae managed wi' a stretch, an' a' used langidge a' sudna, an' a' micht hae been gentler, and no been so short in the temper. A' see't a' noo.

"It's ower late tae mend, but ye 'ill maybe juist say to the fouk that I wes sorry, an' a'm houpin' that the Almichty 'ill hae mercy on me.

"Cud ye . . . pit up a bit prayer, Paitrick?"

"A' haena the words," said Drumsheugh in great distress; "wud ye like's tae send for the minister?"

"It's no the time for that noo, an' a' wud rather hae yersel—juist what's in yir hert, Paitrick: the Almichty 'ill ken the lave (rest) Himsel."

So Drumsheugh knelt and prayed with many pauses.

"Almichty God . . . dinna be hard on Weelum MacLure, for he's no been hard wi' onybody in Drumtochty. . . . Be kind tae him as he's been tae us a' for forty year. . . . We're a' sinners afore Thee. . . . Forgive him what he's dune wrang, an' dinna cuist it up tae him. . . . Mind the fouk he's helpit . . . the weemen an' bairnies . . . an' gie him a welcome hame, for he's sair needin't after a' his wark. . . . Amen."

"Thank ye, Paitrick, and gude nicht tae ye. Ma ain true freend, gie's yir hand, for a'll may be no ken ye again.

"Noo a'll say ma mither's prayer and hae a sleep, but ye 'ill no leave me till a' is ower."

Then he repeated as he had done every night of his life:

> "This night I lay me down to sleep,
> I pray the Lord my soul to keep.
> And if I die before I wake,
> I pray the Lord my soul to take."

He was sleeping quietly when the wind drove the snow against the window with a sudden "swish"; and he instantly awoke, so to say, in his sleep. Someone needed him.

"Are ye frae Glen Urtach?" and an unheard voice seemed to have answered him.

"Worse is she, an' sufferin' awfu'; that's no lichtsome; ye did richt tae come.

"The front door's drifted up; gang roond tae the back, an' ye 'ill get intae the kitchen: a'll be ready in a meenut.

"Gie's a hand wi' the lantern when a'm saidling Jess, an' ye needna come on till daylicht; a' ken the road."

Then he was away in his sleep on some errand of mercy, and struggling through the storm.

"It's a coorse nicht, Jess, an' heavy traivellin'; can ye see afore ye, lass? for a'm clean confused wi' the snaw; bide a wee till a' find the diveesion o' the roads; it's aboot here back or forrit.

"Steady, lass, steady, dinna plunge; it's a drift we're in, but ye're no sinkin'; . . . up noo; . . . there ye are on the road again.

"Eh, it's deep the nicht, an' hard on us baith, but there's a puir wumman micht dee if we didna warstle through; . . . that's it; ye ken fine what a'm sayin'.

"We 'ill hae tae leave the road here, an' tak tae the muir. Sandie 'ill no can leave the wife alane tae meet us; . . . feel for yersel, lass, and keep oot o' the holes.

"Yon's the hoose black in the snaw. Sandie! man, ye frichtened us; a' didna see ye ahint the dyke; hoo's the wife?"

After a while he began again:

"Ye're fair dune, Jess, and so a' am masel: we're baith gettin' auld, an' dinna tak sae weel wi' the nicht wark.

"We 'ill sune be hame noo; this is the black wood, and it's no lang aifter that; we're ready for oor beds, Jess; . . . ay, ye like a clap at a time; mony a mile we've gaed thegither.

"Yon's the licht in the kitchen window; nae wonder ye're nickering (neighing); . . . it's been a stiff journey; a'm tired, lass . . . a'm tired tae deith," and the voice died into silence.

Drumsheugh held his friend's hand, which now and again tightened in his, and as he watched, a change came over the face on the pillow beside him. The lines of weariness disappeared, as if God's hand had passed over it; and peace began to gather round the closed eyes.

The doctor has forgotten the toil of later years, and has gone back to his boyhood.

> "The Lord's my Shepherd, I'll not want,"

he repeated, till he came to the last verse, and then he hesitated.

> "Goodness and mercy all my life
>   Shall surely follow me."

"Follow me . . . and . . . and . . . what's next? Mither said I wes tae haed ready when she cam.

" 'A'll come afore ye gang tae sleep, Wullie, but ye 'ill no get yir kiss unless ye can feenish the psalm.'

"And . . . in God's house . . . for evermore my . . . hoo dis it rin? a' canna mind the next word . . . my, my——

"It's ower dark noo tae read it, an' mither 'ill sune be comin'."

Drumsheugh, in an agony, whispered into his ear, " 'My dwelling-place,' Weelum."

"That's it, that's it a' noo; wha said it?

> "And in God's house for evermore
>   My dwelling-place shall be."

"A'm ready noo, an' a'll get ma kiss when mither comes; a' wish she wud come, for a'm tired an' wantin' tae sleep.

"Yon's her step . . . an' she's carryin' a licht in her hand; a' see it through the door.

"Mither! a' kent ye wudna forget yir laddie, for ye promised tae come, and a've feenished ma psalm.

"And in God's house for evermore
My dwelling-place shall be."

"Gie me the kiss, mither, for a've been waitin' for ye, an' a'll sune be asleep."

The grey morning light fell on Drumsheugh, still holding his friend's cold hand, and staring at a hearth where the fire had died down into white ashes; but the peace on the doctor's face was of one who rested from his labours.

v

THE MOURNING OF THE GLEN

DR. MACLURE was buried during the great snowstorm, which is still spoken of, and will remain the standard of snowfall in Drumtochty for the century. The snow was deep on the Monday, and the men that gave notice of his funeral had hard work to reach the doctor's distant patients. On Tuesday morning it began to fall again in heavy fleecy flakes, and continued till Thursday, and then on Thursday the north wind rose and swept the snow into the hollows of the roads that went to the upland farms, and built it into a huge bank at the mouth of Glen Urtach, and laid it across our main roads in drifts of every size and the most lovely shapes, and filled up crevices in the hills to the depth of fifty feet.

On Friday morning the wind had sunk to passing gusts that powdered your coat with white, and the sun was shining on one of those winter landscapes no townsman can imagine and no countryman ever forgets. The Glen, from end to end and side to side, was clothed in a glistering mantle white as no fuller on earth could white it, that flung its skirts over the clumps of trees and scattered farm-houses, and was only divided where the Tochty ran with black, swollen stream. The great moor rose and fell in swelling billows of snow that arched themselves over the burns, running deep in the mossy ground, and hid the black peat bogs with a thin, treacherous crust. Beyond, the hills northwards and westwards stood high in white majesty, save where the black crags of Glen Urtach broke the line, and, above our lower Grampians, we caught glimpses of the distant peaks that lifted their heads in holiness unto God.

It seemed to me a fitting day for William MacLure's funeral, rather than summer time, with its flowers and golden corn. He had not been a soft man, nor had he lived an easy life, and now he was to be laid to rest amid the austere majesty of winter, yet in the shining of the sun. Jamie Soutar, with whom I toiled across the Glen, did not think with me, but was gravely concerned.

"Nae doot it's a graund sicht; the like o't is no gien tae us twice in a generation, an' nae king wes ever carried tae his tomb in sic a cathedral.

"But it's the fouk a'm conseederin', an' hoo they 'ill win through; it's hard eneuch for them 'at's on the road, an' it's clean impossible for the lave.

"They 'ill dae their best, every man o' them, ye may depend on that, an' hed it been open weather there wudna hev been six able-bodied men missin'.

"A' wes mad at them, because they never said onything when he wes leevin', but they felt for a' that what he hed dune, an', a' think, he kent it afore he deed.

"He hed juist ae faut, tae ma thinkin', for a' never jidged the waur o' him for his titch of rochness—guid trees hae gnarled bark—but he thocht ower little o' himsel.

"Noo, gin a' hed asked him hoo mony fouk wud come tae his beerial, he wud hae said, 'They 'ill be Drumsheugh an' yersel', an' maybe twa or three neeburs besides the minister,' an' the fact is that nae man in oor time wud hae sic a githerin' if it werena for the storm.

"Ye see," said Jamie, who had been counting heads all morning, "there's six shepherds in Glen Urtach—they're shut up fast; an' there micht hae been a gude half dizen frae Dunleith wy, an' a'm telt there's nae road; an' there's the heich Glen, nae man cud cross the muir the day, an' it's aucht mile roond;" and Jamie proceeded to review the Glen in every detail of age, driftiness of road and strength of body, till we arrived at the doctor's cottage, when he had settled on a reduction of fifty through stress of weather.

Drumsheugh was acknowledged as chief mourner by the Glen, and received us at the gate with a laboured attempt at everyday manners.

"Ye've hed heavy traivellin', a' doot, an' ye 'ill be cauld. It's hard weather for the sheep, an' a'm thinkin' this 'ill be a feeding storm.

"There wes nae use trying tae dig oot the front door yestreen, for it wud hae been drifted up again before morning. We've cleared awa the snow at the back for the prayer; ye 'ill get in at the kitchen door.

"There's a puckle Dunleith men——"

"Wha?" cried Jamie in an instant.

"Dunleith men," said Drumsheugh.

"Div ye mean they're here, whar are they?"

"Drying themsels at the fire, an' no withoot need; ane of them gied ower the head in a drift, and his neeburs hed tae pu' him oot.

"It took them a gude fower oors tae get across, an' it wes coorse wark; they likit him weel doon that wy, an', Jamie man"—here Drumsheugh's voice changed its note, and his public manner disappeared—"what div ye think o' this? every man o' them hes on his blacks."

"It's mair than cud be expeckit," said Jamie; "but whar dae yon men come frae, Drumsheugh?"

Two men in plaids were descending the hill behind the doctor's cottage, taking three feet at a stride, and carrying long staffs in their hands.

"They're Glen Urtach men, Jamie, for ane o' them wes at Kildrummie fair wi' sheep, but hoo they've wun doon passes me."

"It canna be, Drumsheugh," said Jamie, greatly excited. "Glen Urtach's steikit up wi' sna like a locked door.

"Ye're no surely frae the Glen, lads?" as the men leaped the dyke and crossed to the back door, the snow falling from their plaids as they walked.

"We're that an' nae mistak, but a' thocht we wud be lickit ae place, eh, Chairlie? a'm no sae weel acquant wi' the hill on this side, an' there wes some kittle (hazardous) drifts."

"It wes grand o' ye tae mak the attempt," said Drumsheugh, "an' a'm gled ye're safe."

"He cam through as bad himsel tae help ma wife," was Charlie's reply.

"They're three mair Urtach shepherds 'ill come in by sune; they're frae Upper Urtach, an' we saw them fording the river; ma certes, it took them a' their time, for it wes up tae their waists and rinnin' like a mill lade, but they jined hands and cam ower fine." And the Urtach men went in to the fire.

The Glen began to arrive in twos and threes, and Jamie, from a point of vantage at the gate, and under an appearance of utter indifference, checked his roll till even he was satisfied.

"Weelum MacLure 'ill hae the beerial he deserves in spite o' sna and drifts; it passes a' tae see hoo they've githered frae far an' near.

"A'm thinkin' ye can colleck them for the minister noo, Drumsheugh. A'body's here except the heich Glen, an' we mauna luke for them."

"Dinna be sae sure o' that, Jamie. Yon's terrible like them on the road, wi' Whinnie at their head;" and so it was, twelve in all, only old Adam Ross absent, detained by force, being eighty-two years of age.

"It wud hae been temptin' Providence tae cross the muir," Whinnie explained, "and it's a fell stap roond; a' doot we're laist."

"See, Jamie," said Drumsheugh, as he went to the house, "gin there be ony antern body in sicht afore we begin; we maun mak allooances the day wi' twa feet o' sna on the grund, tae say naethin' o' drifts."

"There's something at the turnin', an' it's no fouk; it's a machine o' some kind or ither—maybe a bread cart that's focht its wy up."

"Na, it's no that; there's twa horses, ane afore the ither; if it's no a dogcairt wi' twa men in the front; they 'ill be comin' tae the beerial."

"What wud ye sae, Jamie," Hillocks suggested, "but it micht be some o' thae Muirtown doctors? they were awfu' chief wi' MacLure."

"It's nae Muirtown doctors," cried Jamie, in great exultation, "nor ony ither doctors. A' ken thae horses, and wha's ahint them. Quick, man Hillocks, stop the fouk, and tell Drumsheugh tae come oot, for Lord Kilspindie hes come up frae Muirtown Castle."

Jamie himself slipped behind, and did not wish to be seen.

"It's the respeck he's gettin' the day frae high an' low," was Jamie's husky apology; "tae think o' them fechtin' their wy doon frae Glen Urtach, and toiling roond frae the heich Glen, an' his lordship driving through the drifts a' the road frae Muirtown, juist tae honour Weelum MacLure's beerial.

"It's nae ceremony the day, ye may lippen tae it; it's the hert brocht the fouk, an' ye can see it in their faces; ilka man hes his ain reason, an' he's thinkin' on't, though he's speakin' o' naethin' but the storm; he's mindin' the day Weelum pued him oot frae the jaws o' death, or the nicht he savit the gude wife in her oor o' tribble.

"That's why they pit on their blacks this mornin' afore it wes licht, and wrastled through the sna drifts at risk o' life. Drumtochty fouk canna say muckle, it's an awfu' peety, and they 'ill dae their best tae show naethin', but a' can read it a' in their een.

"But wae's me"—and Jamie broke down utterly behind a fir tree, so tender a thing is a cynic's heart—"that fouk 'ill tak a man's best wark a' his days withoot a word an' no dae him honour till he dees. Oh, if they hed only githered like this juist aince when he wes livin', an' lat him see he hedna laboured in vain. His reward hes come ower late, ower late."

During Jamie's vain regret, the Castle trap, bearing the marks of a wild passage in the snow-covered wheels, a broken shaft tied with rope, a twisted lamp, and the panting horses, pulled up between two rows of farmers, and Drumsheugh received his lordship with evident emotion.

"Ma lord . . . we never thocht o' this . . . an' sic a road."

"How are you, Drumsheugh? and how are you all this wintry day?

That's how I'm half an hour late; it took us four hours' stiff work for sixteen miles, mostly in the drifts, of course."

"It wes gude o' yir lordship, tae mak sic an effort, an' the hale Glen wull be gratefu' tae ye, for ony kindness tae him is kindness tae us."

"You make too much of it, Drumsheugh," and the clear, firm voice was heard of all; "it would have taken more than a few snow drifts to keep me from showing my respect to William MacLure's memory."

When all had gathered in a half circle before the kitchen door, Lord Kilspindie came out—every man noticed he had left his overcoat, and was in black, like the Glen—and took a place in the middle with Drumsheugh and Burnbrae, his two chief tenants, on the right and left, and as the minister appeared every man bared his head.

The doctor looked on the company—a hundred men such as for strength and gravity you could hardly have matched in Scotland—standing out in picturesque relief against the white background, and he said:

"It's a bitter day, friends, and some of you are old; perhaps it might be wise to cover your heads before I begin to pray."

Lord Kilspindie, standing erect and grey-headed between the two oldest men, replied:

"We thank you, Dr. Davidson, for your thoughtfulness; but he endured many a storm in our service, and we are not afraid of a few minutes' cold at his funeral."

A look flashed round the stern faces, and was reflected from the minister, who seemed to stand higher.

His prayer, we noticed with critical appreciation, was composed for the occasion, and the first part was a thanksgiving to God for the life-work of our doctor, wherein each clause was a reference to his services and sacrifices. No one moved or said Amen—it had been strange with us—but when every man had heard the gratitude of his dumb heart offered to Heaven, there was a great sigh.

After which the minister prayed that we might have grace to live as this man had done from youth to old age, not for himself, but for others, and that we might be followed to our grave by somewhat of "that love wherewith we mourn this day Thy servant departed." Again the same sigh, and the minister said Amen.

The "wricht" stood in the doorway without speaking, and four stalwart men came forward. They were the volunteers that would lift the coffin and carry it for the first stage. One was Tammas, Annie Mitchell's man; and another was Saunders Baxter, for whose life Mac-Lure had his great fight with death; and the third was the Glen Urtach shepherd for whose wife's sake MacLure suffered a broken leg and three fractured ribs in a drift; and the fourth, a Dunleith man, had his own reasons of remembrance.

"He's far lichter than ye wud expeck for sae big a man—there wesna muckle left o' him, ye see—but the road is heavy, and a'll change ye aifter the first half mile."

"Ye needna tribble yersel, wricht," said the man from Glen Urtach; "the'll be nae change in the cairryin' the day," and Tammas was thankful someone had saved him speaking.

Surely no funeral is like unto that of a doctor for pathos, and a peculiar sadness fell on that company as his body was carried out who for nearly half a century had been their help in sickness, and had beaten back death time after time from their door. Death after all was victor, for the man that saved them had not been able to save himself.

As the coffin passed the stable door a horse neighed within, and every man looked at his neighbour. It was his old mare crying to her master.

Jamie slipped into the stable, and went up into the stall.

"Puir lass, ye're no gaein' wi' him the day, an' ye 'ill never see him again; ye've hed yir last ride thegither, an' ye were true tae the end."

After the funeral Drumsheugh came himself for Jess, and took her to his farm. Saunders made a bed for her with soft, dry straw, and prepared for her supper such things as horses love. Jess would neither take food nor rest, but moved uneasily in her stall, and seemed to be waiting for someone that never came. No man knows what a horse or a dog understands and feels, for God hath not given them our speech. If any footstep was heard in the courtyard, she began to neigh, and was always looking round as the door opened. But nothing would tempt her to eat, and in the night-time Drumsheugh heard her crying as if she expected to be taken out for some sudden journey. The Kildrummie veterinary came to see her, and said that nothing could be done when it happened after this fashion with an old horse.

"A've seen it aince afore," he said. "Gin she were a Christian instead o' a horse, ye micht say she wes dying o' a broken hert."

He recommended that she should be shot to end her misery, but no man could be found in the Glen to do the deed, and Jess relieved them of the trouble. When Drumsheugh went to the stable on Monday morning, a week after Dr. MacLure fell on sleep, Jess was resting at last, but her eyes were open and her face turned to the door.

"She wes a' the wife he hed," said Jamie, as he rejoined the procession, "an' they luved ane anither weel."

The black thread wound itself along the whiteness of the Glen, the coffin first, with his lordship and Drumsheugh behind, and the others as they pleased, but in closer ranks than usual, because the snow on either side was deep, and because this was not as other funerals. They could see the women standing at the door of every house on the hillside, and weeping, for each family had some good reason in forty years to remember MacLure. When Bell Baxter saw Saunders alive, and the coffin of the doctor that saved him on her man's shoulder, she bowed her head on the dyke, and the bairns in the village made such a wail for him they loved that the men nearly disgraced themselves.

"A'm gled we're through that, at ony rate," said Hillocks; "he wes awfu' taen up wi' the bairns, conseederin' he hed nane o' his ain."

There was only one drift on the road between his cottage and the kirkyard, and it had been cut early that morning.

Before daybreak Saunders had roused the lads in the bothy, and they had set to work by the light of lanterns with such good will that, when Drumsheugh came down to engineer a circuit for the funeral, there was a fair passage, with walls of snow twelve feet high on either side.

"Man, Saunders," he said, "this wes a kind thocht, and rael weel dune."

But Saunders' only reply was this:

"Mony a time he's hed tae gang roond; he micht as weel hae an open road for his last traivel."

When the coffin was laid down at the mouth of the grave, the only blackness in the white kirkyard, Tammas Mitchell did the most beautiful thing in all his life. He knelt down and carefully wiped off the snow the wind had blown upon the coffin, and which had covered the name, and when he had done this he disappeared behind the others, so that Drumsheugh could hardly find him to take a cord. For these were the eight that buried Dr. MacLure—Lord Kilspindie at the head as landlord and Drumsheugh at the feet as his friend; the two ministers of the parish came first on the right and left; then Burnbrae and Hillocks of the farmers, and Saunders and Tammas for the ploughmen. So the Glen he loved laid him to rest.

When the bedrel had finished his work and the turf had been spread, Lord Kilspindie spoke:

"Friends of Drumtochty, it would not be right that we should part in silence and no man say what is in every heart. We have buried the remains of one that served this Glen with a devotion that has known no reserve, and a kindliness that never failed, for more than forty years. I have seen many brave men in my day, but no man in the trenches of Sebastopol carried himself more knightly than William MacLure. You will never have heard from his lips what I may tell you today, that my father secured for him a valuable post in his younger days, and he preferred to work among his own people; and I wished to do many things for him when he was old, but he would have nothing for himself. He will never be forgotten while one of us lives, and I pray that all doctors everywhere may share his spirit. If it be your pleasure, I shall erect a cross above his grave, and shall ask my old friend and companion Dr. Davidson, your minister, to choose the text to be inscribed."

"We thank you, Lord Kilspindie," said the doctor, "for your presence with us in our sorrow and your tribute to the memory of William MacLure, and I choose this for his text:

"'Greater love hath no man than this, that a man lay down his life for his friends.'"

Milton was, at that time, held in the bonds of a very bitter theology, and his indignation was stirred by this unqualified eulogium.

"No doubt Dr. MacLure hed mony natural virtues, an' he did his wark weel, but it wes a peety he didna mak mair profession o' releegion."

"When William MacLure appears before the Judge, Milton," said Lachlan Campbell, who that day spoke his last words in public, and they were in defence of charity, "He will not be asking him about his professions, for the doctor's judgment hass been ready long ago; and it iss a good judgment, and you and I will be happy men if we get the like of it.

"It iss written in the Gospel, but it iss William MacLure that will not be expecting it."

"What is't, Lachlan?" asked Jamie Soutar, eagerly.

The old man, now very feeble, stood in the middle of the road, and his face, once so hard, was softened into a winsome tenderness.

"'Come, ye blessed of My Father . . . I was sick, and ye visited Me.'"

AN AFTERWORD ON "A DOCTOR OF THE OLD SCHOOL"

THIS chronicle of Dr. MacLure is the work of a Liverpool minister who died in Iowa in 1907. If, in some crisis of flood or fire, I knew I could keep, in my flight to safety, but one out of all the sacred writings in this book, there would be no moment of hesitation. I should choose *A Doctor of the Old School*.

I have been reading it off and on for forty years. I cannot remember when I read it first. If you, too, grew up in a household of readers, you may recall that even while you were still personally addicted to G. A. Henty or Louisa M. Alcott, as the sex may be, you did sometimes out of curiosity explore a book addressed to grown-ups, if only the Olympians around you talked about it enough. Thus in the nineties, even when I was finding intolerable the week-long interval between issues of *Harper's Young People,* and later, in Germantown, Pa., when I used to sally forth of a Saturday morning to the Wister Library with five grimy library cards (even the Woollcott hired-girl was compelled to join) and a small express-wagon to help me fetch home enough of J. C. Trowbridge and Kirk Munroe to last me over the weekend, I was also aware of certain new books about which my elders were making a great pother. Four bestsellers of the nineties still stand like misted mountains in a receding landscape—*Trilby* (which was such a national obsession as no book has been since), *Richard*

Carvel (in which I first came face to face with my hero, Charles James Fox), *David Harum* (which the late Walter Hines Page of Garden City and the Court of St. James's had, when he was a reader of manuscripts for the *Atlantic Monthly,* rejected as "too vulgar"), and *Beside the Bonnie Brier Bush.* This last was a collection of sketches wherein, under the pen-name of Ian Maclaren, the Rev. John Watson, the Liverpool clergyman aforesaid, set down his fond memories of the Perthshire parish where as a young man he had been just such a little meenister as was later to encounter Babbie in the enchanted moonlight of Caddam Wood.

The great final chapter—one of the most deeply moving of all passages in English letters—was no part of *Beside the Bonnie Brier Bush* when it was first published in England and first pirated in the United States. Like the earlier Kipling stories, this book came into being in a transition period when the recent reciprocal agreements tending to protect international copyright were still shaky, because they had not yet been perfected and buttressed by judicial decisions. I believe that Mr. Watson was asked to add a little something to the book as originally printed in England. Then his accredited American publisher would have a text distinguishable at a glance from the unauthorized one which fly-by-night hucksters were already selling on every street corner. The result was "The Mourning of the Glen."

Most authors are difficult if not impossible. Many of them can no more rewrite a paragraph than you can pour back into the saucepan the nutful fudge which has cooled and hardened on your windswept window-ledge. Whenever a publisher hints to one of these that a change in this or that sentence might improve a newly poured script, the outraged scribe at once behaves as if someone had suggested brightening up the Twenty-Third Psalm. After the kind of scene which then ensues, the battle-scarred publisher finds the cockles of his foolish heart mysteriously warmed by his recollection that Ian Maclaren's undying fame rests most securely on an after-thought instigated by the man who, after all, was going to take his book out and, if possible, sell it.

Long ago the legend of Dr. MacLure escaped from the book of which it was once a part and has had in our time a separate life. Indeed, it is obtainable in the bookshops as a separate volume. I could name you a member of the faculty in one of our great medical schools who each year makes it required reading for his classes. I could name you an actor (Walter Huston, if you must know) who dreams of making a movie out of it with himself as the Doctor and Vermont in 1870 as the background—Vermont, where he would find not only the floods and the snowstorms but just such unpacked hearts as beat in the Glen where Jess and the Doctor used to make their rounds. For that matter, I could name you a radio performer who, each year that he broadcasts, considers it a part of his job on this earth, if he has one at all, to tell again the story of Weelum MacLure.

A. W.

MY
LITTLE BOY

by

CARL EWALD

TRANSLATED FROM THE DANISH
BY
ALEXANDER TEIXEIRA DE MATTOS

MY LITTLE BOY

I

My little boy is beginning to live.

Carefully, stumbling now and then on his little knock-kneed legs, he makes his way over the paving-stones, looks at everything that there is to look at and bites at every apple, both those which are his due and those which are forbidden him.

He is not a pretty child and is the more likely to grow into a fine lad. But he is charming.

His face can light up suddenly and become radiant; he can look at you with quite cold eyes. He has a strong intuition and he is incorruptible. He has never yet bartered a kiss for barley-sugar. There are people whom he likes and people whom he dislikes. There is one who has long courted his favour indefatigably and in vain; and, the other day, he formed a close friendship with another who had not so much as said "Good day" to him before he had crept into her lap and nestled there with glowing resolution.

He has a habit which I love.

When we are walking together and there is anything that impresses him, he lets go my hand for a moment. Then, when he has investigated the phenomenon and arrived at a result, I feel his little fist in mine again.

He has bad habits too.

He is apt, for instance, suddenly and without the slightest reason, to go up to people whom he meets in the street and hit them with his little stick. What is in his mind, when he does so, I do not know; and, so long as he does not hit me, it remains a matter between himself and the people concerned.

He has an odd trick of seizing big words in a grown-up conversation, storing them up for a while and then asking me for an explanation:

"Father," he says, "what is life?"

I give him a tap in his little stomach, roll him over on the carpet and conceal my emotion under a mighty romp. Then, when we sit breathless and tired, I answer, gravely:

"Life is delightful, my little boy. Don't you be afraid of it!"

I I

TODAY my little boy gave me my first lesson.

It was in the garden.

I was writing in the shade of the big chestnut-tree, close to where the brook flows past. He was sitting a little way off, on the grass, in the sun, with Hans Christian Andersen in his lap.

Of course, he does not know how to read, but he lets you read to him, likes to hear the same tales over and over again. The better he knows them, the better he is pleased. He follows the story page by page, knows exactly where everything comes and catches you up immediately should you skip a line.

There are two tales which he loves more than anything in the world. These are Grimm's *Faithful John* and Andersen's *The Little Mermaid*. When anyone comes whom he likes, he fetches the big Grimm, with those heaps of pictures, and asks for *Faithful John*. Then, if the reader stops, because it is so terribly sad, with all those little dead children, a bright smile lights up his small, long face and he says, reassuringly and pleased at "knowing better":

"Yes, but they come to life again."

Today, however, it is *The Little Mermaid*.

"Is that the sort of stories you write?" he asks.

"Yes," I say, "but I am afraid mine will not be so pretty."

"You must take pains," he says.

And I promise.

For a time he makes no sound. I go on writing and forget about him.

"Is there a little mermaid down there, in the water?" he asks.

"Yes, she swims up to the top in the summer."

He nods and looks out across the brook, which ripples so softly and smoothly that one can hardly see the water flow. On the opposite side, the rushes grow green and thick and there is also a bird, hidden in the rushes, which sings. The dragon-flies are whirling and humming. I am sitting with my head in my hand, absorbed in my work.

Suddenly, I hear a splash.

I jump from my chair, upset the table, dart forward and see that my little boy is gone. The brook is billowing and foaming; there are wide circles on the surface.

In a moment, I am in the water and find him and catch hold of him.

He stands on the grass, dripping with wet, spluttering and coughing. His thin clothes are clinging to his thin body, his face is black with mud. But out of the mud gleams a pair of angry eyes:

"There was no mermaid," he says.

I do not at once know what to reply and I have no time to think.

"Do you write that sort of stories?" he asks.

"Yes," I say, shamefaced.

"I don't like any of you," he says. "You make fun of a little boy."

He turns his back on me and, proud and wet, goes indoors without once looking round.

This evening, Grimm and Hans Christian Andersen disappear in a mysterious manner, which is never explained. He will miss them greatly, at first; but he will never be fooled again, not if I were to give him the sun and moon in his hand.

III

My little boy and I have had an exceedingly interesting walk in the Frederiksberg Park.

There was a mouse, which was irresistible. There were two chaffinches, husband and wife, which built their nest right before our eyes, and a snail, which had no secrets for us. And there were flowers, yellow and white, and there were green leaves, which told us the oddest adventures: in fact, as much as we can find room for in our little head.

Now we are sitting on a bench and digesting our impressions.

Suddenly the air is shaken by a tremendous roar:

"What was that?" asks my little boy.

"That was the lion in the Zoological Gardens," I reply.

No sooner have I said this than I curse my own stupidity.

I might have said that it was a gunshot announcing the birth of a prince; or an earthquake; or a china dish falling from the sky and breaking into pieces: anything whatever, rather than the truth.

For now my little boy wants to know what sort of thing the Zoological Gardens is.

I tell him.

The Zoological Gardens is a horrid place, where they lock up wild beasts who have done no wrong and who are accustomed to walk about freely in the distant foreign countries where they come from. The lion is there, whom we have just heard roaring. He is so strong that he can kill a policeman with one blow of his paw; he has great, haughty eyes and awfully sharp teeth. He lives in Africa and, at night, when he roars, all the other beasts tremble in their holes for fear. He is called the king of beasts. They caught him one day in a cunning trap and bound him and dragged him here and locked him up in a cage with iron bars to it. The cage is no more than half as big as Petrine's room. And there the king walks up and down, up and down, and gnashes his teeth with sorrow and rage and roars so that you can hear him ever so far away. Outside his cage stand cowardly people and laugh at him, because he can't get out and eat them up, and poke their sticks through the rails and tease him.

My little boy stands in front of me and looks at me with wide-open eyes:

"Would he eat them up, if he got out?" he asks.

"In a moment."

"But he can't get out, can he?"

"No. That's awfully sad. He can't get out."

"Father, let us go and look at the lion."

I pretend not to hear and go on to tell him of the strange birds there: great eagles, which used to fly over every church-steeple and over the highest trees and mountains and swoop down upon lambs and hares and carry them up to their young in the nest. Now they are sitting in cages, on a perch, like canaries, with clipped wings and blind eyes. I tell him of gulls, which used to fly all day long over the stormy sea: now they splash about in a puddle of water, screaming pitifully. I tell him of wonderful blue and red birds, which, in their youth, used to live among wonderful blue and red flowers, in balmy forests a thousand times bigger than the Frederiksberg Park, where it was as dark as night under the trees with the brightest sun shining down upon the tree-tops: now they sit there in very small cages and hang their beaks while they stare at tiresome boys in dark-blue suits and black stockings and waterproof boots and sailor-hats.

"Are those birds really blue?" asks my little boy.

"Sky-blue," I answer. "And utterly broken-hearted."

"Father, can't we go and look at the birds?"

I take my little boy's hands in mine:

"I don't think we will," I say. "Why should still more silly boys do so? You can't imagine how it goes to one's heart to look at those poor captive beasts."

"Father, I should so much like to go."

"Take my advice and don't. The animals there are not the real animals, you see. They are ill and ugly and angry because of their captivity and their longing and their pain."

"I should so much like to see them."

"Now let me tell you something. To go to the Zoological Gardens costs five cents for you and ten cents for me. That makes fifteen cents altogether, which is an awful lot of money. We won't go there now, but we'll buy the biggest money-box we can find: one of those money-boxes shaped like a pig. Then we'll put fifteen cents in it. And every Thursday we'll put fifteen cents in the pig. By-and-by, that will grow into quite a fortune: it will make such a lot of money that, when you are grown up, you can take a trip to Africa and go to the desert and hear the wild, the real lion roaring and tremble just like the people tremble down there. And you can go to the great, dark forests and see the real blue birds flying proud and free among the flowers. You can't think how glad you will be, how beautiful they will look and how they will sing to you. . . ."

"Father, I would rather go to the Zoological Gardens now."

My little boy does not understand a word of what I say. And I am at my wits' end.

"Shall we go and have some cakes at Josty's?" I ask.

"I would rather go to the Zoological Gardens."

I can read in his eyes that he is thinking of the captive lion. Ugly human instincts are waking up in his soul. The mouse is forgotten and the snail; and the chaffinches have built their nest to no purpose.

At last I get up and say, bluntly, without any further explanation:

"You are *not* going to the Zoological Gardens. Now we'll go home."

And home we go. But we are not in a good temper.

Of course, I get over it and I buy an enormous money-box pig. Also we put the money into it and he thinks that most interesting.

But, later in the afternoon, I find him in the bed-room engaged in a piteous game.

He has built a cage, in which he has imprisoned the pig. He is teasing it and hitting it with his whip, while he keeps shouting to it:

"You can't get out and bite me, you stupid pig! You can't get out!"

I V

We have beer-soup and Aunt Anna to dinner. Now beer-soup is a nasty dish and Aunt Anna is not very nice either.

She has yellow teeth and a little hump and very severe eyes, which are not even both equally severe. She is nearly always scolding us and, when she sees a chance, she pinches us.

The worst of all, however, is that she is constantly setting us a good example, which can easily end by gradually and inevitably driving us to embrace wickedness.

Aunt Anna does not like beer-soup any more than we do. But of course she eats it with a voluptuous expression on her face and looks angrily at my little boy, who does not even make an attempt to behave nicely:

"Why doesn't the little boy eat his delicious beer-soup?" she asks.

A scornful silence.

"Such delicious beer-soup! I know a poor, wretched boy who would be awfully glad to have such delicious beer-soup."

My little boy looks with great interest at Auntie, who is swallowing her soup with eyes full of ecstatic bliss:

"Where is he?" he asks.

Aunt Anna pretends not to hear.

"Where is the poor boy?" he asks again.

"Yes, where is he?" I ask. "What's his name?"

Aunt Anna gives me a furious glance.

"What's his name, Aunt Anna?" asks my little boy. "Where does he live? He can have my beer-soup with pleasure."

"Mine too," I say, resolutely, and I push my plate from me.

My little boy never takes his great eyes off Aunt Anna's face. Meanwhile, she has recovered herself:

"There are many poor boys who would thank God if they could get such delicious beer-soup," she says. "Very many. Everywhere."

"Yes, but tell us of one, Auntie," I say.

My little boy has slipped down from his chair. He stands with his chin just above the table and both his hands round his plate, ready to march off with the beer-soup to the poor boy, if only he can get his address.

But Aunt Anna does not allow herself to be played with:

"Heaps of poor boys," she says again. "Hun-dreds! And therefore another little boy, whom I will not name, but who is in this room, ought to be ashamed that he is not thankful for his beer-soup."

My little boy stares at Aunt Anna like the bird fascinated by the snake

"Such delicious beer-soup!" she says. "I must really ask for another little helping."

Aunt Anna revels in her martyrdom. My little boy stands speechless, with open mouth and round eyes.

I push my chair back and say, with genuine exasperation:

"Now, look here, Aunt Anna, this is really too bad! Here we are, with a whole lot of beer-soup, which we don't care about in the least and which we would be very glad to get rid of, if we only knew some-one who would have it. You are the only one that knows of anybody. You know a poor boy who would dance for joy if he got some beer-soup. You know hundreds. But you won't tell us their names or where they live."

"Why, what do you mean?"

"And you yourself sit quite calmly eating two whole helpings, though you know quite well that you're going to have an omelette to follow. That's really very naughty of you, Aunt Anna."

Aunt Anna chokes with annoyance. My little boy locks his teeth with a snap and looks with every mark of disgust at that wicked old woman.

And I turn with calm earnestness to his mother and say:

"After this, it would be most improper for us ever to have beer-soup here again. We don't care for it and there are hundreds of little boys who love it. If it must be made, then Aunt Anna must come every Saturday and fetch it. She knows where the boys live."

The omelette is eaten in silence, after which Aunt Anna shakes the dust from her shoes. She won't have any coffee today.

While she is standing in the hall and putting on her endless wraps, a last doubt arises in my little boy's soul. He opens his green eyes wide before her face and whispers:

"Aunt Anna, where do the boys live?"

Aunt Anna pinches him and is shocked and goes off, having suf-fered a greater defeat than she can ever repair.

v

My little boy comes into my room and tells me, with a very long face, that Jean is dead. And we put all nonsense on one side and hurry away to the Klampenborg train, to go where Jean is.

For Jean is the biggest dog that has lived for some time.

He once bit a boy so hard that the boy still walks lame. He once bit his own master. He could give such a look out of his eyes and open such a mouth that there was no more horrible sight in the world. And then he would be the mildest of the mild: my little boy could put his hand in his mouth and ride on his back and pull his tail.

When we get there, we hear that Jean is already buried.

We look at each other in dismay, to think how quickly that happens! And we go to the grave, which is in the grounds of the factory, where the tall chimneys stand.

We sit down and can't understand it.

We tell each other all the stories that we know of Jean's wonderful size and strength. The one remembers this, the other that. And, as each story is told, the whole thing becomes only more awful and obscure.

At last we go home by train.

Besides ourselves, there is a kind old gentleman in the compartment, who would like to make friends with my little boy. But the boy has nothing to talk about to the kind old gentleman. He stands at the window, which comes just under his chin, and stares out.

His eyes light upon some tall chimneys:

"That's where Jean is buried," he says.

"Yes."

The landscape flies past. He can think only of *that* and see only *that* and, when some more chimneys appear, he says again:

"That's where Jean is buried."

"No, my little friend," says the kind old gentleman. "That was over there."

The boy looks at him with surprise. I hasten to reassure him:

"Those *are* Jean's chimneys," I say.

And, while he is looking out again, I take the old gentleman to the further corner of the compartment and tell him the state of the case.

I tell him that, if I live, I hope, in years to come, to explain to the boy the difference between Petersen's and Hansen's factories and, should I die, I will confidently leave that part of his education to others. Yes, even if he should never learn this difference, I would still be resigned. Today it is a question of other and more important matters. The strongest, the most living thing he knew is dead. . . .

"Really?" says the old gentleman, sympathetically. "A relation, perhaps?"

"Yes," I say. "Jean is dead, a dog. . . ."

"A dog?"

"It is not because of the *dog*—don't you understand?—but of *death,* which he sees for the first time: death, with all its might, its mystery. . . ."

"Father," says my little boy and turns his head towards us. "When do we die?"

"When we grow old," says the kind old gentleman.

"No," says the boy. "Einar has a brother, at home, in the courtyard, and he is dead. And he was only a little boy."

"Then Einar's brother was so good and learnt such a lot that he was already fit to go to Heaven," says the old gentleman.

"Mind you don't become too good," I say and laugh and tap my little boy in the stomach.

And my little boy laughs too and goes back to his window, where new chimneys rise over Jean's grave.

But I take the old gentleman by the shoulders and forbid him most strictly to talk to my little boy again. I give up trying to make him understand me. I just shake him. He eyes the communication-cord and, when we reach the station, hurries away.

I go with my little boy, holding his hand, through the streets full of live people. In the evening, I sit on the edge of his bed and talk with him about that incomprehensible thing: Jean, who is dead; Jean, who was so much alive, so strong, so big. . . .

VI

OUR courtyard is full of children and my little boy has picked a bosom-friend out of the band: his name is Einar and he can be as good as another.

My little boy admires him and Einar allows himself to be admired, so that the friendship is established on the only proper basis.

"Einar says . . . Einar thinks . . . Einar does," is the daily refrain; and we arrange our little life accordingly.

"I can't see anything out of the way in Einar," says the mother of my little boy.

"Nor can I," say I. "But our little boy can and that is enough. I once had a friend who could see nothing at all charming in you. And you yourself, if I remember right, had three friends who thought *your* taste inexcusable. Luckily for our little boy. . . ."

"Luckily!"

"It is the feeling that counts," I go on lecturing, "and not the object."

"Thanks!" she says.

Now something big and unusual takes place in our courtyard and makes an extraordinary impression on the children and gives their small brains heaps to struggle with for many a long day.

The scarlatina comes.

And scarlatina is not like a pain in your stomach, when you have eaten too many pears, or like a cold, when you have forgotten to put on your jacket. Scarlatina is something quite different, something powerful and terrible. It comes at night and takes a little boy who was playing quite happily that same evening. And then the little boy is gone.

Perhaps a funny carriage comes driving in through the gate, with two horses and a coachman and two men with bright brass buttons on their coats. The two men take out of the carriage a basket, with a red blanket and white sheets, and carry it up to where the boy lives. Presently, they carry the basket down again and then the boy is inside. But nobody can see him, because the sheet is over his face. The basket is shoved into the carriage, which is shut with a bang, and away goes the carriage with the boy, while his mother dries her eyes and goes up to the others.

Perhaps no carriage comes. But then the sick boy is shut up in his room and no one may go to him for a long time, because he is infectious. And anyone can understand that this must be terribly sad.

The children in the courtyard talk of nothing else.

They talk with soft voices and faces full of mystery, because they know nothing for certain. They hear that one of them, who rode away in the carriage, is dead; but that makes no more impression on them than when one of them falls ill and disappears.

Day by day, the little band is being thinned out and not one of them has yet come back.

I stand at my open window and look at my little boy, who is sitting on the steps below with his friend. They have their arms around each other's necks and see no one except each other; that is to say, Einar sees himself and my little boy sees Einar.

"If you fall ill, I will come and see you," says my little boy.

"No, you won't!"

"I will come and see you."

His eyes beam at this important promise. Einar cries as though he were already ill.

And the next day he is ill.

He lies in a little room all by himself. No one is allowed to go to him. A red curtain hangs before the window.

My little boy sits alone on the steps outside and stares up at the curtain. His hands are thrust deep into his pockets. He does not care to play and he speaks to nobody.

And I walk up and down the room, uneasy as to what will come next.

"You are anxious about our little boy," says his mother. "And it will be a miracle if he escapes."

"It's not that. We've all had a touch of scarlatina."

But just as I want to talk to her about it, I hear a fumbling with the door-handle which there is no mistaking and then he stands before us in the room.

I know you so well, my little boy, when you come in sideways like that, with a long face, and go and sit in a corner and look at the two people who owe so much happiness to you—look from one to the other. Your eyes are greener than usual. You can't find your words and you sit huddled up and you are ever so good.

"Mother, is Einar ill?"

"Yes. But he will soon be better again. The doctor says that he is not so bad."

"Is he infectious, Mother?"

"Yes, he is. His little sister has been sent to the country, so that she may not fall ill too. No one is allowed to go to him except his mother, who gives him his milk and his medicine and makes his bed."

A silence.

The mother of my little boy looks down at her book and suspects nothing. The father of my little boy looks in great suspense from the window.

"Mother, I want to go to Einar."

"You can't go there, my little man. You hear, he's infectious. Just think, if you should fall ill yourself! Einar isn't bothering at all about chatting with you. He sleeps the whole day long."

"But when he wakes, Mother?"

"You can't go up there."

This tells upon him and he is nearly crying. I see that the time has come for me to come to his rescue:

"Have you promised Einar to go and see him?" I ask.

"Yes, Father. . . ."

He is over his trouble. His eyes beam. He stands erect and glad beside me and puts his little hand in mine.

"Then of course you must do so," I say, calmly. "So soon as he wakes."

Our mother closes her book with a bang:

"Go down to the courtyard and play, while Father and I have a talk."

The boy runs away.

And she comes up to me and lays her hand on my shoulder and says, earnestly:

"I *daren't* do that, do you hear?"

And I take her hand and kiss it and say, quite as earnestly:

"And I *daren't refuse!*"

We look at each other, we two, who share the empire, the power and the glory.

"I heard our little boy make his promise," I say, "I saw him. Sir Galahad himself was not more in earnest when swearing his knightly oath. You see, we have no choice here. He can catch the scarlatina in any case and it is not even certain that he will catch it. . . ."

"If it was diphtheria, you wouldn't talk like that!"

"You may be right. But am I to become a thief for the sake of a nickel, because I am not sure that I could resist the temptation to steal a kingdom?"

"You would not find a living being to agree with you."

"Except yourself. And that is all I want. The infection is really only a side matter. It can come this way or that way. We can't safeguard him, come what may. . . ."

"But are we to send him straight to where it is?"

"We're not doing that; it's not we who are doing that."

She is very much excited. I put my arm round her waist and we walk up and down the room together:

"Darling, today our little boy may meet with a great misfortune. He may receive a shock from which he will never recover. . . ."

"That is true," she says.

"If he doesn't keep his promise, the misfortune has occurred. It would already be a misfortune if he could ever think that it was possible for him to break it, if it appeared to him that there was anything great or remarkable about keeping it."

"Yes, but . . ."

"Darling, the world is full of careful persons. One step more and they become mere paltry people. Shall we turn that into a likely thing, into a virtue, for our little boy? His promise was stupid: let that pass. . . ."

"He is so little."

"Yes, that he is; and God be praised for it! Think what good luck it is that he did not know the danger, when he made his promise, that he does not understand it now, when he is keeping it. What a lucky beggar! He is learning to keep his word, just as he has learnt to be clean. By the time that he is big enough to know his danger, it will be an indispensable habit with him. And he gains all that at the risk of a little scarlatina."

She lays her head on my shoulder and says nothing more.

That afternoon, she takes our little boy by the hand and goes up with him to Einar. They stand on the threshold of his room, bid him good-day and ask him how he is.

Einar is not at all well and does not look up and does not answer.

But that does not matter in the least.

VII

My little boy is given a cent by Petrine with instructions to go to the baker's and buy some biscuits.

By that which fools call an accident, but which is really a divine miracle, if miracles there be, I overhear this instruction. Then I stand at my window and see him cross the street in his slow way and with bent head; only, he goes slower than usual and with his head bent more deeply between his small shoulders.

He stands long outside the baker's window, where there is a confused heap of lollipops and chocolates and sugar-sticks and other things created for a small boy's delight. Then he lifts his young hand, opens the door, disappears and presently returns with a great paper bag, eating with all his might.

And I, who, Heaven be praised, have myself been a thief in my time, run all over the house and give my orders.

My little boy enters the kitchen.

"Put the biscuits on the table," says Petrine.

He stands still for a moment and looks at her and at the table and at the floor. Then he goes silently to his mother.

"You're quite a big boy now, that you can buy biscuits for Petrine," says she, without looking up from her work.

His face is very long, but he says nothing. He comes quietly in to me and sits down on the edge of a chair.

"You have been over the way, at the baker's."

He comes up to me, where I am sitting and reading, and presses himself against me. I do not look at him, but I can perceive what is going on inside him.

"What did you buy at the baker's?"

"Lollipops."

"Well, I never! What fun! Why, you had some lollipops this morning. Who gave you the money this time?"

"Petrine."

"Really! Well, Petrine is certainly very fond of you. Do you remember the lovely ball she gave you on your birthday?"

"Father, Petrine told me to buy a cent's worth of biscuits."

"Oh, dear!"

It is very quiet in the room. My little boy cries bitterly and I look anxiously before me, stroking his hair the while.

"Now you have fooled Petrine badly. She wants those biscuits, of course, for her cooking. She thinks they're on the kitchen-table and, when she goes to look, she won't find any. Mother gave her a cent for biscuits. Petrine gave you a cent for biscuits and you go and spend it on lollipops. What are we to do?"

He looks at me in despair, holds me tight, says a thousand things without speaking a word.

"If only we had a cent," I say. "Then you could rush over the way and fetch the biscuits."

"Father. . . . " His eyes open very wide and he speaks so softly that I can hardly hear him. "There is a cent on mother's writing-table."

"Is there?" I cry with delight. But, at the same moment, I shake my head and my face is overcast again. "That is no use to us, my little boy. That cent belongs to mother. The other was Petrine's. People are so terribly fond of their money and get so angry when you take it from them. I can understand that, for you can buy such an awful lot of things with money. You can get biscuits and lollipops and clothes and toys and half the things in the world. And it is not so easy either to make money. Most people have to drudge all day long to earn as much as they want. So it is no wonder that they get angry when you take it. Especially when it is only for lollipops. Now Petrine . . . she has to spend the whole day cleaning rooms and cooking dinner and washing up before she gets her wages. And out of that she has to buy clothes and shoes . . . and you know that she has a little girl whom she has to pay for at Madam Olsen's. She must certainly have saved very cleverly before she managed to buy you that ball."

We walk up and down the room, hand in hand. He keeps on falling over his legs, for he can't take his eyes from my face.

"Father . . . haven't you got a cent?"

I shake my head and give him my purse:

"Look for yourself," I say. "There's not a cent in it. I spent the last this morning."

We walk up and down. We sit down and get up and walk about again. We are very gloomy. We are bowed down with sorrow and look at each other in great perplexity.

"There might be one hidden away in a drawer somewhere," I say.

We fly to the drawers.

We pull out thirty drawers and rummage through them. We fling papers in disorder, higgledy-piggledy, on the floor: what do we care? If only, if only we find a cent. . . .

Hurrah!

We both, at last, grasp at a cent, as though we would fight for it . . . we have found a beautiful, large cent. Our eyes gleam and we laugh through our tears.

"Hurry now," I whisper. "You can go this way . . . through my door. Then run back quickly up the kitchen stairs, with the biscuits, and put them on the table. I shall call Petrine, so that she doesn't see. And we won't tell anybody."

He is down the stairs before I have done speaking. I run after him and call to him:

"Wasn't it a splendid thing that we found that cent?" I say.

"Yes," he answers, earnestly.

And he laughs for happiness and I laugh too and his legs go like drumsticks across to the baker's.

From my window, I see him come back, at the same pace, with red cheeks and glad eyes. He has committed his first crime. He has understood it. And he has not the sting of remorse in his soul nor the black cockade of forgiveness in his cap.

The mother of my little boy and I sit until late at night talking about money, which seems to us the most difficult matter of all.

For our little boy must learn to know the power of money and the glamour of money and the joy of money. He must earn much money and spend much money. . . .

Yet there were two people, yesterday, who killed a man to rob him of four dollars and thirty-seven cents. . . .

VIII

It has been decreed in the privy council that my little boy shall have a weekly income of one cent. Every Sunday morning, that sum shall be paid to him, free of income-tax, out of the treasury and he has leave to dispose of it entirely at his own pleasure.

He receives this announcement with composure and sits apart for a while and ponders on it.

"Every Sunday?" he asks.

"Every Sunday."

"All the time till the summer holidays?"

"All the time till the summer holidays."

In the summer holidays, he is to go to the country, to stay with his godmother, in whose house he was pleased to allow himself to be

born. The summer holidays are, consequently, the limits of his calcula-
tion of time: beyond them lies, for the moment, his Nirvana.

And we employ this restricted horizon of ours to further our true
happiness.

That is to say, we calculate, with the aid of the almanac, that, if
everything goes as heretofore, there will be fifteen Sundays before the
summer holidays. We arrange a drawer with fifteen compartments and
in each compartment we put one cent. Thus we know exactly what
we have and are able at any time to survey our financial status.

And, when he sees that great lot of cents lying there, my little boy's
breast is filled with mad delight. He feels endlessly rich, safe for a
long time. The courtyard rings with his bragging, with all that he is
going to do with his money. His special favourites are invited to come
up and view his treasure.

The first Sunday passes in a normal fashion, as was to be expected.

He takes his cent and turns it straightway into a stick of chocolate
of the best sort, with almonds on it and sugar, in short, an ideal stick
in every way. The whole performance is over in five minutes: by that
time, the stick of chocolate is gone, with the sole exception of a remnant in the corners of our mouth, which our ruthless mother wipes
away, and a stain on our collar, which annoys us.

He sits by me, with a vacant little face, and swings his legs. I
open the drawer and look at the empty space and at the fourteen
others:

"So *that's* gone," I say.

My accent betrays a certain melancholy, which finds an echo in his
breast. But he does not deliver himself of it at once.

"Father . . . is it long till next Sunday?"

"Very long, my boy; ever so many days."

We sit a little, steeped in our own thoughts. Then I say, pensively:

"Now, if you had bought a top, you would perhaps have had more
pleasure out of it. I know a place where there is a lovely top: red, with
a green ring round it. It is just over the way, in the toy-shop. I saw it
yesterday. I should be greatly mistaken if the toy-man was not willing
to sell it for a cent. And you've got a whip, you know."

We go over the way and look at the top in the shop-window. It is really a splendid top.

"The shop's shut," says my little boy, despondently.

I look at him with surprise:

"Yes, but what does that matter to us? Anyway, we can't buy the top before next Sunday. You see, you've spent your cent on chocolate. Give me your handkerchief: there's still a bit on your cheek."

There is no more to be said. Crestfallen and pensively, we go home. We sit a long time at the dining-room window, from which we can see the window of the shop.

During the course of the week, we look at the top daily, for it does not do to let one's love grow cold. One might so easily forget it. And the top shines always more seductively. We go in and make sure that the price is really in keeping with our means. We make the shop-keeper take a solemn oath to keep the top for us till Sunday morning, even if boys should come and bid him much higher sums for it.

On Sunday morning, we are on the spot before nine o'clock and acquire our treasure with trembling hands. And we play with it all day and sleep with it at night, until, on Wednesday morning, it disappears without a trace, after the nasty manner which tops have.

When the turn comes of the next cent, something remarkable happens.

There is a boy in the courtyard who has a skipping-rope and my little boy, therefore, wants to have a skipping-rope too. But this is a difficult matter. Careful enquiries establish the fact that a skipping-rope of the sort used by the upper classes is nowhere to be obtained for less than five cents.

The business is discussed as early as Saturday:

"It's the simplest thing in the world," I say. "You must not spend your cent tomorrow. Next Sunday you must do the same and the next and the next. On the Sunday after that, you will have saved your five cents and can buy your skipping-rope at once."

"When shall I get my skipping-rope then?"

"In five Sundays from now."

He says nothing, but I can see that he does not think my idea very brilliant. In the course of the day, he derives, from sources unknown to me, an acquaintance with financial circumstances which he serves up to me on Sunday morning in the following words:

"Father, you must lend me five cents for the skipping-rope. If you will lend me five cents for the skipping-rope, I'll give you *forty* cents back. . . ."

He stands close to me, very red in the face and quite confused. I perceive that he is ripe for falling into the claws of the usurers:

"I don't do that sort of business, my boy," I say. "It wouldn't do you any good either. And you're not even in a position to do it, for you have only thirteen cents, as you know."

He collapses like one whose last hope is gone.

"Let us just see," I say.

And we go to our drawer and stare at it long and deeply.

"We might perhaps manage it this way, that I give you five cents now. And then I should have your cent and the next four cents. . . ."

He interrupts me with a loud shout. I take out my purse, give him five cents and take one cent out of the drawer:

"That won't be pleasant next Sunday," I say, "and the next and the next and the next. . . ."

But the thoughtless youth is gone.

Of course, the instalments of his debt are paid off with great ceremony. He is always on the spot himself when the drawer is opened and sees how the requisite cent is removed and finds its way into my pocket instead of his.

The first time, all goes well. It is simply an amusing thing that I should have the cent; and the skipping-rope is still fresh in his memory, because of the pangs which he underwent before its purchase. Next Sunday, already the thing is not *quite* so pleasant and, when the fourth instalment falls due, my little boy's face looks very gloomy:

"Is anything the matter?" I ask.

"I should so much like a stick of chocolate," he says, without looking at me.

"Is that all? You can get one in a fortnight. By that time, you will have paid for the skipping-rope and the cent will be your own again."

"I should so much like to have the stick of chocolate now."

Of course, I am full of the sincerest compassion, but I can't help it. What's gone is gone. We saw it with our own eyes and we know exactly where it has gone to. And, that Sunday morning, we part in a dejected mood.

Later in the day, however, I find him standing over the drawer with raised eyebrows and a pursed-up mouth. I sit down quietly and wait. And I do not have to wait long before I learn that his development as an economist is taking quite its normal course.

"Father, suppose we moved the cent now from here into this Sunday's place and I took it and bought the chocolate-stick. . . ."

"Why, then you won't have your cent for the other Sunday."

"I don't mind that, Father. . . ."

We talk about it, and then we do it. And, with that, as a matter of course, we enter upon the most reckless peculations.

The very next Sunday, he is clever enough to take the furthest cent, which lies just before the summer holidays. He pursues the path of vice without a scruple, until, at last, the blow falls and five long Sundays come in a row without the least chance of a cent.

Where should they come from? They were there. We know that. They are gone. We have spent them ourselves.

But, during those drab days of poverty, we sit every morning over the empty drawer and talk long and profoundly about that painful phenomenon, which is so simple and so easy to understand and which one must needs make the best of.

And we hope and trust that our experience will do us good, when, after our trip, we start a new set of cents.

·

I X

My little boy is engaged to be married.

She is a big, large-limbed young woman, three years his senior, and no doubt belongs to the minor aristocracy. Her name is Gertie. By a misunderstanding, however, which is pardonable at his age and moreover quite explained by Gertie's appearance, he calls her Dirty—little Dirty—and by this name she will be handed down to history.

He met her on the boulevard, where he was playing, in the fine spring weather, with other children. His reason for the engagement is good enough:

"I wanted a girl for myself," he says.

Either I know very little of mankind or he has made a fortunate choice. No one is likely to take Dirty from him.

Like the gentleman that he is, he at once brings the girl home to us and introduces her. In consequence of the formality of the occasion, he does not go in by the kitchen way, as usual, but rings the front-door bell. I open the door myself. There he stands on the mat, hand in hand with Dirty, his bride, and, with radiant eyes:

"Father," he says, "this is little Dirty. She is my sweetheart. We are going to be married."

"That is what people usually do with their sweethearts," I answer, philosophically. "Pray, Dirty, come in and be welcomed by the family."

"Wipe your feet, Dirty," says my little boy.

The mother of my little boy does not think much of the match. She has even spoken of forbidding Dirty the house.

"We can't do that," I say. "I am not in ecstasies over it either, but it is not at all certain that it will last."

"Yes, but . . ."

"Do you remember what little use it was when your mother forbade me the house? We used to meet in the most incredible places and kiss each other terribly. I can quite understand that you have forgotten, but you ought to bear it in mind now that your son's beginning. And you ought to value the loyalty of his behaviour towards his aged parents."

"My dear! . . ."

"And then I must remind you that it is spring. The trees are budding. You can't see it, perhaps, from the kitchen-window or from your work-table, but I, who go about all day, have noticed it. You know what Byron says:

March has its hares, and May must have its heroine."

And so Dirty is accepted.

But, when she calls, she has first to undergo a short quarantine, while the mother of my little boy washes her and combs her hair thoroughly.

Dirty does not like this, but the boy does. He looks on with extraordinary interest and at once complains if there is a place that has escaped the sponge. I can't make out what goes on within him on these occasions. There is a good deal of cruelty in love; and he himself hates to be washed. Perhaps he is rapt in fancies and wants to see his sweetheart rise daily from the waves, like Venus Anadyomene. Perhaps it is merely his sense of duty: last Friday, in cold blood, he allowed Dirty to wait outside, on the step, for half an hour, until his mother came home.

Another of his joys is to see Dirty eat.

I can quite understand that. Here, as at her toilet, there is something worth looking at. The mother of my little boy and I would be glad too to watch her, if there were any chance of giving Dirty her fill. But there is none. At least, not with my income.

When I see all that food disappear, without as much as a shade of satisfaction coming into her eyes, I tremble for the young couple's future. But he is cheerful and unconcerned.

Of course, there are also clouds in their sky.

A few days ago, they were sitting quietly together in the dining-room and talking of their wedding. My little boy described what the house would be like and the garden and the horses. Dirty made no remarks and she had no grounds for doing so, for everything was particularly nice. But, after that, things went wrong:

"We shall have fourteen children," said the boy.

"No," said Dirty. "We shall only have two: a boy and a girl."

"I want to have fourteen."

"I won't have more than two."

"Fourteen."

"Two."

There was no coming to an agreement. My little boy was speechless at Dirty's meanness. And Dirty pinched her lips together and nodded her head defiantly. Then he burst into tears.

I could have explained to him that Dirty, who sits down every day as the seventh at the children's table at home, cannot look upon children with his eyes, as things forming an essential part of every well-regulated family, but must regard them rather as bandits who eat up other people's food. But I did not feel entitled to discuss the young lady's domestic circumstances unasked.

One good thing about Dirty is that she is not dependent upon her family nor they upon her. It has not yet happened that any inquiries have been made after her, however long she remained with us. We know just where she lives and what her father's name is. Nothing more.

However, we notice in another way that our daughter-in-law is not without relations.

Whenever, for instance, we give her a pair of stockings or some other article of clothing, it is always gone the next day; and so on until all the six brothers and sisters have been supplied. Not till then do we have the pleasure of seeing Dirty look neat. She has been so long accustomed to going shares that she does so in every conceivable circumstance.

And I console the mother of my little boy by saying that, should he fall out with Dirty, he can take one of the sisters and that, in this way, nothing would be lost.

x

My little boy confides to me that he would like a pear.

Now pears fall within his mother's province and I am sure that he has had as many as he is entitled to. And so we are at once agreed that what he wants is a wholly irrelevant, uncalled-for, delightful extra pear.

Unfortunately, it also appears that the request has already been laid before Mamma and met with a positive refusal.

The situation is serious, but not hopeless. For I am a man who knows how mean is the supply of pears to us poor wretched children of men and how wonderful an extra pear tastes.

And I am glad that my little boy did not give up all hope of the pear at the first obstacle. I can see by the longing in his green eyes how big the pear is and I reflect with lawful paternal pride that he will win his girl and his position in life when their time comes.

We now discuss the matter carefully.

First comes the prospect of stomach-ache:

"Never mind about that," says he.

I quite agree with his view.

Then perhaps Mother will be angry.

No, Mother is never angry. She is sorry; and that is not nice. But then we must see and make it up to her in another way.

So we slink in and steal the pear.

I put it to him whether, perhaps—when we have eaten the pear—we ought to tell Mother. But that does not appeal to him:

"Then I shan't get one this evening," he says.

And when I suggest that, possibly, Mother might be impressed with such audacious candour, he shakes his head decisively:

"You don't know Mother," he says.

So I, of course, have nothing to say.

Shortly after this, the mother of my little boy and I are standing at the window laughing at the story.

We catch sight of him below, in the courtyard.

He is sitting on the steps with his arm round little Dirty's neck. They have shared the pear. Now they are both singing, marvellously out of tune and with a disgustingly sentimental expression on their faces, a song which Dirty knows:

> For riches are only a lo-oan from Heaven
> And poverty is a reward.

And we are overcome with a great sense of desolation.

We want to make life green and pleasant for our little boy, to make his eyes open wide to see it, his hands strong to grasp it. But we feel powerless in the face of all the contentment and patience and resignation that are preached from cellar to garret, in church and in school: all those second-rate virtues, which may lighten an old man's last few steps as he stumbles on towards the grave, but which are only so many shabby lies for the young.

X I

Dirty is paying us a visit and my little boy is sitting at her feet.

She has buried her fingers in her hair and is reading, reading, reading. . . .

She is learning the Ten Commandments by heart. She stammers and repeats herself, with eyes fixed in her head and a despairing mouth:

"Thou shalt . . . Thou shalt not . . . Thou shalt . . ."

The boy watches her with tender compassion.

He has already learnt a couple of the commandments by listening to her and helps her, now and then, with a word. Then he comes to me and asks, anxiously:

"Father, must Dirty do all that the Ten Commandments say?"

"Yes."

He sits down by her again. His heart is overflowing with pity, his eyes are moist. She does not look at him, but plods on bravely:

"Thou shalt . . . Thou shalt not . . ."

"Father, when I grow big, must I also do all that the Ten Commandments say?"

"Ye-es."

He looks at me in utter despair. Then he goes back to Dirty and listens, but now he keeps his thoughts to himself.

Suddenly, something seems to flash across his mind.

He comes to me again, puts his arms on my knee and looks with his green eyes firmly into mine:

"Father, do you do all that the Ten Commandments say?"

"Ye-e-es."

He looks like a person whose last hope has escaped him. I would so much like to help him; but what, in Heaven's name, can I do?

Then he collects himself, shakes his head a little and says, with great tears in his eyes:

"Father, I don't believe that I can do all those things that the Ten Commandments say."

And I draw him to me and we cry together because life is so difficult, while Dirty plods away like a good girl.

X I I

THIS we all know, that sin came into the world by the law.

Dirty's Ten Commandments have brought it to us.

When she comes, she now always has Luther's terrible Little Catechism [1] and Balslev's equally objectionable work with her. Her parents evidently look upon it as most natural that she should also cultivate her soul at our house.

Her copies of these two classics were not published yesterday. They are probably heirlooms in Dirty's family. They are covered in thick brown paper, which again is protected by a heavy layer of dirt against any touch of clean fingers. They can be smelt at a distance.

But my little boy is no snob.

When Dirty has finished her studies—she always reads out aloud— he asks her permission to turn over the pages of the works in which she finds those strange words. He stares respectfully at the letters which he cannot read. And then he asks questions.

He asks Dirty, he asks the servant, he asks us. Before anyone suspects it, he is at home in the whole field of theology.

He knows that God is in Heaven, where all good people go to Him, while the wicked are put down below in Hell. That God created the world in six days and said that we must not do anything on Sundays. That God can do everything and knows everything and sees everything.

He often prays, creeps upstairs as high as he can go, so as to be nearer Heaven, and shouts as loud as he can. The other day I found him at the top of the folding-steps:

---

[1] *Luther's Lille Katekismus,* the Lutheran catechism in general use in Denmark.— A. T. de M.

"Dear God! You must please give us fine weather tomorrow, for we are going to the wood."

He says *Du* to everybody except God and the grocer.

He never compromises.

The servant is laying the table; we have guests coming and we call her attention to a little hole in the cloth:

"I must lay it so that no one can see it,"she says.

"God will see it."

"He is not coming this evening," says the blasphemous hussy.

"Yes, He is everywhere," answers my little boy, severely.

He looks after me in particular:

"You mustn't say 'gad,' Father. Dirty's teacher says that people who say 'gad' go to Hell."

"I shan't say it again," I reply, humbly.

One Sunday morning, he finds me writing and upbraids me seriously.

"My little boy," I say, distressfully, "I must work every day. If I do nothing on Sunday, I do nothing on Monday either. If I do nothing on Monday, I am idle on Tuesday too. And so on."

He ponders; and I continue, with the courage of despair:

"You must have noticed that Dirty wants a new catechism? The one she has is dirty and old."

He agrees to this.

"She will never have one, you see," I say, emphatically. "Her father rests so tremendously on Sunday that he is hardly able to do anything on the other days. He never earns enough to buy a new catechism."

I have won—this engagement. But the war is continued without cessation of hostilities.

The mother of my little boy and I are sitting in the twilight by his bedside and softly talking about this.

"What are we to do?" she asks.

"We can do nothing," I reply. "Dirty is right: God is everywhere. We can't keep Him out. And if we could, for a time: what then? A day would come perhaps when our little boy was ill or sad and the priests would come to him with their God as a new and untried miraculous remedy and bewilder his mind and his senses. Our little boy too will have to go through Luther and Balslev and Assens and confirmation and all the rest of it. Then this will become a commonplace to him; and one day he will form his own views, as we have done."

But, when he comes and asks how big God is, whether He is bigger than the Round Tower, how far it is to Heaven, why the weather was not fine on the day when he prayed so hard for it: then we fly from the face of the Lord and hide like Adam and Eve in the Garden of Eden.

And we leave Dirty to explain.

XIII

My little boy has got a rival, whose name is Henrik, a popinjay who not only is six years old, but has an unlimited supply of liquorice at his disposal. And, to fill the measure of my little boy's bitterness, Henrik is to go to the dancing-school; and I am, therefore, not surprised when my little boy asks to be taught to dance, so that he may not be left quite behind in the contest.

"I don't advise you to do that," I say. "The dancing which you learn at school is not pretty and does not play so great a part in love as you imagine. I don't know how to dance; and many charming ladies used to prefer me to the most accomplished ornaments of the ball-room. Besides, you know, you are knock-kneed."

And, to cheer him up, I sing a little song which we composed when we were small and had a dog and did not think about women:

> See, my son, that little basset,
>   Running with his knock-kneed legs!
> His own puppy, he can't catch it:
>   He'll fall down as sure as eggs!
>   Knock-kneed Billy!
>   Isn't he silly?
> Silly Billy!

But poetry fails to comfort him. Dark is his face and desperate his glance. And, when I see that the case is serious, I resolve to resort to serious measures.

I take him with me to a ball, a real ball, where people who have learnt to dance go to enjoy themselves. It is difficult to keep him in a more or less waking condition, but I succeed.

We sit quietly in a corner and watch the merry throng. I say not a word, but look at his wide-open eyes.

"Father, why does that man jump like that, when he is so awfully hot?"

"Yes; can you understand it?"

"Why does that lady with her head on one side look so tired? . . . Why does that fat woman hop about so funnily, Father? . . . Father, what queer legs that man there has!"

It rains questions and observations. We make jokes and laugh till the tears come to our eyes. We whisper naughty things to each other and go into a side-room and mimic a pair of crooked legs till we can't hold ourselves for laughter. We sit and wait till a steam thrashing-machine on its round comes past us; and we are fit to die when we hear it puff and blow.

We enjoy ourselves beyond measure.

And we make a hit.

The steam thrashing-machine and the crooked legs and the fat woman and the hot gentleman and others crowd round us and admire the dear little boy. We accept their praises, for we have agreed not to say what we think to anybody, except to Mother, when we come home, and then, of course, to Dirty.

And we wink our eyes and enjoy our delightful fun until we fall asleep and are driven home and put to bed.

And then we have done with the dancing-school.

My little boy paints in strong colours, for his Dirty's benefit, what Henrik will look like when he dances. It is no use for that young man to deny all that my little boy says and to execute different elegant steps. I was prepared for this; and my little boy tells exultantly that this is only something with which they lure stupid people at the start and that it will certainly end with Henrik's getting very hot and hopping round on crooked legs with a fat woman and a face of despair.

In the meantime, of course, I do not forget that, if we pull down without building up we shall end by landing ourselves in an unwholesome scepticism.

We therefore invent various dances, which my little boy executes in the courtyard to Dirty's joy and to Henrik's most jealous envy. We point emphatically to the fact that the dances are our own, that they are composed only for the woman we love and performed only for her.

There is, for instance, a dance with a stick, which my little boy wields, while Henrik draws back. Another with a pair of new mittens for Dirty. And, lastly, the liquorice dance, which expresses an extraordinary contempt for that foodstuff.

That Dirty should suck a stick of liquorice, which she has received from Henrik, while enjoying her other admirer's satire, naturally staggers my little boy. But I explain to him that that is because she is a woman and that *that* is a thing which can't be helped.

What Bournonville [1] would say, if he could look down upon us from his place in Heaven, I do not know.

But I don't believe that he can.

If he, up there, could see how people dance down here, he really would not stay there.

XIV

THERE is a battle royal and a great hullabaloo among the children in the courtyard.

I hear them shouting "Jew!" and I go to the window and see my little boy in the front rank of the bandits, screaming, fighting with clenched fists and without his cap.

I sit down quietly to my work again, certain that he will appear before long and ease his heart.

---

[1] A famous French ballet-master who figured at the Copenhagen Opera House in the eighteenth century.—A. T. de M.

And he comes directly after.

He stands still, as is his way, by my side and says nothing. I steal a glance at him: he is greatly excited and proud and glad, like one who has fearlessly done his duty.

"What fun you've been having down there!"

"Oh," he says, modestly, "it was only a Jew boy whom we were licking."

I jump up so quickly that I upset my chair:

"A Jew boy? Were you licking him? What had he done?"

"Nothing. . . ."

His voice is not very certain, for I look so queer.

And that is only the beginning. For now I snatch my hat and run out of the door as fast as I can and shout:

"Come . . . come . . . we must find him and beg his pardon!"

My little boy hurries after me. He does not understand a word of it, but he is terribly in earnest. We look in the courtyard, we shout and call. We rush into the street and round the corner, so eager are we to come up with him. Breathlessly, we ask three passers-by if they have not seen a poor, ill-used Jew boy.

All in vain: the Jew boy and all his persecutors are blown away into space.

So we go and sit up in my room again, the laboratory where our soul is crystallized out of the big events of our little life. My forehead is wrinkled and I drum disconsolately with my fingers on the table. The boy has both his hands in his pockets and does not take his eyes from my face.

"Well," I say, decidedly, "there is nothing more to be done. I hope you will meet that Jew boy one day, so that you can give him your hand and ask him to forgive you. You must tell him that you did that only because you were stupid. But if, another time, anyone does him any harm, I hope you will help him and lick the other one as long as you can stir a limb."

I can see by my little boy's face that he is ready to do what I wish. For he is still a mercenary, who does not ask under which flag, so long as there is a battle and booty to follow. It is my duty to train him to be a brave recruit, who will defend his fair mother-land, and so I continue:

"Let me tell you, the Jews are by way of being quite wonderful people. You remember David, about whom Dirty reads at school: he was a Jew boy. And the Child Jesus, Whom everybody worships and loves, although He died two thousand years ago: He was a little Jew also."

My little boy stands with his arms on my knee and I go on with my story.

The old Hebrews rise before our eyes in all their splendour and power, quite different from Dirty's Balslev. They ride on their camels in coats of many colours and with long beards: Moses and Joseph and his brethren and Samson and David and Saul. We hear wonderful stories. The walls of Jericho fall at the sound of the trumpet.

"And what next?" says my little boy, using the expression which he employed when he was much smaller and which still comes to his lips whenever he is carried away.

We hear of the destruction of Jerusalem and how the Jews took their little boys by the hand and wandered from place to place, scoffed at, despised and ill-treated. How they were allowed to own neither house nor land, but could only be merchants, and how the Christian robbers took all the money which they had got together. How, nevertheless, they remained true to their God and kept up their old sacred customs in the midst of the strangers who hated and persecuted them.

The whole day is devoted to the Jews.

We look at old books on the shelves which I love best to read and which are written by a Jew with a wonderful name, which a little boy can't remember at all. We learn that the most famous man now living in Denmark is a Jew.

And, when evening comes and Mother sits down at the piano and sings the song which Father loves above all other songs, it appears that the words were written by one Jew and the melody composed by another.

My little boy is hot and red when he falls to sleep that night. He turns restlessly in bed and talks in his sleep.

"He is a little feverish," says his mother.

And I bend down and kiss his forehead and answer, calmly:

"That is not surprising. Today I have vaccinated him against the meanest of all mean and vulgar diseases."

X V

WE are staying in the country, a long way out, where the real country is.

Cows and horses, pigs and sheep, a beautiful dog and hens and ducks form our circle of acquaintances. In addition to these, there are of course the two-legged beings who own and look after the four-legged ones and who, in my little boy's eyes, belong to quite the same kind.

The great sea lies at the foot of the slope. Ships float in the distance and have nothing to say to us. The sun burns us and bronzes us. We eat like thrashers, sleep like guinea-pigs and wake like larks. The only real sorrow that we have suffered is that we were not allowed to have our breeches made with a flap at the side, like the old wood-cutter's.

Presently, it happens that, for better or worse, we get neighbours.

They are regular Copenhageners. They were prepared not to find electric light in the farm-house; but, if they had known that there was no water in the kitchen, God knows they would not have come. They trudge through the clover as though it were mire and are sorry to find so few cornflowers in the rye. A cow going loose along the roads fills them with a terror which might easily have satisfied a royal tiger.

The pearl of the family is Erna.

Erna is five years old; her very small face is pale green, with watery blue eyes and yellow curls. She is richly and gaily dressed in a broad and slovenly sash, daintily-embroidered pantalets, short open-work socks and patent-leather shoes. She falls if she but moves a foot, for she is used only to gliding over polished floors or asphalt.

I at once perceive that my little boy's eyes have seen a woman.

He has seen the woman that comes to us all at one time or another and turns our heads with her rustling silks and her glossy hair and wears her soul in her skirts and our poor hearts under her heel.

"Now comes the perilous moment for Dirty," I say to the mother of my little boy.

This time it is my little boy's turn to be superior.

He knows the business thoroughly and explains it all to Erna. When he worries the horse, she trembles, impressed with his courage and manliness. When she has a fit of terror at the sight of a hen, he is charmed with her delicacy. He knows the way to the smith's, he dares to roll down the high slope, he chivalrously carries her ridiculous little cape.

Altogether, there is no doubt as to the condition of his heart. And, while Erna's family apparently favour the position—for which may the devil take them!—I must needs wait with resignation like one who knows that love is every man's master.

One morning he proposes.

He is sitting with his beloved on the lawn. Close to them, her aunt is nursing her chlorosis under a red parasol and with a novel in her bony lap. Up in the balcony above sit I, as Providence, and see everything, myself unseen.

"You shall be my sweetheart," says my little boy.

"Yes," says Erna.

"I have a sweetheart already in Copenhagen," he says, proudly.

This communication naturally by no means lowers Erna's suitor in her eyes. But it immediately arouses all Auntie's moral instincts:

"If you have a sweetheart, you must be true to her."

"Erna shall be my sweetheart."

Auntie turns her eyes up to Heaven:

"Listen, child," she says. "You're a very naughty boy. If you have given Dir—Dir——"

"Dirty," says the boy.

"Well, that's an extraordinary name! But, if you have given her your word, you must keep it till you die. Else you'll never, never be happy."

My little boy understands not a word and answers not a word. Erna begins to cry at the prospect that this good match may not come off. But I bend down over the baluster and raise my hat:

"I beg your pardon, Fröken. Was it not you who jilted Hr. Petersen? . . ."

"Good heavens! . . ."

She packs up her chlorosis and disappears with Erna, mumbling something about like father, like son, and goodness knows what.

Presently, my little boy comes up to me and stands and hangs about.

"Where has Erna gone to?" I ask my little boy.

"She mustn't go out," he says, dejectedly.

He puts his hands in his pockets and looks straight before him.

"Father," he says, "can't you have two sweethearts?"

The question comes quite unexpectedly and, at the moment, I don't know what to answer.

"Well?" says the mother of my little boy, amiably, and looks up from her newspaper.

And I pull my waistcoat down and my collar up:

"Yes," I say, firmly. "You can. But it is wrong. It leads to more fuss and unpleasantness than you can possibly conceive."

A silence.

"Are you so fond of Erna?" asks our mother.

"Yes."

"Do you want to marry her?"

"Yes."

I get up and rub my hands:

"Then the thing is settled," I say. "We'll write to Dirty and give her notice. There's nothing else to be done. I will write now and you can give the letter yourself to the postman, when he comes this afternoon. If you take my advice, you will make her a present of your ball. Then she will not be so much upset."

"She can have my gold-fish too, if she likes," says the boy.

"Excellent, excellent. We will give her the gold-fish. Then she will really have nothing in the world to complain of."

My little boy goes away. But, presently, he returns:

"Father, have you written the letter to Dirty?"

"Not yet, my boy. There is time enough. I sha'n't forget it."

"Father, I am so fond of Dirty."

"She was certainly a dear little girl."

A silence.

"Father, I am also so fond of Erna."

We look at each other. This is no joke:

"Perhaps we had better wait with the letter till tomorrow," I say. "Or perhaps it would be best if we talked to Dirty ourselves, when we get back to town."

We both ponder over the matter and really don't know what to do.

Then my eyes surprise an indescribable smile on our mother's face. All a woman's incapacity to understand man's honesty is contained within that smile and I resent it greatly:

"Come," I say and give my hand to my little boy. "Let us go."

And we go to a place we know of, far away behind the hedge, where we lie on our backs and look up at the blue sky and talk together sensibly, as two gentlemen should.

X V I

My little boy is to go to school.

We can't keep him at home any longer, says his mother. He himself is glad to go, of course, because he does not know what school is.

I know what it is and I know also that there is no escape for him, that he must go. But I am sick at heart. All that is good within me revolts against the inevitable.

So we go for our last morning walk, along the road where something wonderful has always happened to us. It looks to me as if the trees have crape wound round their tops and the birds sing in a minor key and the people stare at me with earnest and sympathetic eyes.

But my little boy sees nothing. He is only excited at the prospect. He talks and asks questions without stopping.

We sit down by the edge of our usual ditch—alas, that ditch!

And suddenly my heart triumphs over my understanding. The

voice of my clear conscience penetrates through the whole well-trained and harmonious choir which is to give the concert; and it sings its solo in the ears of my little boy:

"I just want to tell you that school is a horrid place," I say. "You can have no conception of what you will have to put up with there. They will tell you that two and two are four. . . ."

"Mother has taught me that already," says he, blithely.

"Yes, but that is wrong, you poor wretch!" I cry. "Two and two are never four, or only very seldom. And that's not all. They will try to make you believe that Teheran is the capital of Persia and that Mont Blanc is 15,781 feet high and you will take them at their word. But I tell you that both Teheran and Persia are nothing at all, an empty sound, a stupid joke. And Mont Blanc is not half as big as the mound in the tallow-chandler's back-garden. And listen: you will never have any more time to play in the courtyard with Einar. When he shouts to you to come out, you'll have to sit and read about a lot of horrible old kings who have been dead for hundreds and hundreds of years, if they ever existed at all, which I, for my part, simply don't believe."

My little boy does not understand me. But he sees that I am sad and puts his hand in mine:

"Mother says that you must go to school to become a clever boy," he says. "Mother says that Einar is ever so much too small and stupid to go to school."

I bow my head and nod and say nothing.

That is past.

And I take him to school and see how he storms up the steps without so much as turning his head to look back at me.

XVII

Here ends this book about my little boy.

What more can there be to tell?

He is no longer mine. I have handed him over to society. Hr. Petersen, candidate in letters, Hr. Nielsen, student of theology, and Fröken

Hansen, certificated teacher, will now set their distinguished example before him for five hours daily. He will form himself in their likeness. Their spirit hovers over him at school: he brings it home with him, it overshadows him when he is learning the lessons which they zealously mete out to him.

I don't know these people. But I pay them.

I, who have had a hard fight to keep my thoughts free and my limbs unrestrained and who have not retired from the fight without deep wounds of which I am reminded when the weather changes, I have, of my own free will, brought him to the institution for maiming human beings. I, who at times have soared to peaks that were my own, because the other birds dared not follow me, have myself brought him to the place where wings are clipped for flying respectably, with the flock.

"There was nothing else to be done," says the mother of my little boy.

"Really?" I reply, bitterly. "Was there nothing else to be done? But suppose that I had put by some money, so that I could have saved Messrs. Petersen and Nielsen and Fröken Hansen their trouble and employed my day in myself opening out lands for that little traveller whom I myself have brought into the land? Suppose that I had looked round the world for people with small boys who think as I do and that we had taken upon us to bring up these young animals so that they kept sight of horns and tails and fairy-tales?"

"Yes," she says.

"Small boys have a bad time of it, you know."

"They had a worse time of it in the old days."

"That is a poor comfort. And it can become worse again. The world is full of parents and teachers who shake their foolish heads and turn up their old eyes and cross their flat chests with horror at the depravity of youth: children are so disobedient, so naughty, so self-willed and talk so disrespectfully to their elders! . . . And what do we do, we who know better?"

"We do what we can."

But I walk about the room, more and more indignant and ashamed of the pitiful part which I am playing:

"Do you remember, a little while ago, he came to me and said that he longed so for the country and asked if we couldn't go there for a little? There were horses and cows and green fields to be read in his eyes. Well, I couldn't leave my work. And I couldn't afford it. So I treated him to a shabby and high-class sermon about the tailor to whom I owed money. Don't you understand that I let my little boy do *my* work, that I let him pay *my* debt? . . ." I bend down over her and say earnestly, "You must know; do please tell me—God help me, I do not know—if I ought not rather to have paid my debt to the boy and cheated the other?"

"You know quite well," she says.

She says it in such a way and looks at me with two such sensible eyes and is so strong and so true that I suddenly think things look quite well for our little boy; and I become restful and cheerful like herself:

"Let Petersen and Nielsen and Hansen look out!" I say. "My little boy, for what I care, may take from them all the English and geography and history that he can. But they shall throw no dust in his eyes. I shall keep him awake and we shall have great fun and find them out."

"And I shall help him with his English and geography and history," says she.

AN AFTERWORD ON
"MY LITTLE BOY"

IF, among all the works assembled in this volume, there is one that comes closer than any other to representing the editor's notion of what such an anthology as this should look for, that one is this wise, gentle, and unpretentious work which came out of Denmark shortly after the turn of the century. For it is as simple and as modest and as perfect as a Vermeer. First published here in 1906, it would lapse out of print, then somehow be revived and go jogging along down the years. But though it made many friends, somehow it never reached any considerable fraction of the great multitude who—one knows infallibly— would find it dear and cherish it.

Carl Ewald, son of an author more considerable in his native land, died in 1908. The younger Ewald's work was never widely known beyond the frontier of his own country, which is, after all, a tiny one. Once a friend of mine sought to cheer up the morose Georg Brandes by predicting a tremendous *réclame* for his forthcoming work. "But it's in Danish," Brandes complained bitterly. "What is Danish? A barbarous language which a few people whisper to one another in a small corner of the world."

My Little Boy is an interrupted biography. There are always readers who want to know what happened afterward. In this instance the story is still being told and I know few of the details. Did the little boy forget about Dirty? In an age when it matters in Europe, does he remember the lesson in tolerance his father taught him when he was a little boy? I do not know. I can tell you only that the still younger Ewald—his name is Jesper Ewald —is now (1935) a man of forty-two who lives in Naerum, Denmark, and is himself a writer with seven novels to his credit, as the odd, incautious saying goes. Jesper Ewald has done some translation from English into that tongue wherewith the Danish confide to one another in Copenhagen. Into Danish he has done such transpositions from our literature as *British Agent, The Beloved Vagabond,* and—*pour le sport,* I suppose,—*The Green Hat.* Speaking of translations, the task in this instance was entrusted to the late Alexander Teixeira de Mattos, who is sorely missed. In the great post-war flow of books from the continent to America, the work of providing a text for this country more often than not is mystifyingly entrusted to someone whose linguistic equipment does not include a notable familiarity with the resources of the English language.

A. W.

MARY WHITE

by

WILLIAM ALLEN
WHITE

MARY WHITE

THE Associated Press reports carrying the news of Mary White's death declared that it came as the result of a fall from a horse. How she would have hooted at that! She never fell from a horse in her life. Horses have fallen on her and with her—"I'm always trying to hold 'em in my lap," she used to say. But she was proud of few things, and one was that she could ride anything that had four legs and hair. Her death resulted not from a fall, but from a blow on the head which fractured her skull, and the blow came from the limb of an over-hanging tree on the parking.

The last hour of her life was typical of its happiness. She came home from a day's work at school, topped off by a hard grind with the copy on the High School Annual, and felt that a ride would refresh her. She climbed into her khakis, chattering to her mother about the work she was doing, and hurried to get her horse and be out on the dirt roads for the country air and the radiant green fields of the spring. As she rode through the town on an easy gallop, she kept waving at passers-by. She knew everyone in town. For a decade the little figure with the long pig-tail and the red hair-ribbon has been familiar on the streets of Emporia, and she got in the way of speaking to those who nodded at her. She passed the Kerrs—walking the horse—in front of the Normal Library, and waved at them; passed another friend a few hundred feet further on, and waved at her. The horse was walking and, as she turned into North Merchant Street, she took off her cow-boy hat, and the horse swung into a lope. She passed the Tripletts and waved her cowboy hat at them, still moving gayly north on Merchant Street. A *Gazette* carrier passed—a High School boy friend —and she waved at him, but with her bridle hand; the horse veered quickly, plunged into the parking where the low-hanging limb faced her, and, while she still looked back waving, the blow came. But she did not fall from the horse; she slipped off, dazed a bit, staggered, and fell in a faint. She never quite recovered consciousness.

But she did not fall from the horse, neither was she riding fast. A year or so ago she used to go like the wind. But that habit was broken, and she used the horse to get into the open to get fresh, hard exercise and to work off a certain surplus energy that welled up in her and needed a physical outlet. That need has been in her heart for years. It was back of the impulse that kept the dauntless little brown-clad figure on the streets and country roads of this community and built into a strong, muscular body what had been a frail and sickly frame during the first years of her life. But the riding gave her more than a body. It released a gay and hardy soul. She was the happiest thing in the world. And she was happy because she was enlarging her horizon. She came to know all sorts and conditions of men; Charley O'Brien, the traffic cop, was one of her best friends. W. L. Holtz, the Latin teacher, was another. Tom O'Connor, farmer-politician, and Rev. J. H. J. Rice, preacher and police judge, and Frank Beach, music master, were her special friends, and all the girls, black and white, above the track and below the track, in Pepville and Stringtown, were among her acquaintances. And she brought home riotous stories of her adventures. She loved to rollick; persiflage was her natural expression at home. Her humor was a continual bubble of joy. She seemed to think in hyperbole and metaphor. She was mischievous without malice, as full of faults as an old shoe. No angel was Mary White, but an easy girl to live with, for she never nursed a grouch five minutes in her life.

With all her eagerness for the out-of-doors, she loved books. On her table when she left her room were a book by Conrad, one by Galsworthy, *Creative Chemistry,* by E. E. Slosson, and a Kipling book. She read Mark Twain, Dickens, and Kipling before she was ten— all of their writings. Wells and Arnold Bennett particularly amused and diverted her. She was entered as a student in Wellesley in 1922; was assistant editor of the High School Annual this year, and in line for election to the editorship of the Annual next year. She was a member of the executive committee of the High School Y.W.C.A.

Within the last two years she had begun to be moved by an ambition to draw. She began as most children do by scribbling in her school books, funny pictures. She bought cartoon magazines and took a course—rather casually, naturally, for she was, after all, a child with no strong purposes—and this year she tasted the first fruits of success by having her pictures accepted by the High School Annual. But the thrill of delight she got when Mr. Ecord, of the Normal Annual, asked her to do the cartooning for that book this spring was too beautiful for words. She fell to her work with all her enthusiastic heart. Her drawings were accepted, and her pride—always repressed by a lively sense of the ridiculousness of the figure she was cutting—was a really gorgeous thing to see. No successful artist ever drank a deeper draft of satisfaction than she took from the little fame her work was getting among her schoolfellows. In her glory she almost forgot her horse— but never her car.

For she used the car as a jitney bus. It was her social life. She never had a "party" in all her nearly seventeen years—wouldn't have one; but she never drove a block in the car in her life that she didn't begin to fill the car with pick-ups! Everybody rode with Mary White—white and black, old and young, rich and poor, men and women. She liked nothing better than to fill the car full of long-legged High School boys and an occasional girl, and parade the town. She never had a "date," nor went to a dance, except once with her brother Bill, and the "boy proposition" didn't interest her—yet. But young people— great spring-breaking, varnish-cracking, fender-bending, door-sagging carloads of "kids"—gave her great pleasure. Her zests were keen. But the most fun she ever had in her life was acting as chairman of the committee that got up the big turkey dinner for the poor folks at the county home; scores of pies, gallons of slaw, jam, cakes, preserves, oranges, and a wilderness of turkey were loaded in the car and taken to the county home. And, being of a practical turn of mind, she risked her own Christmas dinner by staying to see that the poor folks actually got it all. Not that she was a cynic; she just disliked to tempt folks. While there she found a blind colored uncle, very old, who could do nothing but make rag rugs, and she rustled up from her school friends rags enough to keep him busy for a season. The last engagement she tried to make was to take the guests at the county home out for a car ride. And the last endeavor of her life was to try to get a rest room for colored girls in the High School. She found one girl reading in the toilet, because there was no better place for a colored girl to loaf, and it inflamed her sense of injustice and she became a nagging harpie to those who, she thought, could remedy the evil. The poor she had always with her, and was glad of it. She hungered and thirsted for righteousness; and was the most impious creature in the world. She joined the Congregational Church without consulting her parents; not particularly for her soul's good. She never had a thrill of piety in her life, and would have hooted at "testimony." But even as a little child she felt the church was an agency for helping people to more of life's abundance, and she wanted to help. She never wanted help for herself. Clothes meant little to her. It was a fight to get a new rig on her; but eventually a harder fight to get it off. She never wore a jewel and had no ring but her High School class ring, and never asked for anything but a wrist watch. She refused to have her hair up, though she was nearly seventeen. "Mother," she protested, "you don't know how much I get by with, in my braided pigtails, that I could not with my hair up." Above every other passion of her life was her passion not to grow up, to be a child. The tomboy in her, which was big, seemed to loathe to be put away forever in skirts. She was a Peter Pan, who refused to grow up.

Her funeral yesterday at the Congregational Church was as she would have wished it; no singing, no flowers save the big bunch of red roses from her Brother Bill's Harvard classmen—Heavens, how proud that would have made her!—and the red roses from the *Gazette* force—in vases at her head and feet. A short prayer, Paul's beautiful essay on "Love" from the Thirteenth Chapter of First Corinthians, some remarks about her democratic spirit by her friend, John H. J. Rice, pastor and police judge, which she would have deprecated if she could, a prayer sent down for her by her friend, Carl Nau, and opening the service the slow, poignant movement from Beethoven's *Moonlight Sonata,* which she loved, and closing the service a cutting from the joyously melancholy first movement of Tschaikow-ski's *Pathetic Symphony,* which she liked to hear in certain moods on the phonograph; then the Lord's Prayer by her friends in the High School.

That was all.

For her pall-bearers only her friends were chosen: her Latin teacher, W. L. Holtz; her High School principal, Rice Brown; her doctor, Frank Foncannon; her friend, W. W. Finney; her pal at the *Gazette* office, Walter Hughes; and her brother Bill. It would have made her smile to know that her friend Charley O'Brien, the traffic cop, had been transferred from Sixth and Commercial to the corner near the church to direct her friends who came to bid her good-by.

A rift in the clouds in a gray day threw a shaft of sunlight upon her coffin as her nervous energetic little body sank to its last sleep. But the soul of her, the glowing, gorgeous, fervent soul of her, surely was flaming in eager joy upon some other dawn.

AN AFTERWORD ON
"MARY WHITE"

MARY WHITE died on May 14, 1921, and this portrait of her by her father was printed three days later in the *Emporia Gazette,* of which he is and long has been the editor. Any newspaper man proud of his trade would want it in his Reader.

This is the first of three newspaper clippings which are included in this anthology. Further on you will find an obituary by Rebecca West which caught the mail-packet from Southampton two days after she had received the cable commissioning her to write it. And beyond that is a column by Clarence Day.

It is related of Lawrence Barrett, a once eminent tragedian, that sometimes in his cups he would grow tearful and lament that nightly it was his fate to carve a statue in snow. On this solemn plaint Brander Matthews made the stinging comment that that artist's fame was the more secure who left no work lying around to be coldly appraised by a later generation. Newspaper work, like acting and singing, is perishable. That is the conventional thing to say about it. It is high time someone also said that, like acting and singing, it is therefore profoundly modest. I count it a high honor to belong to a trade in which the good men write each piece, each paragraph, each sentence as painstakingly and as lovingly as any Addison and do so in the full knowledge that by noon next day it will have been used to light a fire or saved, if at all, to line a shelf.

Yet every once in a while, to its own surprise, such a piece, cut out and tucked away in someone's admiring wallet or someone else's cherishing desk-drawer, starts out around the world on a journey of its own. Such a piece is this clipping from the *Emporia Gazette*. Its inclusion in this book is by no means its first reappearance. Nor will it be its last. It is my own notion that it will still be read a hundred years from now. Those who read it then will know, as you and I know, how irreparably impoverished Mary White's town must have been by the death of such a one so young. And perhaps in the background of this portrait they will see, more clearly than it can be seen today, a picture of an American way of life which, in the intervening years, we, the people, may have sold for a mess of pottage.

                                                        ·A. W.

MR. FORTUNE'S
MAGGOT

by

*SYLVIA TOWNSEND
WARNER*

"MAGGOT 2. A nonsensical or perverse fancy; a crotchet." N. E. D.

TO

THEO

MR. FORTUNE'S MAGGOT

THOUGH the Reverend Timothy Fortune had spent three years in the island of Fanua he had made but one convert. Some missionaries might have been galled by this state of things, or if too good to be galled, at least flustered; but Mr. Fortune was a humble man of heart and he had the blessing which rests upon humility: an easy-going nature. In appearance he was tall, raw-boned and rather rummaged looking; even as a young man he had learnt that to jump in first doesn't make the bus start any sooner; and his favourite psalm was the one which begins: My soul truly waiteth still upon God.

Mr. Fortune was not a scholar, he did not know that the psalms express bygone thoughts and a bygone way of life. In his literal way he believed that the sixty-second psalm applied to him. For many years he had been a clerk in the Hornsey branch of Lloyd's Bank, but he had not liked it. Whenever he weighed out the golden sovereigns in the brass scales which tacked and sidled like a yacht in a light breeze he remembered uneasily that the children of men are deceitful upon the weights, that they are altogether lighter than vanity itself.

In the bank too he had seen riches increase. But he had not set his heart upon them; and when his godmother, whose pass-book he kept, died and left him one thousand pounds he went to a training college, was ordained deacon, and quitted England for St. Fabien, a port on an island of the Raritongan Archipelago in the Pacific.

St. Fabien was a centre of Christianity. It had four missions: one Catholic, one Protestant, one Wesleyan, and one American. Mr. Fortune belonged to the Protestant mission. He gave great satisfaction to his superiors by doing as he was bid, teaching in the school, visiting the sick, and carrying the subscription list to the English visitors, and even greater satisfaction when they had discovered that he could keep all the accounts. At the end of ten years Archdeacon Mason was sorry to hear that Mr. Fortune (who was now a priest) had felt a call to go to the island of Fanua.

Fanua was a small remote island which could only be seen in imagination from that beach edged with tin huts where Mr. Fortune walked slowly up and down on evenings when he had time to. No steamers called there, the Archdeacon had visited it many years ago in a canoe. Now his assistant felt a call thither, not merely to visit it in the new mission launch, but to settle there, and perhaps for life.

The two clergymen strolled along the beach in the cool of the evening. The air smelt of the sea, of flowers, and of the islanders' suppers.

"I must warn you, Fortune, you are not likely to make many converts in Fanua."

"What, are they cannibals?"

"No, no! But they are like children, always singing and dancing, and of course immoral. But all the natives are like that. I believe I have told you that the Raritongan language has no word for chastity or for gratitude?"

"Yes, I believe you did."

"Well, well! You are not a young man, Fortune, you will not expect too much of the Fanuans. Singing and dancing! No actual harm in that of course, and no doubt the climate is partly responsible. But light, my dear Fortune, light! And not only in their heels either."

"I am afraid that none of the children of men weigh altogether true," said Mr. Fortune. "For that matter I have heard that many cannibals are fond of dancing."

"Humanly speaking I fear that you would be wasted in Fanua. Still, if you have felt a call I must not dissuade you, I won't put any obstacles in your way. But you will be a great loss."

The Archdeacon spoke so sadly that Mr. Fortune, knowing how much he disliked accounts, wondered for a moment if God would prefer him to wait still in St. Fabien. God tries the souls of men in crafty ways and perhaps the call had been a temptation, a temptation sent to try his humility. He turned his eyes towards where he knew the island of Fanua to lie. What his superior had said about it had not

displeased him, on the contrary he liked to think of the islanders dancing and singing. It would be a beautiful estate to live among them and
gather their souls as a child gathers daisies in a field.

But now the horizon was hidden in the evening haze, and Fanua
seemed more remote than ever. A little cloud was coming up the
heavens, slowly, towards the sunset; as it passed above the place of
Fanua it brightened, it shone like a pearl, it caught the rays of the sun
and glowed with a rosy rim. Mr. Fortune took the cloud to be a sign.

Heartened by a novel certainty that he was doing the right thing he
disappointed the Archdeacon quite unflinchingly, and set about his
preparations for the new life. Since the island was so unfrequented it
was necessary to take with him provisions for at least a year. In the
ordinary course of things the Mission would have supplied his outfit,
but he had a scruple against availing himself of this custom, because
having kept the accounts he knew their poverty and their good works,
and also he was aware that the expedition to Fanua was looked on as,
at best, a sort of pious escapade. Fortunately there were the remains
of his godmother's legacy. With feelings that were a nice mixture of
thrift and extravagance he bought tinned meats, soup-squares, a chest
of tea, soap, a toolbox, a medicine chest, a gentleman's housewife, a
second-hand harmonium (rather cumbrous and wheezy but certainly
a bargain) and an oil-lamp. He also bought a quantity of those coloured glass baubles which hang so ravishingly on Christmas trees,
some picture-books, rolls of white cotton, and a sewing-machine to
make clothes for his converts. The Archdeacon gave him a service of
altar furniture and the other mission-workers presented him with a
silver tea-pot. With the addition of some plate-powder Mr. Fortune
was now ready to embark.

In fancy he had seen himself setting foot upon the island alone
though he knew that in fact someone must go with him if only to
manage the launch. But that someone would be a sailor, a being so
aloofly maritime as scarcely to partake in the act of landing. He was
slightly dashed when he discovered that the Archdeacon, accompanied
by his secretary, was coming too in order to install him with a proper
appearance of ceremony.

"We cannot impress upon them too early," said the Archdeacon, "the solemn nature of your undertaking." And Mr. Fortune hung his head, a grey one, old and wise enough to heed an admonition or a rebuke.

The voyage was uneventful. The Archdeacon sat in the bows dictating to the secretary, and Mr. Fortune looked at the Pacific Ocean until he fell asleep, for he was tired out with packing.

About sunset he was aroused by the noise of surf and by peals of excited laughter; and opening his eyes he found that they were close in under the shadow of the island of Fanua. The launch was manœuvring round seeking for an inlet in the reef, and the islanders were gathered together to view this strange apparition. Some were standing on the rocks, some were in the sea, others were diving from cliff to water, in movement and uproar like a flock of sea-gulls disturbed by a fishing-boat.

It seemed to Mr. Fortune that there must be thousands of them, and for a moment his heart sank. But there was no time for second thoughts; for behold! a canoe shot forward to the side of the launch, a rope was thrown and caught, the Archdeacon, the secretary and himself were miraculously jumped in, the sea was alive with brown heads, everyone talked at once, the canoe turned, darted up the smooth back of a wave, descended into a cloud of spray, and the three clergymen, splashed and stiff, were standing on the beach.

Now Mr. Fortune was properly grateful for the presence of the Archdeacon, for like a child arriving late at a party he felt perfectly bewildered and would have remained in the same spot, smiling and staring. But like the child at the party he found himself taken charge of and shepherded in the right direction until, in the house of the chief islander, he was seated on a low stool with his hat taken off, a garland round his neck and food in his hands, smiling and staring still.

Before dark the luggage was also landed. The evening was spent in conversation and feasting. Everyone who could squeeze himself into Ori's house did so, and the rest of them (the thousands did not seem above a few hundreds now) squatted round outside. Even the babies seemed prepared to sit there all night, but at length the Archdeacon, pleading fatigue, asked leave of his host to go to bed.

Ori dismissed the visitors, his household prepared the strangers' sleeping place, unrolling the best mats and shooing away a couple of flying foxes, the missionaries prayed together and the last good-nights were said.

From where he lay Mr. Fortune could look out of the door. He saw a tendril of some creeper waving gently to and fro across the star Canopus, and once more he realized, as though he were looking at it for the first time, how strangely and powerfully he had been led from his native land to lie down in peace under the constellations of the southern sky.

"So this is my first night in Fanua," he thought, as he settled himself on his mat. "My first night. . . ."

And he would have looked at the star, a sun whose planets must depend wholly upon God for their salvation, for no missionary could reach them; but his eyes were heavy with seafaring, and in another minute he had fallen asleep.

As though while his body lay sleeping his ghost had gone wandering and ascertaining through the island Mr. Fortune woke on the morrow feeling perfectly at home in Fanua. So much so that when he stood on the beach waving farewell to the launch he had the sensations of a host, who from seeing off his guests turns back with a renewed sense of ownership to the house which the fact of their departure makes more deeply and dearly his. Few hosts indeed could claim an ownership equally secure. For when the Archdeacon, visited with a sudden qualm at the thought of Mr. Fortune's isolation, had suggested that he should come again in three months' time, just to see how he was getting on, Mr. Fortune was able to say quite serenely and legitimately that he would prefer to be left alone for at least a year.

Having waved to the proper degree of perspective he turned briskly inland. The time was come to explore Fanua.

The island of Fanua is of volcanic origin, though at the time of Mr. Fortune's arrival the volcano had been for many years extinct. It rises steeply out of the ocean, and seen from thence it appears disproportionately tall for its base, for the main peak reaches to a height of near three thousand feet, and the extremely indented coast-line does not measure more than seventy miles. On three sides of the island there are steep cliffs worked into caverns and flying buttresses by the action of the waves, but to the east a fertile valley slopes gently down to a low-lying promontory of salt-meadow and beach where once a torrent of lava burst from the side of the mountain and crushed its channel to the sea; and in this valley lies the village.

The lower slopes of the mountain are wooded, and broken into many deep gorges where the noise of the cataract echoes from cliff to cliff, where the air is cool with shade and moist with spray, and where bright green ferns grow on the black face of the rock. Above this swirl and foam of tree-tops the mountain rises up in crags or steep tracts of scrub and clinker to the old crater, whose ramparts are broken into curious cactus-shaped pinnacles of rock, in colour the reddish lavender of rhododendron blossoms.

A socket of molten stone rent and deserted by its ancient fires and garlanded round with a vegetation as wild as fire and more inexhaustible, the whole island breathes the peculiar romance of a being with a stormy past. The ripened fruit falls from the tree, the tree falls too and the ferns leap up from it as though it were being consumed with green flames. The air is sleepy with salt and honey, and the sharp wild cries of the birds seem to float like fragments of coloured paper upon the montononous background of breaking waves and falling cataract.

Mr. Fortune spent the whole day exploring, and when he felt hungry he made a meal of guavas and rose-apples. There seemed to be no end to the marvels and delights of his island and he was as thrilled as though he had been let loose into the world for the first time. But he returned with all the day's wonders almost forgotten in the excitement and satisfaction of having discovered the place where he wanted to live.

It was a forsaken hut, about a mile from the village and less than that distance from the sea. It stood in a little dell amongst the woods; before it there was a natural lawn of fine grass, behind it was a rocky spur of the mountain. There was a spring for water and a clump of coco-palms for shade.

The hut consisted of one large room opening on to a deep veranda. The framework was of wood, the floor of beaten earth, and it was thatched and walled with reeds.

Ori told him that it could be his for the taking. An old woman had lived there with her daughter, but she had died and the daughter, who didn't like being out of the world, had removed to the village. Mr. Fortune immediately set about putting it in order, and while he worked almost everyone in the island dropped in at some time or other to admire, encourage or lend a hand. There was not much to do; a little strengthening of the thatch, the floor to be weeded and trodden smooth, the creepers to be cut back—and on the third day he moved in.

This took place with ceremony. The islanders accompanied him on his many journeys to and from the village, they carried the crate containing the harmonium with flattering eulogies of its weight and size, and when everything was transported they sat on the lawn and watched him unpacking. When he unpacked the tea-pot they burst into delighted laughter.

Except for the lamp, the sewing-machine and the harmonium Mr. Fortune's house had not a European appearance, for while on the island he wished to live as its natives did. His bowls and platters and drinking-vessels were made of polished wood, his bed (Ori's gift) was a small wooden platform spread with many white mats. When everything was completed he gave each of the islanders a ginger-bread nut and made a little formal speech, first thanking them for their gifts and their assistance, and going on to explain his reasons for coming to Fanua. He had heard, he said, with pleasure how happy a people they were, and he had come to dwell with them, and teach them how they might be as happy in another life as they were in this.

The islanders received his speech in silence, broken only by crunching. Their expressions were those of people struck into awe by some surprising novelty. Mr. Fortune wondered if he were that novelty, or Huntley and Palmer.

He was anxious to do things befittingly for the Archdeacon's admonition on the need for being solemn still hung about the back of his mind. This occasion, it seemed to him, was something between a ceremony and a social function. It was a gathering, and as such it had its proper routine: first there comes an address, after the address a hymn is sung, then comes a collect and sometimes a collection and after that the congregation disperses.

Mr. Fortune sat down to his harmonium and sang and played through a hymn.

His back was to the islanders, he could not see how they were taking it. But when, having finished the hymn and added two chords for the Amen, he turned round to announce the collect he discovered that they had already dispersed, the last of them even then vanishing noiselessly and enigmatically through the bushes.

The sun was setting behind the mountain, great shafts of glory moved among the topmost crags. Mr. Fortune thought of God's winnowing-fan, he imagined Him holding the rays of the sun in His hand. God winnows the souls of men with the beauty of this world: the chaff is blown away, the true grain lies still and adoring.

In the dell it was already night. He sat for a long time in his veranda listening to the boom of the waves. He did not think much, he was tired with a long day's work and his back ached. At last he went indoors, lighted his lamp and began to write in his diary. Just as he was dropping off to sleep a pleasant thought came to him, and he smiled, murmuring in a drowsy voice: "Tomorrow is Sunday."

In the morning he was up and shaved and dressed before sunrise. With a happy face he stepped on to his lawn and stood listening to the birds. They did not sing anywhere near so sweetly as English blackbirds and thrushes, but Mr. Fortune was pleased with their notes, a music which seemed proper to this gay landscape which might have been coloured out of a child's paint box.

He stood there till the sun had risen and shone into the dell, then he went back into his hut; when he came out again he was dressed in his priest's clothes and carried a black tin box.

He walked across the dell to where there was a stone with a flat top. Opening the box he took out, first a linen cloth which he spread on the stone, then a wooden cross and two brass vases. He knelt down and very carefully placed the cross so that it stood firm on the middle of the stone. The vases he carried to the spring where he filled them with water, and gathering some red blossoms which grew on a bush near-by he arranged them in the vases, which he then carried back and set on either side of the cross. Standing beside the stone and looking into the sun, he said in a loud voice: "Let your light so shine before men that they may see your good works and glorify your Father which is in heaven."

The sun shone upon the white cloth and the scarlet flowers, upon the cross of wood and upon the priest standing serious, grey-headed and alone in the green dell all sparkling with dew as though it had never known the darkness of night.

Once more he turned and went back to the hut. When he came out again he carried in either hand a cup and a dish which shone like gold. These he put down upon the stone, and bowed himself before them and began to pray.

Mr. Fortune knelt very upright. His eyes were shut, he did not see the beauty of the landscape glittering in the sunrise, the coco-palms waving their green feather head-dresses gently to and fro in the light breeze, the wreaths of rosy mist floating high up across the purple crags of the mountain; and yet from the expression on his face one would have said that he was all the more aware of the beauty around him for having his eyes shut, for he seemed like one in an ecstasy and his clasped hands trembled, as though they had hold of a joy too great for him. He knelt on, absorbed in prayer. He did not see that a naked brown boy had come to the edge of the dell, and was gazing at him, and at the stone which he had decked to the glory of God—gazing with wonder and admiration, and step by step coming softly across the grass. Only when he had finished his prayer and stretched out his hands towards the altar did Mr. Fortune discover that a boy was kneeling at his side.

He gave no sign of surprise, he did not appear even to have noticed the newcomer. With steadfast demeanour he took from the dish a piece of bread and ate it, and drank from the cup. Then, rising and turning to the boy who still knelt before him, he laid his hand upon his head, and looked down on him with a long look of greeting. Slowly and unhesitatingly, like one who hears and accepts and obeys the voice of the spirit, he took up the cup once more and with the fore-finger of his right hand he wrote the sign of the cross upon the boy's forehead with the last drops of the wine.

The boy did not flinch, he trembled a little, that was all. Mr. Fortune bent down and welcomed him with a kiss.

He had waited, but after all not for long. The years in the bank, the years at St. Fabien, they did not seem long now, the time of waiting was gone by, drowsy and half-forgotten like a nightwatch. A cloud in the heavens had been given him as a sign to come to Fanua, but here was a sign much nearer and more wonderful: his first convert, miracu-lously led to come and kneel beside him a little after the rising of the sun. His, and not his. For while he had thought to bring souls to God, God had been beforehand with His gift, had come before him into the meadow, and gathering the first daisy had given it to him.

For a long while he stood lost in thankfulness. At last he bade the kneeling boy get up.

"What is your name?" he said.

"Lueli," answered the boy.

"I have given you a new name, Lueli. I have called you Theodore, which means 'the gift of God.' "

Lueli smiled politely.

"Theodore," repeated Mr. Fortune impressively.

The boy smiled again, a little dubiously this time. Then, struck with a happy thought he told Mr. Fortune the name of the scarlet blossoms that stood on either side of the cross. His voice was soft and pleasant and he held his head on one side in his desire to please.

"Come, Theodore, will you help me to put these things away?"

Together they rinsed the cup and the dish in the spring, folded the linen cloth and put them with the cross and the vases back into the black tin box. The flowers Mr. Fortune gave to the boy, who with a rapid grace pulled others and wove two garlands, one of which he put round Mr. Fortune's neck and one round his own. Then discovering that the tin box served as a dusky sort of mirror he bent over it, and would have stayed coquetting like a girl with a new coral necklace had not Mr. Fortune called him into the hut.

In all Lueli's movements there was a swiftness and a pliancy as though not only his mind but his body also were intent on complaisance and docility. A monkey will show the same adaptability, deft and pleased with its deftness, but in a monkey's face there is always a sad self-seeking look, and their eyes are like pebbles unhappily come alive. A bird, or a squirrel, or a lizard whisking over a stone have a vivid infallible grace, but it is inherent, they are made so, and however much one may admire or envy them, they do not touch one into feeling grateful to them for being what they are. As Mr. Fortune watched Lueli folding up the priestly clothes, patting them smooth and laying them in their box, he felt as though he were watching some entirely new kind of being, too spontaneous to be human, too artless to be monkey, too sensitive to be bird or squirrel or lizard; and he wished that he had been more observant of creation, so that he could find out what it was that Lueli resembled. Only some women, happy in themselves and in their love, will show a lover or husband this kind of special grace; but this Mr. Fortune, whose love affairs had been hasty and conventional, did not know.

While they were breakfasting together in the veranda the missionary had a good look at his convert.

Lueli was of the true Polynesian type, slender-boned and long-limbed, with small idle hands and feet: broadminded persons with no colour prejudices might have described him as aristocratic-looking. This definition did not occur to Mr. Fortune, who had no dealings with aristocrats and was consequently unaware of any marked difference between them and other people; but he reflected with satisfaction that the boy looked very refined for one who had been so recently a heathen. His eyes were rather small and his nose was rather snub, but these details did not mar the general good effects of regular features and a neatly-shaped head. Though when he talked he pulled very charming faces, in repose his expression was slightly satirical. In colour he was an agreeable brown, almost exactly the colour of a nutmeg; his hair was thick but not bushy and he wore it gathered up into a tuft over either ear, in much the same manner as was fashionable at the French Court in the year 1671.

In spite of his convert's advantageous appearance and easy manners Mr. Fortune judged that he was not the child of anyone particularly rich or distinguished; for in these islands where the poorest are scrupulously clean and the richest may wear for sole adornment the sophisticated elegance of freshly gathered flowers, social standing may yet be deduced from the degree of tattooing. Lueli had greaves and gaiters of a pattern of interlacing bamboo-shoots, and in addition a bracelet round his left wrist and on his right shoulder-blade an amusing sprig. But this was all. And from the elegance of the designs and their wilful disposition it seemed as though he had been decorated for no better reason than the artist's pleasure.

When Mr. Fortune came to make inquiries he found that he had judged rightly. Lueli was one of a large family, which is rare in these islands. His mother was a fat, giggling creature, without a care in the world; even among the lighthearted people of Fanua she and her brood were a byword for their harum-scarum ways. Their dwelling was a big tumble-down hut in which there was scarcely ever anyone at home except a baby; and though they had no apparent father or other means of sustenance that was no obstacle to well-being in this fertile spot where no one need go hungry who could shake fruit off a tree or pull fish out of the water.

All of the family were popular; Lueli in particular, for his beauty, and amiability, was a regular village pet. But, whether it be that an uncommon share of good looks, like a strain of fairy blood, sets their owners apart, or whether beautiful people are in some way aware of the firebrand they carry with them and so are inclined to solitariness, Lueli, like other beauties, had for all his affability a tincture of aloofness in his character. Although he was a pet, it was not a pet dog he resembled, solicitous and dependent, but a pet cat, which will leap on to a knee to be fondled and then in a moment detach itself, impossible to constrain as a beam of moonlight playing bo-peep through a cloud. So when he deserted the village and attached himself to the newcomer no one was hurt or surprised, they took it for granted that he would go where he pleased.

This complaisance had slightly shocked Mr. Fortune, particularly as it fell in so convenient to his wishes. It was most desirable, indeed almost necessary, that his convert should live with him, at any rate for the present, in order to assure and perfect the work of conversion. Afterwards the finished product could be let loose again, a holy decoy, to lure others into salvation's net. But good men do not expect silver spoons to be slipped into their mouths. Easy fortune finds them unprepared and a trifle suspicious.

Mr. Fortune sought to inoculate his good luck by a scrupulous observance of formalities. He put on his black felt hat and went to pay a call on Lueli's mother. On the fourth visit he happened to find her at home. Taking off the hat and bowing he addressed her with a long speech in which he drew a careful distinction between obedience to God and obedience to lawful authority. Lueli, said he, having become a Christian any attempts on her part to discourage him would be tempting Lueli to disobey God, therefore as God's priest it would be his duty to oppose them. On the other hand as Lueli's only visible parent and lawful guardian she had an absolute right to decide whether Lueli should remain at home, and if she wished him (Lueli) to do so, far from opposing her, he (Mr. Fortune) would enforce her authority with his own and insist upon the boy's return.

Lueli's mother looked rather baffled, and crumpled her face exactly as Lueli crumpled his in the effort to follow Mr. Fortune's explanation. But when he had finished she brightened, said that it was all a very good scheme, and asked if Mr. Fortune would like a netful of shrimps.

He spoke a little longer of his affection for the boy, and his plans for teaching him, explaining that though perhaps a European education might not be much use in Fanua, wherefore he was not proposing to trouble him with much arithmetic, yet a Christian education is useful anywhere and so Lueli must soon learn the Catechism; and then carrying the shrimps he set off to visit Ori.

Ori was the chief man of the island and it would be only civil and politic to consult him. Besides, there was always the chance that Ori might put a spoke in his wheel, a chance not to be missed by any conscientious Englishman. But when Ori had listened to the speech about obedience to God and obedience to lawful authority which Mr. Fortune delivered all over again (with of course suitable omissions and alterations) he also said that it was all a very good scheme. Wouldn't Mr. Fortune like a girl too?

Mr. Fortune refused, as politely as his horror would allow; for he had had more than enough of the girls of Fanua. He wished them no harm, it was his hope to live in charity with all men, girls included, and he had no doubt that when they were converted they would become as much better as they should be. But in their present state they were almost beyond bearing. Once upon a time when he was still a bank clerk and had leisure for literature the phrase "a bevy of young girls" had sounded in his ears quite pleasantly, suggesting something soft as "a covey of partridges" but lighter in colour. Now it sounded like a cross between "a pack of wolves," "a swarm of mosquitoes," and "a horde of Tatars."

The girls of Fanua always went about in bevies, and ever since his arrival they had pestered him with their attentions. He had but to put his nose into the village for a score of brown minxes to gather round him, entangling him in garlands and snatching at his hat. If he walked on the beach at sunset repeating to himself that sonnet of Wordsworth's:

> "It is a beauteous evening, calm and free,
>   The holy time is quiet as a Nun
>   Breathless with adoration; the broad sun
>   Is sinking down in its tranquillity;
>   The gentleness of Heaven is on the sea"

long before he had got to: "Dear child, dear girl that walkest with me here" he was sure to be interrupted by sounds of laughter and splashing, and to find himself encompassed by yet another bevy, naked from the sea, and begging and cajoling him to go bathing with them.

If he fled to the woods they followed him, creeping softly in his tracks. When he thought himself safe and sat down to rest, a head and shoulders would be thrust through the greenery; soon there would be half a dozen of them watching him, commenting and surmising on his person, and egging each other on to approach nearer. If he got up to walk away they burst out after him and taking hands entrapped him in the centre of a dance, wanton enough to inflame a maypole.

Once these nymphs surprised him bathing. Fortunately the pool he was in was only large enough to hold one at a time, so while it continued to hold him he was tolerably safe. But it was tiresome to have them sitting all around gazing at him as though he might shortly turn into a satyr. He told them to go away, he even begged them to do so, for the water was cold and as modesty compelled him to sit with as much of his person in the water as possible he was growing cramped. But all was in vain; they sat there as expectant as a congregation, and for once sat in silence. His zeal told him that, tiresome as it all was, this opportunity for proselytizing should not be missed. Accordingly he began to preach to them with chattering teeth, only his shoulders appearing above the surface of the water, draped in a sort of ruff or boa of water-weed. He preached for an hour and twenty minutes, and then, seeing that they would neither be converted nor go, he reared up out of the pool, strode over the shoulder of the nearest girl and proceeded (the word is more dignified than walked), blue and indignant, toward his clothes. Thank Heaven the young whores had not noticed them!

The best thing that could be said for the girls of Fanua (unless judged as trials of temper, mortifications, and potential stumbling-blocks, in which case they would have received very high marks) was that they afforded an admirable foil to Lueli's maidenly demeanour. Day by day he unrolled such a display of the Christian virtues, was so gentle, so biddable, so deft to oblige, so willing to learn, and just sufficiently stupid to be no trouble, that Mr. Fortune felt he could have endured even twice as many girls as the price of being soothed by one such boy. He had never beheld, he had never dreamed of such a conversion. Indeed if it had been his own work he would have been uneasy, wondering if it were not too good to be true. But he acknowledged it to be the Lord's doing and so he was prepared for anything.

But he was not prepared for his paragon to disappear without a word of warning and stay away for three days and four nights. For the first twenty-four hours he thought little or nothing of it: Lueli was gone birding or gone fishing: he was playing with his friends in the village, or he might be on a visit to his mother. Mr. Fortune had no objection. On the contrary, he was rather pleased that the convert should thus hie him back to the company of his old acquaintance. There had been something disquieting, almost, in the calm way Lueli had given his former life the go-by. He would not like to think him lacking in natural affection. So he slept through the first night and dabbled through the first day without feeling any uneasiness; but on the second night he dreamed that Lueli had come back, and waking from his dream he ran out into the dell to see if it were a true one.

There was no one there. He called: at first loudly, then he thought that Lueli might be hiding in the bushes afraid to come out lest he should be angry, so he called softly. Then he sat down in the veranda, for he knew there would be no more sleep for him that night, and began to worry, imagining all the dreadful things that might have befallen the boy, and reproaching himself bitterly for having allowed so much time to slip by before he awoke to the possibility of danger. Perhaps Lueli had been drowned. Mr. Fortune knew that he could swim like a fish, but he thought of drowning none the less. Perhaps running through the woods he had been caught like Absalom, or perhaps he had broken his leg and now, tired of calling for help, was lying snuffling with his face to the wet ground. Perhaps he had been carried off in a canoe by natives from some other island to serve as a slave or even as a meal.

"This is nonsense," said Mr. Fortune. "The boy is probably somewhere in the village. I will go down as soon as it is day, and inquire for him. Only when I know for certain that he is not there will I allow myself to worry."

For all that he continued to sit on the veranda, shredding his mind into surmises and waiting for the colour of day to come back to the whispering bushes and the black mountain. "In a little while," he thought, "the moon will be in her first quarter and Lueli will not be able to see his way back if he comes by night."

As soon as he decently could (for he had his dignity as a missionary to keep up) he walked to the village and made inquiries. No one had seen Lueli; and what was worse, no one could be persuaded into making any suggestions as to his whereabouts or being in the least helpful. There was some sort of feast toward: people were hurrying from house to house with baskets and packages, and the air was thick with taboos. Mr. Fortune hung about for a while, but no one encouraged him to hang on them. Presently he returned to the hut, feeling that the Fanuans were all very heathen and hateful.

Anxious and exasperated he spent the greater part of the day roaming about the woods, harking back every hour or so to the dell and the bathing pool on the chance that Lueli might have re-appeared. In the dell the shadows moved round from west to east and the tide brimmed and retrenched the pool; everything seemed to be in a conspiracy to go on as usual. By sunset he had tormented himself out of all self-control. His distress alternated with gusts of furious anger against his convert. Blow hot, blow cold, each contrary blast fanned his burning. At one moment he pictured Lueli struggling in the hands of marauding cannibals: in the next he was ready to cast him off (that is if he came back) as a runagate, and began to prepare the scathing and renouncing remarks which should dismiss him. "Not that I am angry," he assured himself. "I am not in the least angry. I am perfectly cool. But I see clearly that this is the end. I have been deceived in him, that is all. Of course I am sorry. And I shall miss him. He had pretty ways. He seemed so full of promise."

And instantly he was ravaged with pity for the best and most ill-prized convert the world had ever seen; and now, perhaps, the world saw him no longer. Even if he had run away and was still frolicking about at his own sweet will, there was every excuse to be made for him. He was young, he was ignorant, he had not a notion how much suffering this little escapade entailed on his pastor, he belonged to a people to whom liberty is the most natural thing in the world. And anyhow, had he not a perfect right to run away if he chose to? "Good

Heavens, do I want him tethered to me by a string?" So his passions whisked him round again, and he was angrier than ever with Lueli because he was also angry with himself for being ridden by what was little better than an infatuation, unworthy of a man and far more unworthy of a missionary, whose calling it is to love all God's children equally, be they legitimated or no. And he remembered uneasily how in visiting the village that morning he had not breathed a word of conversion.

The idea of having to worry about his own conduct as well as Lueli's agitated him so extremely that he fell on his knees and took refuge in prayer, imploring that his deficiencies might be overlooked and that his sins might not be visited upon Lueli; for it was no fault of the child's, he began to point out to the All-Knowing, that his pastor had chosen to erect him into a stumbling-block. But he was in too much of an upset to pray with any satisfaction, and finding that he was only case-making like a hired barrister he opened his prayer-book and set himself to read the Forms of Prayer to be Used by Those at Sea, for these seemed appropriate to his case. Thence he read on through the Form and Manner of Making, Ordaining, and Consecrating of Bishops, Priests, and Deacons, and had persevered into the Accession Service when there was a noise behind him. He leapt up to welcome the truant. But it was only a stray pig, looking curiously in on him from the doorway.

"O pig!" Mr. Fortune exclaimed, ready just then to disburden himself to anybody. But the emotion betrayed in his hurt voice was so overwhelming that the pig turned tail and bolted.

He addressed himself once more to the Accession Service. The prayer-book lay face-downward, something had fallen out of it, and lay face-downward too. It was a little old-fashioned picture with a lace-paper frame, one of those holy valentines that lurk in pious prayer-books, and in course of time grow very foxed. He looked at it. It was a print of the Good Shepherd, who with His crook was helping a lost sheep out of a pit. Careless of His own equilibrium, the Good Shepherd leant over the verge of the rocks, trying to get a firm grip on the sheep's neck and so haul him up into safety.

Smitten to the heart and feeling extremely small, Mr. Fortune closed up the print in the prayer-book. He had a shrewd suspicion that this incident was intended as a slightly sarcastic comment on his inadequacies as a shepherd. But he took comfort too, for he felt that God had looked on his distress, even though it were with a frown. And all night (for he lay awake till dawn) he held on to this thought and endeavoured to wait still.

Having been so tossed up and down, by the morrow he was incapable of feeling anything much. He spent the day in a kind of stoical industry, visiting the islanders and preaching to them, though they heard him with even less acceptance than usual, for they were all engaged in sleeping off the feast. During the afternoon he washed his clothes and cleaned the hut and in the evening he practised the harmonium till his back smouldered with fatigue; and all night he lay in a heavy uncomfortable sleep, as though he were cased up in an ill-fitting leaden armour.

He awoke stupefied to bright daylight. He could scarcely remember where he was, or who he was, and his perplexity was increased by finding a number of presences, cold, sleek, and curved, disposed about his limbs. Serpents! In a panic that was half nightmare he sat up. His bed was full of bananas, neatly arranged to encircle him as sausages are arranged to encircle a Christmas turkey. Who had put bananas in his bed? Could it be—? He went swiftly and silently to the door and peered into the dell. There by the spring sat Lueli, arranging shells round the water's edge as though he were laying out a garden. His back was turned, he was so absorbed in his game that he did not discover that he was being watched. Presently he rolled over and lay on his stomach, gently kicking his heels in the air.

Mr. Fortune had a good stare at him. Then he tiptoed back again and began to dress.

As a rule, Mr. Fortune was rather careless about his appearance, and compared to the islanders he was decidedly dirty, for whereas they would bathe themselves three times a day or more he considered that once was enough. But now he made his toilet with extraordinary circumspection and deliberation. He shaved himself as minutely as though he were about to attend an archidiaconal meeting, he parted his hair, he fastened every button with a twitch, he pulled his coat forward so that it should sit well on his shoulders, he wound up his watch and knotted his bootlaces so that they should not come undone. He even put on a hat.

All the while he had a curious sensation that he was dressing a man of stone that must needs be dressed like a dummy for of itself it was senseless and immovable. Yet *he* was the man of stone, his fingers that slowly and firmly pushed the buttons through the button-holes and knotted the bootlaces were so remorselessly and stonily strong that if he had not been managing them with such care they would have ground the buttons to powder: and if he had allowed them for one moment to tremble the bootlaces would have snapped off in his grasp like black cotton threads.

Walking terribly and softly, and still in this curious stony dream, he stepped into the dell and advanced on Lueli. Lueli turned round. It seemed to Mr. Fortune that he was looking frightened but he could not be sure of this for his eyes also were partaking of the nature of stone, they did not see very clearly. He came up to Lueli and took hold of him by the shoulder and jerked him on to his feet.

Then, still holding fast to Lueli's shoulder he said:

"Where have you been?"

Lueli said: "I have been fishing with my two cousins. For three days we went in our boats and at night we sang."

But Mr. Fortune did not seem to have heard him, and said again: "Where have you been?"

Lueli said: "We paddled round this island and away to the north-west to an islet of shells. I have brought you back these—look!—as a present."

For the third time Mr. Fortune asked:

"Where have you been?"

But this time he did not wait for an answer. Putting his face close to Lueli's and speaking with his eyes shut and in a low secret voice he began to scold him.

"Don't tell me where you've been. I don't care. Why should I care where you go? You made off without asking my leave, so what is it to me where you go to or how long you stay away? Nothing! For I cannot allow myself to love a boy who flouts me. While you were good I loved you, but that goodness didn't last long and I don't suppose it meant much. Why did you run away? If you had told me, if you had asked my leave I would have given it gladly. But of course you didn't, you went off without a word, and left me to worry myself half out of my mind. Not that I worried for long. I soon saw that you didn't care a snap of your fingers for me. If you were sorry I would forgive you, but you are not sorry, you are only frightened. I am very angry with you, Lueli,—for I cannot call you Theodore now."

Mr. Fortune's eyes were shut but he knew that Lueli was frightened for he could feel him trembling. After a minute he began again.

"I can feel how you tremble, but that is silly of you, it only shows how little you understand me. You have no reason to be frightened, don't think I would punish you with blows for I would never do such a thing, I don't approve of it. But something I must do. I must tell you when you do wrong, for it seems that you yourself don't know the difference between good and bad. Why did you run away without telling me where you were going? Was that like a Christian? Was that like a child of God? Do you suppose Samuel would have behaved so, whom you pretend to take such an interest in?"

Mr. Fortune had almost talked himself out. He was feeling dazed by the sound of his own voice, sounding so different too, and he wished Lueli would take a turn. But Lueli continued to tremble in silence, he did not even wriggle, so Mr. Fortune exerted himself to say a few last words.

"Come now, Lueli, what is it to be? Don't be frightened of me. I mean you nothing but good. Perhaps I spoke too angrily; if so, you must forgive me. I was wrong to scold; but you really are maddening, and I have been very anxious about you and not slept much since you ran away. Anxiety always makes people seem stern."

Now he spoke almost pleadingly, but he still had his hand fast on Lueli's shoulder. At length he noticed this, for his hand was no longer stone but flesh and blood which ached from the intensity of its grip. He withdrew it, and in an instant Lueli had ducked sideways and with a spring like a frightened deer he fled into the bushes.

Mr. Fortune was in a state to do anything that was desperate, though what, he had not the slightest idea. But suddenly, and completely to his surprise, he found himself convulsed with laughter. He did not know what he was laughing at till in a flash he remembered Lueli's bolt for safety, and the ludicrous expression, half abject, half triumphantly cunning, with which he had made off. To run away again when he was in such disgrace for running away—this stroke, so utterly unexpected, so perfectly natural, rapt him into an ecstasy of appreciation. He forgave everything that had gone before for leading up to this. And the brat had done it so perfectly, too. If he had practised nothing else for years he could not have surpassed that adroit, terror-stricken bound, nor the glance he cast over his shoulder—deprecating, defiant, derisive, alive.

He had never been so real before.

Mr. Fortune propped himself against a tree and laughed himself weak. He had laughed his hat off, his ribs ached, and he squealed as he fetched his breath. At last he could laugh no more. He slid to the ground and lay staring up into the branches with a happy and unseeing interest. He was looking at his thoughts: thoughts that at a less fortunate juncture might have pained him but that now seemed as remote and impersonal a subject for consideration as the sway and lapse of the fronds moving overhead.

How near he had gone to making an irremediable fool of himself, and perhaps worse than a fool! This came of letting oneself get into a fuss, of conscientiously supposing oneself to be the centre of the universe. A man turned into stone by a fury of self-justification, he had laid hold of Lueli and threatened him with pious wrath whilst all the time his longing had been to thrash the boy or to smite his body down on the grass and ravish it. Murder or lust, it had seemed that only by one or the other could he avenge his wounded pride, the priestly rage again the relapsed heretic. And then by the grace of God Lueli had leapt aside with that ludicrous expression, that fantastic agility: and by a moment's vivid realization of his convert's personality, of Lueli no longer a convert but a person, individual, unexpected, separate, he was released, and laughed the man of stone away.

He looked back on it without embarrassment or any feelings of remorse. Remorse was beside the point for what was so absolutely over and done with. Lueli had nothing to fear from him now—unless it were indigestion; for he proposed to make him some coco-nut buns as a peace-offering. They were quite easy to make. One just grated the coco-nut into a bowl, added a little water and drove the contents round with a spoon till they mixed. Then one formed the mixture into rocks, made each rock into a package with leaves, and baked them under the ashes. The results were quite palatable while they remained hot. And Lueli would take it as a compliment.

He would set about it presently. Meanwhile he would lie here, looking up at the tree and taking an interest in his sensations. "I suppose it is partly reaction," he thought, "but I do feel most extraordinarily happy. And as mild as milk—as mothers' milk." He was not only happy, he was profoundly satisfied and rather pleased with himself, with his new self, that is.

"And why shouldn't I be? It is a great improvement on the old. It would be absurd to pretend now that I am not entirely different from what I was then. I might as well refuse to feel pleased at waking from a nightmare. A nightmare, a storm of error. The heavens after a thunderstorm, and the air, are so radiant, so fresh, that they seem to be newly-created. But they are not: the heavens and the eternal air were created once for all, it is only in man, that creature of a day, so ignorant and fugitive, that these changes can be wrought. The great thing, though, is not to make too much fuss about it. One should take things as they come, and keep reasonably busy. Those buns . . . How I must have frightened that pig!"

This time there were no bananas round him when he woke and no sign of Lueli. He did not fret himself: knowing how very unfrightening he was, he could not seriously apprehend that his convert was much frightened of him.

Nor was he. For hearing his name called he came out from where he had been reconnoitring in the bushes with scufflings so soft and yet so persistent that they might have been self-commendatory, serene, perfectly at his ease, with a pleasant smile and his head only slightly to one side. He showed no tactless anxiety to sound himself in Mr. Fortune's good graces. Only when Mr. Fortune ventured on a few words of apology did he seem at a loss, frowning a little, and wriggling his toes. He made no answer, and presently introduced a new topic. But he made it quite sufficiently clear that he would prefer an act of oblivion.

From that day the two friends lived together in the greatest amity. True, the very next week Lueli disappeared again. But this time Mr. Fortune remembered his psalm and waited with the utmost peacefulness and contentment. Indeed he found himself quite pleased to be left to the enjoyment of his own society. It had never seemed very enjoyable in old days but it was now. For on this enchanting island where everything was so gay, novel and forthcoming his transplanted soul had struck root enough to be responding to the favouring soil and sending up blossoms well worth inspection.

Beyond a few romantic fancies about bathing by moonlight and a great many good resolutions to keep regular hours, Mr. Fortune had scarcely propounded to himself how he would be suited by the life of the only white man on the island of Fanua. In the stress of preparation there had been no incitement to picture himself at leisure. It seemed that between converting the islanders and dissolving soup-squares he would scarcely have an unoccupied minute. Now he found himself in possession of a great many—hours, whole days sometimes, without any particular obligation, stretching out around him waste and tranquil as the outstretched blue sky and sparkling waves.

Leisure can be a lonely thing: and the sense of loneliness is terrifically enhanced by unfamiliar surroundings. Some men in Mr. Fortune's position might have been driven mad; and their madness would have been all the more deep and irrevocable because the conditions that nursed it were so paradisal. A delightful climate; a fruitful soil; scenery of extreme and fairy-tale beauty; agreeable meals to be had at the minimum of trouble; no venomous reptiles and even the mosquitoes not really troublesome; friendly natives and the most romantic lotus—these, and the prospect of always these would have mocked them into a melancholy frenzy.

But Mr. Fortune happened to be peculiarly well fitted to live on the island of Fanua. Till now there had been no leisure in his life, there had only been holidays; and without being aware of it, in body and soul he was all clenched up with fatigue, so that it was an intuitive ecstasy to relax. He could not have put a name to the strange new pleasure which was come into his existence. He supposed it was something in the air.

As it was with leisure, so it was with luxuriance. Most Englishmen who visit the South Sea Islands are in the depths of their hearts a little shocked at the vegetation. Such fecundity, such a largesse and explosion of life, trees waving with ferns, dripping with creepers, and as it were flaunting their vicious and exquisite parasites, fruits like an emperor's baubles, flowers triumphantly gaudy or tricked out with the most sophisticated improbabilities of form and patterning, all this profusion unbridled and untoiled for and running to waste disturbs them. They look on it as on some conflagration and feel that they ought to turn the hose on it. Mr. Fortune was untroubled by any such thoughts, because he was humble. The reckless expenditure of God's glory did not strike him as reckless, and his admiration of the bonfire was never overcast by a feeling that he ought to do something about it. Indeed the man who ten years ago had been putting down in Mr. Beaumont's pass-book: Orchid Growers Ltd., £72 15s. od. had presently ceased to pay any special attention to the vegetables of Fanua, and was walking about among them as though they were the most natural thing in the world; which if one comes to reflect on it, in that part of the world they were.

But though he came to disregard the island vegetation he never ceased to be attentive to the heavens. To have time to watch a cloud was perhaps the thing he was most grateful for among all his leisurely joys. About a mile or so from the hut was a small grassy promontory, and here he would lie for hours on end, observing the skies. Sometimes he chose out one particular cloud and followed it through all its changes, watching how almost imperceptibly it amassed and reared up its great rounded cauliflower curves, and how when it seemed most proud and sculptural it began to dissolve and pour itself into now moulds, changing and changing, so that he scarcely had time to grasp one transformation before another followed it. On some days the clouds scarcely moved at all, but remained poised like vast swans floating asleep with their heads tucked under their wings. They rested on the air, and when they brightened, or changed their white plumage to the shadowy pallor of swans at dusk, it was because of the sun's slow movement, not their own. But those days came seldom, for as a rule the sea-wind blew, buoying them onward.

Lying on his stomach Mr. Fortune would watch a cloud come up from the horizon, and as it approached he would feel almost afraid at the silent oncoming of this enormous and towering being, an advance silent as the advance of its vast shadow on the sea. The shadow touched him, it had set foot on the island. And turning on his back he looked up into the cloud, and glancing inland saw how the shadow was already climbing the mountain side.

Though they were silent he imagined then a voice, an enormous soft murmur, sinking and swelling as they tumbled and dissolved and amassed. And when he went home he noted in his diary the direction of the wind and any peculiarities of weather that he had noticed. At these times he often wished, and deeply, that he had a barometer: but he had never been able to afford himself one, and naturally the people of the Mission had thought of a tea-pot.

On the first really wet day, however, he rushed out with joy and contrived a rain-gauge. And having settled this in and buttered its paws, he went for a long rejoicing walk, a walk full of the most complicated animal ecstasy, or perhaps vegetable would be the truer word; for all round him he heard the noise of the woods guzzling rain, and he felt a violent sympathy with all the greenery that seemed to be wearing the deepened colour of intense gratification, and with the rich earth trodden by the rain, and sending up a steam of mist as though in acknowledgment. And all the time as he trudged along he was pretending to himself how hardy he was to be out in such disagreeable weather, and looking forward to how nice it would be to get back to the hut and change into dry clothes, and boil a kettle for tea.

He was behaving as though he had never been out in the rain before. It had rained quite often in St. Fabien, indeed there were times when it seemed never to do anything else. But rain there had been a very different matter, veiling the melancholy quayside, clanking on the roofs of the rabble of tin church premises, and churning the soft grit of the roads into mud. It had rained in St. Fabien and he had constantly been out in it, but with no more ecstasy than he had known when it rained in Hornsey. No doubt the ownership of a rain-gauge accounted for much; but there was more to it than that—a secret core of delight, a sense of truancy, of freedom, because now for the first time in his life he was walking in the rain entirely of his own accord, and not because it was his duty, or what public opinion conceived to be so.

Public opinion was waiting for him in the hut when he got back. While he was still shaking himself like a dog in the veranda, Lueli appeared in the doorway, looking very dry and demure, and began to pet and expostulate in the same breath.

"How very wet! How very silly! Come in at once! Why do you go out when it rains?"

"It is healthy to go for a walk in the rain," replied Mr. Fortune, trampling firmly on public opinion.

"It would be better to stay under a roof and sleep."

"Not at all. In England it rains for days at a time, but everyone goes out just the same. We should think it very effeminate to stop indoors and sleep."

"I haven't been asleep the whole time," Lueli remarked in a defensive voice. "That new pot of yours—I've been out to fetch it in case it got spoilt."

While he was drinking his tea (Lueli drank tea also, because his affection and pride made him in everything a copycat, but he sipped it with a dubious and wary expression), Mr. Fortune found himself thinking of England. He thought about his father, a sanguine man who suddenly upped and shot himself through the head; and thence his thoughts jumped to a Whitsuntide bank holiday, which he had spent in a field near Ruislip. The sky was a pale milky blue, the field was edged with some dowdy elms and beyond them was a view of distant gasworks. At two o'clock he had eaten his lunch—a cold pork chop; and clear as ever he could recall the exquisite unmeaning felicity of that moment.

How little pleasure his youth had known, that this outing should remain with him like an engraved gem! And now he scarcely knew himself for happiness. The former things were passed away—the bank with its façade trimmed with slabs of rusticated stone—a sort of mural tripe; his bed-sitting-room at "Marmion," 239 Lyttleton Road, N. E., so encumbered and subfusk, and the horrible disappointment of St. Fabien. There had passed the worst days of his life; for he had expected something of them, he had gone there with an intention of happiness and doing good. But though he had tried his best he had not been able to love the converts, they were degenerate, sickly, and servile; and in his discouragement he had thought to himself: "It's a good thing I know about bookkeeping, for I shall never be fit to do anything better." And now he was at Fanua, and at his side squatted Lueli, carving a pattern on the rain-gauge.

The next day it rained again, and he went for another walk, a walk not so ecstatic as the former, but quite as wet and no doubt quite as healthy. Hollow peals of thunder rumbled through the cold glades, the chilling South wind blew and the coco-nuts fell thumping from the trees. He walked to his promontory and stood for some time watching the clouds—which were today rounded, dark and voluminous, a presentation to the eye of what the thunder was to the ear—and the waves. He felt no love for the sea, but he respected it. That evening the rain-gauge recorded 1.24.

The project of bathing by moonlight never came to much, for somehow when the time came he was always too sleepy to be bothered; but he was extremely successful in keeping regular hours, for all that so many of them were hours of idleness. Morning prayers, of course, began the day, and after prayers came breakfast. A good breakfast is the foundation of a good day. Mr. Fortune supposed that a great deal of the islanders' lack of steadfastness might be atributed to their ignorance of this maxim. Lueli, for instance, was perfectly content to have no breakfast at all, or satisfied himself with a flibberty-gibberty meal of fruit eaten off the bushes. Mr. Fortune made tea, softened and sweetened at once by coco-milk, and on Sundays, coffee. With this he had three boiled eggs. The eggs were those of the wild pigeon, eggs so small that three was really a quite moderate allowance. Unfortunately there was no certainty of them being new-laid, and very often they were not. So it was a notable day when it occurred to him that a native dish of breadfruit sopped into a paste was sufficiently stodgy and sticky to be perfectly well eaten in lieu of porridge.

After breakfast and a pipe shared with Lueli—he did not really approve of boys of Lueli's years smoking, but he knew that pipe-sharing was such an established Polynesian civility that Lueli's feelings would be seriously wounded if he didn't fall in with the custom—the hut was tidied, the mats shaken in the sun, and the breakfast things put away. Then came instruction in befitting branches of Christian lore: then, because the pupil was at hand, and it was well to make sure of him while he had him. For all that there were a good many holidays given and taken. With such an admirable pupil one could afford oneself the pleasure of bestowing it.

Since the teachings had to be entirely conversational, Lueli learnt much that was various and seemingly irrelevant. Strange alleys branched off from the subject in hand, references and similes that strayed into the teacher's discourse as the most natural things in the world had to be explained and enlarged upon. In the middle of an account of Christ's entry into Jerusalem, Mr. Fortune would find himself obliged to break off and describe a donkey. This would lead naturally to the sands of Weston-super-Mare, and a short account of bathing machines; and that afternoon he would take his pupil down to the beach and show him how English children turned sand out of buckets, and built castles with a moat round them. Moats might lead to the Feudal system and the Wars of the Barons. Fighting Lueli understood very well, but other aspects of civilization needed a great deal of explaining; and Mr. Fortune nearly gave himself heat apoplexy by demonstrating in the course of one morning the technique of urging a golf ball out of a bunker and how English housewives crawl about on their hands and knees scrubbing the linoleum.

After dismissing Lueli from his lessons, Mr. Fortune generally strolled down to the village to enlarge the work of conversion. By now he had given up general preaching and exhortation—not that he thought it a bad way to go to work, on the contrary, he knew that it had been sanctioned by the best Apostolic usage; but preaching demands the concurrence of an audience, even though it be one of fishes or pigs; and since he was no longer a novelty, the islanders had become as slippery as the one, as artful and determined in dodging away as the other. He practised instead the Socratic method of pouncing upon any solitary and defenceless person who happened to pass by. And like Socrates he would lead them aside into the shade and ask them questions.

Many charming conversations took place. But nothing ever came of them, and the fields so white for the harvest continued to ripple and rustle in the sun, eluding all his efforts to reap and bind them into sheaves and carry them into God's barn in time for the harvest-home.

He had now been on the island for nearly six months and every day he knew himself to have less attractive power. How he wished that he had thought of bringing some fireworks with him! Two or three rockets touched off, a green Bengal light or a Catherine wheel, he would have been sure of a congregation then. And there is no religious reason why fireworks should not be used as a means to conversion. Did not God lure the fainting Israelites by letting Himself off as a pillar of fire by night? He thought, though, that had he fireworks at his command, he would draw the line at that variety which is known as British Cannon. They are very effective, but they are dangerous; and he did not wish to frighten his flock.

From mid-day till about two or three in the afternoon, there was no possibility of converting anybody, for the islanders one and all went firmly to sleep. This was the time when Mr. Fortune went for his daily walk. After so much endeavour he would have been quite pleased to take a nap himself; but he knew the value of regular exercise and by taking it at this time of day he was safe from molestation by the bevies. He usually ate a good deal of fruit on these walks, because he had not yet accustomed himself to such a long stretch between breakfast and dinner. Indeed for some time after his arrival on the island he felt rather underfed. Dinner consisted of more breadfruit, messes prepared by Lueli, fish sometimes, roots flavoured with sea-water. Lueli preferred his fish raw. Sometimes Mr. Fortune made soup or opened a tin of sardines.

Dinner was immediately followed by afternoon tea. Mr. Fortune would not forgo that comfortable meal, so they had it as a sort of dessert. Then followed a long sub-afternoon, spent in various ways of doing nothing in particular. Lueli always went bathing then. He had no theories about it being dangerous to bathe on the heels of a large meal, and after an interval for digestion Mr. Fortune bathed too. Sometimes they paid visits, or received them. On these occasions Mr. Fortune never spoke of religion. He produced his pocket magnifying glass and showed them his pores. At other times they went sailing or took a stroll.

These were all pleasant doings, but perhaps the moment he enjoyed best was when, dusk having fallen, he lit the lamp. He had a peculiar affection for his lamp. It hung from the ridge pole of the hut and he felt about it much as Sappho felt about the evening star. It shone as though with a kindness upon everything that was dear to him: upon his books, and the harmonium; upon the bowls and dishes and woven mats that were both dear in themselves as tokens of the islanders' goodwill, and endeared by use; upon the wakeful shine of the tea-pot and the black tin box, and upon Lueli's sleepy head. He would often walk out into the darkness for the pleasure of seeing his hut lighted up within, the rays of warm light shining through the chinks in the latticed walls as though they were shining through a very large birds' nest. Overhead were the stars trembling with the intensity of their remote fires. The air was very sweet and the dark grass gentle underfoot as he walked round about his home.

He whistled to himself, softly, an air that Delilah sings in the oratorio of Samson—a rather foolish chirruping tune, in which Handel expressed his private opinion of soprano Delilahs: but he liked the words—

How charming is domestic ease,
A thousand ways I'll strive to please:

(after that they ceased to be appropriate).

A thousand, thousand ways he would strive to please until he had converted all the islanders. And planning new holy wiles for the morrow he re-entered the hut to eat a slight supper, and perhaps to darn a rent or replace a button, and then to write up his diary, to read prayers, and so to end another day.

Saturday and Saints' days were holidays, for himself and Lueli both. Lueli disported himself as he pleased, and Mr. Fortune watched clouds. On Sundays they performed the services appointed by the Church of England.

There was a week or two when he believed that he was in the way to make another convert. She was a very old woman, extremely ugly, not very agreeable and rather doting. But she seemed perfectly able to understand about eternal life, and showed great anxiety to lay hold on it. Mr. Fortune visited her daily and tried hard to teach her the love of God, and the Christian belief. But she seemed deaf to all topics save one—and her anxiety to lay hold became as the days went by positively grasping.

One day the wife of Teioa, a sensible woman whom Mr. Fortune had a great respect for, came in with some food for the invalid and overheard part of their colloquy.

"Live for ever," she remarked rather scornfully to the missionary as they left the house. "Why, isn't she old enough already? How much more does she want?" And though Mr. Fortune deplored her blindness, yet in this particular instance he admitted to himself that she had perceived clearly enough, and that his old woman was no sort of genuine convert, only very old and frightened and rapacious. None the less he continued to visit her, and to do what he could to comfort her. And often as he sat by her bedside he thought what a mystery this business of eternal life is and how strangely, though almost all desire it, they differ in their conception of what it is they desire; some, like Shakespeare (and how many others unknown?), coolly confident of an immortality

> Where breath most breathes, even in the mouths of men;

some, like Buddha, hoping for an eternal life in which their own shall be absolved and lost; some, like this old woman, desiring an eternity like an interminable piece of string which she could clutch one end of and reel for ever about herself. "And how do I desire it?" he thought. "I want to feel it on every side, more abundantly. But I want to die first."

In the end he grew quite attached to the old creature, and when she died, he was sorry. He would have liked, as a mark of respect, to attend her funeral (he certainly did not feel that he had any claim to conduct it himself). But no one suggested that he should, and he hesitated to suggest it, lest he should be offending against some taboo. So he went off by himself for a day in the woods and thought about her, and said a prayer or two. And in the evening he returned to Lueli. One convert at any rate had been granted to him, and perhaps it would be greedy to want more, especially as that one was in every way so exemplary and delightful.

The two friends—for such they were despite more than sixty degrees of latitude and over thirty years between them (and the latter is a more insuperable barrier than an equator)—lived together in the greatest amity. Lueli had now quite given up running away. He settled down to Mr. Fortune's ways and curled himself up amidst the new customs and regulations as peacefully as though he had never known any other manner of existence. Indeed Mr. Fortune was sometimes obliged to pack him off to the village to play with the other boys, thinking that it would harm him never to be with company of his own age.

Lueli was no anchorite, he enjoyed larking about the island with his friends as much as any boy should do, but what he loved beyond anything was novelty, and for this he worshipped Mr. Fortune, whose every action might reveal some new and august entertainment. The faces he made in shaving, the patch of hair on his chest, his ceremonious method of spitting out pips into his hand, the way in which his bootlaces went round the little hooks, his watch, his pockets and the things he kept in them—Lueli might grow accustomed to these daily delights, but he did not tire of them any more than Wordsworth tired of the Lesser Celandine. And there was more than this, and much more: prayer, the harmonium, the sewing-machine, religious instruction and occasional examples of European cookery. Prayer Lueli had taken to from the start, but the harmonium required more getting used to. At first when Mr. Fortune played to him he would sit as close as possible to the instrument, quivering like a dog and tilting up his chin with such an ecstaticized and woebegone look that Mr. Fortune almost expected him to howl; and thinking that he didn't really enjoy it he would leave off playing. But Lueli would then edge a little closer and beg for more and Mr. Fortune was only too glad to comply.

Like the harpsichord, the harmonium has a repertory of its own, pieces that can only be properly rendered on this instrument. Naturally I do not speak of the harmonium compositions of such recent composers as Schoenberg, or Max Reger: these would have been too difficult for Mr. Fortune to play even if they had been stocked by the music-shop he had frequented. But without being in any way a virtuoso—and some think that the harmonium, being essentially a domesticated instrument, sober and of a religious nature, is inherently unsuited for displays of skill—Mr. Fortune played quite nicely and had a repertory of many classical larghettos and loud marches, besides of course, the usual hymns and chants. Haydn was his favourite composer; and arrangements from the string quartets go rather well on the harmonium.

Lueli too was a musician after a simpler fashion. He had a wooden pipe, rather like a flageolet, of a small compass and a sad squeaky tone; and the two friends passed many happy evenings entertaining each other with their performances. First Mr. Fortune obliged, leaning forward at an acute angle on the music stool, his knees rising and falling like parts of a machine, his face very close to the music, his large hands

manœuvring among the narrow keys, or sometimes hovering like a bee
in a flower-border over the ranks of stops, pulling out one, hitting
another back with a tap, as though his fingers could read, though
rather short-sightedly, in black Gothic lettering on the ivory knobs
such names as Gamba, Corno di Bassetto, Bourdon, or Dulciana. And
then, when rising he released the last throbbing chord and stretched
himself (for he was a tall man and in order to adjust his body and
legs to the instrument he had to assume a rather cramped position),
it was pleasant to see Lueli discoursing music in his turn, and a
curious study in contrasts. For the boy sat cross-legged on the floor,
or leant against the wall in the attitude of the boy in the statue, an
attitude so physically nonchalant, so spiritually intent that whoever
looks at the statue, or even a cast of it or a photograph, understands,
sometimes with a kind of jealous horror, how musicians are free of a
world of their own, inhabiting their bodies as it were nominally or by
proxy—just as we say of a house: That is Mr. So and So's; but the
house is empty save for a sleepy caretaker, the owner is away travelling
in Africa.

Lueli's tunes were very long tunes, though the phrases composing
them were short; the music seemed to waver to and fro, alighting unexpectedly and then taking another small flight, and listening to it
was like watching a bird flitting about in a bush; the music ends, the
bird flies away; and one is equally at a loss to explain why the bird
stayed so long and seemed so busy or why it suddenly made up its
mind that the time had come for a longer flight, for a flight that dis-
misses it from our vision.

To tell the truth, Mr. Fortune was not as much impressed by Lueli's
music as Lueli was by his. His chin sunk even further into his chest
as he sat, his listening flesh was unmoved and he never felt the least
impulse to howl. Mr. Fortune, in spite of his superior accomplishments, his cultivated taste and enough grasp of musical theory to be
able to transpose any hymn into its nearly related keys, was not so
truly musical as Lueli. For instance, he never had the least idea
whether Lueli's tunes were lively or sad. They all seemed alike to
him. But Lueli learnt almost immediately to distinguish between a

march and a sentimental piece, and as the harmonies grew more and more passionate his chin would lift higher, his mouth would contract, and the shadow of his long eyelashes would shorten up over his cheek.

It would have been pleasant if the two musicians could have joined forces. Mr. Fortune by listening very often and pretty intently to Lueli's rambling tunes was able to memorize two of them, as he believed, perfectly. Sending Lueli down to the village he spent an afternoon practising these two melodies on the harmonium and putting in a part for the left hand. It would make an agreeable surprise for his boy, he thought, to hear his tunes played by someone else; and then with Lueli playing his pipe while he supported the melody with chords and figurations they would achieve a duet. But the surprise fell quite flat; perhaps Mr. Fortune's European harmonies had queered the pitch, perhaps he had misunderstood the time-values; in any case, Lueli showed no signs of recognizing the tunes, and even when their identity was pointed out to him he seemed doubtful. As for the duet plan, it was not feasible, for the harmonium was tuned to the meantone temperament and Lueli's pipe obeyed some unscientific native scale; either alone sounded all right but in conjunction they were painfully discordant.

Finding it impossible to convert Lueli's pipe, Mr. Fortune next essayed to train his voice to Christian behaviour. In this he was more successful; Lueli's voice was of a nondescript newly-broken timbre. He couldn't always control it and Mr. Fortune had to smoke his pipe very hard in order not to laugh at the conjunction of Lueli's expression, so determined in well-doing, and the vagaries of his voice wandering from the straight path and ricochetting from note to note.

He also taught him to whistle, or tried to, for he was rather shocked at the idea of a boy not knowing how to whistle, explaining to him before hand the secular nature of the act, and forbidding him to whistle tunes that had any especially sacred associations. But though Lueli screwed up his lips and almost burst himself taking in breath his whistling remained of a very girlish incompetent kind. On the other hand he showed an immediate aptitude for the vulgar kind of whistling which is done with a blade of grass. The first hearing of this was one of the pleasantest surprises that his pastor gave him. He mastered the technique in a few minutes and raced off to show the new accomplishment to his friends in the village. The fashion caught on like wildfire, and soon every boy on the island was looking for the proper blades of grass which are called squeakers. The woods rang with their performances and the parrots looked down with awe and astonishment at hearing men producing sounds so much more ear-splitting than anything they could achieve themselves.

The fashion raged like wildfire and like wildfire burnt itself out. The groves were peaceful again, that is to say peaceful as any groves can be with parrots in them (not that the reader should suppose that the parrots at Fanua were like the parrots in the Zoological Gardens: oppression makes them much noisier); and everyone was out in the salt-meadows, passionately flying kites.

The islanders were like that; enthusiastic and fickle, they would wear a whim to shreds and cast it away in the course of a week. Lueli was as bad, if it had not been for Mr. Fortune he would never have persevered in anything. It was provoking for a master to find his pupil so changeable and inconstant, all the more so because of Lueli's extraordinary docility and aptitude in learning. Nothing could have exceeded the readiness with which he accepted a new idea; and finding him so swift to become a Christian Mr. Fortune used to wonder why the other islanders would not respond as pleasantly to his teaching, for at this time he was still in hopes of converting the whole island. He preached to them, he prayed among them, every night and morning he prayed for them, he gave them biscuits and showed them pictures. They behaved themselves to him most charmingly, tactfully overlooking his blunders in etiquette, accepting him as their friend, though an unaccountable one. But his message they would not accept, it slid off them as though their very innocence and guilelessness had spread a fine impermeable film over their souls.

"After all," thought Mr. Fortune: "I have not made a single convert in this island though it is now almost a year since I came. For I did not convert Lueli, God gave him to me (by the way I must remember to call him Theodore). And God still withholds the others."

This was a comfortable point of view. It satisfied Mr. Fortune, all the more so since it agreed so aptly with his psalm, of which the last verse runs: "And that Thou, Lord, art merciful: for Thou rewardest every man according to his work." And he quoted this verse of it in the report which he handed to Archdeacon Mason on returning to St. Fabien to buy more stores and give an account of his ministry.

The Archdeacon frowned slightly when he laid down the report, which was a pretty piece of work, for Mr. Fortune had written it in his neatest hand and Lueli (under his direction) had tinted blue, fawn-colour and green the little sketch-map of the island which embellished it as a frontispiece.

The next day Mr. Fortune called upon his superior.

"My dear Fortune," said he after a few polite questions about the soil of Fanua and its marriage ceremonies, "this is excellent," (here he tapped the report which lay on the table). "Indeed I may say it is idyllic. But you must allow me to make one comment, you must let me tell you that there is such a thing as being too modest. Believe me, conversions at the rate of one *per annum* are not an adequate reward of your works. God's grace is infinite, and I am sure that your labours have been most truly conscientious; and yet you say you have only made one convert. This is not enough—mind, I would not speak a word of blame. I only say—if I may so express myself—that there must have been a leakage somewhere, a leakage!"

He paused. Mr. Fortune looked at his hands and realized how sun-burnt they had become.

"Compel them to come in, you know."

Mr. Fortune wondered if he should confess to his superior the one so nearly disastrous occasion when he had tried to use compulsion. But the Archdeacon's metaphor about the leakage had pained him and he decided not to. Instead he asked the Archdeacon how he would advise him to act in order to convert the whole island.

It was rather a shock to him to be recommended to take a leaf out of the Jesuits' book. However on the first evening of his return to the island he began to make some discreet inquiries of Lueli about what gods the islanders worshipped, though being very careful to convey by his tone and choice of words that he thought it a terrible pity that they should not worship his.

"Oh, they," said Lueli, offering him some more fruit, which Mr. Fortune refused since he had been stuffed with gifts in kind ever since the moment he got out of the launch. "Oh, they—they only worship one god."

This answer did not sound quite as it should: and in deference to his recent memories of the Archdeacon Mr. Fortune ran his convert through the Apostle's Creed before proceeding with his inquiries. It was quite all right. Lueli remembered the creed without a single lapse, and on further questioning Mr. Fortune discovered that the islanders worshipped one god each, a much more suitable state of affairs for heathens; although on thinking it over before he fell asleep the missionary reflected that in the island of Fanua conversion must necessarily be a slow business since he would have to break the faggot stick by stick. Just before he lost consciousness he began to wonder what sort of god Lueli had worshipped.

In the morning he remembered his curiosity. He said to Lueli: "What god had you before I came and taught you to know the true God?"

"I'll show him to you," said Lueli; and running into the bushes he presently returned with an idol about two feet long.

Mr. Fortune looked at the idol very seriously, almost respectfully, as though he were measuring swords with an adversary. It was a rather well-looking idol, made of wood and nicely polished, and he was pleased to note that it was not obscene; but for all that a slight shudder ran through his flesh, such as one feels on looking at a dead snake even though one knows that it is a dead one.

"Drop it," he commanded, and the boy laid it down on the grass between them. Mr. Fortune remembered the words of a female missionary from China who had visited St. Fabien on a tour. "The first thing I make my converts do," she had said, and as she spoke she clenched her hands till the knuckles showed up as bones: "is to destroy their idols. Then I can feel sure of them. And not till then."

Talking over her lecture afterwards Mr. Fortune had been of the opinion of the majority: that the lady missionary had been right. "I don't agree at all," said his friend, Henry Merton. "We teach that idols are the works of men's hands, things of wood and stone. To insist on their destruction is to show our converts that we believe in them ourselves, that we look on them with anxiety and attribute power to them. No, no, it is silly to take any idol so seriously!" And Mr. Fortune, who was humble before others, thought that after all he had judged too hastily and that his friend was in the right of it.

Soon after that, Henry Merton had died, and the words of the dead have a special value. Mr. Fortune remembered his friend's opinion, but he also remembered the female missionary. She had spoken with an air of authority, and for all he knew she might be dead too, she might even be a martyr. He stood and looked at Lueli's idol which lay on the grass between them and he wondered if he should tell Lueli to burn it. At last without saying anything he walked into the hut. When he came out again Lueli was scouring a wooden bowl and the idol was gone.

One of the Archdeacon's first questions about the convert of Fanua was: Had Mr. Fortune dressed him properly? And Mr. Fortune had replied with perfect candour that he had been too busy caring for his soul to think of his clothing. This too the Archdeacon had objected to, saying that dress made a great difference, and that when the other islanders saw Lueli dressed befittingly they would become aware of their nakedness and wish to be converted and wear white raiment.

"But they have seen me, I have never omitted to dress myself since I have lived at Fanua."

"No, no, of course not," answered the Archdeacon, a little testily, for really the missionary's simplicity was making him very argumentative and tiresome. "But that is not to the point, for you surely don't suppose that they look on you as one of themselves. You must clothe that boy, Fortune, you must make him wear trousers and a tunic. And at night he must wear a nightshirt."

So now, seeing that the idol was gone, Mr. Fortune called Lueli into the hut and began to measure him. He had never learnt tailoring, however he supposed that by taking great care and doing his best he could turn out a suit of clothes which might insinuate the fact of their nakedness to the islanders of Fanua, even if it had no other merit. He measured Lueli, he wrote down the measurements, he made his calculations and drew a sort of ground plan. Then he fetched a roll of white cotton and having laid it upon the floor and tethered it with some books he crawled about on all fours cutting out the trousers and the tunic with a pair of nail-scissors; for he thought that the nightshirt might rest in abeyance for the present.

The nail-scissors could only manage very small bites, and by the time the cutting-out was completed he was rather dizzy and very hot from taking so much exercise on his knees.

"That will do for the present," he thought, rolling up the pieces. "This afternoon I will visit my parishioners. Perhaps as they have not seen me for a week they will be more inclined to listen to my teaching. And I must keep my eyes open for idols."

But early on the morrow Mr. Fortune got out the sewing-machine and continued his career as a tailor. The sewing-machine was suffering from the sea-air, it needed a great deal of oil and adjustment before it could be got to run smoothly, but he mastered it in the end and began to sew up the seams. As time went on he grew more and more excited. He worked the treadles faster and faster, he had never, even for the most spirited march, trodden the pedals of his harmonium so frantically; the machine rocked under his zeal and all the time the needle kept darting up and down, piercing the cotton with small accurate stabs in a way that seemed to express a kind of mechanical malevolence. The seams were all finished, the hems were turned up; now it was evening, there was nothing left but the buttons. Those he must put on by hand.

All day Lueli had sat beside him watching his performance with rapture. It was the machine which ravished him, he was not so much interested in the clothes. But when Mr. Fortune called him in a rather solemn voice and began to dress him, holding up the tunic above his head as though it were a form of baptism, he too began to put on looks of solemnity and importance.

The tunic fitted tolerably enough though there was no elegance about it; but alas! the trousers were a sad blow to Mr. Fortune. For he had designed them on a two-dimensional basis, cutting out the back and the front in one operation on a doubled fold of the cloth, and forgetting that even the slimmest boy is bulkier behind than in front; so that when attired in these unfortunate garments it was difficult for Lueli to move and almost impossible for him to sit down. He, in his innocence, thought the trousers all that they should be, and late as it was he wished to run down to the village in order to wake up his friends and show them his fine clothes. But Mr. Fortune bade him take them off. It made his heart bleed to see his boy made such a figure of fun, and when the living Lueli emerged from his white cotton sepulchre he privately called the Archdeacon a fool and foreswore the idea of the nightshirt for good and all. But on the next day and on the next again he struggled to make a practicable pair of trousers, and in the end he produced a pair that were rather on the baggy side perhaps, but still they were tolerable.

Unfortunately by this time his convert's ardour was somewhat quenched. He had been measured so often, he had stood still to be fitted when he wanted to go fishing, he had had pins run into him and all this had made this particular novelty seem rather a tedious example of his pastor's odd ways. So though he put on his white raiment at command and walked decorously through the village beside Mr. Fortune to be an object lesson, his demeanour while admirably meek and civil, wasn't much of an advertisement for the happiness of those who are clothed in the whole armour of God.

The Archdeacon's theory was not borne out by events. The islanders were too much struck and roused to speculation by the sight of Lueli's apparel to spare a thought for their own nakedness. At first they were of the opinion that this was some new and powerful taboo invented by the stranger. They shrank back, and averted their eyes as if from some improper spectacle. Lueli's mother was actually moved to a display of maternal feeling. She rushed weeping from the crowd, hurled herself at Mr. Fortune's knees and began to implore him not to ruin the boy's prospects. Disentangling himself a little pettishly from her pleadings Mr. Fortune explained that clothing such as this would do Lueli nothing but good: indeed, she herself would be none the worse for something of the sort. She took him at his word, before he could stay her she had torn the clothes off her son and was squirming into them. She was several sizes too fat and Mr. Fortune saw his seams being rent open in all directions. He had to bribe her with a promise of the blue glass mulberries from his Christmas tree selection before she would consent to undress. Finally he had to ease her out himself. It was a good thing that the Archdeacon was not present, but for all that Mr. Fortune half wished that he had been.

On their return he sewed up the seams once more and called Lueli. The boy began to protest and argue. Then he changed his methods and started coaxing. Mr. Fortune had his own ideas as to how Lueli should be managed. Rising discreetly he opened the harmonium and said that it was time to study another hymn.

That night he lay awake, wondering what he would do if his convert rebelled. He had already decided to drop the Archdeacon's tactics at the first seemly opportunity: but he wished to choose the opportunity and do the dropping himself. He might have spared himself this anxiety. On the morrow Lueli donned the trousers and the tunic with a very matter of course air, and half an hour later went off to bathe. And it was a sure thing that if formerly he had bathed twice or thrice a day he now bathed as often again, undressing with a bland smile and folding up his white raiment with the utmost neatness. Of course it was a pretext; and the missionary wondered if his charge was learning to be deceitful. But Lueli's deceitfulness was so very open and unconcerned that it could scarcely be reckoned as the genuine article.

The clothes were always deposited very carefully in some place where they would have every opportunity of happening to fall into the sea. At the end of a week they were so saturated with brine as to be quite unwearable. Exercising his authority Mr. Fortune forbade Lueli to wear them any more.

Lueli would bathe anywhere; he seemed equally happy lolling on the Pacific Ocean or folded up in a pool the size of a bedroom basin with a little waterfall splashing on his head. Mr. Fortune was more ceremonious. It was he who instituted the bathing pool as a regular adjunct to their life.

About a half mile from the hut and near the cloud observatory was a small rocky cove with a half-moon of white shell-beach and a slope of fine sward running back into the woods. A small rivulet debouched here, very convenient for washing off the sea-salt in; and as the mouth of the cove was guarded by a barrier of coral-reef the water within was almost as still as a lake and so clear that one could look down and see the weeds twenty feet below slowly twirling their vast brown or madder-coloured ribbons, and the fish darting among them.

Mr. Fortune often thought of Robinson Crusoe and his man Friday as he sat on the rocks watching Lueli at his interminable diversions in the pool. Living on an island alone with his convert, spiritually alone at any rate, for though he had not given up hope of the other Fanuans and still visited them pretty frequently he could never feel the kinship with them which he felt so securely with Lueli, the comparison could scarcely fail to occur to him. And he thought gratefully how much happier he was than the other man. *He* was ideally contented with his island and with his companion, he had come there by his own wish and he liked the life so well that he proposed to continue in it until his death. So little did it distress him to be away from civilization that he was of his own will paring away the slender bonds that tied him to the rest of the world. For after the first visit to St. Fabien he had paid no more, and for the last twelve-month he had not even bestirred himself to write a report to be sent by canoe to the island of Maikalua, where a local steamer touched once a month. But poor Crusoe had no such contented mind. His is a tragic story, albeit considered so entertaining for school-boys: and though his stay on the island taught him to find religion it did not teach him to find happiness, but whether at work or at leisure he was always looking with a restless and haggard stare at the rigid horizon, watching for a sail, enemy or friend, he knew not.

"I see numbers of goats. Melancholy reflections." What a world of sombre and attentive ennui, thought Mr. Fortune, is summed up in those words! The goats might supply him with suppers and raiment, but not with a cheerful thought. Their antics were wasted on him, he observed them without a smile, without sympathy, as unresponsive to natural history as the traduced Alexander Selkirk of Cowper's poem; for the real Alexander was a much more congenial character who sometimes danced and sang with his troop of pet animals. True, Robinson was fond of his dog, and kind to him, setting him on his right hand at meal times even after he was grown "very old and crazy." He also gave a decent burial to the two cats. But these were English animals, fellow-countrymen, assuring relics of the time when he had been knolled to church with other Christians: and it was for this he cherished them, clinging to them with a trivial and desperate affection.

No! In spite of his adventurous disposition and his knowledge of the world, he was not really suited to life on an island, this man who is for all time the representative of island-dwellers. Of course, his island was very different from Fanua: larger, not so beautiful probably; certainly not so convenient. And no doubt the presence of natives would have made a great difference to him. He was the sort of man who would soon marry. "But to be honest with myself," thought Mr. Fortune, "though I came here to convert the islanders, except for my Friday I don't think I should miss their company if it were withdrawn. My happiness is of a rather selfish and dream-like kind and I take my life very much for granted. Why, I have not even walked round the island. That would seem strange to some, they would not believe in me. I should seem as absurd and idyllic as those other Robinsons, that Swiss family, who whenever they needed anything found it cast up on shore or growing on a tree. I should be even more unlikely than Leila."

And he began to ponder on how many years had gone by since he last thought of Leila. She came in a book belonging to his stepsister, and he had read it secretly and rather bashfully because it was a book for girls. But he had been obliged to read on for the subject of islands had always enthralled him. Leila was shipwrecked on a desert island with her papa, her nurse, a spaniel, and a needle. One day the needle was dropped by Leila and lost in the sand. Here was a sad to-do! But the nurse, a very superior politic woman, bade the spaniel Go seek; and presently he uttered a yelp and came running towards them with the needle sticking in his nose.

A very thin story! Yet it might have happened for all that it was so fortunate. Things do sometimes fall out as we would have them, though perhaps not often, for it is always the happy coincidences which are hardest to credit. Man, however gullible and full of high ideals for his own concerns, is suspicious of good-fortune in general. If Robinson had enjoyed himself on the island he would not have been received as somebody in real life.

"But I am in real life," thought Mr. Fortune, adroitly jerking a limpet to assure himself of being so, "although I am so happy in my lot. I am real too, as real as Robinson. Some people might even say I was more real than he, because my birth is mentioned in the church register, and I used to pay income-tax, whereas he was only entered at Stationers' Hall. But I don't agree with them. I may seem to have the advantage of him now, but it is only temporary. In twenty years' time, maybe less, who will even remember my name?"

From such reflections he would be diverted by Lueli politely handing him a long streamer of sea-weed, dripping and glistening, and freshly exhaling its deep-sea smell—a smell that excites in one strongly and mysteriously the sense of life—or beckoning to him with a brown hand that held a silver fish. These advances meant that Lueli thought it time for Mr. Fortune to bathe too, and to take his swimming-lesson —a turning of the tables which the convert considered extremely amusing and satisfactory. Mr. Fortune was a very poor pupil. As a child he had never done more than to paddle about, and now he was too old to learn easily. He did not lack goodwill or perseverance, but he lacked faith. Faith which can remove mountains can also float. Mr. Fortune had not enough of it to do either. In the depths of his heart he mistrusted the sea, an ambiguous element. The real sea beyond the reef he never dreamed of venturing in, he could imagine how the long nonchalant rollers would pick him up and hurl him with their casual strength upon the rocks. Even in this sheltered pool he could gauge their force; for though scarcely a ripple traversed the surface, to every leisurely surge that crashed on the reef the pool responded throughout its depth with a thrill, a tremor, an impulsion, and the streamers of sea-weed turned inland one after another as though they were obeying a solemn dance music.

But for all his mistrust he enjoyed bathing, indeed the mistrust put a tang into his enjoyment. And with looks of derring-do he struck out into the middle of the pool, his teeth set, his eyes rolling, splashing horribly and snorting a good deal, labouring himself along with uncouth convulsions, while Lueli swam beside him or round him or under him as easily as a fish and with no more commotion, seeming like a fish to propel himself and change his direction with an occasional casual flip.

The further half of the pool, under the wall of rocks whence Lueli used to dive, was extremely deep. Whenever he had got so far Mr. Fortune was afraid and not afraid. He had a natural fear but he had a reasonable trust; for he knew that while Lueli was by he would never drown. It was sweet to him to be thus relying upon his convert—that was part of the pleasure of bathing. On shore it was fit and proper that Lueli should look up to him and learn from him; but every affectionate character even though it be naturally a dominant one, spending itself by rights in instruction and solicitude, likes sometimes to feel dependent. People, the most strong-minded people, perfectly accustomed to life, being ill may discover this; and as they lie there, passive, tended and a little bewildered, may be stirred to the depths of their being by finding themselves wrapped once more in the security of being a good child. Mr. Fortune bathing in the pool did not go quite so far as this. His dependence was not quite so emotional and he was too busy keeping himself afloat to analyse his feelings very carefully; but he liked to depend on Lueli, just as he liked Lueli to depend on him.

Though so ready to learn swimming from Lueli he was less favourably inclined to another of his convert's desires: which was to oil him. He would not for the world have had Lueli guess it but at the first proposal of these kind offices he was decidedly shocked. Lueli oiled himself as a matter of course, and so did everybody on the island. They also oiled each other. Mr. Fortune had no objection. It was their way. But below all concessions to broadmindedness his views on oiling were positive and unshakable. They were inherent in the very marrow of his backbone, which was a British one. Oiling, and all that sort of thing, was effeminate, unbecoming, and probably vicious. It was also messy. And had Hector and Achilles, Brutus and Alexander detailed before him, all of them sleek and undeniably glistening as cricket-bats, he would have been of the same opinion still.

"No, thank you," he said, firmly putting aside the flask of scented coco-nut oil (scented, too!). Or: "Not just now, Lueli, I am going for a walk. Exercise is the best thing after bathing." Or again: "Unfortunately oil has a very painful effect on my skin."

But he knew all the time that sooner or later he would have to muffle up his prejudices and give in, for every day Lueli began to look, first more hopeful and then more hurt, and was perpetually (if figuratively) standing on his head in the attempt to produce some unguent which could not injure his friend's sensitive skin. So when he sprained his knee jumping off a rock he welcomed the pretext with feelings intricately compounded of relief and apostasy. For some weeks he confined the area of effeminacy to his left knee, and on one occasion he was base enough to lacerate the flesh in secret with a fishhook in an attempt to justify the statement about his skin. But Lueli was so piteously full of compunction and so certain that if he climbed a yet higher tree or went in a canoe to another island he would be able to procure a balm entirely blameless that Mr. Fortune was ashamed of the prank and counterfeited no more. Indeed he was beginning to enjoy what he assured himself was not oiling, nothing of the sort, but a purely medicinal process. And by the time he had finished with the sprain it struck him that something of the same kind might be good for his rheumatism. After all there was nothing but what was manly and might quiet him in Elliman's Embrocation—used extensively by many athletes and as far as he could remember by horse-doctors.

Mr. Fortune kept his rheumatism up and down his back, but inevitably a little of the embrocation slopped over his shoulders. By the end of six months he was stretching himself out for Lueli's ministrations as methodically as when in the old days at the corner of the Hornsey Parade he offered one foot and then the other to the bootblack. It did him a great deal of good and improved his appearance tenfold, though that did not matter to him. Nothing could make him fat, but he began to look quite well-living. The back of his hands grew smooth and suent, he ceased to have goose-flesh on his thighs, and one day, regarding himself more attentively than usual in the little shaving mirror, he discovered that somehow his expression had changed. How and why he would not stoop to examine into; but Lueli could have told him. For when he came to the island his face was so parched and wrinkled that it was like a mask of rough earthenware, and his eyes being the only surface in it that looked alive, also looked curiously vulnerable. But now his face had come alive too and instead of wrinkles had rather agreeable creases that yielded and deepened when he laughed. And his eyes were no longer vulnerable, but just kind.

But if Mr. Fortune had altered during his three years on the island, Lueli had altered a great deal more. Not in character though—he was still the same rather casual compendium of virtues and graces; nor in behaviour—for he still hung affectionately and admiringly round Mr. Fortune with a dependence which for all its compliance and intimacy yet remained somehow gaily and coolly aloof, so that the priest felt more and more that what he was rearing up was in truth a young plant, a vine or a morning glory, which while following all the contours of the tree it clings to draws from its own root alone a secret and mysterious life in which the very element of dependence is as secret and mysterious as the rest.

In the beginnings of an intimacy one seems to be finding out day by day more about another person's inner life and character. But after a certain stage has been reached not only does further exploration become impossible but things which one thought were discoveries become suddenly meaningless and irrevelant and one finds that one really knows nothing about them, nothing at all. They sit beside one, they turn their heads and make some remark, and the turn of the head and the tone of the voice and even what they say seem all familiar and already recognized in one's heart: but there can be no knowing why they turned and spoke at that moment and not at another nor why they said what they did and not something totally different. Though one might expect this realization to be agonizing it is so much part of the natural course of things that many people do not notice it at all and others, whilst acknowledging that something has happened, account for it perfectly to their own satisfaction by hypotheses which are entirely inapplicable.

Mr. Fortune, for instance, finding that he knew no more of Lueli than at the moment when he first beheld him kneeling on the grass, said to himself that he now knew him so well that he had grown used to him. In the same breath he was able to rejoice in a confidence that no phase of Lueli's development could catch him napping; and he plumed himself on his acuteness in observing that Lueli was growing older every day and was now of an age to assert himself as a young man.

For all that, Mr. Fortune could never quite compass thinking of him as such. Time in this pleasant island where the seasons passed so lightly and where no one ever showed the smallest sense of responsibility was like a long happy afternoon spent under the acacia with the children. However, Lueli was grown up (or would be, the moment he noticed the fact himself) and something would have to be done about it. Something particularly—for in matters of this sort it is best to go straight to the point—must be done about providing him with a wife.

A Christian wife. And of late he had made several inspections of the village with this end in view, keeping an open eye for all the young women, scanning them as searchingly as Cœlebs, artfully devising the like cheese-paring tests for them and pondering which would be the most eligible for conversion and holy matrimony. There were plenty of charming possibilities—by now he had quite got over his empirical aversion to them as bevies—though at first sight they

seemed more eligible for holy matrimony than for conversion, for one
and all they were smiling, wholesome and inclined to giggle. But of
course convertibility was the prime consideration. Perhaps by catching his hare and making a special effort? Mr. Fortune admitted that
during this last year his labours as a missionary had been growing
rather perfunctory.

Not that he loved his flock less. Rather he loved them more, and
to his love was added (and here was the rub) a considerable amount
of esteem. For seeing the extraordinarily good hand they made at the
business of living to their own contentment—a business that the wise
consider so extremely laborious and risky—and reflecting that for all
their felicity they yet contrived to do nobody any harm, he felt some
diffidence in his mission to teach them to do better.

And then he would pull himself up with a jerk and remember
fiercely that they were loose livers and worshipped idols. Moreover
they had rejected the word of God, and had made their rejection if
anything worse by making it with such flippancy and unconcern. The
seed he scattered had fallen into a soil too rich and easy so that the
weeds sprang up and choked it. Alas, all their charming good qualities
were but a crop of fragrant and exotic groundsel and their innocence
was like the pure whiteness and ravishing classical contours of the
blossom of the common bindweed, which strangles the corn and looks
up from the crime with its exquisite baby face.

Yet after all, he consoled himself by thinking, the apparent reluctance of the Fanuans to become Christians might all be part of God's
dealings. God proceeds diversely in divers places, and where His
servants had prepared the ground for wheat He may overrule them
and set barley. In some islands He may summon the souls with a loud
immediate thunderclap; in others He would go about it differently,
knowing the secrets of all hearts. God's time is the best. And perhaps
it was his intention in Fanua to raise up a people from the marriage
of Lueli as He had prepared Himself a people in the seed of Abraham
and Sarah. At this thought Mr. Fortune went off into one of his
dreams and he grew cold with emotion as he gazed into the future,
seeing in a vision Lueli's children and grandchildren and great-

grandchildren, mild and blessed, stretching away into the distance like a field of ripened wheat which the wind flows over and the sun shines on. They would remember him, for their fathers would have told them. But no, he thought, there was no need for them to remember him. For it is only the unsatisfied who want to be remembered: old Simeon in the fullness of his joy, beholding the light and the glory had no plea but to depart in peace.

Meanwhile, which girl? Ori's tall daughter, gentle Vaili, or the little plump one who laughed so much that he could never remember her name? It occurred to him that since it was Lueli's wife he was choosing Lueli might well be consulted.

Lueli was out fishing. Mr. Fortune sat till dusk by the spring, thinking out what he would say and choosing his metaphors and turns of speech with unusual pleasure and care as though he were preparing a sermon.

The long shadows had merged into shadow and the western sky was a meditative green when Lueli returned. In one hand he held a glistening net of fish and in the other a bough of fruit, so that he looked like some god of plenty, a brown slip of Demeter's who had not got into the mythology.

Mr. Fortune admired the fish and admired the fruit; but inwardly he admired Lueli more, this beautiful young man smelling of the sea. He gave a little cough and began his speech.

Marriage, he said, was a most excellent thing. It was God's first institution, and in the world's loveliest garden the flowers had asked no better than to be twined into a wreath for the bride. Men's stories commonly end with a marriage, but in God's story the marriage comes at the beginning. The ancient poets when they would celebrate the sun compared him to a bridegroom, the saints could find no tenderer name for Christ than the spouse of the soul, and in the vision of the last things John the Evangelist saw the church descending out of Heaven like a bride, so that God's story which begins with a mortal marriage ends with a marriage too, but an immortal one.

What did Lueli think? Did he not agree that marriage was a good thing?

Lueli nodded. His face wore an admiring and far-away expression, as though he were listening to the harmonium.

Marriage, Mr. Fortune continued, is a gracious act, a bestowal, and a token of man's gratitude to his Maker. When we are happy we needs must give; Lueli himself was always giving, be it fruit or fish, a strand of sea-weed or a flower. These gifts are transient and incomplete; the weed begins to lose its gloss from the moment it is taken out of the ocean, the fish and the fruit (unless, of course, eaten) go bad, the flower is broken from the stem, its petals will discolour and fold up in death; but whoever begets children gives life itself, gives that from which all gifts are drawn.

The procreation of children is the first end for which marriage is ordained. But that was not all. There was also the love of man and woman and the pleasure they had in one another's company. When he was a young man, Mr. Fortune said, he had often wished for a wife to be merry with. Now he was too old to think much of such things but none the less marriage did not seem to him less desirable, for now he understood as he did not and could not in his youth how sweet it would be to have the faithful company of one with whom he had shared his best days if it were only, as a celebrated English divine once expressed it in a sermon, that he might have someone to whom he could say: "How our shadows lengthen as our sun goes down!"

Mr. Fortune stopped. Lueli's silent consenting and his own thought had led him too far. He had not meant to introduce such serious considerations into a discourse on marriage, and the mournful sound of his own voice alone in the shadow of night suddenly revealed to him that he was sorrowful, although he had not thought he was.

"Tell me, Lueli, have you thought at all about whom you would prefer?"

"Vaili is a nice girl and her father would give her a good dowry——"

Lueli pressed up the tip of his nose with the tip of his finger and spoke in a soft considering voice.

"Or there is Fuma, or Lepe who loves singing. But I think Vaili would suit you best, so you had better marry her."

"I marry! No, no, Lueli, you are mistaken, I was not talking of myself but of you. It is your marriage I was thinking about."

"Oh! Were you?"

"Wouldn't you like a wife, Lueli? As you were saying, Vaili is a nice girl. She is gentle and fond of children, we could soon teach her to become a Christian if we gave our minds to it. I'm sure you could be very happy with Vaili."

A decided shake of the head.

"Fuma, then."

Another shake.

"Well, what about Lepe or Tialua?"

Mr. Fortune proceeded to recite the names of all the girls on the island, feeling not very respectable as he did so, but going steadfastly on because he was in for it now, he could not go back on his own sermon. But he might as well have recited the Kings of Israel and Judah or the Queens consort of England from Matilda of Flanders down to Adelaide of Saxe-Meiningen for all the effect it had on Lueli, who sat beside him listening decorously as though to a lesson and silently waving away each one of Mr. Fortune's nominees.

"But, Lueli, if you don't approve of any of these, whom do you want?"

A terrible possibility had flashed upon him. Suppose like the traditional young man, Lueli had placed his affections on some mature married woman? What steps should he take, indeed what steps could he take? He would not even have public opinion on his side.

"I don't want anyone. I am quite happy as I am."

"But, Lueli, you are young and vigorous. This is not natural and I don't think it is at all advisable. Why St. Paul himself—" And Mr. Fortune gave a short summary of St. Paul's views on the marrying or burning question, toning them down a little, for privately he considered the saint's conclusions a trifle acrid. But there was no shaking Lueli, who continued to asseverate that he found chastity an easier matter than St. Paul supposed, and in any case preferable to the nuisance of taking a wife.

It seemed rather odd and improbable to Mr. Fortune. But he let the matter drop and did not speak of it again. Lueli would change his tune all in good time no doubt. Meanwhile things could go on as before, and certainly nothing could be pleasanter. Of course, he was properly desirous to see the beginnings of that Christian family and he was much looking forward to becoming a godfather. He had already settled that since the proper consecrated kind of mugs were unprocurable the first child should have the tea-pot and the second the sovereign he still kept for luck. After that he supposed he would have to sacrifice the magnifying glass and the tuning fork, and after that again—well, he still had time to think about it. Indeed at present even the tea-pot seemed indefinitely postponed.

He was puzzled by Lueli, but he was not uneasy about him; when he went off by himself he did not speculate as to what he was up to, nor ask strategic questions on his return. He trusted the boy and he also trusted himself. He did not think he could be deceived in Lueli.

And so things went kindly and easily on till the day when he was to find out his mistake.

It was very hot weather. Mr. Fortune had been suffering from a severe headache, and had spent the whole day lying down in the shade with wet cloths on his head. About sundown he decided to go for a short stroll, hoping that the dusk and the cool airs from the sea would refresh him. He called for Lueli to come too, but Lueli was nowhere about, so he set forth alone, crossing the dell and going down toward the sea. As he went he admired the brilliance of the afterglow, a marvellous rose-coloured bloom that seemed to hang on the air like a cloud of the finest metallic dust. Perhaps his eyes were weakened by headache and so more sensitive to light than usual; but as he roamed up and down the shadowy strand, at each turn that brought him to face the west he marvelled, thinking that in all his evenings at Fanua he had never beheld the sky so vibrating with colour nor so slow to fade; for sunsets in the tropics are fleeting things, but tonight there was a strange steadfastness in the west. He admired it so much that it was not possible for him to admire it for very long, and there was still light in the sky as he turned homeward.

Ordinarily he kept to the same routes as faithfully as though they had been ruled for him with red ink. But tonight, lost in thoughts of he knew not what, he strayed from his direction and found himself approaching a little grove of coco-palms. They grew prettily together, laced with creepers and thickened with an undergrowth of ferns; there was something about the innocence of their arrangement which reminded him of an English copse, and the resemblance was increased by a little path that turned and twisted its way in among them. But in an English copse even the slenderest path is wide enough for two lovers to walk it with their arms about each other, while this path was so narrow that it was clearly the path of one who visited the thicket alone.

A parrot flew off from a bough above his head, uttering a loud cry. Mr. Fortune roused himself from his dream. He was not in an English copse, looking for bluebells and being careful not to tread on a nightingale's nest, he was in a grove of coco-palms on the island of Fanua, an island in the midst of the Pacific Ocean like an island in a story book. And he was looking for—? He was not looking for anything; for in all his time at Fanua though he admired the flowers he had rarely picked any. It did not occur to him to do so. One picks only the flowers that one learned to pick as a child—cowslips and primroses and cuckoo-pint, and pale starwort that grows in the dusty summer hedge and fades before one can carry it home.

Lueli was always picking flowers. Perhaps he came here for them, perhaps he had been along this path but an hour ago? At any rate some flower gatherer had; for lying at his feet Mr. Fortune observed a dark-coloured blossom like a stain. He stooped and picked it up. Yes, it was freshly gathered, it had not begun to wither yet, but it was moist with dew and felt cold and forsaken.

Presently Mr. Fortune came on a trail of lilac-flowered creeper caught up on a fern. He disentangled this and carried it along with him.

"Extravagant creature!" he said; for now he felt sure that he was on Lueli's track. "I could make myself a bouquet out of what he spills and scatters."

He still followed the path, wondering what next he would pick up.

A little further on he perceived a whole garland lying on a patch of greensward. He was in the heart of the little wood and here the path seemed to end.

"I declare that he's still child enough to be playing at houses. And this is the young man I've been trying to find a wife for!"

It looked exactly as though Lueli had been playing at house. The ferns and bushes were hung with trailing sprays of blossom which looped them into a pretence of being walls, and in the midst beside the garland was a platter arranged with fruits and leaves.

"What a child!" exclaimed the priest. "Yet after all it may not be Lueli. Why should I be so sure that this is his fancy-work?"

In an instant he was to be made quite sure. Something slim and dusky and motionless was reared up behind the platter of fruit. He looked closer. It was dreadfully familiar. He snatched it up and stared close into its face, a face he had seen before. And trampling on the garland he stood glaring at Lueli's idol, which looked back at him with flowers behind its ears.

It was quite obvious, quite certain. There was no chance of being mistaken, no hope of doubt. For all these years Lueli had been playing a double game, betraying him, feigning to be a Christian, and in secret, in the reality of secretness, worshipping an idol.

"It's my fault," said the priest, speaking aloud because of his desperate loneliness. "Not his at all, nor yours either," and he gave the idol a sort of compassionate shake.

"I have deluded myself wilfully, I have built my house on the sand. . . .

"I have forgotten the fear of God," he went on. "All this time I have gone on pretending that religion is a pleasant, is a gentle thing, a game for good children.

"But it is an agony!" he suddenly shouted out.

There was no echo. The sultry twilight was closing in on him like a dark fleece. He could scarcely see the idol now, but in his mind's eye he could see it, a face coldly and politely attentive, and the narrow polished shoulders over which a doll's necklace slipped and sidled as it shook with his trembling hands.

"It is torments, wounds, mutilation, and death. It is exile and weariness. It is strife—an endless strife—it is bewilderment and fear and trembling. It is despair."

Turning abruptly he left the thicket by the path which had led him in, and stumbling in the dark and feeling his body heavy and cold in the hot night he made his way to the hut.

It was all dark; but that was no reason why Lueli should not be within, for he had been so often warned to handle the lamp carefully that he was a coward about it and never touched it if he could avoid doing so.

Mr. Fortune threw down the idol and lit the lamp from his tinderbox. Then he looked round. Lueli was curled up on his mat. He had been asleep and now he opened his eyes and looked drowsily at his friend. Mr. Fortune said nothing. He stood in the centre of the hut under the hanging lamp and waited for Lueli to notice the idol.

Lueli parted his lips. He was just about to speak when he saw what lay on the ground. He raised his eyes to Mr. Fortune's countenance, for a moment he put on a confused smile, then with an ill-feigned yawn he turned over and pretended to have fallen asleep again.

"Deceit," said Mr. Fortune, as though he were reading from a notebook.

A faint grunt answered him.

"Lueli, my poor Lueli, this is useless. You can't get out of it like this. Get up and tell me what it is that I have found."

Lueli sat up. The pupils of his eyes were still distended by sleep and this gave him a frightened look; but his demeanour was perfectly calm.

"That?"

He shook his head as if to say that he really couldn't tell what it was.

"Look again."

Mr. Fortune spoke curtly, but it was from pure sorrow.

"It is an idol."

"Yes, and it is your idol."

Lueli gave a sigh of distress. Mr. Fortune knew exactly how much that was worth. Lueli hated any unpleasantness.

"You don't ask me how I came by it. I found it in a thicket near the beach, the lonely one. And there were flowers round it, and offerings of fruit, and look, there are flowers stuck behind its ears."

"So there are."

"Is this your doing? Why do I ask you, for I know it is. Lueli, you mustn't lie to me. I implore you not to lie. Is this your doing, have you been worshipping this object?"

"I picked the flowers."

Mr. Fortune groaned. Then he sat down like one who foresees a long and weariful business before him. Lueli edged himself a little nearer. He had rumpled up his brow into a grimace of condolence, he looked like a beautiful and sympathetic marmoset.

He said in a voice at once tender and sly:

"But why are you unhappy? I have done nothing, it is only my idol, and I just happened to pick it a few flowers. That is all."

"Listen. I will tell you why I am unhappy. When I came to Fanua I came to teach you not to worship idols but to worship God. I came to teach you all, but the others would have none of me. You were my only convert, you received my teaching. I thought you loved it, and I trusted you. Now I have found out my mistake. If you worship your idol still I am to blame. It is my fault. If I had done my duty by you you would have known better. But I have not shown you the true God, so you have kept to the old one, the false one, a wooden thing, a worship so false that you can treat him like a toy. As I came back tonight I was tempted with the thought that perhaps after all your fault was only childishness. And for a moment (to spare myself and you) I had half a mind to pretend to God that your idol was only a doll. But we will have none of that."

Now he spoke sternly, and at the last words he beat one fist against the other. Lueli started.

"I blame myself, I say, not you. I should have been on my guard. When I saw that thing four years ago I should have acted then. But I shut my eyes (I am most horribly to blame) and now, see what has come of it. You are in fault too, for you have been deceiving me. But

I know you are rather cowardly and very affectionate; your deceitfulness after all is not so surprising."

He could have gone on talking like this for some time and finding it soothing, but he knew by experience that Lueli would find it soothing too. He raised his eyes from his heavily folded hands and looked at the boy. Sure enough, there was the familiar expression, the lulled face of one who listens to a powerful spell.

He stopped short, nerved himself to deliver the blow and said in a slow dull voice:

"You must destroy your idol. You had better burn it."

With a vehement gesture of refusal Lueli sprang to his feet.

"Burn it," repeated the priest.

Such a wild and affronted antagonism defied him from the tautened brown body and the unswerving, unbeholding gaze that for a moment the priest was appalled. But his looks gave back defiance for defiance. They bore the other's down, and averting his eyes Lueli gave a sudden shrug and made as though to walk out of the hut.

Mr. Fortune was between him and the door. He jumped up and barred the line of retreat. Lueli wavered. Then he went back to his corner and sat down without a word. Mr. Fortune half expected him to weep, but he did nothing so obliging.

For a good hour Mr. Fortune talked on, commanding, reasoning, expostulating, explaining, persuading, threatening. Lueli never answered him, never even looked at him. He sat with downcast eyes in utter stubbornness and immobility.

The night was sultry and absolutely still. Mr. Fortune dripped with sweat, he felt as though he were heaving enormous boulders into a bottomless pit. He continued to heave his words into silence, a silence only broken by the hissing of the lamp, or the creak of his chair as he changed from one uneasy position to another, but the pauses grew longer between each sentence. He was weary, and at his wits' end. But he could see nothing for it but to go on talking. And now he became so oppressed by the silence into which he spoke that he could foresee a moment when he would have to go on talking because he would be afraid to hold his tongue.

A frightful imagination took possession of him: that Lueli was become like his idol, a handsome impassive thing of brown wood, that had ears and heard not, that had no life in its heart. Would nothing move him? He would have been thankful for a look of hate, for a curse or an insult. But with the same show of inanimate obstinacy Lueli continued to bend his look upon the ground, a figure too austere to be sullen, too much withdrawn into itself to be defiant.

Mr. Fortune heard himself say at the top of his voice: "Lueli! Don't you hear me?"

It seemed that his outcry had broken the spell. Lueli suddenly looked up and began to listen, to listen with such strained, absorbed, animal attention that Mr. Fortune found himself listening too. There was a sound: a sound like a violent gust of wind strangely sweeping through the motionless night. It came rapidly, it came near, brushing its way through the tree-tops. Like an actual angry presence the wind came vehemently into the hut and as though an invisible hand had touched it Mr. Fortune saw the hanging lamp begin to sway. It swayed faster and faster, widening its sweep at every oscillation; and while he stared at it in a stupor of amazement he felt the earth give a violent twitch under his feet as though it were hitting up at him and he was thrown to the ground. There was a noise of rending and bellowing, the lamp gave a last frantic leap, again he felt the ground buffet him like the horns of a bull and then with a crash and a spurt of fire the roof of the hut caved in.

At the same moment he felt something large and heavy topple across his body.

He could not move and he could not think. He saw flames rising up around him and heard the crackle of the dried thatch. Again the ground began to quiver and writhe beneath him, and suddenly he knew what was happening—an earthquake!

The bulk that lay on top of him was the harmonium. He was pinned beneath it—presently the flames would reach him and he would be burnt to death.

He felt no kind of fear or emotion, only a calm certainty as to what was happening, and with it a curious detached satisfaction at being able to understand it all so well. The flames would enclose him and he would be burnt to death, unless the ground opened first and swallowed him up. Then he remembered Lueli. What of him? He struggled again, but he could not get out from under the harmonium. The struggle reminded him that he was a human being, not only an intelligence but a creature defencelessly sentient that must perish by fire. Fear came on him, and self-pity, and with it a sort of pique; for he said to himself: "I know now he never cared for me. He has made off and left me to burn, just what I should expect." And at the same moment he heard himself cry out: "Save yourself, Lueli! Be quick, child! Never mind me, I am all right." And then, seeing Lueli bending over him, he said in a voice of command: "Lueli, I tell you to save yourself. Get out of this while there's time."

He saw Lueli in the light of the flames, he saw him put his shoulder against the harmonium and begin to heave it up; he saw the muscles leap out along the thrusting body—all with a sort of anger and impatience because his friend would not attend to what he was saying. Even when it was jolted backward and he was freed he lay where he had fallen, half-stunned, with no definite thought except to compel Lueli to obey him and get away before the next tremor sent the whole hut crashing down on them.

He felt Lueli put his arms round his shoulders, shaking him and hauling him on to his feet, and he noticed with surprise how stern the boy looked, not frightened, but extraordinarily stern, like a stranger, like an angel. The earth began to quake again, another sheaf of thatch slid from the roof and the flames leaped up to seize upon it. Mr. Fortune suddenly came out of his stupor. Stumbling and losing his footing on the wavering floor he caught hold of Lueli's arm and together they ran out of the hut.

Three times in crossing the dell they were thrown to the earth. There was something horribly comic in this inability to stand upright. It was as though they were being tossed in a blanket. They did not speak to each other; all thought of speech was forbidden by the appalling novelty of the uproar that was going on, rumblings and bellowings underground, trees beating against each other or crashing to the ground, the cries of terror-struck creatures. Lueli dragged him on, hastening toward the mountain. There was a little path that led up by the ravine, difficult to mount at any time and more difficult still in an earthquake.

"Why do you go this way?" Mr. Fortune asked, when the tremor had subsided enough for him to be able to remember how to speak. Lueli turned on him a face of terror.

"The sea," he said. "The sea."

Mr. Fortune had forgotten the sea. Now he remembered what he had read in books of adventure as a boy: how after an earthquake comes a tidal wave, a wall of water frantically hurling itself upon the land. And not daring to look behind him he followed Lueli up the steep path as though the sea were at his heels.

At last they came out upon a little grassy platform, overlooking the ravine. They were only just in time, for the earthquake began again. They sat side by side, holding on to one another. Mr. Fortune discovered that it was a brilliant and impassive moonlight night. He looked toward the ocean. It seemed strangely calm, incredibly vast, more solid than the tormented earth. A glittering path of silver across it reflected the moon.

They were close to the cataract. Tonight, instead of the usual steady roar of falling water, the noise was coming in curious gouts of sound, now loud, now almost nothing. He turned his eyes and saw the slender column of falling water all distorted, and flapping like a piece of muslin in a draught. For some reason this sight was overwhelmingly piteous and a sort of throe hollowed him as if he were going to cry.

At every shock thousands of birds flew up from the tossing tree-tops. In wild excitement they circled overhead, flying in droves, sweeping past with a whirr of innumerable wings, soaring higher and higher, then suddenly diving aslant, shot from the wake of their own vortex. Their continual angry clamour, passionate and derisive, swayed above the uproar of trampling earth and clashing forest. One bird came volleying so close to Mr. Fortune that he saw its beak flash in the moonlight and put up his hand to shield his face. As it passed it screamed in his ear like a railway whistle. He thought: "I should like to scream like that."

Although he and Lueli sat holding on to each other, Mr. Fortune had no sense of companionship. In this appalling hour there did not seem to be anyone alive save himself. He was the Last Man, alone in a universe which had betrayed him, abandoned on the face of an earth which had failed under his feet. He was isolated even from himself. There was no Mr. Fortune now, a missionary who had been a bank-clerk, an Englishman and a member of the Church of England. Such a one would have been behaving quite differently. At the best he might have been behaving much better, he might have been in the village, keeping troth with his fellow-men; at the least he would have been trembling for his own skin and calling on God. But this man sat on the reeling mountain side with but one sensation: a cold-hearted excitement, a ruthless attentive craving that at the height of horror would welcome another turn of the screw, another jab of the spur, another record broken.

The shocks were now coming so continuously that it was scarcely possible to say when one followed another; but he went on keeping count and comparing them, and if they seemed to be slackening off he was disappointed. He sat with his eyes shut, for so he could both feel and hear more unmitigatedly. At intervals he looked out seaward for the coming of the tidal wave. But the sea was always calm, as coldly calm as himself and a great deal more solid. "Yet it must come," he told himself. "It is certain to come." And after a terrific shock, accompanied by sounds of rending and shattering as though the whole island were splitting asunder, he thought with certainty: "It will come now," and opened his eyes once more.

Something had happened. There was a difference in the air, in the colour of the night. Had dawn come already? His faculties were so cramped with attention that he could scarcely receive a new sensation, still less analyse it. Yet he felt that there was something he must account for, some discrepancy between this light and the light of dawn. The sun rose—yes, the sun rose in the east, over the sea: but this light seemed to come from behind him. He turned and saw the sky lit up with the light of fire.

"The mountain is on fire!" he cried out. And at the sound of his own words he suddenly understood what had happened. The mountain was on fire. Its ancient fires had come back to it, Fanua was once more an active volcano.

Below the bed of the cold and heavy sea, below the foundations of the great deep, into an unimaginable hell of energy and black burning those fires had withdrawn. They had rejoined the imprisoned original frenzy that lies in the heart of the earth, working and wallowing in unknown tides, and once more the fiery spring had mounted, revolting against the encompassing pressure, fumbling in darkness, melting its way, flooding along its former channels until now it flared on the crest of the island, brightening and brightening upon the sky, a glow of such intense and vivid rose-colour that by contrast the moonlight turned to an icily-piercing blue. Cloud upon cloud of smoke rolled upwards and at every fresh surge of fire the vault of heaven appeared to grow more vast and haughty, and the stars seemed recoiling into space. The mountain shouted and bellowed as though it were triumphing because its fires had come back to it.

Mr. Fortune leapt to his feet. He waved his arms, he stood on tiptoe in order to see better. Though the next moment might engulf him he was going to make the most of this. But there was no need to be so provident, so economical. This bonfire had been preparing for decades, it would not burn out in a minute or two. Realizing this he sat down again and relinquished himself to an entire and passive contemplation, almost lulled by the inexhaustible procession of fire and smoke, warming his mind at the lonely terrific beauty of a mountain burning by night amid an ocean.

Clouds began to gather at daybreak. Only a pallor showed where the sun groped upwards among them, and the sea which but a few hours ago had looked so lustrous, and solid like a floor of onyx, was now pale and weltering.

The earthquake seemed to be over; sometimes the ground gave

a sort of twitch and a tremble like an animal that dreams a bad dream; but this happened at longer and longer intervals and each disturbance was fainter than the last. Except for the plume of foul smoke that issued from the crater and sagged over the mountain side as it was checked by the morning airs there was nothing to distinguish this daybreak from any other, unless, thought Mr. Fortune, that it was a peculiarly dreary one.

He was chilled with watching, and oppressed with the indigestion common to those who have sat up all night. He was also bruised with so much falling about, and his ribs ached from being crushed under the harmonium. But his excitement which in spite of all the adventures of the last twelve hours was still a deferred excitement, unsatisfied and defrauded of its prey, wouldn't let him settle down into a reasonable fatigue, but still kept his muscles strung up and his vision strained.

It seemed an age since he had last thought of Lueli. He looked at him now as though from a long way off and rather crossly and it seemed as though his vague irritation were in a way to be justified, for Lueli lay as though asleep.

That Lueli should sleep while he waked was enough. It showed that he was inconsiderate, incapable of true sympathy, an inferior being who hadn't got indigestion. Mr. Fortune heaved a loud short sigh. Lueli didn't stir. No doubt of it. He was asleep. He lay so that Mr. Fortune could only see the curve of his cheek and half his mouth, which bore the sad resigned expression of those who slumber. But bending a little over him to make sure, Mr. Fortune discovered that the boy's eyes were open and fixed mournfully upon the empty and tormented sea. There was something so devastated about that blank and unmoving gaze that the priest was awed. Why did Lueli look so old, so set and austere? The face so well known seemed that of a stranger: and suddenly he recalled Lueli bending over him in the burning hut as he lay helpless under the harmonium, and remembered that then his face had worn the same look, grave and stern.

Lueli had saved his life at the risk of his own, he had shown that greatest love which makes a man ready to lay down his life for his friend. And now the rescued one sat coldly beside the rescuer eyeing his unknown sorrow, and but a moment ago seeking some pretext for scorning and disliking him.

"What a hateful creature I am," thought Mr. Fortune, "and how this earthquake has shown me up! But Lueli has behaved well throughout, he saved my life, he kept his head, he didn't want to cheer and behave like a tripper when the mountain exploded." And in his thoughts he begged Lueli's pardon.

Still Lueli lay beside him, staring out to sea with the same mournful look. His silence was like a reproach to Mr. Fortune. It seemed to say: "You have slighted me unjustly and now I must forget you." Mr. Fortune waited patiently, he had a confused idea that his patience now must repair his former impatience. But at length his love could endure no longer, and he laid his hand gently on Lueli's arm. There was no response. Lueli didn't even turn his eyes.

"He is tired out," thought the priest. "That is why he looks so miserable." He said aloud: "Wake up, Lueli, you will make yourself ill if you lie there any longer so still on the cold ground. Wake up. Rouse yourself. It is all over now." And he gave him an encouraging slap on the shoulder.

At last Lueli sighed and stretched himself and turned and met Mr. Fortune's anxious gaze.

"I think the earthquake is over," he remarked in an everyday voice.

"Just what I said a minute ago," thought Mr. Fortune. "But he doesn't know I said it. What can he have been thinking of that he didn't hear me?"

He still felt slightly worried about the boy.

"We had better walk about a little," he said. "Ow! I've got cramp."

Taking Lueli's arm he staggered down the little rocky path. The morning was cold and now it began to rain. The rain was dirty rain, full of smuts and fine grit from the volcano. It might have been raining in London or Manchester.

Exercise soon restored Mr. Fortune to an ordinary frame of mind. He looked with interested horror at the wood they passed through. Many trees were uprooted or hung tottering with their roots half out of the ground, the shrubs and grass were crushed and trampled, boughs and torn creepers were scattered everywhere. It was as though some savage beast had run amuck through the glades, tearing and havocking and rooting up the ground with its horns. Lueli picked up a dead parrot, and once they skirted by a swarm of angry bees. Their hive had been broken in the fall of its tree, the honeycomb was scattered on the grass and the affronted insects were buzzing hither and thither, angrier than ever because now the rain was making its way through the dishevelled green roof.

"But it will soon quench them," thought Mr. Fortune. "And if some bees and some parrots are the only deaths by this earthquake we shall be well out of it."

He was uneasy about the villagers, all the more so because he had run away from them in their hour of peril. Also he wanted to talk to someone about the stream of lava which he knew would soon flow down from the crater. Provided it only flows to the south, he thought. He questioned Lueli but could learn nothing; Lueli had never been in an earthquake before, he had heard the old men of the island talking about them but the last earthquake had happened long before his day.

On nearing the village Mr. Fortune heard a great hub-hub, but it was impossible to discover from the noise of everyone talking at once whether they were lamenting or merely excited; all he could conclude was that at any rate they were not all dead.

When he appeared, with Lueli following sedately behind, a crowd of gesticulating islanders rushed forward, all waving their arms and shouting. The thought leapt up in his mind: "Suppose they think that *I* am responsible for this earthquake? Perhaps they will kill me to appease the mountain!" He had never felt less in the mood for martyrdom. The last twelve hours had given him more than enough to cope with. Yet even if the fervour of his faith were lacking he could make a shift to die decently: and he stiffened himself and went forward. But Lueli? Suppose they wanted to martyr him too? No! That he would not allow. While there was a kick left in him he would see to that. He glanced back as though to reassure him, but as he caught sight of him he remembered that Lueli was not a Christian, nor ever had been one. What a sell if they should sacrifice him before there was time to explain! Well, this made it even more urgent a matter to defend him: martyrdom was one thing, miscarriage of justice quite another.

But Mr. Fortune need not have been agitated. The islanders had no intention but to welcome him and Lueli, and to rejoice round them over their safety; which they did with the pleasanter excitement and conviction since naturally, in the emotions of the night, they had not given them a thought till now.

Half smothered and quite deafened, Mr. Fortune pushed through the throng, saying: "Where is Ori?" For having lived so long on the island he had fallen into the proper respect for a chief, and depended on Ori rather more than he would have liked to admit. "He is almost like another European,"—so the priest explained to himself. At this juncture Ori was behaving very much like a European, for he was partaking of one of those emergency breakfasts, sketchy in form but extremely solid and comprehensive in content, with which the white races consummate and, as it were, justify any fly-by-night catastrophe. Seeing Mr. Fortune he politely invited him to sit down and take a share. "But the flow of lava?" inquired Mr. Fortune, wiping his mouth. "Do you think it will come this way?" Ori took another handful of stirabout. "There are no signs of it so far and if it comes this way it will not come here yet."

"But do you think it will come this way?"

"My god says, No."

When breakfast was finished Ori got up and went off with the other men of consequence to make an inquisition into the damage done by the pigs. They had come bolting down from the woods and wrought even more serious havoc than the earthquake, which had only shaken down a house or two, whereas the pigs had trespassed into every enclosure and eaten all the provisions. Mr. Fortune felt a little slighted that he was not invited to go too. Apparently Ori did not quite regard him as another Fanuan. "Oh, well," he said. "Perhaps they meant it politely, seeing that I had not finished my breakfast." But though he felt as if he were hungry he had no real appetite, and rising he prepared to walk back to his hut.

It was as though the earthquake had literally shaken his wits. All his recollections were dislodged and tumbled together, he knew they were there somewhere, but he could not find them, just as he had mislaid the discovery of overnight until, turning to view Lueli as a possible martyr, he beheld and recognized him as the idolater he was and always had been. Now he was walking to the hut in the same kind of oblivion. He must have remembered the lamp tossing its flame up to the roof, the burning sheaves of thatch falling down around him, for he had a very clear vision of Lueli's face bending over him, so violently modelled by the flames that it had looked like the face, sad and powerful, of a stranger, of an angel. But his thoughts went no further; and even when the smell of charred wood came sadly to his nostrils through the falling rain he did not put two and two together.

"I wonder if those pigs have messed up my place too," he said. A sigh out of the air answered him. He had not noticed till then that Lueli was following.

"Poor Lueli, you must be so tired!" There was no answer and still the boy lagged behind. He must be tired indeed. Mr. Fortune stopped. He was about to speak once more, bidding Lueli to lean on him and take heart, when suddenly the boy shot past him, running desperately, and whispering to himself as he ran as though he were imploring his own mind.

Mr. Fortune hastened after him. Would all this strangeness, this bewilderment, this nightmare of familiar living confounded and turned backward never come to an end? He hastened on into the smell of burning and pulling aside the drooping fronds of a banana tree which, uprooted, had fallen and lay across the pathway like a screen, he beheld the ruins of the hut.

One wall was still standing, a few pale flames licking wistfully over it. The rest was charred logs and hummocks of grey ash, sizzling under the rain—for now it was raining more and more heavily. Looking round on the devastation he began to recognize the remains of his belongings. Those shreds of tinder were his clothes. That scrap of shrivelled leather, that wasting impalpable bulk of feathery print was his Bible; there lay the medicine chest and there the sewing-machine, and this, this intricate ruin of molten metal tubes, charred rubber and dislocated machinery was the harmonium, its scorched ivory keys strewed round about it like teeth fallen from a monstrous head.

Lueli was there, but he seemed to have no thought for the unfortunate priest amid the ruins of his home. Wading among the hot ashes, crouching close to the wreckage, turning over this and that with rapid and trembling hands, Lueli was searching with desperate anxiety for— Mr. Fortune knew not what. At length he gave a bitter cry and cast himself upon the ground.

Instantly Mr. Fortune was kneeling beside him, patting his shoulder, trying to lift the averted head.

"What is it, Lueli? What is it, my dear, dear friend?"

Lueli sat up and turned on him a face discoloured and petrified into an expression of such misery that he could hardly endure to look at it.

"What is it? Are you hurt? Are you ill?"

The expression never changed.

"Are you frightened, Lueli? Has it upset you to find our home burnt to the ground? But never mind! We will soon have another, it is nothing to grieve for."

He would have said that Lueli did not hear him, so unmoving he sat, so utterly aloof, but that at these last words a very slight smile of scorn quivered on the dry lips.

Then Mr. Fortune remembered. He hung his head and when he spoke again it was with the grave voice in which we address the bereaved.

"Is it your god you were looking for? Is he gone?"

Lueli did not answer. But it was clear that he had both heard and understood, for he fixed his eyes on the priest's face with the look of an animal which knows itself at man's mercy but does not know what man intends to do to it.

"My poor Lueli! Is that it? . . . Is it so dreadful? Yes, I know it must be, I know, I know. I would do anything to comfort you, but I cannot think now, I can only tell you how I pity you with my whole heart. I do, indeed I do. Believe me, though I told you to burn your god, yet at this moment, if it were possible for me, I think I would even give it to you again."

He spoke very slowly, scarcely daring to lift his gaze to the sorrow which sat beside him, not answering, not crying out, meek with the meekness of despair. And still Lueli listened, and still looked, with his expression wavering between timidity and antagonism.

"Lueli, I spoke very harshly to you last night, not like a Christian, not as one sad human being should speak to another. In blaspheming against your god I blasphemed against my own. And now I can't comfort you. I don't deserve to. I can only sit beside you and be sorry."

Lueli never answered and Mr. Fortune acted his last words, sitting mournfully beside him in the rain. After an hour or so Lueli began to topple forward, then suddenly he lay down and fell asleep.

Now Mr. Fortune had time to think, and though he was dog-tired think he must. For after a while Lueli would wake again, and then the missionary must have some settled reasonable comfort for him, some plan of consolation. On the face of it nothing could be clearer. He should say something of this sort: "Your god, Lueli, was only made of wood, perishable and subject to accidents, like man who is made of flesh. He is now burnt, and his ashes are lost among the other ashes. Now will you not see that my God is a better God than yours, and turn to Him? For my God is from everlasting, even though the earth shake. He cannot be moved."

Yes, that was the sort of thing to say, but he felt a deep reluctance to saying it. It seemed ungentlemanly to have such a superior invulnerable God, part of that European conspiracy which opposes gunboats to canoes and rifles to bows and arrows, which showers death from the mountains upon Indian villages, which rounds up the Negro in an empire and tricks him of his patrimony.

Mr. Fortune remembered the Man of Sorrows. Would Lueli accept in the place of his wooden god a God that had once been made flesh? In the old days Lueli had enjoyed hearing about Jesus, though Mr. Fortune had always suspected him of preferring Joshua. Many, very many must have taken Jesus to their hearts out of pity; following the example of the woman who washed His feet although to her they were most likely but the feet of a wayfaring man. But it was rare to find a Polynesian accepting Him for these mortal motives, they themselves were not sorrowful enough. Probably despite the loss of his god Lueli would still prefer the more robust and stirring character of Joshua.

The trumpet that shall awaken the dead with the sanction of the resurrection is louder than all the rams' horns that blew down Jericho. As an honest priest it was Mr. Fortune's duty to preach, not only Christ crucified but also Christ arisen to comfort His followers awhile with neighbourly humanity ere He ascended to His Father. If this were all, it might suit Lueli very well: but in a twinkling it would lead him on to the Trinity, a mysterious sign revolving in the heavens from everlasting, a triangle that somehow is also a sphere. And so he was back again where he started from, embarrassed with a God so superior to poor Lueli's that to insist upon him now would be heartless boasting, would be exploiting an unfair advantage, wouldn't be cricket.

"If I were a proper missionary,"—he burst out in a cross voice. And then with a wry grin he added: "It doesn't look as though I were any sort of missionary. Lord, what a mess I've made of it!"

He had indeed. The mess amid which he sat was nothing to it. Disconsolately, he looked at his watch. It had stopped. In the stress of overnight he had forgotten to wind it up, and now it recorded the epoch at which his last link with European civilization had been snapped—eight hours thirty-five minutes. It could not be much later than that now. But a miss is as good as a mile, and for the rest of his sojourn on the island, for the rest of his life maybe, he would not know what o'clock it was. This circumstance, not serious in itself and not to be compared with the loss of the medicine chest or his books, upset him horribly. He felt frightened, he felt as small and as desperate as a child lost. "I must set it as best I can," he thought. "After all, time is a convention, just like anything else. My watch will measure out my days and remind me to be up and doing just as well though it be a little askew. And no doubt I shall die at my appointed hour however erroneously I reckon to it."

But what time was it? The sky was overcast, he could not guess by the sun and he could not guess by his own time-feeling either, for his body had lost touch with ordinary life. He sat debating between nine-seventeen, five past ten, ten-forty-three, eleven-twenty—indecisive times which all seemed reasonably probable, and noon exactly, which was bracing and decisive, a good moment to begin a new era—but too good to be true. At last he settled on ten twenty-five; but even so he still delayed, for he felt a superstitious reluctance to move the hands and so to destroy the last authentic witness his watch could bear him. Five minutes, he judged, had been spent in this weak-minded dallying: so resolutely he set the hands to ten-thirty and wound the poor machine up. It began to tick, innocently, obediently. It had set out on its fraudulent career.

It was a good watch, painstaking and punctual, its voice was confident, it had an honest face; but henceforth its master had lost his trust in it, and though he wore it (like a wife) at bed and board and wound it up regularly and hung it on a tree when he went bathing, yet he never could feel it was his true wife (watch, I mean) again.

Still Lueli slept.

"I make all this fuss," thought Mr. Fortune. "I even feel helpless and abandoned, because I have lost my reckoning of time. How much worse to lose one's God!"

Thus the watch diversion over and done with, and the new time being ten-thirty-one, he was back on the old problem. What could he do for poor Lueli who had lost his god? "And it was for me that he lost it," he thought, with a poignancy of feeling that was almost irritation. "He might have picked up his god and run out of the hut with it, but he would not leave me under the harmonium." It was heroic, desperately heroic. . . . Yet there might have been time to save both? A god that could be picked up in one hand. Had Lueli in the flurry of the moment forgotten that the idol lay on the floor of the hut? But no, one would not forget one's god, thought he, even in an earthquake.

Now he could understand why Lueli had seemed so cold in the early morning, so aloof and unlike his usual self. When he had lain staring out to sea with that strange expression he had been tasting what it feels like to be without a god. And when they approached the hut that was why he had lagged behind until the last explosion of hope had sent him running to seek his god among the wood-ashes. Now he was asleep. But he would not sleep much longer. Already he had stirred once or twice, and sighed, as those do who must soon awaken. And still Mr. Fortune had not settled how to deal with him when he awoke. Would the Man of Sorrows fit his sorrowful case, He who had once cried out, *"Eloi, Eloi, lama sabachthani?"* Or would it be better to try Jehovah, a tribal character whose voice was in the clouds, whose arrows stuck very fast? The worst of it was that Lueli knew all about them already. For three years he had been living on the terms of the greatest intimacy with them, he was even at home with the Trinity. And so all that Mr. Fortune could tell him now would be but a twice-told tale; and that was not likely to be of much effect, for Polynesians are fickle, they tire as easily as children and must be bribed with novelties.

Mr. Fortune grew increasingly despondent. He was even growing bored, and more and more quickly he turned over in his mind the various expedients of Godhead which might appeal to Lueli, like a woman tossing over a piece-bag in search of something she cannot find. The blue print, the grey merino, the long and ever more tangled trail of metal lace, a scrap of corduroy: none of these is what she looks for, and what she looks for is not there.

"I can do nothing," he cried out; and then an inner voice finishing the quotation for him added, "without Thee."

Of course he could do nothing without God. Why had he not thought of that before? Why, instead of vain thinking, hadn't he prayed?

He looked about him. He was alone in a mesh of rain. For leagues around the rain was falling, falling upon the quenched ashes of his homestead where were mingled and quenched too the ashes of Lueli's god, falling upon the motionless forest, falling upon the moving ocean, on that vast watery and indivisible web of tides and currents, falling everywhere with an equal and unstaying pressure. Only upon the newly-open mouth of the pit was the rain not falling, for there the flames rushed up and caught and consumed it.

There had been an earthquake and now it was raining. Both events were equally natural, equally accountable for, equally inevitable. There was nowhere any room for chance; no happening from the greatest to the least could be altered or provoked or turned aside. And why should he specify into greatest or least? In causation there is no great or small. He himself was as great as the mountain, as little as the least of the ashes of Lueli's god.

Still he looked about him. But he was not looking for anything now nor did he need to raise his eyes to heaven or close them before any presence unseen. The God who had walked with him upon the island had gone. He had ascended in the flames that had burst roaring and devouring from the mountain-top, and hiding His departure in clouds of smoke, He had gone up and was lost in space.

Mr. Fortune no longer believed in a God.

It had all happened quite quietly, just like that. Once he put out his hand as though to arrest something that was floating away out of reach, but in a moment it dropped again. And there it was before him, resting upon his knees, the hand of a man who didn't any longer believe in a God, with fingers idly patting out a slow and flagging rhythm, tick-tock like a time-piece that is running down. The real time-piece went on nimbly enough, it was now (he noticed) five minutes to eleven of the new era. If his diary had not been burnt he could have mentioned in it with impressive accuracy: "At 10:45 a.m. (N. T.) I ceased to believe in God." This quaint fancy gave him pleasure.

How differently to Lueli was he taking his loss. The reason must be that Lueli though losing his god had kept his faith. Lueli had lost something real, like losing an umbrella; he had lost it with frenzy and conviction. But *his* loss was utter and retrospective, a lightning-flash loss which had wiped out a whole life-time of having. In fact the best way of expressing it, though it sounded silly and paradoxical, was to say that what he had lost for ever was nothing. "For ever is a word that stretches backward too," he explained to himself. If any proof were needed his own behaviour was supplying it. He had ceased to believe in God but this was making no difference to him. Consequently what he had ceased to believe in had never been.

He sighed—the loud horse's sigh of one who has come to the end of a long stint. Then he stood up amid the rain and the ashes and stretched himself. He had got pins and needles in his legs from sitting still for so long, but it was a pleasure to his body to stretch and he stretched once more. The air struck cold on the muscles and skin which had, as it were, started to live again. He felt at once both tired and vigorous. In an odd way he was feeling rather pleased with himself, a pleasure that was perhaps the independent pleasure of his flesh which had waited patiently around his motionless thinking as a dog waits at the feet of its master absorbed in writing. The pen is thrown down rather wantonly, so that the ink may give a little spurt on to the page that a moment ago was all the world, that now is finished and prostrate and floutable. The master gets up and stretches, the dog gambols round him with congratulations. "Now you have come home to your senses again, now we can be reasonable and go for a walk!"

He leant down and gave Lueli a little shake, affectionate but brisk.

"Wake up, wake up. We are going down to the village now to find a lodging. You cannot sleep here in the rain all day or you will get rheumatism."

A policeman could not have been kinder, a mother more competent. He had got Lueli up and walking through the wet woods and eating stirabout by Ori's fire before he had had time to bethink him of his unhappiness.

Lueli sat swallowing and blinking and looking very debauched and youthful while Mr. Fortune and Ori made arrangements. For the present they could live under the chief's ample roof. Meanwhile the burnt hut could be rebuilt, or some dwelling could be fitted up to receive them as lodgers, whichever Mr. Fortune thought best. As for the volcano, that would not interfere with anybody's plans. The pigs had been corralled once more, the earthquake was already half-forgotten. Ori had sent an old woman up to the mountain to make a reconnaissance, and she had reported that the lava was flowing down the south side of the mountain where nobody lived. Everything was all right again, and the rain would freshen things up nicely. Tomorrow he would invite a few friends in, and there would be roast meat and a party in honour of his guest.

Personally Mr. Fortune would have preferred to have the former

hut re-built and to go on living there, much as of old except for religion, the harmonium, and other European amenities. But he feared
that Lueli would mope and be miserable. It would be better for him
to have a change of scene, company and gaiety, Accordingly, he arranged that for the future they should lodge with Teioa, a lesser chief,
whose family included several lively sons and daughters, and an extremely vivacious great-grandmother.

Unfortunately this plan worked badly. Mr. Fortune was much happier than he expected to be. He was now engaged in growing a beard,
and freed from any obligation to convert his housemates he found their
society very agreeable. The great-grandmother was especially good
company. She was a celebrated story-teller, and when she had exhausted her stock of scandals about everyone in the village she fell back
upon legends and fairy-tales. Mr. Fortune was interested to find that
many of these were almost word for word the stories of the Old Testament. One hot afternoon as they sat bathing their legs in a pool and
waving away the flies from each other, she recounted the story of
Joseph and his Brethren. Joseph was called Kila and was carried to the
land of Egypt in a canoe, but all the familiar characters were there, all
the familiar incidents, even to where Kila turned away from the
brothers he was threatening, to hide the tears which he could no longer
keep back. The only variation was in the character of Isaac, who had
changed his sex and split into Joseph's mother and aunt. But in truth
the change made little difference, nor did it detract from the dignity
of the story, for in spite of our English prejudice there is nothing inherently ridiculous about a mother's sister. Mr. Fortune was not perturbed to hear the history of the Jews from the lips of a wrinkled and
engraved old Polynesian harridan. He reflected that everywhere mankind is subject to the same anxious burden of love and loneliness, and
must in self-defence enchant their cares into a story and a dream. In
return for Joseph and his Brethren he told the old dame of the adventures of Mr. Pickwick, many of which were new to her.

But while Mr. Fortune was getting on so nicely Lueli was very unhappy. His playmates had soon found out his misfortune. They teased
him, saying that he had lost his god and would soon go to Hell. Every

day the boy grew more dispirited. He shunned his fellows and went slinking off to hide himself in the woods, where he could mope in peace and quiet. Late in the evening he would creep back, smelling of damp forest earth and wild spices; and without a word he would lie down on his mat and fall into a dreary slumber.

One day Teioa remarked to Mr. Fortune: "That boy has lost his god. I expect he will die soon."

"What nonsense!" shouted Mr. Fortune in a loud rude voice. He felt too suddenly sick to choose his words. He remembered what he had once read in a book about the Polynesians: that they can renounce life at their own will, not with the splash of suicide but slowly, sullenly, deliberately, driving death into themselves like a wedge. Was Lueli doing this—gay, inconsequent, casual Lueli? But since the loss of his god Lueli was gay no longer, and his casualness had taken on a new and terrible aspect, as though it were the casualness of one who could not be bothered to live, who was discarding life as naturally and callously as he had picked flowers and thrown them down to die.

Just then a troop of boys and girls danced by. They were dancing after Lueli and pelting him with small glittering fishes. "Catch!" they cried. "Here's a god for you, Lueli. Catch him!"

Lueli walked on as if he hadn't noticed them. He looked down and saw one of the fish lying at his feet. Like an animal he picked it up and began eating it, but he ate inattentively, without appetite. He was like a sick dog that snatches listlessly at a tuft of grass. Mr. Fortune stepped out from the veranda. His intention had been to drive the dancers away, but instead of that he put his arm through Lueli's and began walking him down to the beach.

"Let us bathe together," he said. "It is a long time since you gave me a swimming lesson."

Lueli swam so beautifully that it was hard to believe he was not happy. Mr. Fortune surpassed himself in flounderings. He tried to catch a fish in his mouth.

When they were sitting on the beach again he said: "Where shall we live when we leave Teioa's house? Shall we make a new hut or shall we build up our old one again?"

"Go back to the old," Lueli replied instantly in a soft fearful whisper.

"Yes, I think so too. Our own bathing-pool is much the best."

"Yes. It's deeper than the one here."

"I think the fish are tamer, too."

"Yes."

"I was wondering if we couldn't make a small wickerwork bower on a pole and teach the parrots to sleep in it. In England people do so, only the birds are doves, not parrots. Perhaps you remember me telling you about our doves and pigeons?"

"They take messages."

"Yes, those are carrier pigeons. There are also pouters and fantails and tumbling pigeons that turn head over heels in the air. But parrots would be very nice too. You could feed them."

"Won't they be able to feed themselves?"

"Oh, yes, certainly. But they would be more apt to stay with us if we fed them."

"Must they stay?"

"Now am I diverting him from his grief"—thought Mr. Fortune, "or am I only boring him?"

The new hut that rose on the place of the old had a faint whiff of burning. Mr. Fortune had superintended the building of it and because the islanders were fond of him they allowed him to introduce several novelties, such as window-boxes and a kitchen dresser. He also threw out a bay. The parrot-cote stood in a corner of the lawn and leading up to it was a narrow serpentining path with crazy paving made out of flat shells. On the other side of the house to balance the parrot-cote was a pergola, constructed in bamboo. In front of the house, in fact exactly where it always had been, but uprooted by the earthquake, was the flat stone on which he had celebrated Holy Communion on that first Sunday morning. He looked at it a little sadly. He bore it no malice, although it reminded him of a special kind of happiness which he could taste no more. He decided that he would make it the head-stone of a rock-garden.

Mr. Fortune attached special importance to these European refinements because he felt that to the eyes of the world he must now present

such an un-European appearance. The earthquake had left him nothing save the clothes he stood up in, the contents of his pockets and a
good-sized rubbish-heap. As for the rubbish-heap, he had with his own
hands grubbed a large hole among the bushes and buried therein the
bones of the harmonium, lamp, sewing-machine, etc., also the molten
images of the communion plate and the tea-pot. He had done this by
night, working by moonlight in the approved fashion of those who
have a past to put away, and when he had covered in the hole and
stamped down the earth he went back and forth from the ruins to
the bushes, scooping up the ashes in a gourd and scattering them in
the undergrowth.

His clothes he had folded and put away, thinking that as they were
all he had, he had better save them up for future emergencies, such as
a shipwreck, a visit of American tourists, the arrival of a new missionary or somebody dropping in from a flying-machine. In their stead he
wore a kilt and a mantle of native cloth, soberly contrived without any
fringes or fandangos, and sandals of plaited bark. Since this new garb
was pocketless, the contents of his pockets were ranged on the shelf of
honour of the kitchen dresser—a pocket magnifying-glass, a whistle,
a nail-file, a graduated medicine spoon, a flint-and-steel lighter, a
copper medal commemorating Parnell which Henry Martin had
brought from Ireland as a curiosity, nineteen mother-of-pearl counters
in a wash-leather bag, a pencil-sharpener blunted by sand getting into
it, a tape-measure that sprang back into a boxwood nut, several buttons, a silver pencil-case with no pencil and a small magnet, painted
scarlet. There was also the knife with two blades, but this he carried
on a string round his neck.

He looked on this array without sentiment. The parrot-cote and the
pergola were also without charms for him. His intentions were severely
practical. These things were all part of his designs on Lueli, they were
so many fishhooks to draw him from despair. Not by their proper
qualities, of course. Mr. Fortune was not so simple as to expect that,
even of the magnet. But indirectly they would build up around their
owner and designer a compelling spiritual splendour, a glamour of
mysterious attributes, fastidious living and foreign parts. After three

years of such familiarity it would not be easy to re-construct his first fascination as something rich and strange. But it must be done if he were to compete successfully with his rival in Lueli's affections. It must be done because that rival was death.

He thought as little as he could help about his progress in this contest. He dared not allow himself to be elated when he seemed to be gaining a little, he dared not admit the possibility of failure. He fought with his eyes turned away from the face of the adversary, like Perseus attacking the Gorgon. He fought by inches, by half-hours; he dared not attempt a decisive victory for he could not risk a decisive defeat. And when he crept out of the hut at night to refresh himself with solitude and darkness, the sullen red light kindling and wavering above the blackness of the crags betokened to him that his enemy was also awake and weaving his powerful spells of annihilation.

He had no time to think of his own loss. He was entirely taken up with solicitude for Lueli, a soul no longer—as he supposed—immortal, and for that reason a charge upon him all the more urgent, as one is more concerned for a humming-bird than for a tortoise. Only at such times as when he had received a serious set-back or was feeling especially desperate did he find himself on the point of taking refuge in prayer; and then remembering the real state of things he would feel exactly like a person who makes to cast himself down on a chair but recalls just in time (or maybe just too late) how all the furniture has been moved, and that the chair is no longer in its old place.

It was sometimes hard for him with his English prejudices not to grow irritated at Lueli's abject listlessness and misery. He could not have believed that his friend could be so chicken-hearted. And since when one is down everything falls on one, circumstances seemed to conspire in twitting and outraging the luckless youth.

Mr. Fortune thought he would try games. Lueli was agile and dexterous, surely it would comfort him to exhibit those qualities? Mr. Fortune introduced him to ping-pong. They played with basket-work bats and small nuts. On the second day a nut hit Lueli and made his nose bleed. He turned green, cast down his bat and began to whimper.

Since ping-pong was too rough, what about spellikins? He carved a set of pieces out of splinters, dyed them with fruit juice to make them look more appetizing, and made a great show of excitement to tempt the other on. Whenever it was Lueli's turn to hook a piece from the tangle he sighed and groaned as though he had been requested to move mountains. Dicing and skittles were no better received.

Deciding that neither games nor gaming (they diced for the mother-of-pearl counters) were likely to rouse Lueli from his dejection, Mr. Fortune cast about for some new expedient. Perhaps a pet animal might have charms? He caught a baby flying-fox and reared it with great tenderness on guavas and coco-milk. The flying-fox soon grew extremely attached to him and learnt to put its head out of the cage when he called "Tibby!" But whenever Lueli could be induced to take an interest in it and to prod it up with a cautious finger, it scratched and bit him. Still persevering with natural history, Mr. Fortune spat on the magnifying glass, polished it, and began to show off the wonderful details of flowers, mosses, and water-fleas. Lueli would look, and look away again, obediently and haplessly bored.

Though the idea of such cold and rapacious blood-thirstiness was highly repugnant to him, he resolved to sacrifice his own feelings (and theirs) and make a moth collection. He prepared a mess of honey and water and took Lueli out that evening on an expedition to lime the trees. Two hours later they went out again with a string of candle-nuts for a lantern and collected a quantity of moths and nocturnal insects, poignantly beautiful and battered with their struggles to escape. But he stifled his sense of shame, all the more in that Lueli seemed inclined to rise to this lure, of his own accord suggesting a second expedition. He had not quite grasped the theory, however. Two days later Mr. Fortune, returning from an errand in the village, was surprised to hear a loud and furious buzzing proceeding from the dell. It was full of wild bees, and Lueli, very swollen and terrified, came crawling out of the bushes. He had smeared the parrot-cote and the posts of the veranda with honey and it seemed as though every bee and wasp on the island were assembled together to quarrel and gorge themselves. It was not possible to approach the hut until after nightfall, and drunk and disorderly bees hovered about it for days, not to speak of a sediment of ants.

Worse was to come. Since his arrival on the island Mr. Fortune had never ailed. But now, whether by exposure to night dews and getting his feet damp out mothing or by some special malignity of Fate, he found himself feeling sore at the back of the throat and sneezing; and presently he had developed a streaming cold. Lueli caught it from him and if his cold were bad, Lueli's was ten times worse. He made no effort to struggle against it; indeed, he was so overwhelmed that struggling was practically out of the question. He crouched on his mats, snorting and groaning, with a face all chapped and bloated, blear eyes, a hanging jaw, and a sullen and unhealthy appetite; and every five minutes or so he sneezed as though he would bring the roof down.

Mr. Fortune was terrified, not only for Lueli, but for the whole population of the island. He knew how direly European diseases can rampage through a new field. He set up a rigid quarantine. Since the loss of his god Lueli had been at pains to avoid his friends, but naturally he was now seized with a passionate craving for their society; and there was some excuse for him as Mr. Fortune was not just now very exhilarating company. But he did his best to be, in spite of an ear-ache which followed the cold, and between Lueli's paroxysms of sneezing he strove to cheer him with accounts of the Great Plague and the Brave Men of Eyam.

At last they were both recovered. But though restored in body Lueli was as mopish as ever. Mr. Fortune went on bracing, and beat his brains for some new distraction. But he had lost ground in this last encounter, and the utmost he could congratulate himself upon was that Lueli was still, however indifferently or unwillingly, consenting to exist. The worst of it was that he couldn't allow himself to show any sympathy. There were times when he could scarcely hold himself back from pity and condolence. But he believed that if he were once to acknowledge the other's grief he would lose his greatest hold over him —his title of being someone superior, august and exemplary.

And then one morning when they had been living in the new hut for about six weeks he woke up inspired. Why had he wasted so much time displaying his most trivial and uncompelling charms, opposing to the magnetism of death such fripperies and titbits of this world, such gewgaws of civilization as a path serpentining to a parrot-cote (a parrot-cote which hadn't even allured the parrots), or a pocket magnifying glass, while all the time he carried within him the inestimable treasures of intellectual enjoyment? Now he would pipe Lueli a tune worth dancing to, now he would open for him a new world. He would teach him mathematics.

He sprang up from bed, full of enthusiasm. At the thought of all those stretches of white beach he was like a bridegroom. There they were, hard and smooth from the tread of the sea, waiting for that noble consummation of blank surfaces, to show forth a truth; waiting, in this particular instance, to show forth the elements of plane geometry.

At breakfast Mr. Fortune was so glorified and gay that Lueli caught a reflection of his high spirits and began to look more life-like than he had done for weeks. On their way down to the beach they met a party of islanders who were off on a picnic. Mr. Fortune with delight heard Lueli answering their greetings with something like his former sociability, and even plucking up heart enough for a repartee. His delight gave a momentary stagger when Lueli decided to go a-picnicking too. But, after all, it didn't matter a pin. The beach would be as smooth again tomorrow, the air as sweet and nimble; Lueli would be in better trim for learning after a spree, and, now he came to think of it, he himself wouldn't teach any the worse for a little private rubbing-up beforehand.

It must be going on for forty years since he had done any mathematics; for he had gone into the Bank the same year that his father died, leaving Rugby at seventeen because, in the state that things were then in, the Bank was too good an opening to be missed. He had once got a prize—*The Poetical Works of Longfellow*—for Algebra, and he had scrambled along well enough in other branches of mathematics; but he had not learnt with any particular thrill or realized that thrill there might be until he was in the Bank, and learning a thing of the past.

Then, perhaps because of that never-ending entering and adding up and striking balances, and turning on to the next page to enter, add up and strike balances again, a mental occupation minute, immediate and yet, so to speak, wool-gathering, as he imagined knitting to be, the absolute quality of mathematics began to take on for him an inexpressibly romantic air. "Pure Mathematics." He used to speak of them to his fellow-clerks as though he were hinting at some kind of transcendental debauchery of which he had been made free—and indeed there does seem to be a kind of unnatural vice in being so completely pure. After a spell of this holy boasting he would grow a little uneasy; and going to the Free Library he took out mathematical treatises, just to make sure that he could follow step by step as well as soar. For twenty pages perhaps, he read slowly, carefully, dutifully, with pauses for self-examination and working out the examples. Then, just as it was working up and the pauses should have been more scrupulous than ever, a kind of swoon and ecstasy would fall on him, and he read ravening on, sitting up till dawn to finish the book, as though it were a novel. After that his passion was stayed; the book went back to the Library and he was done with mathematics till the next bout. Not much remained with him after these orgies, but something remained: a sensation in the mind, a worshipping acknowledgment of something isolated and unassailable, or a remembered mental joy at the rightness of thoughts coming together to a conclusion, accurate thoughts, thoughts in just intonation, coming together like unaccompanied voices coming to a close.

But often his pleasure flowered from quite simple things that any fool could grasp. For instance he would look out of the bank windows, which had green shades in their lower halves; and rising above the green shades he would see a row of triangles, equilateral, isosceles, acute-angled, right-angled, obtuse-angled. These triangles were a range of dazzling mountain peaks, eternally snowy, eternally untrodden; and he could feel the keen wind which blew from their summits. Yet they were also a row of triangles, equilateral, isosceles, acute-angled, right-angled, obtuse-angled.

This was the sort of thing he designed for Lueli's comfort Geometry would be much better than algebra, though he had not the same certificate from Longfellow for teaching it. Algebra is always dancing over the pit of the unknown, and he had no wish to direct Lueli's thoughts to that quarter. Geometry would be best to begin with, plain plane geometry, immutably plane. Surely if anything could minister to the mind diseased it would be the steadfast contemplation of a right angle, an existence that no mist of human tears could blur, no blow of fate deflect.

Walking up and down the beach, admiring the surface which to-morrow with so much epiphany and glory was going to reveal the first axioms of Euclid, Mr. Fortune began to think of himself as possessing a universal elixir and charm. A wave of missionary ardour swept him along and he seemed to view, not Lueli only, but all the islanders rejoicing in this new dispensation. There was beach-board enough for all and to spare. The picture grew in his mind's eye, some-what indebted to Raphael's Cartoon of the School of Athens. Here a group bent over an equation, there they pointed out to each other with admiration that the square on the hypotenuse equalled the sum of the squares on the sides containing the right angle; here was one delighting in a rhomboid and another in conic sections; that enrap-tured figure had secured the twelfth root of two, while the children might be filling up the foreground with a little long division.

By the morrow he had slept off most of his fervour. Calm, me-thodical, with a mind prepared for the onset, he guided Lueli down to the beach and with a stick prodded a small hole in it.

"What is this?"

"A hole."

"No, Lueli, it may seem like a hole, but it is a point."

Perhaps he had prodded a little too emphatically. Lueli's mistake was quite natural. Anyhow, there were bound to be a few misunder-standings at the start.

He took out his pocket knife and whittled the end of the stick. Then he tried again.

"What is this?"

"A smaller hole."

"Point," said Mr. Fortune suggestively.

"Yes, I mean a smaller point."

"No, not quite. It is a point, but it is not smaller. Holes may be of different sizes, but no point is larger or smaller than another point."

Lueli looked from the first point to the second. He seemed to be about to speak, but to think better of it. He removed his gaze to the sea.

Meanwhile, Mr. Fortune had moved about, prodding more points. It was rather awkward that he should have to walk on the beach-board, for his footmarks distracted the eye from the demonstration.

"Look, Lueli!"

Lueli turned his gaze inland.

"Where?" said he.

"At all these. Here; and here; and here. But don't tread on them."

Lueli stepped back hastily. When he was well out of the danger-zone he stood looking at Mr. Fortune with great attention and some uneasiness.

"These are all points."

Lueli recoiled a step further. Standing on one leg he furtively inspected the sole of his foot.

"As you see, Lueli, these points are in different places. This one is to the west of that and consequently that one is to the east of this. Here is one to the south. Here are two close together, and there is one quite apart from all the others. Now look at them, remember what I have said, think carefully and tell me what you think."

Inclining his head and screwing up his eyes Lueli inspected the demonstration with an air of painstaking connoisseurship. At length he ventured the opinion that the hole lying apart from the others was perhaps the neatest. But if Mr. Fortune would give him the knife he would whittle the stick even finer.

"Now what did I tell you? Have you forgotten that points cannot be larger or smaller? If they were holes it would be a different matter. But these are points. Will you remember that?"

Lueli nodded. He parted his lips, he was about to ask a question. Mr. Fortune went on hastily.

"Now suppose I were to cover the whole beach with these: what then?"

A look of dismay came over Lueli's countenance. Mr. Fortune withdrew the hypothesis.

"I don't intend to. I only ask you to imagine what it would be like if I did."

The look of dismay deepened.

"They would all be points," said Mr. Fortune, impressively. "All in different places. And none larger or smaller than another.

"What I have explained to you is summed up in the axiom: a point has position but not magnitude. In other words if a given point were not in a given place it would not be there at all."

Whilst allowing time for this to sink in he began to muse about those other words. Were they quite what he meant? Did they indeed mean anything? Perhaps it would have been better not to try to supplement Euclid. He turned to his pupil. The last words had sunk in at any rate, had been received without scruple and acted upon. Lueli was out of sight.

Compared with his intentions actuality had been a little quelling. It became more quelling as time went on. Lueli did not again remove himself without leave; he soon discovered that Mr. Fortune was extremely in earnest, and was resigned to regular instruction every morning and a good deal of rubbing-in and evocation during the rest of the day. No one ever had a finer capacity for listening than he, or a more docile and obliging temperament. But whereas in the old days these good gifts had flowed from him spontaneously and pleasurably he now seemed to be exhibiting them by rote and in a manner almost desperate, as though he were listening and obliging as a circus animal does its tricks. Humane visitors to circuses often point out with what alacrity the beasts run into the ring to perform their turn. They do not understand that in the choice of two evils most animals would rather flourish round a spacious ring than be shut up in a cage. The activity and the task is a distraction from their unnatural lot, and they tear through paper hoops all the better because so much of their time is spent behind iron bars.

It had been a very different affair when Lueli was learning Bible history and the Church Catechism, "The King of Love My Shepherd Is" and "The Old Hundredth." Then there had been no call for this blatant submission; lessons had been an easy-going conversation, with Lueli keeping his end up as an intelligent pupil should and Mr. Fortune feeling like a cross between wise old Chiron and good Mr. Barlow. Now they were a succession of harangues, and rather strained harangues to boot. Theology, Mr. Fortune found, is a more accommodating subject than mathematics; its technique of exposition allows greater latitude. For instance when you are gravelled for matter there is always the moral to fall back upon. Comparisons too may be drawn, leading cases cited, types and antetypes analysed and anecdotes introduced. Except for Archimedes mathematics is singularly naked of anecdotes.

Not that he thought any the worse of it for this. On the contrary he compared its austere and integral beauty to theology decked out in her flaunting charms and wielding all her bribes and spiritual bonuses; and like Dante at the rebuke of Beatrice he blushed that he should ever have followed aught but the noblest. No, there was nothing lacking in mathematics. The deficiency was in him. He added line to line, precept to precept; he exhausted himself and his pupil by hours of demonstration and exposition; leagues of sand were scarred, and smoothed again by the tide, and scarred afresh: never an answering spark rewarded him. He might as well have made the sands into a rope-walk.

Sometimes he thought that he was taxing Lueli too heavily, and desisted. But if he desisted for pity's sake, pity soon drove him to work again, for if it were bad to see Lueli sighing over the properties of parallel lines, it was worse to see him moping and pining for his god. Teioa's words, uttered so matter-of-factly, haunted his mind. "I expect he will die soon." Mr. Fortune was thinking so too. Lueli grew steadily more lacklustre, his eyes were dull, his voice was flat; he appeared to be retreating behind a film that thickened and toughened and would soon obliterate him.

"If only, if only I could teach him to enjoy an abstract notion! If he could once grasp how it all hangs together, and is everlasting and harmonious, he would be saved. Nothing else can save him, nothing that I or his fellows can offer him. For it must be new to excite him and it must be true to hold him, and what else is there that is both new and true?"

There were women, of course, a race of beings neither new nor true, yet much vaunted by some as a cure for melancholy and a tether for the soul. Mr. Fortune would have cheerfully procured a damsel (not that they were likely to need much of that), dressed her hair, hung the whistle and the Parnell medal round her neck, dowered her with the nineteen counters and the tape measure and settled her in Lueli's bed if he had supposed that this would avail. But he feared that Lueli was past the comfort of women, and in any case that sort of thing is best arranged by the parties concerned.

So he resorted to geometry again, and once more Lueli was hurling himself with frantic docility through the paper hoops. It was really rather astonishing, how dense he could be! Once out of twenty, perhaps, he would make the right answer. Mr. Fortune, too anxious to be lightly elated, would probe a little into his reasons for making it. Either they were the wrong reasons or he had no reasons at all. Mr. Fortune was often horribly tempted to let a mistake pass. He was not impatient: he was far more patient than in the palmiest days of theology—but he found it almost unendurable to be for ever saying with various inflexions of kindness: "No, Lueli. Try again," or: "Well, no, not exactly," or: "I fear you have not quite understood," or: "Let me try to make that clearer." He withstood the temptation. His easy acceptance (though in good faith) of a sham had brought them to this pass, and tenderness over a false currency was not likely to help them out of it. No, he would not be caught that way twice. Similarly he pruned and repressed Lueli's talent for leaking away down side-issues, though this was hard too, for it involved snubbing him almost every time he spoke on his own initiative.

Just as he had been so mistaken about the nature of points, confounding them with holes and agitating himself at the prospect of a beach pitted all over, Lueli contrived to apply the same sort of well-meaning misconceptions to every stage of his progress—if progress be the word to apply to one who is hauled along in a state of semiconsciousness by the scruff of his neck. When the points seemed to be tolerably well-established in his mind Mr. Fortune led him on to lines, and by joining up points he illustrated such simple figures as the square, the triangle and the parallelogram. Lueli perked up, seemed interested, borrowed the stick and began joining up points too. At first he copied Mr. Fortune, glancing up after each stroke to see if it had been properly directed. Then growing rather more confident, and pleased—as who is not?—with the act of drawing on sand, he launched out into a more complicated design.

"This is a man," he said.

Mr. Fortune was compelled to reply coldly:

"A man is not a geometrical figure."

At length Mr. Fortune decided that he had better take in sail. Pure mathematics were obviously beyond Lueli; perhaps applied mathematics would work better. Mr. Fortune, as it happened, had never applied any, but he knew that other people did so, and though he considered it a rather lower line of business he was prepared to try it.

"If I were to ask you to find out the height of that tree, how would you set about it?"

Lueli replied with disconcerting readiness:

"I should climb up to the top and let down a string."

"But suppose you couldn't climb up it?"

"Then I should cut it down."

"That would be very wasteful: and the other way might be dangerous. I can show you a better plan than either of those."

The first thing was to select a tree, an upright tree, because in all elementary demonstrations it is best to keep things as clear as possible. He would never have credited the rarity of upright trees had he not been pressed to find one. Coco-palms, of course, were hopeless: they all had a curve or a list. At length he remembered a tree near the bathing-pool, a perfect specimen of everything a tree should be, tall, straight as a die, growing by itself; set apart, as it were, for purposes of demonstration.

He marched Lueli thither, and when he saw him rambling towards the pool he recalled him with a cough.

"Now I will show you how to discover the height of that tree. Attend. You will find it very interesting. The first thing to do is to lie down."

Mr. Fortune lay down on his back and Lueli followed his example.

Many people find that they can think more clearly in a recumbent position. Mr. Fortune found it so too. No sooner was he on his back than he remembered that he had no measuring-stick. But the sun was delicious and the grass soft; he might well spare a few minutes in exposing the theory.

"It is all a question of measurements. Now my height is six foot two inches, but for the sake of argument we will assume it to be six foot exactly. The distance from my eye to the base of the tree is so far an unknown quantity. My six feet however are already known to you."

Now Lueli had sat up, and was looking him up and down with an intense and curious scrutiny, as though he were something utterly unfamiliar. This was confusing, it made him lose the thread of his explanation. He felt a little uncertain as to how it should proceed.

Long ago on dark January mornings, when a septic thumb (bestowed on him by a cat which he had rescued from a fierce poodle) obliged him to stay away from the Bank, he had observed young men with woollen comforters and raw-looking wind-bitten hands practising surveying under the snarling elms and whimpering poplars of Finsbury Park. They had tapes and tripods, and the girls in charge of perambulators dawdled on the asphalt paths to watch their proceedings. It was odd how vividly fragments of his old life had been coming back to him during these last few months.

He resumed:

"In order to ascertain the height of the tree I must be in such a position that the top of the tree is exactly in a line with the top of a measuring-stick—or any straight object would do, such as an umbrella—which I shall secure in an upright position between my feet. Knowing then that the ratio that the height of the tree bears to the length of the measuring-stick must equal the ratio that the distance from my eye to the base of the tree bears to my height, and knowing (or being able to find out) my height, the length of the measuring-stick and the distance from my eye to the base of the tree, I can, therefore, calculate the height of the tree."

"What is an umbrella?"

Again the past flowed back, insurgent and actual. He was at the Oval, and out of an overcharged sky it had begun to rain again. In a moment the insignificant tapestry of lightish faces was exchanged for a noble pattern of domes, blackish, blueish and greenish domes, sprouting like a crop of miraculous and religious mushrooms. The rain fell harder and harder, presently the little white figures were gone from the field and, as with an abnegation of humanity, the green plain, so much smaller for their departure, lay empty and forsaken, ringed round with tier upon tier of blackly glistening umbrellas.

He longed to describe it all to Lueli, it seemed to him at the moment that he could talk with the tongues of angels about umbrellas. But this was a lesson in mathematics: applied mathematics, moreover, a compromise, so that all further compromises must be sternly nipped. Unbending to no red herrings he replied:

"An umbrella, Lueli, when in use resembles the—the shell that would be formed by rotating an arc of curve about its axis of symmetry, attached to a cylinder of small radius whose axis is the same as the axis of symmetry of the generating curve of the shell. When not in use it is properly an elongated cone, but it is more usually helicoidal in form."

Lueli made no answer. He lay down again, this time face downward.

Mr. Fortune continued: "An umbrella, however, is not essential. A stick will do just as well, so find me one, and we will go on to the actual measurement."

Lueli was very slow in finding a stick. He looked for it rather languidly and stupidly, but Mr. Fortune tried to hope that this was because his mind was engaged on what he had just learnt.

Holding the stick between his feet, Mr. Fortune wriggled about on his back trying to get into the proper position. He knew he was making a fool of himself. The young men in Finsbury Park had never wriggled about on their backs. Obviously there must be some more dignified way of getting the top of the stick in line with the top of the tree and his eye, but just then it was not obvious to him. Lueli made it worse by standing about and looking miserably on. When he had placed himself properly he remembered that he had not measured the stick. It measured (he had had the forethought to bring the tape with him) three foot seven, very tiresome: those odd inches would only serve to make it seem harder to his pupil. So he broke it again, drove it into the ground, and wriggled on his stomach till his eye was in the right place, which was a slight improvement in method, at any rate. He then handed the tape to Lueli, and lay strictly motionless, admonishing and directing while Lueli did the measuring of the ground. In the interests of accuracy he did it thrice, each time with a different result. A few minutes before noon the height of the tree was discovered to be fifty-seven foot, nine inches.

Mr. Fortune now had leisure for compassion. He thought Lueli was looking hot and fagged, so he said:

"Why don't you have a bathe? It will freshen you up."

Lueli raised his head and looked at him with a long dubious look, as though he had heard the words but without understanding what they meant. Then he turned his eyes to the tree and looked at that. A sort of shadowy wrinkle, like the blurring on the surface of milk before it boils, crossed his face.

"Don't worry any more about that tree. If you hate all this so much we won't do any more of it, I will never speak of geometry again. Put it all out of your head and go and bathe."

Still Lueli looked at him as though he heard but didn't understand. Then in the same sleepwalking fashion he turned and went down towards the bathing-pool.

Presently, looking between the trees, Mr. Fortune saw him reappear on the rock above the deep part of the pool. He was going to dive. Very slowly and methodically he took off everything that was on him, he even took off his earrings. Then he stretched his arms in a curve above his head and leapt in.

A beautiful dive—Mr. Fortune found himself thinking of the arc of a stretched bow, the curve and flash of a scimitar, the jet of a harpoon—all instruments of death, all displaying the same austere and efficient kind of beauty, the swiftness to shed blood. A beautiful dive— and a long one. Had he come up already? Hardly; from where he sat Mr. Fortune could see almost the whole surface of the bathing-pool. Perhaps though he had come up behind the rock, swimming back under water.

Mr. Fortune rose to his feet. Instantly, with the movement, agonizing fear took hold of him. He ran down to the pool, and out along the rocks, shouting and calling. No sign, only the quietly-heaving water under the impervious blue sky. No sound, except the parrots and sea-birds, squawking in answer to his disturbing voice. Lueli was staying down on purpose. He was holding on to the sea-weed, drowning himself, with the resolute fatal despair of his lighthearted race.

Mr. Fortune leapt over his own fear of deep water. Where Lueli had dived, he could dive too. He hurled himself off the rock, he felt the water break like a stone under him, he felt himself smothered and sinking; and the next moment he was bouncing about on the surface, utterly and hopelessly afloat. He kicked and beat the water, trying to force a passage downward. It would not let him through.

He swam to the rock and scrambled out into the weight of air, and dived for a second time. Once more the sea caught him and held him up.

"Damn!" he said, softly and swiftly, as though he were pursuing a pencil which had rolled into a dark corner out of reach.

Since diving was out of the question he must run to the village to fetch helpers. The village was nearly a mile away, there might be no one there but old women and babies, he would be breathless, everyone would shout and wave their arms, by the time he got back with a rescue party it would be too late, Lueli would be drowned.

This time it was harder to haul himself out of the water, for he had forgotten to throw off his large draperies and they were now waterlogged. After the shadow of the pool the sunlight seemed black and blinding. He started to run, loosening the knots as he went, for he would run quicker naked. As he threw off the cloak he caught sight over his shoulder of a canoe out to sea. It was heading away from the island but perhaps it was still within earshot. He shouted and waved the cloak and shouted and coo-eed again. Each cry came out of his body like a thing with jagged edges, tearing him inwardly. The canoe kept on its course. The sweat ran down and blinded him, so that he thought for a moment that the canoe had changed its direction and was coming towards him; but it was only the sweat in his eyes which had enlarged it.

He began to run again. It was a pity that he had wasted so much good breath shouting. He was among the trees now, rushing down a vista of light and shadow. Each tall tree seemed to gather speed as he approached it till it shot past him with a whirr of foliage and a swoop of darkness. His going shook the ground and the fruit fell off the bushes as he ran by.

The path began to wind downhill and grew stonier. He was about halfway to the village, he could hear the noise of the brook. He shot round a corner, tripped over something, and fell headlong into a group of human beings, falling among smooth brown limbs and cries of astonishment. It was one of those bevies, half-a-dozen young women who had come out to the brook to net crayfish. To his horror they all leapt to their feet and began to run away. Lying along the ground as he fell, with his head in the brook, he caught hold of an ankle.

"Stop! Don't be little fools!" he cried out, sobbing for breath. "Lueli is drowning in the bathing-pool. You must come back with me and save him."

The ankle belonged to Fuma, a hoyden whom he had once loathed beyond words; but now he adored her, for she was going to play up. She called back the other girls, rallied them, sent one back to the village, and bade the others run as fast as they could to the pool, and in a twinkling she and Mr. Fortune were following them up through the woods. Fuma caught hold of his arm and patted it encouragingly.

"He is in the deep hole under the black rock," he said. "He is lying there holding on to the weed. I have been shouting, and I may not be able to keep up with you. But you must run on without me and dive until you find him."

"Silly boy! Silly Lueli! He told me three days ago that he meant to die. Such nonsense! Never mind, we will pull him up and breathe him alive again."

They ran on side by side. Presently Mr. Fortune said: "You know, Fuma, this is all my fault."

Fuma laughed under her breath. "Lueli thinks the world of you," she said. "He is always telling us how lovable you are."

After a few more yards Mr. Fortune said: "Fuma, you must run on alone now."

She gave his arm a gentle nip, and shot ahead. He saw her join the others as a starling flies into the flock and then they were out of sight. He could only think of quite small immediate things, Fuma's eyebrows, a beautiful clear arch, and the soft quick sound of her breathing. He was thinking more of her than of Lueli. She seemed more real.

He was still running but now every time that he put a foot down it was with a stamp that disintegrated his balance, so that he could not guide his direction. Then he heard a splash, and another and another. They had reached the pool and begun diving. Then he heard Fuma's voice crying: "Further to the left. He's down here." Then a babble of voices and more splashings. Then silence.

He gathered up his will for the last thirty yards, was down on to the beach and out breast-high into the water. He saw a girl's head rise above the surface of the empty pool. She shook the hair from her eyes, saw him standing there, and came swimming towards him.

"We've got him," she said. "But Fuma has to cut the weed with a shell for we can't loosen his hands."

Mr. Fortune took the pocket-knife from his neck and held it out to her. Then he saw a strangely intricate and beautiful group emerge and slowly approach. They had brought up Lueli and were bearing him among them. His head lolled and dipped back into the water from Fuma's shoulder, where it lay. His eyes were open in a fixed and piteous stare, his mouth was open too, and a little trickle of blood ran down from his lip, where he had bitten it. His inanimate body trailed in the water with gestures inexpressibly weary. But two long streamers of weed still hung from his clenched hands.

Death comes with her black ruler and red ink and scores a firm line under the long tale of more or less, debit and credit, all the small multitudinous entries which have made up the relationship between one's self and another. The line is drawn, the time has come to audit; and from the heart of her shadow a strange clarity, dream-like and precise, is shed upon the page, so that without any doubt or uncertainty we can add up the account which is now at an end, and perceive the sum-total of the expenditure of time. While the others were ministering around the body of Lueli, squeezing water out of his lungs, rubbing him, breathing into his nostrils, burning herbs and performing incantations, Mr. Fortune sat under a tree, a little apart, and audited the past. In the tree sat a parrot, uttering from time to time its curious airy whistle—a high, sweet, meditative note. It seemed to Mr. Fortune that the bird was watching the process of his thoughts, and that its whistle, detached from any personal emotion, even from that of astonishment, was an involuntary and philosophic acknowledgment of the oddity of men's lives and passions.

"I loved him," he thought. "From the moment I set eyes on him I loved him. Not with what is accounted a criminal love, for though I set my desire on him, it was a spiritual desire. I did not even love him as a father loves a son, for that is a familiar love, and at the times when Lueli most entranced me it was as a being remote, intact, and incalculable. I waited to see what his next movement would be, if he would speak or no—it was the not knowing what he would do that made him dear. Yes, that was how I loved him best, those were my happiest moments: when I was just aware of him, and sat with my senses awaiting him, not wishing to speak, not wishing to make him notice me until he did so of his own accord because no other way would it be perfect, would it be by him. And how often, I wonder, have I let it be just like that? Perhaps a dozen times, perhaps twenty times all told, perhaps, when all is put together, for an hour out of the three years I have had with him. For man's will is a demon that will not let him be. It leads him to the edge of a clear pool; and while he sits admiring it, with his soul suspended over it like a green branch and dwelling in its own reflection, will stretches out his hand and closes his fingers upon a stone—a stone to throw into it.

"I'd had a poor meagre turnpike sort of life until I came here and found Lueli. I loved him, he was a refreshment to me, my only pleasant surprise. He was perfect because he *was* a surprise. I had done nothing to win him, he was entirely gratuitous. I had had no hand in him, I could no more have imagined him beforehand than I could have imagined a new kind of flower. So what did I do? I started interfering. I made him a Christian, or thought I did, I taught him to do this and not to do the other, I checked him, I fidgeted over him. And because I loved him so for what he was I could not spend a day without trying to alter him. How dreadful it is that because of our wills we can never love anything without messing it about! We couldn't even love a tree, not a stone even; for sooner or later we should be pruning the tree or chipping a bit off the stone. Yet if it were not for a will I suppose we should cease to exist. Anyhow it is in us and while we live we cannot escape from it; so however we love and whatever we love it can only be for a few minutes, and to buy off our will for those few minutes we have to relinquish to it for the rest of our lives whatever it is we love. Lueli has been the price of Lueli. I enslaved him, I kept him on a string. I robbed him of his god twice over—first in intention, then in fact. I made his misery more miserable by my perpetual interference. Up till an hour ago I was actually tormenting him with that damned geometry. And now he is dead. . . . Yes, parrot! You may well whistle. But be careful. Don't attract my attention too much lest I should make a pet of you, and put you in a cage, and then in the end, when you had learnt to talk like me instead of whistling like a wise bird, wring your neck because you couldn't learn to repeat *Paradise Lost.*"

At these words the parrot flew away, just as though it had understood and wished to keep on the safe side; and looking up Mr. Fortune saw some of the islanders running towards him. He got up and went to meet them. "Well, is he dead?" he asked, too deeply sunk in his own wan-hope to pay any attention to their looks and greetings.

It was some time before they could make him understand that Lueli was alive. He followed them, dumb, trembling and stupefied, to where Lueli was sitting propped up under a tree. He looked rather battered, and rather bewildered, and slightly ashamed of himself, like a child that has been at a rich tea-party, grown over-excited and been sick. But the hag-ridden look he had worn since the earthquake was gone, and he was answering the congratulations and chaff of those around him with a semblance of his old gaiety.

Mr. Fortune stood looking down on him in silence, confused at meeting him whom he had not thought to meet again. Lueli was infected by his embarrassment, and the two regarded each other with caution and constraint, as dear friends do who meet unexpectedly after long separation. Lueli was the first to speak.

"How ill you look. Your face is all holes."

"Lueli, you would have laughed if you could have seen me trying to dive in after you. Twice I threw myself in, but I could do nothing but float."

"I expect you let yourself crumple up."

"Yes, I expect I did."

"But it was very kind of you to try."

"Not at all."

The situation was horrible. Mr. Fortune was tongue-tied, very jealous of the others and haunted with the feeling that behind all this cause for rejoicing there was some fatal obstacle which he ought to know all about but which his mind was shirking the contemplation of. Lueli fidgeted and made faces. The awkwardness of being raised from the dead was too much even for his *savoir-faire*.

"Why can't I be natural?" thought Mr. Fortune. "Why can't I say how glad I feel? And why don't I feel my gladness? What have I done? Why is it like this, what is the matter with me?"

Lueli's thoughts were something like this: "He has a blemish on his neck, but didn't I ever notice it before? It must have grown larger. I hope they won't begin to laugh at him because he can't dive. I love him, but Oh dear! what a responsibility he is. I don't think I can bear it much longer, not just now. I don't want responsibilities. I only want to go to sleep."

Round them stood half the population of the island, raging with congratulations, jokes and inquiries. Even when they had escorted them back to the hut, superintended Lueli's falling asleep, and eaten all the provisions which Mr. Fortune brought out to them, they would not go away but sat among their crumbs and on the rock-garden imploring Fuma to tell them once more how Mr. Fortune had come bounding through the wood and fallen headlong into the girls' laps.

For no reason that he could see he had suddenly become immensely popular. And as he walked to and fro in the twilight waiting for his guests to take themselves off he heard his name being bandied about in tones of the liveliest affection and approval. He had one consolation: by the morrow he would be out of fashion again. As for Lueli, they scarcely mentioned him. If he had been drowned they would have spent the evening wailing and lamenting; not for him but for themselves, at the reminder of their own mortality, after the natural way of mourning. And there would have been just as much gusto, he thought—but tenderly, for he felt no animosity to them now, only a desire to get rid of them and be left to his own soul— and just as many crumbs.

The moon had set before they went away. Mr. Fortune stole into the hut and listened for a while to Lueli's quiet breathing, a slight human rhythm recovered that day from the rhythm of the sea. He knelt down very quietly and creakingly and taking hold of Lueli's limp warm hand he put it to his lips. "Good-bye, my dear," he murmured under his breath. Lueli stirred, and uttered a drowsy inarticulate good-night.

Both rhythms were in Mr. Fortune's ears as he lay down to rest. He did not sleep, at least not for some hours; but he lay unharried in a solemn and dream-like repose, listening to the gentle fanning of Lueli's slumber and the slow tread of the sea.

Thus, tranquil and full of long thoughts, he had lain on his first night in Fanua, gazing at the star Canopus and watching the trail of

creeper stir at the sweet breath of night. All that he had then of hope
and faith was lost. But now at the last he seemed strangely to have
resumed the temper of that night, and the thought of his renuncia-
tion was as full and perfect as the former thought of his vocation had
been. "It is not one's beliefs that matter," he told himself, "but to be
acting up to them. To have come to Fanua and now to have made up
my mind to go away—it is the decision that fills me with this amazing
kind of joy."

To go away. It was the only solution, he had the parrot's word for
it. The slow tread of the sea told him the same story. "I brought you
here," it said, "and presently I shall bear you away. My ebbing tides
will return to Fanua, and ebb and return again and ebb and return
again. But for you there will be no return." And the tread of the sea
became the footfall of a warder. It was this necessity, still implicit and
unrealized, which had lain like a stone in his heart when he saw
Lueli brought back from the dead. If he had not thought of Lueli as
being dead, he would never have understood. But Death had vouchsafed him a beam of her darkness to see clearly by; and having seen,
he could not sin against that light. He must go away, that was the
only stratagem by which love could outwit its own inherent treachery.
If he stayed on, flattering himself with the belief that he had learnt
his lesson, he would remember for a while no doubt; but sooner or
later, inevitably he would yield to his will again, he would begin to
meddle, he would seek to destroy.

To see everything so clearly and to know that his mind was made up
was almost to be released from human bondage. This must be the
boasted calm joy of mathematicians which he had once pretended to
share. Euclid had failed him or he had failed Euclid; but the contemplation of his own reasoning and resolved mind gave him a felicity
beyond even that which the rightness of right-angles could afford. He
would keep awake a little longer and make the most of it. He could
be sure it would not last. But when it had shattered and desolation
came in its stead there would still be common-sense and common
manliness and several practical preoccupations with which to keep
desolation at bay.

First he must get a message to St. Fabien. In the pocket of the coat he had worn on the night of the earthquake were a couple of sheets torn out of an exercise book. He had carried them on his stroll on the chance that he might feel impelled to write a sonnet (Petrarchan sonnets were the only poetical form he attempted because they were so regular, and even so he did them very badly) On the Setting Sun, or To a Hermit Crab. He had not done so, partly because he had forgotten to take a pencil too; but now, when he had smoothed the crumples out, these sheets would come in handy for his letter to the Archdeacon.

In the morning he gathered some purple fruit whose juice he knew from experience to be indelible, squeezed them into a bowl, and with a reed pen wrote as follows:

"Fanua.

"My dear Archdeacon.

"I am sorry to trouble you but I must ask that the launch may be sent to fetch me away from Fanua. My ministry here has been a failure. I have converted no one, moreover I think that they are best as they are.

"I am aware that I shall seem to you an unprofitable servant, and I am prepared for reproof. But I must tell you that in my present state of mind nothing that you can say, either of blame or consolation, is likely to make much difference.

"I should be very much obliged if you could send with the launch a pair of stout black boots (size eleven), some collars (sixteen and a half inch), and a bottle of Aspirin tablets.

"Yours sincerely,

"TIMOTHY FORTUNE.

"P.S. Also some bone collar-studs. There was an earthquake and I lost those which I had."

When the letter was written he put it away. His mind was quite made up as to leaving Fanua, there was no danger that a week's delay or so in sending off the letter would weaken his resolution. Indeed if he had consulted his own feelings he would not have delayed for an hour. But he did not wish to leave Lueli until he was quite certain the boy was able to stand on his own feet.

One thing was beyond doubt: Lueli would not try to kill himself again. He had been frightened by the dark look of Death under the water. Though he said nothing about his drowning or his rescue it was obvious that he had set himself to get on good terms with the life he had then thought fit to abandon. Never before had he been so beautiful, nor moved so lithely, nor sprawled so luxuriously on the warm grass. Sleek, languid and glittering, he was like a snake that has achieved its new skin. He was grown more sociable too, and with a quite new form of sociability; for instead of seeking the company of others he exerted himself to make others seek his. Although his drowning had done him no harm whatsoever and he had never been in better trim, he chose to preen himself as an interesting invalid. At all hours of the day the youth and beauty of the island would appear with offerings of fruit and invalid delicacies. Since the Fanuans are a people unequalled in kindness and idleness this was not such a great tribute to Lueli's fascinations. But what was really remarkable was the success with which he imposed himself upon them as a young hero. Even Fuma, who had stood out against his pretensions for several days, laughing at him and pulling his hair and making sarcastic remarks about people who couldn't swim, suddenly dropped her sisterly airs and attended on him as devoutly as the rest. As though this were the last plum that he had been proposing should drop into his mouth Lueli began to feel a little better now; was able to go sailing or swimming—not even the waters that drowned him could quench his love for water—or to take a stroll in the woods. Presently he was addressing Fuma as "Child."

If he had not so utterly forsworn meddling, if the letter to the Archdeacon were not put away in his coat pocket, Mr. Fortune might have yielded himself to a glow of matchmaking. Perhaps Fuma was not quite the girl he would have chosen; perhaps for that matter Lueli's choice of her was not quite to the exclusion of other girls; but having been so heart-rent over the defeated estate of that spiritless and godless boy whom even his own younger brothers had been able to tease out of the village it would have been sweet now to abet the happiness of this triumphant young man.

As things were Lueli's recovery must be the waving of the flag which signalled his departure. So one morning he set off to find Ori and explained to him that he wished to send a message by canoe to Maikalua. Would Ori as usual see about it and oblige?

Early in the morning the canoe was launched: and singing and shouting the boatmen set out on their voyage.

As he watched them depart Mr. Fortune had a sudden vision of a pillar-box. It seemed to spring up before him, a substantial scarlet cylinder, out of the glittering untenanted beach. He remembered how long ago, one August afternoon, he had posted a note accepting with pleasure an invitation to play tennis, an invitation which came from some people called Tubbs who lived at Ealing; and how having done so, he stood with the sun beating down upon him, just outside the station, with people jostling past him and the newspaper man shouting: "Star, Standard, Westminster! Surrey all out!" wishing with despair that he could get his note back, for it seemed to him that nothing could be more distasteful than to play tennis at Ealing with those rollicking Tubbses.

But now he had no wish to recall his letter, though he was still sick with the wrench of definitely dispatching it. His only thought was to leave Fanua as soon as possible; and until the moment of departure came he could not imagine how he would pass away the time. Gradually the pillar-box faded out before him and he saw the ocean-waste, the narrow diminishing boat, the empty indifferent sky. His head was aching again and he put his hand to his forehead. There was that deluded watch, mincing complacently on. It was much better at passing away time than he. Half-past seven. Another thirteen hours and he would be getting himself supper, and Lueli might come in or he might not. And after supper he would be going to bed. But if he fell asleep too soon he would wake early with another shining unending morning before him. No! It would be better to sit up late, to midnight if possible. For time passes more tolerantly at night when the body is drowsy and the mind tired; but in the morn-

ing hours there is no release from one's faculties, and every second is
a needleprick to consciousness.

The sand had dribbled out between his fingers, he found himself
staring at the palm of his hand. It would be the better for washing;
and he turned back toward the bathing-pool. While he was still the
headache was not so bad; but every step jolted it and sent a heavy
sick tingle up his spine to jar against his temples.

As the bathing-pool came in sight through the lattice of ferns and
bushes he paused, for it came into his mind that Lueli might be there
with his friends. And dropping on his hands and knees he crawled
through the undergrowth, holding his breath and cautiously poking
out his head from the greenery to scout if the coast were clear. He
need not have been so discreet. The pool was empty. There was no
foot-print on the sandy rim.

He undressed and bathed his body wearily in the fresh cool water—
it was always exquisitely cool under the shadow of the rock. It did not
occur to him that by going a little further he could drown. He hauled
himself up on a ledge and began to clean his toes with a wisp of
sea-weed.

The shade on his wet limbs, the sound of the sea, the breathing
murmur of the woods in the soft steady wind were comforting to his
headache. He began to feel slightly lachrymose and a good deal better,
and with the tenderness of a convalescent he watched the fish darting
in and out of the streaming weed. Of course he might have gone
himself by the canoe instead of sending his request for the launch.
But though he now realized that it would have been perfectly feasible
to have done so, something within him assured him that it would not
really have been possible. Things must take their course: and thus
to wait still in Fanua for the launch to come and fetch him away was
the natural course for his departure. He could see himself leaving the
island in the launch, but not any other how.

That bull-faced fish had dodged in and out from the weed a
dozen times at least. It was as persistent as a swallow. His body was
dry now and his headache smoothed away. Only the heartache remained; and he was getting used to that.

All this while, as he was crawling through the bushes, and cleaning his toes, and watching the fish, there had been but one deep pre-occupying thought at the back of his mind—the thought of Lueli and a longing for his presence. It was on the chance that Lueli might come down to bathe that he was waiting now. And he imagined the conversation that must take place between them.

"Lueli, I am going away from Fanua."

"But you will come back again?"

"No. I am going away for ever."

It would be quite simple—as simple as that. "I am going away from Fanua." Above all he was determined that there should be no explanations. It would never do to tell Lueli that he was going away because of him. No smirch of complicity, no blight of responsibility should fall upon Lueli, happy Lueli who had done him no wrong, and whom so often he had sought to injure from the best, worst, most fatal and affectionate motives. How could he have so teased him in his misery with that idiotic geometry—a misery, too, in which he was the agent, for it was through him that Lueli had lost his idol. That was bad enough, at any rate it was damnably silly. Though what else could he have done? Something equally senseless, no doubt. But what was it to his behaviour in the hut, when the idol lay between them, and Lueli crouched in his last refuge of silence while he sought with menaces and blackmailing to rob him of his faith, and bade him cast his god into the fire? Ah! of the two gods who had perished that night it was the wooden one he would now fetch back again.

But this he could never say. He must not give any reason for his departure lest he should at length fall into giving the true one and seeming to involve Lueli in his own blunders. "I am going away from Fanua." That must be all. Little to say: so little that he must postpone saying it till the last hour came, the hour when one says good-bye. And for that reason he must shun Lueli's presence, hide from him if need be and crawl through bushes, for if he once allowed himself to resume their old familiar intercourse he would not be able to keep back the words: "Lueli, I am going away. I am going away for ever."

He said it aloud, and as it were heard the words for the first time. He put on his clothes and began mechanically to walk back toward the hut. Then he had a good idea. Since he was leaving the island it would be a pity not to go up the mountain and have a look at the crater. Very likely he would never have another opportunity of inspecting an active volcano.

It would be a taxing expedition, and not without danger. He put up some food, cut himself a stout walking-stick and gathered a bunch of plantain leaves to stick in his boots—for it was decidedly an occasion for boots. Preparations always pleased him, for he had a housewifely mind, and by the time he set out he was feeling, if not less miserable, at any rate a point or two deflected from his misery.

The new crater was on the further side of the mountain. He decided that the best way of approach would be to walk up through the woods by tracks which he knew and thence to skirt round under the foot of the crags, keeping against the wind in order to avoid the smoke and fumes. As he mounted through the woods he could hear, at first the sea and the tree-tops, presently the murmuring tree-tops alone. Soothed by their company and their shade he climbed on peacefully enough for a couple of hours, keeping a sharp look-out for rents and fissures; for however weary one may be of life one would not choose to discard it by starving, or suffocating in a deep crevice as hot as an oven.

At last he came out upon the tract of scrub and clinker which covered the upper slopes of the mountain. After the cool depth of the woodland it was like a pale hell, a prospect bleached and brittle, such as even the greenest garden will offer if one sits and looks at it suddenly after lying with the sun strong on one's eyelids. After a moment of dizziness the garden will revive again, but the longer Mr. Fortune looked at this landscape the more spectral and repellent it seemed. And because the air quivered with heat the face of the mountain side seemed to be twitching with fear.

There were the crags, some two miles away yet, but looking as though he could throw a stone and splinter them. They were not rhododendron-coloured now, but a reddish and scabby mottle. They reminded him of a group of ruined gas-vats with the paint scaling off them, standing in the middle of a brick-field. It smelt of brick-fields too; and in the place of the former sounds of the sea and the tree-tops new sounds came to his ear, ugly to match the landscape, and of a kind of baleful insignificance like the landscape—far-off crashes and rumblings, the hiss and spurt of escaping steam: the noise of a flustered kitchen.

Now was the moment to put the plantain leaves in his boots. Those which he had gathered were faded, he threw them away and gathered fresh. Then, with a heart beating harshly and remotely, he set forth on the second stage of his climb.

It was hateful going—slippery bents, bristling scrubs, sharp-edged clinker which hurt his feet. He tripped and fell constantly, and when he fell the clinker cut his hands. Twice he remained crumpled on the ground just as he had fallen, gasping for breath, and cowed by the frantic beating of his heart, which did not seem to belong to him, behaving like some wild animal which, terrified and apprehensive, is dragged struggling to the summit of the mountain to be sacrificed there. And as he went on, the brick-field smell grew stronger, and the kitchen noises grew louder, and the sun striking down on him from the motionless sky, striking up at him from the ground, reverberating upon him from the parched landscape, enclosed him in its burning net.

He remembered the story of the woman Kapiolani, the Christian convert of Hawaii. Followed by a crowd of trembling islanders she had gone up the burning mountain to manifest her faith in the true God. When she was come to the crater of Kilauea she had scrambled down to the very edge of the burning lake, and there, half hidden in clouds of smoke, she called on Pele the Fire-Goddess, and flouted her, calling her an impostor and challenging her, if goddess she were, to rise up out of her everlasting fiery den and overwhelm her accuser with its waves. Pele did not answer: she sulked in the heart of her fire, powerless before the name of Christ. And when she had waited long enough Kapiolani climbed up again out of the pit and showed herself once more to the crowd who had been cowering at the crater-side, trembling, and listening to the loud voice of her faith. And when they saw her, they believed.

Her faith, thought Mr. Fortune, had carried her lightly up the mountain side, and over the lava-flow which she had trodden with scorched and bleeding feet. But he, though a man, and born free from the burden of heathen fears, and wearing boots, was already tired out and reluctant, and only a cold tourist's curiosity could carry him onward, and a bargain-hunting spirit which told him that having gone so far it would be a waste not to go on to the end.

Kapiolani had made her act of faith in the year 1825. And after that, as though for her courage she were like the prophetess Deborah, the land had peace thirty years. Then Pele shook herself contemptuously and fell to her tricks again. At her first shake the island trembled, as though it knew what was to come. "Yet a little," said the Fire-Goddess; and slept for another ten years. This time she woke angrier. The island quivered like the lid of a boiling pot, a river of fire, flowing terribly underground, rent open a green and fertile plain, and five times a tidal wave reared up and fell upon the helpless land. And once more Pele fell asleep, but fell asleep to dream; snarling to herself, and hotly, voluptuously, obscurely triumphing in a dream of what her next awakening would be.

Kapiolani would not know of that awakening at any rate. It was to be hoped that she had been spared the others. A simple faith like hers would be cruelly jolted by such ambiguities in God's law. She might even have lost it thereby, as did Voltaire, another blunt, straightforward thinker, at a rather similar exhibition; for she could hardly be expected to take the subtler view of those long-standing and accustomed believers who can gloss over an eruption as a very justifiable protest against the wickedness of their neighbours. And as for saying that it is all a mystery—well, there is not much satisfaction to be got out of that.

These thoughts carried him over the last mile, and looking up he was surprised to find himself under the crags. He began to skirt round them. Now the noises and the smells were so strong that as he rounded every jut of the crags he expected to come on the new crater. Just as he had climbed on to the top of a large rock a gust of wind, veering among the crags, brought with it a volley of foul smoke, which rose up from beneath him and smothered him round, just as smoke comes suddenly belching out of the vent of a tunnel. He stood for a moment coughing and stifling; and then the wind shifted again, and the smoke lifted away from him, and looking out underneath it he saw that he was come to the end of his search.

The rock on which he stood was the last westernmost redoubt of the crags, and before him extended the other side of the island of Fanua. Far off and strangely high up he saw the sea-line. The ocean seemed to fall steeply and smoothly downhill to where it broke upon the reef in a motionless pattern of foam. Stretching away down the mountain side was a long, serpentining slab of lava—the thickly-burning torrent which had torn apart the flanks of the mountain on the night of the eruption, wallowing downward with an ever more heavy and glutted motion until now it was solidifying into rock; a brutal surface of formless hummocks and soppy and still-oozing fissures. Everything around was deep in ashes, and here and there little gushes of steam showed where the heat still worked under the outer crust. It was like the surface of a saucepan of porridge which has been lifted off the fire but still pimples and undulates with its own heat.

Another jet of smoke belched up. Holding his breath Mr. Fortune crept over the rock on his hands and knees and looked down into the crater.

By night the spectacle might have had a sort of Medusa's head beauty, for ever wakeful and writhing and dangerous; but in the light of day it was all sordid and despairing. Thick smoke hung low over the burning lava, and thin gaseous flames flickered on the surface, livid and cringing, like the ghosts of bad men still haunting around the corrupting body. Below the play of dun smoke and shadowy flame the lava moved unceasingly, impelled to the south, on and on and over and over as though its torment were bound upon an axle. Every now and then two currents would flow into each other with a heavy impact, a splash and a leap of fire. And then it was as though it clapped hands in its agony.

Slowly, because he was cramped with having watched it so long, Mr. Fortune raised himself to his feet and turned away. He had no thoughts, no feelings. What he had seen was something older than the earth; but vestigial, and to the horror of the sun what the lizard is to the dragon: degenerate. Shuddering and cold he went down past the shadow of the crags and over the scorched expanse of hell-ground towards the woods, hastening, still having in his ears the growlings and concussions of the pit and with that foul smell still in his nostrils.

When he came into the woods he stopped and looked up. The green boughs hid away the skies. He was glad. He did not want to look at anything eternal just now. He sat down on a fallen tree. Moss covered it, and creepers and tree-ferns were springing out of it; but he parted the ferns and creeper and scratched away the moss and put down his nose to snuff up the scent of decay. Everywhere in the woods was the odour of mortality; it was sweet to him, like a homecoming. He lay down and buried his face in the leaf-mould, pressing his eye-lids to the warm mouldering softness, trying to forget the rock.

When he felt better he went on again; and coming to a stream he bathed himself, and ate some fruit. He was not very sure of his whereabouts, so to follow the stream seemed the best plan. It was a pleasant guide. He heard it singing ahead as he followed its windings. All this part of the woodland was unknown to him. It seemed very venerable and solitary. The solemn girth and glossy great leaves of the breadfruit trees pleased him all the better because he was thinking of them as beings transient and subject to laws of growth and decay. They were steadfast, he thought, because they knew of their appointed end. They soothed him, bearing faithful witness that his own should be no other—that he too should one day lie along the earth and be gathered into it.

It occurred to him for the first time that now he would not, as he had hoped, be buried in Fanua. And as though the thought had called up a vision, he saw what appeared to be a graveyard before him. It was a sort of pound or enclosure, built of rough stones. Whatever the purpose of the place it was clearly unfrequented, perhaps forsaken; for the mossy walls were breached and tumbled and the grass grew clean and untrodden in the entry. Overhead the breadfruit trees mingled their large boughs like a roof of wings. He turned and went in. He found himself surrounded by ranks of idols, idols of all sizes and all fashions, idols of wood and stone, all very old, subdued with weather, moss-grown, with the grass tangling round their bases. He knew well what they must be: in this island where everyone had his own god these were the gods of the dead. At the death of their worshippers the gods were carried here and left to their repose, till they too in their time failed and sank into the earth. He remembered who had died since he came to the island and peered among the idols for some more recent than the others which might be those of his acquaintance. Yes, that was Akau's god perhaps, and that pot-bellied fellow with the humorous squint might be the god of poor old Live-for-Ever. Only Lueli's god would never come here.

Sad Lueli! Just now in his flourish of youth and affability he might forget his lost god and do quite as well without him; but one day Lueli would be growing old and then—then he would feel his loss. For the day must come when a man turns from the companionship of flesh and blood, be it flesh and blood failing like his own, or the flesh and blood he has begotten, and seeks back into the traditions of his race for a companionship more ghostly and congenial—old habits, old beliefs, old stories—the things his childhood accepted and his fore-fathers lived by. In that day Lueli would need his god. The lack of it would be a kind of disgrace, a mutilation.

"I cannot go from Fanua," said Mr. Fortune, standing among the idols: "until I have given Lueli back his god."

The knife hung round his neck: it would be easy to take one of the idols, re-trim its features, scrape off the moss and make a new idol of it. But a feeling of decorum stayed his hand. However, he might study them, for he would need an example. He spent half an hour or so in the enclosure, kneeling before the idols, examining the details of their workmanship and trying to acquire the convention. Then, for it was still afternoon, he spent some time wandering round in search of a suitable piece of wood. It must be about two feet long, straight, without knots, not so fresh as to tear, not so old as to crumble, of an easy grain to carve, and for choice, of a pleasant colour. He sought out several pieces and experimented on them with his knife before he found one to his liking. It was of rather dark, sweet-smelling wood, of what tree he knew not, for he found it lying beside the stream. A freshet must have carried it there, perhaps from the hands of some other woodman; for there seemed to be cutting-marks about one end of it.

He sat down and began to rough out the image he had in his mind: a man with a bird perched on his wrist, his head a little inclined towards the bird as though it were telling him something; and seated at his feet a plain smooth dog, also looking at the bird, but quite kindly. After so many failures, great and small: the trousers, the introduction to mathematics, all his very indifferent attempts at cookery, boiled bad eggs and clammy coco-nut buns, the conversion of the islanders and the domestication of the parrots, it might have been expected of Mr. Fortune that he would put forth on sculpture with diffidence. But his heart was in it; he had never attempted anything of the kind before; and anyhow, it is the vainglorious people who expect difficulties. Mr. Fortune in his modesty supposed that cookery, conversion, etc., were really quite easy matters, and that it was only he who made a botch of them. So when after an hour or so of whittling and measuring and whittling again, he found himself possessed of a considerable aptitude for wood-carving, and the man, the dog and the bird emerging from the billet with every promise of looking very much as he intended them to, he was pleased but without any amazement.

He worked while there was light; then wrapping the idol carefully in soft grasses and leaves and tying it into a parcel with vines he set out to follow the stream by starlight.

Now into the solemn caverns of the wood came rolling solemnly the noise of the ocean. Wafts of sweet scent wandered to him from flowering shrubs whose flowers he could not discern, and large soft moths brushed across his face. He was foot-sore and perhaps sorrowful, and he knew that soon he must quit this island which was so beautiful and romantic under its crown of horror, and go, he knew not whither, but certainly never again to any place like this; but nothing disturbed his enjoyment of the hour. His thoughts were slow and peaceful, and looking up through the trees he saw the heavens without disquiet, although they were eternal. The stream laughed and ran joyously forward to the waterfall. He looked about him and knew where he was. The stream which had borne him such pleasant company was the same whose torrent he had seen wavering and distorted on the night of the earthquake.

He hitched the god a little closer up under his arm and turned into a path he knew. As he neared the village he heard voices not far off. He stopped. Yes, that was Fuma's voice: and the laugh—only Lueli could laugh like that. Standing in the darkness he blessed them. The god weighed on his arm, and it occurred to him that this was the first time he had ever returned from a walk bringing with him a present for Lueli. Lueli never came back without some gift or other; he was as prodigal as his native clime. Trails of flowers which festooned the doorway and wound themselves round Mr. Fortune's neck whenever he went in or out. Shells, which were casually thrown down on his mat and ran into his sleep when he turned over in the night. Perfectly uneatable shell-fish because they were so pretty, feathers and fantastic ornaments which he wore with gratified embarrassment round his neck. He too had sometimes brought things back with him, but things practical or edible. Never real presents, objects perishable, useless and inconvenient, friendship's tokens, emblems of love, that passion which man, for all his sad conscience and ingenuity, will never be able quite to tame into something useful.

Well, at last he was making some atonement where he had been so remiss. He was a poor hand at presents: an Englishman with a public school training still lurking in his heel, he would never be able with any sort of grace or naturalness to offer garlands of morning-glories or small gay striped crabs. But he was doing his best; he was bringing Lueli a god.

When Lueli came into the hut Mr. Fortune had eaten his supper and was almost asleep.

"Where have you been all day?" inquired Lueli. "I kept on looking for you, and wondering where you had gone. I was growing very anxious, I assure you."

"I have been to the mountain."

"To the mountain?"

"Yes, right to the top of it."

"Oh! did you see the flames and the smoke they talk about? What's it like? Are there a great many flames? Does it make a great noise? Did you feel frightened? I hope you were careful not to fall in. Tell me all about it."

"It is a very impressive sight."

"Well? Go on!"

"I will tell you the rest tomorrow. Now it is time you went to bed. You needn't trouble about Tibby. I've fed her."

He turned over and fell asleep. All night he lay with the idol close against his side.

For three days he worked on it in secret, chipping and scooping and shaving, rubbing it smooth with fine sand, oiling it, treating it as tenderly as a cricket-bat. As he worked, intent and unflurried, strange thoughts concerning it stole into his mind. Sometimes he thought that the man was himself, listening to the parrot which told him how the doom of love is always to be destroying the thing it looks upon. At other times the man seemed to be Christ, and the bird on His wrist the Holy Ghost. In these suppositions there was no part for the dog, save as an adjunct to the design, steadying the base of the composition, and helping it to stand upright. But there was yet a third fancy; and then the man was Lueli, the bird neither parrot nor dove but the emblem of his personality, while the dog was he himself, looking up at Lueli's bird but on trust not to snatch at it or frighten it away.

On the afternoon of the third day the idol was finished. So far it had been his, the creature of his brain, the work of his hands. In an approving look he took his farewell of it, and dismissing it from his care he put it to stand upright on the rock before the hut. Then, moving very quietly, for inside the hut Lueli was taking his afternoon nap and must not be disturbed till everything was ready, he went to the bush by the spring where the red flowers grew. Of these he wove a rather uncouth garland, after the style of the daisy-chains that children make, but a daisy-chain like slow drops of blood. He arranged this round the idol and walked into the hut.

"Lueli!"

Under the smooth brown eye-lids the eyes flickered and awakened. Lueli blinked at him, shut his eyes once more and stretched protestingly. It was all most right: he would hear the words as he should hear them, he would hear them as in a dream.

"Lueli, on the rock outside there is something waiting for you. Go out and see what it is."

He was conscious of Lueli rising and passing him by, and pausing for a moment on the threshold. He sat down with his face to the wall, for he dared not watch an encounter that must be so momentous. Even the eyes of his mind he turned away, and sat in a timeless world, listening. Then, at last, he heard and was released—for what he heard, a murmur, a wandering wreath of sound, was Lueli talking softly to his god.

He made a movement to arise, and then stayed himself. This time he would not intrude, would not interfere. Lueli should be left in peace. He too was at peace, wasn't he? His atonement had been accepted, his part was done. Now there was nothing left for him but to go away. He began to reckon the days. His letter had caught the boat, he knew; for last night the canoe had returned and Moki told him that he had seen the Captain and put the letter into his hands. That was two days ago, and so by now Archdeacon Mason had hitched on his gold-rimmed eyeglasses and was scanning the letter at arm's length in that dignified way he had, a way of reading letters which was as much as to announce: "Whilst reserving my judgment I remain perfectly infallible." At any rate by tomorrow morning he would learn that Mr. Fortune wished to be recalled from Fanua: for though the boat touched at two or three ports before reaching St. Fabien, she was never more than half a day out of her time. By this reckoning the launch might be expected, perhaps tomorrow evening, perhaps on the day following. Then the canoe would push out to the opening of the reef and dodge forward between two waves. He would stand up in the canoe, catch hold of a rope, push against that footing, buoyant and unsteady almost as the sea. He would be on the launch, looking at the neat life-belt, and smelling brass-polish again and warm machine oil. He would be off, he would be gone.

Outside among the birds and the sliding shadows of the palmfronds Lueli was still talking to his god—a happy noise. Mr. Fortune listened for a minute or two and then went on thinking. He would have no luggage and that was a pity, for he felt the need of doing something business-like, packing would have been a solace. Stay! There would of course be presents: the islanders would not allow him to depart without gifts. They would give him mats, carved bowls and platters, a pig-sticker hung with elaborate tassels, a pipe. A pleasant people, and very beautiful, with their untrammelled carriage and arabesqued nakedness. He glanced down at his forearm where he had allowed old Hina to prick out a vignette of a fish with whiskers. While she was jabbing and chattering he had thought: "A man who has lost his faith in God may perfectly well allow himself to be tattooed." After Lueli, Hina was the islander with whom he had gone nearest to a feeling of intimacy. In extreme old age as in infancy, distinctions of nationality scarcely exist; and Hina had seemed to him very little different from any legendary old lady in an English chimneycorner. She might almost have been his godmother, grown so aged as to be grown gay, and without her wig.

Tomorrow he must go round and bid good-bye to everybody. They would be very surprised, very exclamatory: he did not think that they would be very much upset. If they had seemed rather unreal to him how much more unreal must he have seemed to them! They had been on easy terms with him—they would be on easy terms with anybody; they had accepted his odd ways without demur. While he still preached they had sometimes listened, and when he ceased preaching they asked no questions. When he was happy they smiled back, and when he was parched with anxiety they had not appeared to notice much difference. And at all times they continued to supply him with food and to perform any service he required of them.

They had grown accustomed to him but they had not assimilated him; and his odd ways they had taken as something quite natural since he himself was an oddity. His departure would affect them much as if a star had fallen out of their sky: that is to say it wouldn't really affect them at all. There were once three stars where now you see two: there was once a white man with a magic box which groaned when he trampled it, who came to Fanua. In the course of time the few remaining people who had seen the lost star would brag a little about its superior size and lustre, saying that there were no such stars in these days; and similarly in times to come a black and white being ten feet high and able to speak in a voice of thunder for seven days and seven nights might haunt the groves of Fanua. The ginger-nuts, they too might be commemorated in the fact that he fed men with red-hot pebbles. All he hoped was that they would not use him to frighten children with. But alas!—he was fooling himself. There would soon be plenty of white men to frighten the children of Fanua, to bring them galvanized iron and law-courts and commerce and industry and bicycles and patent medicines and American alarm clocks, besides the blessing of religion. The island could not hope to keep its innocence much longer. Had he not come, a single spy? And soon there would come battalions. Poor islanders! He almost said: "Poor flock!" Well, tomorrow he must bid them good-bye, and tomorrow too, before he bade farewell to the rest he must say: "I am going away, Lueli, I am going away for ever."

And then—*suppose the launch didn't come?* Suppose that the earthquake at Fanua had been but a ripple of an enormous earthquake which had swallowed up St. Fabien?

It would not do to fancy such things. He got up and walked out of the hut. Lueli was gone and had taken his god with him; maybe he had carried him off to the little copse where he had cherished the old one. Absently Mr. Fortune sat down on the altar. His hand touched something cold and flabby. It was the garland of red flowers which he had woven in order to give the idol a more festive and Christmas-tree appearance—for a present is a present twice over if it be tied up prettily. He smiled, and hung it round his neck.

He was still sitting on the altar when Lueli came strolling back for supper. He came singing to himself, and as he walked he tossed a couple of small fish from hand to hand.

"Why didn't you come and bathe too? Look! I caught these in my fingers."

"How beautiful they are!"

They were silvery fish with black and vermilion markings and rose-coloured fins. Their strange blue eyes were yet bright, and they retained the suppleness and shine of life. One does not admire things enough: and worst of all one allows whole days to slip by without once pausing to see an object, any object, exactly as it is.

"We will have them for supper," he said. "I am sorry that I forgot to come bathing. But I'll tell you what. There will be a moon tonight, we might bathe after supper by moonlight. Unless you want to go down to the village."

"No. It would be a lark to bathe."

The night was so mild that after bathing they lounged on the rocks, dangling their legs in the water, which felt even more surprisingly tepid because its black and silver pattern looked so cold. The ledge where they sat was padded with the soft tough growth of sea plants. Out on the reef some gulls were complaining.

The shadow hid his own face but Lueli sat in full moonlight. It was a good moment to speak.

"Lueli, I am going away from Fanua."

There would be no need to add: "I am going away for ever." Somehow, from the tone of his voice or by some curious sympathy, Lueli had guessed. He started so violently that he lost his balance and slipped off the rock. He swam a few strokes out into the pool and then turned and came back again and caught hold of Mr. Fortune's knees to moor himself.

"But if you go you will leave me," he said, lying along the water and looking up into his friend's face. "Don't go!"

"I must, my dear. It is time."

"Are you going back to your own country?"

"Yes. I expect so. Anyhow, I must go. A boat will come for me, the same boat which brought me when I came to the island. Perhaps tomorrow, perhaps the day after."

"Not tomorrow!" Lueli cried out, his face suddenly convulsed with distress.

Mr. Fortune nodded.

"Tomorrow or the next day."

"But why do you only tell me now? Now there will be no time to do anything, I can't even make you a pipe. Stay longer! Stay even a little longer! I thought you would stay for ever."

"I'm sorry if I have left it too late. I did it for the best, I didn't want to spoil our last days."

"But when did you know that you would go away?"

"A long time ago. A bird—" He stopped. It would not do to tell Lueli what the bird had said to him. He would not understand, he was incapable of understanding, because he was incapable of feeling that sad, civilized and proprietary love which is anxious and predatory and spoil-sport. Even now despite his distress at hearing that his friend was about to leave him he wasn't attempting to interfere or to do anything about it.

"Lueli, you know how sorry I am to be leaving you. I will not speak of it much, I don't think we need upset each other by telling our feelings. We know them already. But I have one consolation. I am not leaving a weakling, someone that I should have to feel uneasy about. When I think of you, as I shall do constantly, it will be with admiration and confidence."

He looked down at the face raised toward his. Affection, grief, the most entire attention were depicted thereon; but for all these Lueli's countenance still kept its slightly satirical air. And this, because it was the expression most essentially and characteristically his, the aspect that nature had given him, was dearest of all.

"When I came here you were still almost a child. How the three years have changed you! You are as tall as I am now, and a great deal stronger. You are almost as strong as Kaulu whom you used to tell me about—Kaulu the strong boy, who broke the waves with his hands and forced open the jaws of the King Shark who had swallowed his brother. And you are intelligent too, and as you grow older you will become more so. Perhaps you may become as wise and prudent as Kana, who rescued the sun and moon and stars and put them back into the sky. And when he held up the sun the cock crowed. Do you remember telling me that? And as for charm—why, I think you the most popular young man on the island and the best-loved. It delights me to see it."

"You flatter me," answered Lueli in a pleased voice.

Then he sighed. "I wish you were not going," he said, "I shall miss you. I shall miss you terribly. Oh, why must you leave me?" And he hung his head, and kicked his heels disconsolately.

The water splashed up, drops of spray fell on Mr. Fortune. He shivered, but it was not the falling spray which chilled him. What could he say, how was he to comfort this child?

"Do you remember how I used to tell you about my God?"

"Yes, of course I remember."

"I haven't spoken of Him lately and perhaps you have noticed that."

"Yes."

"Well, the reason why I didn't speak of Him was—I have lost Him. I lost Him on the same night that you lost yours, the night of the earthquake. No!"—Lueli had made a sudden movement of inquiry— "He wasn't anything in the hut, He wasn't any of the things that were burnt. He wasn't the kind of God that could be burnt. But He was the kind of God that could perfectly well be lost; and, as I say, I have lost Him."

"But perhaps you will find Him, perhaps He will come back. I—my god——"

Lueli's voice sank into a warm cautious silence, the silence of a lover. Mr. Fortune put out a hand and stroked the wet head.

"No. I am quite sure I shall never find Him. But I have no doubt He is somewhere around, and that is why I am telling you of my loss. Because, you see, when I go I shall leave Him behind; my God will remain here on the island where I lost Him. And while He remains, a part of me will remain too. I do not leave you utterly."

"Like a keepsake?" ventured Lueli after thinking it over.

"Yes. Like a keepsake. But rather more than a keepsake. Almost like leaving part of myself."

"Yes. I think I understand."

"So now do you feel happier?"

"Not now. But I shall later on."

It had not been anywhere near as bad as he had dreaded that it would be. It had even been a rather comfortable conversation and one that he would be able to look back upon with kindness.

The next day, the last day, was spent in packing and leave-taking. The news of his approaching departure was received with genuine regret, and from everyone he met with such kind concern that it would have been impossible not to feel gratified even if he had wished to be above that sort of feeling. Ori, Teioa and the other important islanders got up a farewell feast in his honour. Speeches were made, his health was drunk, and afterwards Mr. Fortune sat on the best mats, flushed with praise and wearing as many garlands as a May Queen or a coffin, while presentations were made to him. A necklace of carved sharks-teeth, bracklets of scented nuts, mother-of-pearl earrings, several pipes, spears, paddles and carved walking-sticks, rolls of tapa and fine mats, coloured baskets, polished bowls, sweet-meats and cosmetics, several remembrance-knots of curiously plaited hair and charms of all sorts—these were piled up on his lap and all around him. Only Lueli brought no gift. He sat beside him, examining and praising the gifts of the others and pointing out their beauties.

"I do hope he isn't feeling out of it because he has brought no present," thought Mr. Fortune. "My blessed child, he is too generous to have anything left to give. But I can't bear to think that he might be put out of countenance. I could almost wish——"

At that moment he became aware that Lueli was no longer by his side. The conversation suddenly died down, there was a conscious, premonitory pause and people were looking toward the door of the house. They wriggled to either side, opening a sort of lane. And then Lueli stepped over the threshold, carrying a resplendent head-dress of straw-coloured and scarlet feathers.

Walking solemnly, with a rapt and formal face, he advanced down the lane, bearing on high the softly-waving and coloured crown, till with a deep bow he laid the head-dress at Mr. Fortune's feet.

"But, Lueli!" exclaimed Mr. Fortune, too much overcome for words of thanks. "This lovely thing, this marvellous thing! Is it—can it be——?"

"Lueli is your especial friend," said Ori. "It is right that he should make you the best gift."

There was a loud hum of approval. Mr. Fortune raised the head-dress, admired it all round, and put it on. The hum of approval swelled into acclamations and loud cheers.

Then it was Mr. Fortune's turn to produce gifts. He had spent most of the forenoon going over his possessions, such as they were, and in between spells of working on the idol he had contrived to make an assortment of pipe-stoppers, tooth-picks, bodkins and suchlike small items. With these, and the mother-of-pearl counters and almost all his buttons he was enabled to produce a tolerable array; and though he apologized a great deal over their inadequacy there was no need to apologize, for the recipients were overjoyed with objects so distinguished and far-fetched.

The knife, at once his most personal and valuable possession, was naturally for Lueli, and so was his pipe. Ori received the magnifying glass and his two sons the whistle and the flint-and-steel lighter respectively. To Teioa he presented the magnet and to Mrs. Teioa the medicine spoon. Lueli's mother went into fits of rapture over the measuring tape, Tekea, a handsome, rather taciturn fellow who had helped a great deal with the new hut, was much gratified by the nail-file, the Parnell medal was hung round Fuma's neck and the pencil-case round Vaili's. The pencil sharpener he gave to Lei-lei, village sorceress, doctoress and midwife, who declared that it would be an invaluable asset. At the last moment he remembered Hina, the old story-teller. He gave her the wash-leather bag.

After songs and dances the party broke up at a late hour; and still wearing his crown Mr. Fortune walked home with Lueli by moonlight. The other gifts he had left behind, for Ori had undertaken to see that they were packed properly, ready for the morrow. A night-bird was calling among the trees—a soft breathy note like an alto flute—and the roof of the hut shone in the moonlight.

"Will you go on living here, Lueli?"

"Of course. Where else should I like to live so well?"

"I am glad. I shall know how to picture you when I am thinking of you."

"When I think of you I shall not know where you are."

"Think of me here."

As a result of the party they overslept themselves, and they were still breakfasting when Tekea came running up to say that the launch had been sighted. Mr. Fortune became a man of action. He knew instantly that no one from St. Fabien could be allowed to set foot on his island. He gave instructions to Tekea accordingly: a canoe might go out to the reef to keep them in play, but no one was to be taken off the launch on any account.

"What shall I tell them," asked Tekea: "if they want to land?"

"Tell them—" What could they be told? Small-pox, tigers, taboos, hornets in swarm; he ran over a few pretexts but nothing seemed quite suitable. "Tell them," he said, "tell them I say so. By the way, you might take them out a few bananas."

Tekea grinned. He was an understanding fellow. He ran back to the village while Mr. Fortune and Lueli followed at a more leisurely pace. There was nothing to delay them: Mr. Fortune was already dressed in his European clothes, and the feather head-dress was carefully packed in a large leafy frail. Just as they were crossing the dell he stopped. "Wait a minute," he said, "we never washed up the breakfast things."

"I can do that afterwards."

"No, indeed! That would be dismal. We will do it now, and shake out the mats. There is plenty of time, and if there isn't it won't hurt them to wait. They'll have the bananas to amuse them."

Together they put all straight and tidy, folded up Mr. Fortune's island clothes, threw away the garlands of overnight and the unused twigs and vines that had been plucked for the packing of the head-dress, and removed every trace of departure. Then they set forth for the village once more.

Everyone was out to see Mr. Fortune off and wish him good-luck. The launch was outside the reef and his luggage was being conveyed on board. There was a vast amount of it and it seemed even more numerous because of the quantity of helping hands outstretched to deal with it. It was all so exactly like what he had foreseen that he felt as though he were in a dream: the beach, the lagoon, thronged with excited well-wishers, canoes getting their out-riggers entangled and nearly upsetting, hands thrust out of the water to right them, everyone laughing and exclaiming. Everyone that is, except Lueli: Mr. Fortune had not been able to include him in his foreseeing of the last act. He had been lively and natural at breakfast; but now he was silent, he was pale, he was being brave. "If I say something cheerful," thought Mr. Fortune: "I may upset him. What shall I say?" At the water's edge he turned to him. "Forgive me if—" He got no further for Lueli's arms were flung about his neck. Mr. Fortune gently patted him on the back.

He got into the canoe and the dream began again. The canoe manœuvred at the opening of the reef, it dodged forward between the waves. He stood up, he felt the sea sidle and thrust under him as the earth had done on the night of the earthquake, the rope was thrown, he touched the side of the launch, he was on board.

In the launch was the Secretary, grown bald and corpulent, who immediately began to tell Mr. Fortune about the Great War, saying that the Germans crucified Belgian children, were a disgrace to humanity, and should be treated after the same fashion themselves.

Mr. Fortune sat listening and saying at intervals: "Indeed," and: "How terrible!" and: "Of course I have heard nothing of all this." His eyes were fixed upon the coral reef where Lueli stood, poised above the surf, and waving a green frond in farewell. As the launch gathered speed Lueli's figure grew smaller and smaller; at last he was lost to sight, and soon the island of Fanua appeared to be sinking back into the sea whence it had arisen.

Now the Secretary was abusing the French; and from them he

passed to the Turks, the Italians and King Ferdinand of Bulgaria. Mr. Fortune could not yet gather who was fighting whom, still less what they were all fighting about. However there seemed no doubt but that it was a very comprehensive dog-fight.

"Shall I go back to Europe?" he thought. "I couldn't fight but perhaps I might pick up the wounded. No! I am too old to be of any use; and besides, I have no money to pay my passage."

The launch scurried on with a motion that might have been described as rollicking if it had not also been so purposeful and business-like. The paint which used to be white picked out with dark blue was now buff picked out with chocolate. The mechanic was a new one. He had stared at Mr. Fortune when the latter came aboard, and now he came out of the engine house with a rag in his hand and began polishing the brass-work, turning round at frequent intervals to have another look at him.

"Perhaps he expected me to carry a goatskin umbrella," thought Mr. Fortune.

The Secretary displayed no such interest. He asked no questions about Fanua, a negligible peaceful spot, not like Europe, not to be compared to St. Fabien, where there was a gun-boat and a fermenting depot for the Red Cross Fund. And as for Mr. Fortune he had known years ago all that there was to know about him and that wasn't much.

His conversation shifted from the wife of an ex-prime minister who was certainly in the pay of the Germans to the proprietor of the Pension Hibiscus who had attempted to charge for teas served to the ladies of the Swab Committee and was probably a spy. Meanwhile the island of Fanua was sinking deeper into the Pacific Ocean.

At last he stopped talking. Mr. Fortune knew that he ought now to say something but he felt incapable of comment. He did not seem to have an idea left. Everything that was real, everything that was significant had gone down with the island of Fanua and was lost for ever.

No. After all there was one thing he might ask, one small interest which had been overlooked in the pillaging of his existence.

"By the by, can you tell me the exact time?"

He was an hour and twenty minutes out. A bad guess on his part.

But perhaps it was not quite such bad guessing as it now appeared to be; for he had spent three and a half years in Fanua, and his watch might well have lost half an hour or so in that time. It was a good watch once; but Time will wear out even watches, and it had seen its best days.

ENVOY

My poor Timothy, Good-bye! I do not know what will become of you.

AN AFTERWORD ON
"MR. FORTUNE'S MAGGOT"

SYLVIA TOWNSEND WARNER has, to my notion, best earned our gratitude by this odd, perverse, and deeply endearing story and by an earlier novel of hers called *Lolly Willowes,* of which all but its unsatisfying conclusion would delight anyone who found pleasure, let us say, in reading Jane Austen. The conclusion of *Mr. Fortune's Maggot,* however, was, to most of us, eminently satisfactory when the tale was first told, but seemingly it nagged at Miss Warner herself and gave her no peace until several years later she had made at least at attempt to tell what did become of her poor Timothy.

You will find this attempt in a sometimes exquisite but singularly uncommunicative short story of hers called "The Salutation," through which, nameless but unmistakable, Mr. Fortune moves, his first entrance signaled by a cough which disturbs the siesta of an elderly but tender Argentinian widow dozing in the heat of a summer afternoon. Angustias had always been a good sleeper. Indeed, Miss Warner tells us she practiced sleep with such mastery that she had a repertory of different slumbers which she could command at will, slumbers ranging from the gauze of inattention suitable for sermons and too prolonged explanations to the quilted oblivion fit for a winter's night. It is from a middling stupor that she is awaked by the cough which is promptly traced to a dusty, white-haired wayfarer who has lain him down and gone to sleep in the shadow cast by her house. She gives him shelter and little by little you identify him as Mr. Fortune, and

460

learn (not without rigorous attention) something of what has befallen him inside and out.

Thus we learn that, after leaving the island, Mr. Fortune lived by the sea, shipping on strange craft and picking up odd jobs in this port and that. Thus in Buenos Aires he was engaged for a time to give English lessons to an aging harlot who was proposing to found a brothel.

Four thousand miles away, across a continent, across an ocean, was an island. And there, secure in the timelessness of all things irretrievably lost, was happiness—local, like a bird singing or a flower growing. He had possessed it, he had misused it—for to do anything with happiness but to receive it as the ear receives the song of a bird or the nostril the scent of a flower is to misuse it; he had left it. But because he had left it of his own will it had given him—a parting gift—this touchstone to carry for ever in his heart, wherewith to try and infallibly dismiss any solace, whether of chance or plotted by the treachery of his desires, that might come to him and say, I too am happiness. Turn in with me.

Self-exiled, he still carried with him this divine right of not being taken in by imitations. And often he had known a strange mental pleasure in the exercise of this faculty, a faculty so sharp and unerring that the pinchbeck pretences of pleasure had become harmless, tolerable, indeed almost endeared, just because it was so easy to see through them. If from the first we could look into the hearts of those we meet, we should look on all men mildly. It is not our enemies that we seek to destroy, but our own illusions which mistook them for friends.

But what brought him to the pampas was his quest for a place where there might be elbow-room for sorrow.

Make haste, make haste! There was so little time, and he might die before he came there, and be defrauded of his grief. Happiness was on the island, where he had left it; but there, awaiting him on those green plains, if only he could get so far, was sorrow, an experience as deep and assuaging as the other. In all these years of dingy exile he had never once had time to put on his sorrow. It had lain folded and hidden within him like a garment folded in a travelling-trunk. And unless he made haste he might never wear it, for with every day it grew more crumpled, more sullied with disuse, its embroideries perishing, its texture rotting and creased. This heavenly treasure laid up in an earthly carcass, he had lugged it about from port to port. It's a wonder, he thought, that I didn't present it to a museum with all the other things I brought from the island. *Example of a sorrow, full-length. Made by an Englishman in the Southern Hemisphere. Presented by, etc.*

With which sample I leave you to seek out "The Salutation," if you are interested, and decide for yourself whether Miss Warner ever did know what became of her poor Timothy. If, when it was new in this country, her first account of him did not find its way to half the readers who would have relished it, some blame must attach to the title. In England, folks are used to thinking of a maggot as "a whimsical or perverse fancy; a crotchet," a meaning which long ago must have been lost overboard somewhere in mid-Atlantic.

The tale of Mr. Fortune entertains me as another instance of one English phenomenon. The people of that astounding island have roamed the earth for so many generations that they can now manage such explorations in spirit. The enchanting invasion of Tibet called *Lost Horizon* was the work of a young Briton whose traveling, I believe, had been limited to a fortnight in a Swiss *pension,* and Miss Warner was able to traipse through Polynesia with Mr. Fortune without ever putting foot out of Kent. As for "The Salutation," her only preparation, I understand, was a letter asking a colleague in New York to straighten her out on two points. Did South Americans shoot off fireworks on saints' days? And would the Andes be visible from a tram in Valparaiso?

A. W.

THE CHILDREN'S CRUSADE

by

MARCEL SCHWOB

ENGLISH VERSION BY ALEXANDER WOOLLCOTT

Circa idem tempus pueri sine rectore sine duce de universis omnium regionum villis et civitatibus versus transmarinas partes avidis gressibus cucurrerunt, et dum quaereretur ab ipsis quo currerent, responderunt: Versus Jherusalem, quaerere terram sanctam . . . Adhuc quo devenerint ignoratur. Sed plurimi redierunt, a quibus dum quaereretur causa cursus, dixerunt se nescire. Nudae etiam mulieres circa idem tempus nichil loquentes per villas et civitates cucurrerunt. . . .

THE CHILDREN'S CRUSADE

A VAGRANT PRIEST SPEAKS

THOUGH I be but a wretched, outcast cleric who must wander the forests and highways to beg, in the name of Our Lord, my daily bread, I have seen a sight most holy and heard the words of little children. I know my life is not a godly one and that sometimes under the lime trees by the roadside I have given in to temptation. The brothers who offer me wine can see well enough that I am little used to drink. But I am not one of these mutilators. There be wicked men who gouge out the eyes of babies and cut off their legs and bind their hands in order to show them off for pity. Therefore was I sore afraid when I beheld all those children. But without doubt Our Lord will protect them. I rattle on this way because I am filled to the brim with happiness. The springtime and everything I see makes me laugh. My mind is none too good. I was but ten years old when they gave me the tonsure, and all the Latin words I have clean forgot. I am like a locust, for I leap about here and there and make a great buzzing. At times I spread my coloured wings and you can see right through my little empty head. They say that Saint John the Baptist lived on locusts in the wilderness. He must have eaten a great many. But Saint John was not made like the rest of us.

I am full of adoration for Saint John, because he too was a wanderer, and the words he spoke did not always follow one upon another. I think they must have been all the sweeter for that. The spring is sweet too this year. Never have I seen so many pink and white flowers. The meadows are new-washed. Everywhere the blood of Our Lord glistens in the hedgerows. The blessed Lord Jesus is the colour of the lily but His blood is the colour of a ruby. Why? I do not know. Doubtless it is all explained in a parchment somewhere. Had I been taught my letters I would get me a parchment now and write upon it. In that way I would be able to eat my fill every night. I would go into the monasteries to pray for the dead of the brotherhood and write their names upon my scroll. From one abbey to another I would carry my death-scroll. The brothers would like that. But I do not know the names of the dead. Perhaps Our Lord does not bother to know them either. All these children seem to me to have no names, yet it is quite certain that they have the favour of Our Lord Jesus. They filled all the highway like a swarm of white bees. I know not whence they came. They were all small pilgrims. They carried staffs of hazelwood and birch. They had crosses on their shoulders and these crosses were of many colours. I saw some green ones which must have been made of leaves sewn together. These children are wild and ignorant. They are headed for I know not where. They believe in Jerusalem. Me, I think that Jerusalem is far away and that Our Lord must be much nearer to us. They will not come to Jerusalem. But Jerusalem will come to them. And to me. The end of all holy things is joy. Our Lord is here under this scarlet thorn and on my lips and in the poor words I speak, for I think of Him and in my thought lies His sepulchre. Amen. I will lie down here in the sunlight. It is a holy place. The feet of Our Lord have made all places holy. I will go to sleep. May Jesus bring sleep to all the white little children who carry the cross. Verily to Him I say it. I am very sleepy. Verily I say it to Him, for perhaps He has not seen them and He should watch over little children. The hour of noon weighs upon me. All things are white. So be it. Amen.

A LEPER SPEAKS

IF you would understand that which I am about to tell you, know that my head is covered with a white cowl and that I shake a rattle made of hard wood. I no longer know what my face is like, but my hands terrify me. They run before me like scaly creatures the colour of death. I would like to cut them off. Everything that they touch fills me with shame. It seems to me that they blight the red fruits I gather. And the poor roots which I pluck from the ground seem to wither at their touch. *Domine ceterorum libera me!*

The Saviour has not expiated my ghastly sin. I am forgotten until the resurrection. Like the toad sealed in the dark of the moon in some unnoticed rock, I shall stay locked up in my hideous lode when all the rest arise with their shining bodies. *Domine ceterorum fac me liberum: leprosus sum.* I am alone and frightened. Only my teeth have kept their natural whiteness. All animals fear me and my very soul would like to run away from me. The daylight avoids me. Twelve hundred and twelve years ago this Saviour of theirs saved *them,* but on me He had no pity. I was not touched by the bloody spear that pierced His side. Perhaps the blood of their Lord would have healed me. Often I dream of blood. I could bite it with my teeth, for *they* are sound. Since He has been unwilling to give to me, I have a great yearning to take that which belongs to Him. That is why I kept watch on these children who came down from the Vendôme to this woodland on the Loire. They carried crosses, for they were His subjects. Their flesh is His flesh and He has not made me part of His flesh. On this earth I am surrounded by a pale damnation. I lay in wait to suck the innocent blood from the neck of one of these children of His. *Et caro nova fiet in die irae.* On the Day of Judgment my flesh will be new. Loitering behind the others there was a rosy child with red hair. I marked him out. My leap was sudden. I seized his mouth with my dreadful hands. He wore only a rough shirt; his feet were bare and his eyes remained tranquil. Unastonished, he looked at me. Then, knowing that he was not going to cry out, I was seized with a great desire to hear a human voice. I took my hands from his mouth and he did not wipe his lips. His eyes were far away.

"Who art thou?" I said to him.

"Johannes the Teuton," he answered. And his speech was clear and healing.

"Whither goest thou?" I asked him then.

And he answered: "To Jerusalem to conquer the Holy Land."

Then I began to laugh and I asked him: "Where is Jerusalem?"

And he answered: "I do not know."

And then I said: "What is Jerusalem?"

And he answered: "It is Our Lord."

Then I began to laugh anew and I asked him: "What is this Lord of thine?"

And he said: "I do not know. He is white."

And this word threw me into a fury and I opened my teeth under my cowl and I bent towards his rosy throat and he did not draw back and I said: "Why dost thou not fear me?"

And he said: "Why should I have fear of thee, O man all white?"

Then great tears shook me and I stretched myself upon the earth. I kissed the ground with my terrible lips and I cried: "Because I am a leper."

And the child looked at me and said in his limpid voice: "I do not understand."

He was not afraid of me! He was not afraid of me!

To him my monstrous whiteness was like the whiteness of his Lord and I took a handful of grass and wiped his lips and his hands and I said to him: "Go in peace to your white Lord and tell Him that He has forgotten me."

And the child from the North looked at me and said nothing. I went along with him out of the darkness of the forest. He walked without trembling. From afar I watched his red locks vanish into the sunlight. *Domine infantium, libera me!* May the sound of my wooden rattle reach Thee pure as the sound of bells! Master of all who do not understand, deliver Thou me!

POPE INNOCENT III SPEAKS

When I leave the incense and the chasubles behind me and come to the one room in all my palace that has no gold left on its walls, I find it quite easy to talk to God. With no one standing by to prop me up, I come here to give thought to my old age. During the mass, my heart is uplifted and my body straightens up. The sparkle of the sacred wine fills my eyes and my thinking is eased by the precious oils. But in this lonely spot in the house of my Lord, I am free to bend under my earthly weariness. *Ecce homo!* For the Lord cannot really hear the voice of His priests through all the thunder of edicts and bulls. Haply the purple is not pleasing to Him. Nor the jewels, nor the paintings. Then He may have pity on my faulty babbling when it rises from this little cell. Lord, I am very old and behold me clad in white before Thee and my name is Innocent and Thou knowest that I know nothing. Pardon Thou my papacy for it was a thing already set up and I gave in to it. It was not I who ordained these honours. I would rather see Thy sun through this round window than in the magnificent glitter of my stained glass. Let me kneel before Thee as would any old man and turn towards Thee the pallid and wrinkled face which I find it so hard to keep above the waves of the eternal night. As the rings slip along my shrunken fingers, so slide away the last days of my life.

Oh, God, I am Thy vicar here and towards Thee I reach out a hand cupped to hold the pure wine of Thy faith. There are great crimes. There are very great crimes. We can give them absolution. There are great heresies. There are very great heresies. We should punish them without pity. In this hour when, all in white, I kneel in this small white cell, I am in great anguish, Lord, for I know not whether these crimes and heresies fall within the imposing domain of my papacy or within the little circle of sunlight in which an old man clasps his simple hands together. Then, too, I am troubled in this matter of Thy sepulchre. Always the infidels encircle it. No one knows how to take it from them. No one has led Thy cross to the Holy Land, yet are we sunk in torpor. The knights have laid down their arms and there are no longer kings who know how to command them. And I, Lord, reproach myself and beat my breast. I am too weak and too old.

Now, O Lord, hear Thou the tremulous whisper rising from this little cell in my basilica and give me counsel. My men have brought me strange tidings from Flanders and from Germany and from all along the roads that lead to Marseilles and to Genoa. Unheard-of sects are about to be born. There have been seen running about the cities naked women who speak no word at all. These shameless mutes kept pointing to heaven. In the public squares madmen have been preaching ruin. Hermits and wandering friars are full of strange tales. And I know not by what magic more than seven thousand children have been enticed from their homes. Seven thousand are on the march with cross and staff. They have nothing to eat. They carry no arms. They cannot fend for themselves and they discredit us. They are ignorant of all true religion. My men questioned them. They said they were going to Jerusalem to conquer the Holy Land. My men told them they could not cross the sea. They made answer that the waters of the sea would part and dry up to let them pass. Their own God-fearing and worthy people tried to hold them back by force but they broke the locks in the night and climbed over the walls. Many are sons begotten by noblemen with sinful women. It is a great pity. Lord, all these innocents will be given over to shipwreck and to the worshippers of Mahomet. I can see the Sultan of Baghdad lying in wait for them in his palace. I tremble lest the sailors lay hands on them and sell them into slavery.

Lord, let me speak to you in the formulas of religion. This children's crusade is no work of piety. It will never win the sepulchre for the Christians. It but adds to the number of vagabonds who are astray on the fringe of the true faith. Our priests cannot defend it. We are forced to believe that the Evil One has possession of these poor creatures. They flock towards the precipice as the swine ran towards the steep place. Lord, Thou knowest how gladly the Evil One takes possession of children. Once he assumed the guise of a ratcatcher and seduced with his flute-notes all the little children of Hamelin. Some say these unfortunates were drowned in the river Weser. Others say he shut them up in the side of a mountain. It is to be feared that Satan is leading all our children into the toils of those who have not our faith. Lord, you know yourself it is not a good thing for belief to take new forms. It had no sooner appeared in the burning bush, than you shut it up in a tabernacle. And when it was wrung from your lips upon Golgotha, you ordained that it be enclosed in many a pyx and monstrance. These little prophets will shake the edifice of your church. We must keep them out of it. Will you in scorn for the consecrate—who wear in your service their albs and their stoles and who, to win you, have sternly resisted all temptation—will you now find acceptable these who know not what they do? We should suffer little children to come unto you, but only by the avenue of your faith. Lord, I speak to you according to your own laws. These children will perish. Let there not be under Innocent a new massacre of the innocents.

Pardon me, O God, if, though I wear Thy diadem, I still seek counsel. The palsy of old age seizes me anew. See Thou my poor hands. I am a very old man. I no longer have the faith all little children have. Time has worn the gold from the walls of this cell. They are white. This bit of Thy sunlight is white. My robe is white, too. And my withered heart is without stain. I have spoken according to Thy law. There are crimes. There are very great crimes. There are heresies. There are very great heresies. My head shakes from weakness. Perhaps we should neither punish nor absolve. When life has gone by, it makes our resolutions falter. I have never seen a miracle. Give me light. Is this a miracle? What sign hast Thou given them? Is the day at hand? Is it Thy wish that a very old man such as I am be as white as Thy stainless children? Seven thousand! What if theirs be an ignorant faith, wilt Thou punish the ignorance of seven thousand innocents? I, too, am Innocent. Lord, I am as innocent as they. Do not punish me in my old age. The long, long years have taught me that this flock of children *cannot* succeed. And yet, Lord, is it a miracle? This cell of mine remains as calm as when I have meditated here before. I know there is no need of imploring Thee to make Thyself manifest, and yet, from the height of my great age, from the dizzy height of Thy papacy, I do so implore Thee. Teach me, for I do not understand. Lord, these are Thy little innocents and I, Innocent, I do not understand. I do not understand.

TWO CHILDREN SPEAK

WE three—Nicolas, who cannot talk, and Alain and Denis—we are on our way to Jerusalem. We have been walking a long time. White voices called out to us in the night. They were calling all little children. They were like the voices of birds who died in the winter time. At first we saw many poor birds stretched upon the frozen ground, many small birds with red throats. Then we saw the first flowers and the first leaves, and from these we braided crosses. We sang outside the villages just as we always used to at New Year's. And all the children ran towards us. And we moved forward like an army. Some men cursed us because they did not know the Lord. There were women who caught us by the arms and questioned us and covered our faces with kisses. And then there were kind people who brought us wooden bowls with warm milk and fruits. And everybody was sorry for us, for they did not know where we were going and they had not heard the voices.

There are dense forests on this earth, and rivers and mountains and pathways full of brambles. At the end of the land is the sea, which we shall soon be crossing. And at the end of the sea is Jerusalem. We have no leaders or guides but we have found all the roads good. Although he does not know how to talk, Nicolas walks just as we, Alain and Denis, do. And all countries are alike, one as dangerous for children as another. Everywhere there are thick forests and rivers and mountains and thorns. But everywhere the voices will be with us.

There is a child here whose name is Eustace and who was born with his eyes closed. He keeps his arms outstretched and he smiles. We see no more than he does. A little girl leads him and carries his cross. Her name is Allys. She never speaks and she never cries. She keeps her eyes fixed upon Eustace's feet so that she can hold him up when he stumbles. We love them both. Eustace will not be able to see the sacred lamps of the sepulchre. But Allys will take his hands and see that he touches the slabs of the tomb.

Oh, how beautiful the things of this earth are! We remember nothing because we never learned anything. Yet we have seen old trees and red rocks. Sometimes we pass through long shadows. Sometimes we walk until sunset in bright pastures. We have shouted the name of Jesus into Nicolas's ears and he knows it well. But he cannot say it. He enjoys what we see. His lips part out of happiness and he pats us on the shoulders. They are not unhappy, for Allys looks after Eustace and we, Alain and Denis, we look after Nicolas.

They told us we should meet ogres and werewolves in the woods. Those were lies. No one has frightened us. No one has done us any harm. Hermits and sick people come to look at us and old women light rush-candles for us in the huts. They ring the churchbells for us. Peasants stand up in the furrows and stare at us. The cattle look at us too, and do not run away. And since we have been on the march the sun has grown warmer, and the flowers we pick are different. But all the stems can be braided into the same forms and our crosses are always fresh. So our hopes are high and soon we shall see the blue sea. And at the end of the blue sea is Jerusalem. And the Lord will suffer all little children to come to his tomb. And the white voices will be happy in the night.

REPORT OF FRANÇOIS LONGUEJOUE, SCRIVENER

TODAY, *the fifteenth day of September in the twelve-hundred-and-twelfth year after the incarnation of Our Lord, there came into the shipyard of my master, Hugues Ferré, several children asking that they might cross the sea to visit the Holy Sepulchre. And because the aforesaid Ferré did not have enough merchantmen in the port of Marseilles, he bade me call upon Master Guillaume Porc in order to complete the number. The said Hugues Ferré and the said Guillaume Porc will sail the ships all the way to the Holy Land for the love of Our Lord, J. C. Just now more than seven thousand children are spread around the city of Marseilles, and some of them speak strange and savage tongues. So the Honourable Aldermen, fearing with some reason that there might be a shortage of food, met at the town hall where, after deliberation, they summoned the aforesaid shipmasters to urge and beg them to dispatch the ships with all convenient speed. Because of the equinox, the weather at sea is none too good, but one must bear in mind that such a mob might be dangerous to our good city, all the more because these children are starved after their long march and know not what they are doing. I have had a call put in for sailors at the port and have had the ships outfitted. They can set sail at the vesper hour. The swarm of children is not inside the city, but they are running all along the shore gathering up shells as tokens of the voyage. And it is said they are amazed at the starfish and think these must have fallen alive from heaven to point out their road to the Lord. And of this extraordinary happening, here is what I have to say: first, it is much to be desired that Master Hugues Ferré and Master Guillaume Porc should conduct this alien disorder outside our city with all promptness; second, it has been a harsh winter so that the soil is poor this year, as the merchants of the town know full well; third, the church received no notice of the plan of this horde from the north and will take no part in all this nonsense of a childish army. (Turba infantium.) Also it is meet to praise Master Hugues Ferré and Master Guillaume Porc as much for the love they bear our good city as for their obedience to Our Lord, sending forth their ships and sailing them at the equinox, in great danger, moreover, from attack by the infidels who, in their feluccas from Algiers and Bougie, do scour this sea which belongs to us.*

THE KALANDAR SPEAKS

GLORY be to God! All praise to the Prophet who has let me be poor and wander from city to city calling on the name of the Lord! Thrice blessed be the holy companions of Mahomet, who founded the divine order to which I belong! For I am like unto him when he was stoned out of the infamous city which I will not name and when he hid in a vineyard where in pity a Christian slave gave him grapes and was reached by the words of the faith at sundown. God is great! I have passed through the cities of Mosul and of Baghdad and of Basrah, and I have known Sala'h-ud-Din (may God keep his soul) and his brother, the Sultan Seif-ud-Din, and I have looked upon the Commander of the Faithful. I live well enough on the little rice I beg and on the water people pour into my calabash. I keep my body pure, but the greatest purity is of the soul. It is written that the Prophet, before his mission, once fell into a deep sleep upon the ground. And two men in white came down to the right and to the left of his body and stood there. And the man on the left cut open his breast with a golden knife and drew out his heart from which he squeezed the black blood. And the man on the right cut open his belly with a golden knife and drew out the entrails which he purified. And they put the entrails back in place and thus did the Prophet become pure so that he might proclaim the faith. That was a more than human purity, which chiefly belongs to the angels. Yet children are pure, too. Theirs is the kind of purity which the witch-woman wished to conceive when she saw the halo around the head of Mahomet's father and tried to have union with him. But the Prophet's father joined with his wife, Aminah, and when the halo vanished from his forehead, the witch-woman knew that Aminah had conceived a pure being. Glory to God Who purifies!

Here in the portico of this bazaar I can rest myself and call out to passers-by. Squatting here alongside me are rich merchants of fabrics and jewels. That caftan there must be worth a thousand dinars. Me, I have no need of money and I am as free as a dog. Glory be to God! Now that I am in the shade, I recall the start of my discourse. First I spoke of God, for there is but one God, and of our holy Prophet who revealed the faith. For that is the origin of all thoughts, whether they issue from the mouth or are writ with a reed-pen. Next, I dwelt upon the purity which God has given to the saints and to angels. In the third place, I reflected upon the purity of children.

As it happens, I have just seen a great number of Christian children who were bought by the Commander of the Faithful. I saw them on the highway. They were going along like a flock of sheep. Some say they came from Egypt and that the ships of the Franks had unloaded them there. Satan had entered into them, tempting them to cross the sea to Jerusalem. Glory be to God! He would not let so great a cruelty be carried out, for the poor children would have died along the way, having no one to help them and no food to eat. They are altogether innocent. And at the sight of them I cast myself upon the earth and I beat the ground with my forehead, blessing the Lord at the top of my voice. This is how it was with these children. They were dressed in white and they had crosses sewn upon their clothing. They appeared not to know where they were but they did not seem troubled. Always their look was faraway. I noticed that one of them was blind and a little girl led him by the hand. Many of them had red hair and green eyes. These were Franks, who belong to the Roman Emperor. The Franks make the mistake of adoring the prophet Jesus. This error of theirs is obvious. To begin with, it has been proven by the books and the miracles that there is no law save that of Mahomet. Then, God lets us glorify Him every day and beg for our living, and He has ordained that His faithful shall protect our order. Finally, He has denied clairvoyance to these children who, tempted by Iblis, left their far-off country without His giving them a warning sign. If they had not luckily fallen into the hands of the faithful, they would have been seized by the fire-worshippers and chained in deep caves. These damnable people would have offered them up as sacrifices to their devouring and loathsome idol. Praised be our God Who does all things well and protects even those who do not confess Him. God is great! Now I shall go over to that goldsmith's shop there and demand my share of the rice. And at the same time I shall proclaim my contempt of riches. If it be pleasing to God, all these children will be saved by the faith.

LITTLE ALLYS SPEAKS

I CANNOT walk much farther for we are in a burning country to which two wicked men from Marseilles brought us. Then there was that day when all was blackness and we were tossed about on the sea with the fires of heaven all around us. But my little Eustace was not afraid because he saw nothing and I held his two hands. I love him dearly and I came here for his sake. For I do not know where we are going. It is such a long time ago that we started out. People told us about the city of Jerusalem at the end of the sea. And about Our Lord who would be there to receive us. And Eustace knows Our Lord Jesus, but he does not know what Jerusalem is. Nor what a city is. Nor the sea. He ran away to obey the voices he heard every night. It was in the night he heard them because of the stillness. For he does not know the difference between night and day. And he asked me about these voices but I could not tell him anything. I know nothing and my only worry is about Eustace. We used to walk with Nicolas and Alain and Denis but they got on to another ship, and when the sun rose next day, all the other ships were gone. Alas, what has become of them? Will we find them again when we come close to Our Lord? It is still very far off. Some say there is a great king who has sent for us and who holds the city of Jerusalem in his power. In this country everything is white, the houses white and the garments. And the faces of the women are covered with veils. Poor Eustace can't see this whiteness but I tell him about it and it makes him happy, for he says it is a sign of the end. The Lord Jesus is white. Little Allys is very tired but she holds Eustace by the hand that he may not fall and she has no time to think of her own weariness. We will rest this evening and Allys will sleep as always close to Eustace. And if the voices have not deserted us she will try to hear them in the clear night. And she will hold Eustace by the hand until the shining end of the long journey. For she must point out the Lord to him. And surely the Lord will have pity because of Eustace's patience and will suffer Eustace to see Him. And perhaps then Eustace will see little Allys.

POPE GREGORY IX SPEAKS

BEHOLD the devouring sea, which looks so blue and so innocent. Its folds are soft and edged with white like a heavenly robe. It is a liquid sky with living stars. I meditate upon it from this rocky throne whither I have had myself borne from my litter. It is well named for, in all truth, it is the centre of Christendom. Into it pours the holy water wherewith once the Forerunner washed away sins. All the sainted faces have bent over its brink, and its tremulous mirror has held for a time their transparent reflections. Anointed and mysterious font, which has neither ebb nor flow, azure cradle set like a liquid jewel in an earthly ring, my eyes interrogate thee. O Mediterranean, give me back my children. Why hast thou taken them?

I never knew them. My old age was never caressed by their sweet breaths. They never came begging to me with their tender lips parted. Alone, little vagabonds full of a blind and raging faith, they flung themselves towards the Promised Land and were annihilated. From Germany and from Flanders, from France and Savoy and Lombardy, they came towards thy treacherous waves, O holy sea, so that there was a mighty humming sound made from their half-heard words of worship. They went as far as the city of Marseilles. They went as far as the city of Genoa. And thou didst carry them in ships upon thy great foam-crested back. And thou didst twist and stretch out towards them thy grey-green arms. And thou didst hold them fast. And others thou didst betray, carrying them to the infidels, so that now, captives of those who worship Mahomet, they sigh in the palaces of the East.

Once upon a time, a proud king of Asia had thee beaten with rods and loaded with chains. O Mediterranean, who will pardon thee? Thou art sadly guilty. It is thou I accuse. Thou alone. So treacherously limpid and clear, evil mirage of the sky! I call thee to account before the throne of the Most High, whence come all things created. Consecrated sea, what hast thou done with our children? Lift towards Him thy cerulean face, stretch towards Him thy fingers all shimmering with bubbles, unleash thy measureless wine-dark laughter, turn thy murmurous voice into speech and render account unto Him.

Silent in every one of thy white mouths which have just breathed their last at my feet upon this shore, thou sayest naught. In my palace at Rome there is a chipped old cell which time has made white as an alb. Pope Innocent used to shut himself away in it. They say he meditated long upon those children and on their faith and sought a sign from the Lord. Here from this high rock-throne in the open air, I declare that Pope Innocent himself had the faith of a child and that he shook in vain his weary locks. I am much older than Innocent. I am the oldest of all the vicars whom the Lord has placed here below and I am only beginning to understand.

God never manifests Himself. Did He stand by His son at Gethsemane? Did He not abandon Him in His supreme anguish? What childish folly to invoke His aid! All evil and all ordeal lie only in ourselves. He has perfect confidence in the work fashioned by His hands and thou hast betrayed His confidence. O sea divine, be not astonished at what I say. All things are equal before the Lord. Reckoning by infinity, man's mighty reason is worth no more than the tiny, starry eye of one of the creatures that dwell in thy depths. God allots the same share to the grain of sand and to the emperor. The gold ripens in the mine, sinless as the monk meditating in the monastery. All worldly factions are equally guilty when they do not follow the lines of goodness, for these issue from Him. In His eyes there are no rocks, nor plants, nor animals, nor men. There are only creations. I see all these whitening heads which leap above thy waves and vanish into thy waters. Damned or elect, they glisten but for a moment in the light of the sun. Great age can give pride a lesson and make religion clear. I have as much pity for this little pearly shell as I have for myself.

That is why I accuse thee, devouring sea, who hast swallowed up my little children. Remember the Asian king by whom thou wast punished. But he had not lived to be a hundred, that king. He had not been through enough years. The universe still mystified him. I will not punish thee, for my complaint and thy murmur, they will die together at the feet of the Most High, just as the whisperings of thy tiniest drops have this moment died at my feet. O Mediterranean, I pardon thee and I absolve thee. I give thee most holy absolution. Go thou and sin no more. Like thee, I am guilty of faults of which I know nothing. In every moment of time thy myriad murmurous lips make confession on the shore. With my withered lips I confess to thee, great sacred sea. We confess to each other. Absolve thou me and I will absolve thee. Let us both relapse into honest ignorance. So be it.

What shall I do on earth? There shall be a monument in expiation, a monument to uncomprehending faith. The ages to come should recognize our piety and not despair. By the sanctified sin of the sea, God drew the little crusaders to Him. There was a massacre of innocents. Their bodies shall find asylum. On the Reef of the Hermit seven ships foundered. I will build a church of the New Innocents on that island and I will set up twelve canons there. And thou shalt return to me the bodies of my children, O innocent and consecrated sea. And thou shalt bear them towards the shores of the island and the canons shall place them in the crypts of the temple. And above them they shall light eternal lamps wherein the holy oils will burn and they shall show to pious travellers all these little whitened bones stretched out in the night.

AN AFTERWORD ON
"THE CHILDREN'S CRUSADE"

IT was on a June night in 1914 that Walter Duranty of Moscow and elsewhere, who was then toiling fitfully as leg-man for the Paris correspondent of *The New York Times,* came up to me on the *terrasse* of the Closerie des Lilas in the Boul' Miche and gave me, as a book to read on the boat going home, a yellow-backed miscellany by Marcel Schwob called *La Lampe de Psyché,* marking in it for my special attention the small dossier of imagined testimony called "La Croisade des Enfants." The English version given here is the result of the editor's determination to include the work in this anthology and the publisher's implacable refusal to admit the French text to the canon. No satisfactory translation appearing to be available, the evasive Duranty was vainly besought to make one. Past master of the fine art of not writing at all, he gave as his excuse this time the impossibility of capturing in English the hypnotic beauty of Schwob's prose. He may have been right.

André-Mayer Marcel Schwob, who sometimes employed Loyson-Bridet as his *nom de guerre,* was born on the outskirts of Paris (at Chaville, Seine-et-Oise) three years before the Franco-Prussian war. He died before he was forty. Heir to a long line of distinguished Jewish scholars, he "learned the lore rabbinic at the grandparental knee." His wife was Marguerite Moréno of the Comédie Française and lately we encountered them both as recurrent figures in the Parisian entries of Arnold Bennett's diary, through which Schwob moves frail and intense, a man consumed, a haunted little man with huge, burning eyes.

Just after the turn of the century America knew him best as the Frenchman who made the prose translation of *Hamlet* which Bernhardt played. About that translation a tale is told which belongs in the archives of the universal and eternal theater. In her younger days at the Théâtre Français, Sarah was often the Ophelia to the Hamlet of Mounet-Sully, but in 1900 the Divine One set herself the bold and unprecedented task of playing the Melancholy One herself. Schwob, who had a passion for English literature and who had in his time done much translation from English into French, was commissioned to prepare the version. When his first act was finished, he read it to her and she was delighted with it. But what about the other acts? They would, he assured her, be of much the same caliber. And the last act? That, too, Schwob said, would be of a piece with the rest. "No, no," Madame Sarah protested, "you misunderstand me. I want to know what happens in the last act. Doubtless Hamlet dies. But just how?" It is quite true. She had never known. In the old days, her Ophelia had always gone buckety-buckety off home as soon as she was drowned and never did hear tell what happened to the Sweet Prince.

The Schwob text from which the translation for this Reader was made begat in the French composer, Gabriel Pierné, a four-part musical legend called *The Children's Crusade* which has been heard in this country. Then I am under the impression that Yvette Guilbert once staged the eight narratives in a recital in Paris.

A. W.

THE SCHARTZ=
METTERKLUME
METHOD

by

SAKI (H. H. Munro)

THE SCHARTZ-METTERKLUME METHOD

Lady Carlotta stepped out on to the platform of the small wayside station and took a turn or two up and down its uninteresting length, to kill time till the train should be pleased to proceed on its way. Then, in the roadway beyond, she saw a horse struggling with a more than ample load, and a carter of the sort that seems to bear a sullen hatred against the animal that helps him to earn a living. Lady Carlotta promptly betook her to the roadway, and put rather a different complexion on the struggle. Certain of her acquaintances were wont to give her plentiful admonition as to the undesirability of interfering on behalf of a distressed animal, such interference being "none of her business." Only once had she put the doctrine of non-interference into practice, when one of its most eloquent exponents had been besieged for nearly three hours in a small and extremely uncomfortable may-tree by an angry boar-pig, while Lady Carlotta, on the other side of the fence, had proceeded with the water-colour sketch she was engaged on, and refused to interfere between the boar and his prisoner. It is to be feared that she lost the friendship of the ultimately rescued lady. On this occasion she merely lost the train, which gave way to the first sign of impatience it had shown throughout the journey, and steamed off without her. She bore the desertion with philosophical indifference; her friends and relations were thoroughly well used to the fact of her luggage arriving without her. She wired a vague non-committal message to her destination to say that she was coming on "by another train." Before she had time to think what her next move might be she was confronted by an imposingly attired lady, who seemed to be taking a prolonged mental inventory of her clothes and looks.

"You must be Miss Hope, the governess I've come to meet," said the apparition, in a tone that admitted of very little argument.

"Very well, if I must I must," said Lady Carlotta to herself with dangerous meekness.

"I am Mrs. Quabarl," continued the lady; "and where, pray, is your luggage?"

"It's gone astray," said the alleged governess, falling in with the excellent rule of life that the absent are always to blame; the luggage had, in point of fact, behaved with perfect correctitude. "I've just telegraphed about it," she added, with a nearer approach to truth.

"How provoking," said Mrs. Quabarl; "these railway companies are so careless. However, my maid can lend you things for the night," and she led the way to her car.

During the drive to the Quabarl mansion Lady Carlotta was impressively introduced to the nature of the charge that had been thrust upon her; she learned that Claude and Wilfrid were delicate, sensitive young people, that Irene had the artistic temperament highly developed, and that Viola was something or other else of a mould equally commonplace among children of that class and type in the twentieth century.

"I wish them not only to be *taught*," said Mrs. Quabarl, "but *interested* in what they learn. In their history lessons, for instance, you must try to make them feel that they are being introduced to the life-stories of men and women who really lived, not merely committing a mass of names and dates to memory. French, of course, I shall expect you to talk at mealtimes several days in the week."

"I shall talk French four days of the week and Russian in the remaining three."

"Russian? My dear Miss Hope, no one in the house speaks or understands Russian."

"That will not embarrass me in the least," said Lady Carlotta coldly.

Mrs. Quabarl, to use a colloquial expression, was knocked off her perch. She was one of those imperfectly self-assured individuals who are magnificent and autocratic as long as they are not seriously opposed. The least show of unexpected resistance goes a long way towards rendering them cowed and apologetic. When the new governess failed to express wondering admiration of the large newly-purchased and expensive car, and lightly alluded to the superior advantages of one or two makes which had just been put on the market, the discomfiture of her patroness became almost abject. Her feelings were those which might have animated a general of ancient warfaring days, on beholding his heaviest battle-elephant ignominiously driven off the field by slingers and javelin throwers.

At dinner that evening, although reinforced by her husband, who usually duplicated her opinions and lent her moral support generally, Mrs. Quabarl regained none of her lost ground. The governess not only helped herself well and truly to wine, but held forth with considerable show of critical knowledge on various vintage matters, concerning which the Quabarls were in no wise able to pose as authorities. Previous governesses had limited their conversation on the wine topic to a respectful and doubtless sincere expression of a preference for water. When this one went as far as to recommend a wine firm in whose hands you could not go very far wrong Mrs. Quabarl thought it time to turn the conversation into more usual channels.

"We got very satisfactory references about you from Canon Teep," she observed; "a very estimable man, I should think."

"Drinks like a fish and beats his wife, otherwise a very lovable character," said the governess imperturbably.

"My *dear* Miss Hope! I trust you are exaggerating," exclaimed the Quabarls in unison.

"One must in justice admit that there is some provocation," continued the romancer. "Mrs. Teep is quite the most irritating bridge-player that I have ever sat down with; her leads and declarations would condone a certain amount of brutality in her partner, but to souse her with the contents of the only soda-water siphon in the house on a Sunday afternoon, when one couldn't get another, argues an indifference to the comfort of others which I cannot altogether overlook. You may think me hasty in my judgments, but it was practically on account of the siphon incident that I left."

"We will talk of this some other time," said Mrs. Quabarl hastily.

"I shall never allude to it again," said the governess with decision.

Mr. Quabarl made a welcome diversion by asking what studies the new instructress proposed to inaugurate on the morrow.

"History to begin with," she informed him.

"Ah, history," he observed sagely; "now in teaching them history you must take care to interest them in what they learn. You must make them feel that they are being introduced to the life-stories of men and women who really lived——"

"I've told her all that," interposed Mrs. Quabarl.

"I teach history on the Schartz-Metterklume method," said the governess loftily.

"Ah, yes," said her listeners, thinking it expedient to assume an acquaintance at least with the name.

"What are you children doing out here?" demanded Mrs. Quabarl the next morning, on finding Irene sitting rather glumly at the head of the stairs, while her sister was perched in an attitude of depressed discomfort on the window-seat behind her, with a wolf-skin rug almost covering her.

"We are having a history lesson," came the unexpected reply. "I am supposed to be Rome, and Viola up there is the she-wolf; not a real wolf, but the figure of one that the Romans used to set store by—I forget why. Claude and Wilfrid have gone to fetch the shabby women."

"The shabby women?"

"Yes, they've got to carry them off. They didn't want to, but Miss Hope got one of father's fives-bats and said she'd give them a number nine spanking if they didn't, so they've gone to do it."

A loud, angry screaming from the direction of the lawn drew Mrs. Quabarl thither in hot haste, fearful lest the threatened castigation might even now be in process of infliction. The outcry, however, came principally from the two small daughters of the lodge-keeper, who were being hauled and pushed towards the house by the panting and dishevelled Claude and Wilfrid, whose task was rendered even more arduous by the incessant, if not very effectual, attacks of the captured maidens' small brother. The governess, fives-bat in hand, sat negligently on the stone balustrade, presiding over the scene with the cold impartiality of a Goddess of Battles. A furious and repeated chorus of "I'll tell muvver" rose from the lodge children, but the lodge-mother, who was hard of hearing, was for the moment immersed in the preoccupation of her washtub. After an apprehensive glance in the direction of the lodge (the good woman was gifted with the highly militant temper which is sometimes the privilege of deafness) Mrs. Quabarl flew indignantly to the rescue of the struggling captives.

"Wilfrid! Claude! Let those children go at once. Miss Hope, what on earth is the meaning of this scene?"

"Early Roman history; the Sabine women, don't you know? It's the Schartz-Metterklume method to make children understand history by acting it themselves; fixes it in their memory, you know. Of course, if, thanks to your interference, your boys go through life thinking that the Sabine women ultimately escaped, I really cannot be held responsible."

"You may be very clever and modern, Miss Hope," said Mrs. Quabarl firmly, "but I should like you to leave here by the next train. Your luggage will be sent after you as soon as it arrives."

"I'm not certain exactly where I shall be for the next few days," said the dismissed instructress of youth; "you might keep my luggage till I wire my address. There are only a couple of trunks and some golf-clubs and a leopard cub."

"A leopard cub!" gasped Mrs. Quabarl. Even in her departure this extraordinary person seemed destined to leave a trail of embarrassment behind her.

"Well, it's rather left off being a cub; it's more than half-grown, you know. A fowl every day and a rabbit on Sundays is what it usually gets. Raw beef makes it too excitable. Don't trouble about getting the car for me, I'm rather inclined for a walk."

And Lady Carlotta strode out of the Quabarl horizon.

The advent of the genuine Miss Hope, who had made a mistake as to the day on which she was due to arrive, caused a turmoil which that good lady was quite unused to inspiring. Obviously the Quabarl family had been woefully befooled, but a certain amount of relief came with the knowledge.

"How tiresome for you, dear Carlotta," said her hostess, when the overdue guest ultimately arrived; "how very tiresome losing your train and having to stop overnight in a strange place."

"Oh, dear, no," said Lady Carlotta; "not at all tiresome—for me."

AN AFTERWORD ON
SAKI

O N a raw Wednesday morning, in a few ill-chosen words, she told the cook that she drank. She remembered the scene afterwards," Reginald said, "as vividly as though it had been painted in her mind by Abbey. The cook was a good cook, as cooks go; and as cooks go she went."

There, if you will, is the kind of paragraph the devotees of Saki chuckle over as characteristic of him. Then many of them have a great enthusiasm (which not all of us share) for the slightly exhausting energy which he expended on the invention of such proper names as Brope, Thropplestance and Quabarl. But he was unexcelled in reducing the short story to the dimensions of an exquisite cameo and the best of his work—the twilit *Unbearable Bassington,* for example—has a bitter-sweet bouquet from which the passing years have taken nothing. But perhaps one should observe Christopher Morley's warning. There is, he said, no greater compliment to be paid the right kind of friend than to hand him Saki, without comment.

"The Schartz-Metterklume Method" has been offered here not only as a fair sample of the man's comedic gift but as a way of suggesting to whomever it may concern that it would make an admirable one-act play for Beatrice Lillie, let us say, or Hope Williams.

Hector Hugh Munro was born in Akyab, Burma, in 1870. From old Omar's final quatrains

491

Yon rising Moon that looks for us again—
How oft hereafter will she wax and wane;
How oft hereafter rising look for us
Through this same Garden—and for *one* in vain!

And when like her, oh, Saki, you shall pass
Among the Guests Star-scattered on the Grass,
And in your joyous errand reach the spot
Where I made One—turn down an empty Glass.

he took the pen name which he signed to the sketches he began contributing to the *Westminster Gazette* as long ago as 1896. Later he was a foreign correspondent and political writer of considerable pungency. In 1914 he was keeping an eye on Parliament for the *Outlook*. He stuck at it until August 3 and had only scorn for those voices lifted even then against England's entering the war. "If these men are on the side of the angels," Saki wrote, "may I always have a smell of brimstone about me," and, dispatching his copy to the *Outlook*, off he went into the ranks—in what mood and with what shifting experience you might best recall by rereading C. E. Montague's *Disenchantment*. On November 14, 1916, in a shell-hole near Beaumont Hamel, Lance Sergeant H. H. Munro died of his wounds in the forty-seventh year of his age.

A. W.

THE
TRAWNBEIGHS

by

*CHARLES
MACOMB FLANDRAU*

THE TRAWNBEIGHS

FROM "VIVA MEXICO!" BY C. M. FLANDRAU. USED BY PERMISSION OF
D. APPLETON-CENTURY COMPANY, PUBLISHERS, NEW YORK, N. Y.

THE TRAWNBEIGHS

When my first New Year's party dispersed, I walked back to the center of the town with a man who had lived for many years in Mexico, who had been everywhere and had done everything, and who seemed to know something funny or tragic or scandalous about everybody in the world. He loved to talk, to describe, to recall; and while we had some drinks together at a café under the sky-blue portales, he aroused my interest in people I never had heard of and never should see. He told me, among other things, about the Trawnbeighs.

This, as nearly as I can remember, is what he told me about the Trawnbeighs:

The Trawnbeighs, he said, were the sort of people who "dressed for dinner," even when, as sometimes happened, they had no dinner in the house to dress for. It is perhaps unnecessary to add that the Trawnbeighs were English. Indeed, on looking back, I often feel that to my first apparently flippant statement it is unnecessary to add *anything*. For to one who knew Mr. and Mrs. Trawnbeigh, Edwina, Violet, Maud, and Cyril, it was the first and last word on them; their alpha and omega, together with all that went between. Not that the statement *is* flippant—far from it. There is in it a seriousness, a profundity, an immense philosophic import. At times it has almost moved me to lift my hat, very much as one does for reasons of state, or religion, or death.

This, let me hasten to explain, is not at all the way I feel when I put on evening clothes myself, which I do at least twice out of my every three hundred and sixty-five opportunities. No born American could feel that way about his own dress coat. He sometimes thinks he does; he often—and isn't it boresome!—pretends he does, but he really doesn't. As a matter of unimportant fact, the born American may have "dressed" every evening of his grown-up life. But if he found himself on an isolated, played-out Mexican coffee and vanilla finca, with a wife, four children, a tiled roof that leaked whenever there was a "norther," an unsealed sala through the bamboo partitions of which a cold, wet wind howled sometimes for a week at a time, with no money, no capacity for making any, no "prospects," and no cook— under these depressing circumstances it is impossible to conceive of an American dressing for dinner every night at a quarter before seven in any spirit but one of ghastly humor.

With the Trawnbeighs' performance of this sacred rite, however, irony and humor had nothing to do. The Trawnbeighs had a robust sense of fun (so, I feel sure, have pumpkins and turnips and the larger varieties of the nutritious potato family); but humor, when they didn't recognize it, bewildered them, and it always struck them as just a trifle underbred when they did.

Trawnbeigh had come over to Mexico—"come out from England," he would have expressed it—as a kind of secretary to his cousin, Sir Somebody Something, who was building a harbor or a railway or a canal (I don't believe Trawnbeigh himself ever knew just what it was) for a British company down in the hot country. Mrs. Trawnbeigh, with her young, was to follow on the next steamer a month later; and as she was in mid-ocean when Sir Somebody suddenly died of yellow fever, she did not learn of this inopportune event until it was too late to turn back. Still I doubt whether she would have turned back if she could. For, as Trawnbeigh once explained to me at a time when they literally hadn't enough to eat (a hail storm had not only destroyed his coffee crop, but had frozen the roots of most of his trees, and the price of vanilla had fallen from ten cents a bean to three and a half), leaving England at all, he explained, had necessitated "burning their bridges behind them." He did not tell me the nature of their bridges, nor whether they had made much of a blaze. In fact, that one vague, inflammatory allusion was the nearest approach to a personal confidence Trawnbeigh was ever known to make in all his fifteen years of Mexican life.

The situation, when he met Mrs. Trawnbeigh and the children on the dock at Vera Cruz, was extremely dreary, and at the end of a month it had grown much worse, although the Trawnbeighs apparently didn't think so. They even spoke and wrote as if their affairs were "looking up a bit." For, after a few weeks of visiting among kindly compatriots at Vera Cruz and Rebozo, Mrs. Trawnbeigh became cook for some English engineers (there were seven of them) in a sizzling, mosquitoey, feverish mudhole on the Isthmus of Tehuantepec. The Trawnbeighs didn't call it "cook," neither did the seven engineers. I don't believe the engineers even thought of it as cook. (What Mrs. Trawnbeigh thought of it will never be known.) How *could* they when that lady, after feeding the four little Trawnbeighs (or rather the four young Trawnbeighs; they had never been little) a meal I think they called "the nursery tea," managed every afternoon, within the next two hours, first to create out of nothing a perfectly edible dinner for nine persons, and, secondly, to receive them all at seven forty-five in a red-striped, lemon satin ball gown (it looked like poisonous wall paper), eleven silver bangles, a cameo necklace, and an ostrich tip sprouting from the top of her head. Trawnbeigh, too, was in evening clothes. And they didn't call it cooking; they spoke of it as "looking after the mess" or "keeping an eye on the young chaps' livers." Nevertheless, Mrs. Trawnbeigh, daughter of the late the Honorable Cyril Cosby Godolphin Dundas and the late Clare Walpurga Emmeline Moate, cooked—and cooked hard—for almost a year; at the end of which time she was stricken with what she was pleased to refer to as "a bad go of fevah."

Fortunately, they were spared having to pass around the hat, although it would have amounted to that if Trawnbeigh hadn't, after the pleasant English fashion, come into some money. In the United States people know to a cent what they may expect to inherit, and then they sometimes don't get it; but in England there seems to be an endless succession of retired and unmarried army officers who die every little while in Jermyn Street and leave two thousand pounds to a distant relative they have never met. Something like this happened to Trawnbeigh, and on the prospect of his legacy he was able to pull out of the Tehuantepec mudhole and restore his wife to her usual state of health in the pure and bracing air of Rebozo.

Various things can be done with two thousand pounds, but just what *shall* be done ought to depend very largely on whether they happen to be one's first two thousand or one's last. Trawnbeigh, however, invested his ("interred" would be a more accurate term) quite as if they never would be missed. The disposition to be a country gentleman was in Trawnbeigh's blood. Indeed, the first impression one received from the family was that everything they did was in their blood. It never seemed to me that Trawnbeigh had immediately sunk the whole of his little fortune in an old, small, and dilapidated coffee place so much because he was dazzled by the glittering financial future the shameless owner (another Englishman, by the way) predicted for him, as because to own an estate and live on it was, so to speak, his natural element. He had tried, while Mrs. Trawnbeigh was cooking on the Isthmus, to get "something to do." But there was really nothing in Mexico he *could* do. He was splendidly strong, and in the United States he very cheerfully, and with no loss of self-respect or point of view, would have temporarily shoveled wheat or coal, or driven a team, or worked on the street force, as many another Englishman of noble lineage has done before and since; but in the tropics an Anglo-Saxon cannot be a day laborer. He can't because he can't. And there was in Mexico no clerical position open to Trawnbeigh because he did not know Spanish. (It is significant that after fifteen consecutive years of residence in the country, *none* of the Trawnbeighs knew Spanish.) To be, somehow and somewhere, an English country gentleman of a well-known, slightly old-fashioned type, was as much Trawnbeigh's destiny as it is the destiny of, say, a polar bear to be a polar bear or a camel to be a camel. As soon as he got his two thousand pounds, he became one.

When I first met them all, he had been one for about ten years. I had recently settled in Trawnbeigh's neighborhood, which in Mexico means that my ranch was a hard day-and-a-half ride from his, over roads that are not roads, but merely ditches full of liquefied mud on the level stretches, and ditches full of assorted bowlders on the ascent. So, although we looked neighborly on a small map, I might not have had the joy of meeting the Trawnbeighs for years if my mule hadn't

gone lame one day when I was making the interminable trip to Rebozo. Trawnbeigh's place was seven miles from the main road, and as
I happened to be near the parting of the ways when the off hind leg
of Catalina began to limp, I decided to leave her with my mozo at an
Indian village until a pack train should pass by (there is always someone in a pack train who can remove a bad shoe), while I proceeded
on the mozo's mule to the Trawnbeighs'. My usual stopping place for
the night was five miles farther on, and the Indian village was—well,
it was an Indian village. Time and again I had been told of Trawnbeigh's early adventures, and I felt sure he could "put me up" (as he
would have said himself) for the night. He "put me up" not only that
night, but as my mozo didn't appear until late the next afternoon, a
second night as well. And when I at last rode away, it was with the
feeling of having learned from the Trawnbeighs a great lesson.

In the first place they couldn't have expected me; they couldn't possibly have expected anyone. And it was a hot afternoon. But as it was
the hour at which people at "home" dropped in for tea, Mrs. Trawnbeigh and her three plain, heavy-looking daughters were perfectly prepared to dispense hospitality to any number of mythical friends. They
had on hideous but distinctly "dressy" dresses of amazingly stamped
materials known, I believe, as "summer silks," and they were all four
tightly laced. Current fashion in Paris, London, and New York by no
means insisted on small, smooth, round waists, but the Trawnbeigh
women had them because (as it gradually dawned on me) to have had
any other kind would have been a concession to anatomy and the
weather. To anything so compressible as one's anatomy, or as vulgarly
impartial as the weather, the Trawnbeighs simply did not concede. I
never could get over the feeling that they all secretly regarded weather
in general as a kind of popular institution, of vital importance only to
the middle class. Cyril, an extremely beautiful young person of twenty-
two, who had been playing tennis (by himself) on the asoleadero, was
in "flannels," and Trawnbeigh admirably looked the part in gray, middle-aged riding things, although, as I discovered before leaving, their
stable at the time consisted of one senile burro with ingrowing hoofs.

From the first it all seemed too flawless to be true. I had never visited in England, but I doubt if there is another country whose literature gives one so definite and lasting an impression of its "home life." Perhaps this is because the life of families of the class to which the Trawnbeighs belonged proceeds in England by such a series of definite and traditional episodes. In a household like theirs, the unexpected must have a devil of a time in finding a chance to happen. For, during my visit, absolutely nothing happened that I hadn't long since chuckled over in making the acquaintance of Jane Austen, Thackeray, George Eliot, and Anthony Trollope; not to mention Ouida (it was Cyril, of course, who from time to time struck the Ouida note), and the more laborious performances of Mrs. Humphrey Ward. They all of them did at every tick of the clock precisely what they ought to have done. They were a page, the least bit crumpled, torn from *Half Hours with the Best Authors,* and cast, dear Heaven! upon a hillside in darkest Mexico.

Of course we had tea in the garden. There wasn't any garden, but we nevertheless had tea in it. The house would have been cooler, less glaring, and free from the venomous little rodadoras that stung the backs of my hands full of microscopic polka dots; but we all strolled out to a spot some fifty yards away where a bench, half a dozen shaky, homemade chairs, and a rustic table were most imperfectly shaded by three tattered banana trees.

"We love to drink tea in the dingle dangle," Mrs. Trawnbeigh explained. How the tea tray itself got to the "dingle dangle," I have only a general suspicion, for when we arrived it was already there, equipped with caddy, cozy, a plate of buttered toast, a pot of strawberry jam, and all the rest of it. But try as I might, I simply could not rid myself of the feeling that at least two footmen had arranged it all and then discreetly retired; a feeling that also sought to account for the tray's subsequent removal, which took place while Trawnbeigh, Cyril, Edwina, and I walked over to inspect the asoleadero and washing tanks. I wanted to look back; but something (the fear, perhaps, of being turned into a pillar of salt) restrained me.

With most English-speaking persons in that part of the world, conversation has to do with coffee, coffee, and—coffee. The Trawnbeighs, however, scarcely touched on the insistent topic. While we sat on the low wall of the dilapidated little asoleadero we discussed pheasant shooting and the "best places" for haberdashery and "Gladstone bags." Cyril, as if it were but a matter of inclination, said he thought he might go over for the shooting that year; a cousin had asked him "to make a seventh." I never found out what this meant and didn't have the nerve to ask.

"Bertie shoots the twelfth, doesn't he?" Edwina here inquired.

To which her brother replied, as if she had shown a distressing ignorance of some fundamental date in history, like 1066 or 1215, "Bertie *always* shoots the twelfth."

The best place for haberdashery in Mr. Trawnbeigh's opinion was "the Stores." But Cyril preferred a small shop in Bond Street, maintaining firmly, but with good humor, that it was not merely, as "the pater" insisted, because the fellow charged more, but because one didn't "run the risk of seeing some beastly bounder in a cravat uncommonly like one's own." Trawnbeigh, as a sedate parent bordering on middle age, felt obliged to stand up for the more economical "Stores," but it was evident that he really admired Cyril's exclusive principles and approved of them. Edwina cut short the argument with an abrupt question.

"I say," she inquired anxiously, "has the dressing bell gone yet?" The dressing bell hadn't gone, but it soon went. For Mr. Trawnbeigh, after looking at his watch, bustled off to the house and rang it himself. Then we withdrew to our respective apartments to dress for dinner.

"I've put you in the north wing, old man; there's always a breeze in the wing," my host declared as he ushered me into a bamboo shed they used apparently for storing corn and iron implements of an agricultural nature. But there was also in the room a recently made-up cot with real sheets, a tin bath tub, hot and cold water in two earthenware jars, and an empty packing case upholstered in oilcloth. When Trawnbeigh spoke of this last as a "wash-hand-stand," I knew I had indeed strayed from life into the realms of mid-Victorian romance.

The breeze Trawnbeigh had referred to developed in the violen

Mexican way, while I was enjoying the bath tub, into an unmistakable norther. Water fell on the roof like so much lead and then sprang off (some of it did) in thick, round streams from the tin spouts; the wind screamed in and out of the tiles overhead, and through the "north wing's" blurred windows the writhing banana trees of the "dingle dangle" looked like strange things one sees in an aquarium. As soon as I could get into my clothes again—a bath was as far as I was able to live up to the Trawnbeigh ideal—I went into the sala where the dinner table was already set with a really heart-rending attempt at splendor. I have said that nothing happened with which I had not a sort of literary acquaintance; but I was wrong. While I was standing there wondering how the Trawnbeighs had been able all those years to keep it up, a window in the next room blew open with a bang. I ran in to shut it; but before I reached it, I stopped short and, as hastily and quietly as I could, tiptoed back to the "wing." For the next room was the kitchen and at one end of it Trawnbeigh, in a shabby but perfectly fitting dress-coat, his trousers rolled up halfway to his knees, was patiently holding an umbrella over his wife's sacred dinner gown, while she—bebangled, becameoed, beplumed, and stripped to the buff —masterfully cooked our dinner on the brasero.

To me it was all extremely wonderful, and the wonder of it did not lessen during the five years in which, on my way to and from Rebozo, I stopped over at the Trawnbeighs' several times a year. For, although I knew that they were often financially all but down and out, the endless red tape of their daily life never struck me as being merely a pathetic bluff. Their rising bells and dressing bells, their apparent dependence on all sorts of pleasant accessories that simply did not exist, their occupations (I mean those on which I did not have to turn a tactful back, such as "botanizing," "crewel work," painting horrible water colors, and composing long lists of British-sounding things to be "sent out from the Stores"), the informality with which we waited on ourselves at luncheon and the stately, punctilious manner in which we did precisely the same thing at dinner, the preordained hour at which Mrs. Trawnbeigh and the girls each took a candle and said good-night, leaving Trawnbeigh, Cyril, and me to smoke a pipe and "do a whisky peg" (Trawnbeigh had spent some years in India), the whole inflexibly insular scheme of their existence was more, infinitely more, than a bluff. It was a placid, tenacious clinging to the straw of their ideal in a great, deep sea of poverty, discomfort, and isolation. And it had its reward.

For after fourteen years of Mexican life, Cyril was almost exactly what he would have been had he never seen the place; and Cyril was the Trawnbeighs' one asset of immense value. He was most agreeable to look at, he was both related to and connected with many of the most historical-sounding ladies and gentlemen in England, and he had just the limited, selfish, amiable outlook on the world in general that was sure (granting the other things) to impress Miss Irene Slapp of Pittsburgh as the height of both breeding and distinction.

Irene Slapp had beauty and distinction of her own. Somehow, although they all "needed the money," I don't believe Cyril would have married her if she hadn't. Anyhow, one evening in the City of Mexico he took her in to dinner at the British Legation where he had been asked to dine as a matter of course, and before the second entrée, Miss Slapp was slightly in love with him and very deeply in love with the scheme of life, the standard, the ideal, or whatever you choose to call it, he had inherited and had been brought up, under staggering difficulties, to represent.

"The young beggar has made a pot of money in the States," Trawnbeigh gravely informed me after Cyril had spent seven weeks in Pittsburgh—whither he had been persuaded to journey on the Slapps' private train.

"And, you know I've decided to sell the old place," he casually remarked a month or so later. "Yes, yes," he went on, "the young people are beginning to leave us." (I hadn't noticed any signs of impending flight on the part of Edwina, Violet, and Maud.) "Mrs. Trawnbeigh and I want to end our days at home. Slapp believes there's gold on the place—or would it be petroleum? He's welcome to it. After all, I've never been fearfully keen on business."

And I rode away pondering, as I always did, on the great lesson of the Trawnbeighs.

AN AFTERWORD ON
"THE TRAWNBEIGHS"

CHARLES MACOMB FLANDRAU (the second syllable of the middle name is pronounced not to rhyme with comb but with tomb) is a graduate of Harvard in the class of 1896. In *The Diary of a Freshman* (a serial requisitioned for *The Saturday Evening Post* in the early days of Mr. Lorimer's fateful editorship), Flandrau wrote the most engaging college story ever published and, in *Viva Mexico!,* the best book I have come upon among those which attempt the alluring but difficult task of introducing the people of one country to the people of another.

The second book was published in 1908, a mere seven years after the first, but later Flandrau proceeded at a more leisurely rate. In an inkstained world where most of us write too much, he must be named along with A. E. Housman and the late Kenneth Grahame as one of the great underwriters. One could elaborately ascribe this abstinence to the self-mockery which always gives the philosophic pause. Or to the lack of any external necessity whipping him to work. But it might be simpler and more accurate just to set him down as lazy.

Viva Mexico! was published as the uncalculated by-product of his adventures on a coffee plantation in the years after he left college. Being himself one who, according to his own prescription, "is not inclined to exaggerate the importance of exactitude and is perpetually interested in the casual, the florid, and the problematical," he found Mexico one long, carelessly written, but absorbing romance. The editor of this anthology, thwarted by sundry dark forces in his attempt to include the complete work, broke, for once, his own all-or-nothing rule and let in an excerpt. This celebrated Trawnbeigh chapter has been chosen not because it is the best or even the most characteristic—it is neither—but because it is the one which can be plucked out with the least protest from the wounded context. Perhaps that is because it is the least Mexican. This unforgettable vignette of the exotic Trawnbeighs who see to it that the sun should never, never set on the English tea-cozy was based on an actual household of exiled Britons whom Flandrau encountered, I have been told, not in Mexico at all but marooned in the less tropical wilds of Minnesota.

When Philip Guedalla made his own duly recorded visit south of the Rio Grande, he approached that stream by way of New York, after first poring over *Viva Mexico!* as though it were Holy Writ. In New York, at a luncheon party of writing folk, he chanced to ask what manner of fellow this Flandrau was, and learned with surprise that none of the assorted authors present had ever so much as clapped eyes on him. Then, from below the salt, there spoke up a broker chap who had been invited by mistake. "Flandrau was in my class at Harvard," the broker said dreamily, "and I remember only this about him. Once, during his undergraduate days, he invented a cocktail and named it the I-Know-That-My-Redeemer-Liveth." If no further biographical data was vouchsafed that day, it may have been because New York finds it hard to keep track of an intermittent writer who perversely clings either to his ancestral acre in Minnesota or to the fond hideaway he has discovered on the Seine not far from Les Andelys. But from the very mood and flavor of *Viva Mexico!* you could guess it had been written by one who would always lurk in shadows and that, as for booksy teas where authors do get a chance to meet and dislike one another, he would avoid them as though they were pestilential. Of all American writers, it is hardest to imagine that one autographing his works in Macy's window.

A. W.

KAMONGO

by

HOMER W. SMITH

TO

C. G. S.

KAMONGO

I

THE shout of a sailor awakened him and Joel opened his eyes to peer into the blackness beyond the aura of the deck-lights. He could barely distinguish the faint colour of the sandy shore and, above it, the dark shadows of trees outlined against the sky. He heard a winch wheezing as a boat was lowered forward, and men's voices as they unhooked the lines and rowed away from the ship.

He turned his head quickly to either side as though apprehensive someone might be watching him. He had only one companion—on his right an Anglican priest was stretched, like himself, in a long canvas deck-chair. Far aft, hidden in the shadows cast by the feeble yellow lamps, there were other recumbent figures relaxed in sleep. A hand here, a face there was struck by the light and stood out pallidly in the shadows. He got up slowly and walked over to the side of the deck. Once outside the light of the covered passage his eyes took in the narrow strip of black water which separated the ship from the shore, and beyond it, softly lit by the brilliant stars, the grey outlines of sand-dunes rolling back to where a few palms and feathery trees were silhouetted against the sky. After a moment of searching he made out the figures of several sailors who were hauling on a ship's line, preparatory to making her fast to the piles that were set at intervals along the bank of the canal. Quietly, so as not to disturb his companion, he stepped back into the shadows and crossed the deck; but he returned almost immediately and, straddling his deck-chair, dropped into it heavily as though he had returned from a fatiguing journey.

"Another tanker?"

Joel looked around at the priest.

"Sorry, did I wake you? Yes, we are tying up again. We'll be lucky if we get into Said before dawn."

The priest looked at his watch. "Nine-thirty. Yes, we'll have breakfast in Port Said. Do you know that we have been asleep for two hours?" He laughed as he added: "I feel as though it had been ten."

Joel smiled but remained silent as he let his glance rest upon his companion, who was wiping his moist face with a handkerchief. The priest was a big man, broad-shouldered and straight, at least three inches taller than Joel and probably a few years older. Joel guessed him to be about thirty-three. He was smooth-shaven and his regular features and tanned skin suggested a soldier who had spent most of his life in the open. He was dressed in black broadcloth coat and trousers and a black waistcoat buttoned up closely around a stiff white collar. But in spite of his heavy clothes he seemed to feel nothing of the oppressive heat.

Joel took out a handkerchief and, mopping his own face and neck, looked down at himself, at the soft slippers on his feet, the linen trousers clinging limply to his legs, and the wrinkled coat soiled from restless contortions in a deck-chair. His hand went self-consciously to his neck, caressing the throat within the open collar. He wondered how long it had been since he had worn a tie. So he had slept two hours? Well, it was the first two hours in a long, long time. But he did feel better, at that. He pushed himself out in an all-embracing stretch and slowly enjoyed the delight of the muscular movement.

He rose stiffly, still stretching, toning the muscles of his arms and shoulders, and walked over to the edge of the deck. Resting his arms upon the rail he leaned out to peer through the darkness at the sand-dunes. A cur got up out of the band of light and slunk into the shadows to lie down beside some white-robed figures chattering in Arabic. A faint breath of air touched his cheek. He closed his eyes and turned his face upward as though he could confirm the impression by his sense of smell. In the darkness of his concentration the breeze came again, neither cool nor warm, without sensory quality, but like a ghostly hand brushing lightly across his face. So that was why he had slept? Cool! Cool!

The relief of moving air! The unrest, the muscular tension that had pervaded him slipped away gradually before a sense of well-being, of sheer animal comfort. His head dropped forward and his shoulders rose and fell in deep, deliberate respirations. His mind, awakening as the physical strain passed off, ran back as though unreeling a belated record that moved quickly past his indifferent attention.

Nearly a week ago they had come to anchor at Aden. . . . Weary of the ship's monotony they went ashore, hoping to find some diversion and to get a decent drink. A decent drink, uhh! All they got was a warm, sweet lemon squash, for the hotels had run out of ice! There was nothing for them to do but wander from one curio store to another; to stare at the water-carts that were dragged along the hot asphalt streets by slobbering camels; to push off the eternal obsequious venders of junk who slithered out of every shadow to importune the stranger; to shut their eyes against the glare from white walls and white, sterile dust, and to wonder why in the world the British wanted Aden. . . .

Bored with the dust and heat and flies, somebody suggested that they motor through the mountain pass and up to the Wells of Solomon. So they went along the tourist trail, a motley string of trippers dressed in white duck, black broadcloth, tweeds, linen, sun-hats, terais, climbing over the flanks of the crumbling hills that rise abruptly out of the Desert of Arabia. Old weathered peaks, worn into sharp hog-backs and deep crevasses by the wind and rain, with jagged shoulders decorated in many colours by Nature's hieroglyphics. Across the deep ravines the Wells of Solomon looked like giant buttresses set in to keep the hills apart; curving walls and deep pits built by some forgotten Persian—and recently veneered with modern rock and mortar by the optimistic British—to keep back the rain, they rise up tier after tier across the sheer gorges like a gargantuan honeycomb thrown down for ants to scramble over. Gigantic vats—could they be filled with water the desert down below might blossom in green squares of palms and patches of exotic flowers. But not in the memory of man had they been filled, not in five years had their dust been wet by rain. . . . Tremendous industry made futile by a shift in wind!

They went back to the ship, satiated with the desert landscape, to loll upon the deck and fan themselves despairingly while they stared up at the mountains around them; barren mountains pitted with decay and ribbed with broad fans of rotten rock, fired into red and yellow colours by the setting sun. Sea, rock, and sky confused to make a quivering mist, unreal, unearthly. It might have been the gate to Hell, itself!

Being French, the *Dumbea* had crossed the Arabian Sea to call Djibuti, as though it were not enough to pass through this torrid penance without prolonging it. From sundown to sunup she steamed across a barely broken sea, her passengers tossing in their bunks in a vain effort to sleep, or pacing the decks waiting for the dawn.

But when that dawn came it was like the splitting of the heavens. Naked, white, the light came down as though even the blanket of thin air above them had been torn away; the world seemed to be taken up and engulfed in the sun's incandescent substance. As the *Dumbea* made her way through the elongated channel of Djibuti Harbour the tar flowed in her deck-seams and her woodwork burned the flesh. She might have been a furnace belching heat rather than a ship taking it in. Her human cargo came sprawling out of her and wandered restlessly from shadow to shadow, mopping—fanning—mopping—fanning.

Boredom and curiosity can drive men to absurd ends, Joel thought, but it was neither of these that had driven them ashore that midday. To suffer in confinement is a double agony; to move about and curse and move again brings some relief. They had not expected to be cooled by walking into the doors of that furnace; they had not expected the parched hills and choking dust of Somaliland to bring forth a cooling spring to meet their need as had the rock of Horeb beneath the Hebrew's staff. No, they had simply rushed from the hot ship into the hotter town as they might have danced about upon a searing griddle.

Joel laughed as he recalled the picture of himself struggling along the dusty road to fetch a taxi to the landing wharf, pushing through the blinding glare as though it were something fluid, corporeal. Exhausted at the end, he threw himself down in the shadow of a wall to rest—but only to rise hastily from sand too hot to bear against his body.

They found some relief in the darkness of the hotel bar—coatless, collars open, sleeves rolled back, mopping, fanning, beating off the flies. They drank innumerable Tom Collinses, with ice, real ice, long bitter drinks of lime and gin that wet the mouth and cooled the gullet and that sent faint waves of coldness down the back and arms. Under the eaves and through the shutters the white light poured, radiated by a world whitewashed with liquid fire. They drank and joked and mopped and drank again, and begged the boy to work the punkah faster, faster! They thrust their hands from under cover to appraise the naked sun—and hurried back to drink again. From the shadows of tiled roofs that broke its force they cursed the heat, their bodies stretched out before the swinging punkah, drinking its air, seeking its caress, living by it. To sweat was to endure, to defeat the demoniacal energy of that broiling oven. . . . But what, when sweat should be of no avail? They sensed, as they climbed back aboard the ship, avoiding its hot iron and hunting out its shadows, that they were further cursed, that punkahs could no longer save them.

The dinner-gong rang as the *Dumbea* rounded the outflung arm of Somaliland hills and turned her course into the Red Sea. The land fall was a prismatic band around the horizon, violet near the water and blending in yellow and gold above, where the light struck off at an angle from the peaks. Bearing a thin, levelled streak of cloud across its face the sun glared through the red haze of dust as though charged with living hatred. Defeated in its efforts to annihilate it seemed to promise a renewed attack, sharpened by accumulated cunning, on the morrow. The walls of the ship threw their radiation against the body as though there were so little room for that all-pervading fluid in them that it must be poured with increased concentration into the haggard bodies of men and the dark spaces where they tried to hide. At the thresholds of the companionways there hung a curtain of intolerable warmth, a blast that by its greater force arrested them. It stank of vile things, long dead, hardly remembered things buried in the ship's bowels and now stirred up like ghosts to seek the outside air. Men wandered disconsolately toward the shadowed doors to stop arrested by the pall; until driven by the urgency of despair, monotony, or human need they bent their heads and forced themselves into the nether world.

Like a thin veneer, Joel thought, our pleasure is spread upon the base of vital needs, thinning or thickening as the animal beneath thrusts up or draws below the level of attention. But even the lowest state of living demands distraction, demands that the sheer monotony of consciousness be shattered here and there by some diversion. Men forced themselves into the stifling ship to eat and drink, no longer from an honest need but because the mind, in order to endure, requires that it be fed a pabulum of sense and be permitted to exercise itself in motion, however futile. So they ate and drank even while their clothes clung to their bodies with wet transparency, and the sweat matted their hair and ran down their faces in little rivulets to drop off into their food. They became nauseated with the smell and rushed back on deck, swearing that they would not go below again.

They wandered aimlessly up and down the ship or threw themselves into their chairs with complete exhaustion. They took off their coats, their collars and their shoes and left their legs outstretched to block the road of passers-by. They mopped their faces and arms and shoulders and hung their handkerchiefs upon the rail or waved them slowly back and forth to get them dry; and when they would not dry they mopped with them wet, and cursed the eternal sweat that ran down their bodies in perpetual streams. They looked up as though expecting to see the oppressive blanket that enveloped them but there was only the blue sky; never a cloud, never a bird but only the funnel smoke rising straight and then curving back to disappear into the haze; and on every side of them only the darker blue oily water, rolling a little. They thought of the soldiers cooped up in the steerage, six to a cabin with hardly enough deck-space to stand in, and only heavy woollen clothes to wear. They wondered how they survived the stifling heat. But they were not moved to pity, only casual curiosity. It was too hot to pity anybody, even the woman pacing the deck with her baby, incessantly muttering, *"Mon enfant, mon enfant, regarde l'eau!"*

By night they dragged their mattresses on deck and stared up at the stars which swayed from side to side in a perpetual, nauseating motion. They looked down at the sea and saw the stars, swaying again. They wondered where the air began and sea left off. Throughout the endless hours they tossed and turned, their bodies leaving pools of water behind them when they moved. Under the dim aura of the night-lamps the deck-boards were brown with wetness and the rails dripped, dripped an incandescent dew.

Day after day, sunup, sundown, the *Dumbea* pushed on through the slightly rolling water. . . . The old Russian Count was the first to go: they took up a collection to buy him a tin coffin so that he could be buried at home. The ship's carpenter hastily soldered him in it, the while cursing and dripping with perspiration over the hot torch and soldering iron. Then two of the stokers followed the Russian into hastily soldered coffins. Lascars they were, for even Negroes cannot stand the heat; Lascars who drink salt water to prevent the cramps brought on by too quickly diluted blood . . . then two soldiers . . . and the little cockney barber from Dar-es-Salaam had almost gone—he had been picked up in the bar and carried to his bunk, pallid and in collapse. For twelve hours the men had taken turns fanning his white body until he came around. . . . The children stood it best, but always in torment from the big red weals of heat-rash, crying, crying throughout the night. . . . Night after night, pacing the deck or lying in a pool of sweat . . . if you could only sleep . . . Christ, sleep. . . .

Joel straightened up and rubbed his eyes and arms. He turned back to his companion. "So we slept two hours?"

The Padre was staring off into the darkness, seeing, perhaps, some bit of England miraged above the sands of Egypt. "I did," he answered after a moment of blankness, laughing. "Didn't you?"

"Dead to the world!" Joel replied. "Two hours isn't much, but it helps." He came back to his chair and stretched out in it. The Padre had fallen back into his meditation, his eyes fixed on his toes which he was slowly moving back and forth. Joel tried to recall if he had

once seen him during that appalling week without his coat, or even
without that stiff white collar. The man seemed to be imperturbable,
undaunted by the physical and mental strain that had played havoc
with the rest of them. Was he insensible to physical discomfort, or did
he possess some superhuman gift of fortitude?

"Does it get hot in Tanganyika? Like that?" he added, nodding his
head back into time and space.

"No, not like that," the Padre answered. "That was the worst I've
ever seen. It is indiscreet to come home by Suez in August. One should
go around the Cape."

Joel laughed. "That's what the doctor said the Russian and the
Lascars died of—indiscretion! Well—if I live through mine I intend to
celebrate at Port Said. We'll have some coffee that hasn't been sea-
sick for three months. How about it?"

He reached into his pocket and drew out a crumpled package of
cigarettes and tried to light one. The cigarette refused to burn. He
struck another match without success; so he took the cigarette out of
his mouth and rolled it quizzically between his fingers.

The Padre was laughing at him: "It's got worm-holes in it. Didn't
you know that there are special French worms that eat holes in French
cigarettes?"

Joel bent the cigarette between his fingers as though it were elastic
and in a sudden gesture of disgust and temper hurled it from him, but
it fell short of the rail and rolled inconsequently into the scupper. The
Padre laughed again at the violent but futile gesture.

"Let me get you a cigar," he said, and getting up out of his chair
stiffly he disappeared into a nearby companionway. He returned shortly
with an hermetically sealed humidor which he opened, giving Joel a
cigar and taking one himself.

"Thanks, Padre. I'll reward you with a box when we get to Said.
This must be at least the tenth I've had of you—where'd you get
them?"

"In Aden. They're not the best—but they haven't any worm-holes,
anyway. You know, I don't believe that worms like real tobacco."

"No, I don't think that you can hang the French tobacconists on that theory. Worms have queer tastes—I suppose as queer as the rest of us."

"Perhaps not, but my experience tells me that there is a presumption of guilt. I have kept cigars in Tanganyika for months and the only worms that ever got into them were big black ones, sneaking about on two legs. They put their white teeth into them and sneaked off into the bushes somewhere to smoke them. I've often hoped they were made beastly sick. You don't get many cigars in Tanganyika."

"No. Nor many other luxuries, I suppose?"

"No."

"Nor many necessities?"

"No . . . I had some books with me when I first went out, but I lost the lot of them on the way up. One of the canoes upset and spilled the boxes into the Ruvuma River. I had some more sent out from home, but it wasn't pleasant losing my few hand-picked books. Oh, I forgot—I had an almanac left, for which I was thankful."

"How long were the new ones coming?"

"About four months. It takes three weeks to get from Mwambo to Lukoniba. One has to walk most of the way because the river's not navigable. Then it's three or four days overland to the station. That is, in the dry season; it takes longer during the rains because you can't march in the afternoon. Then, too, you have to wait for a tramp steamer from Lindi down to Mwambo. We are in an out-of-the-way sort of place." He looked at Joel and half-way smiled with the last statement, as though he took some pride, like a frontiersman, in the inaccessibility of his post.

"And you have cigars there?"

"Most of the time. We get them sent up from Zanzibar. We have a lot of things—we have a gramophone now, and about thirty-five records; and two years ago when that expedition from Chicago came through shooting big game they left us a whopping big load of stuff— a field desk, three cots, some aluminum cooking utensils—of course, *they* weren't much good to us because our boys melted them on the fire the first thing—but best of all, they left us an ice machine. Did you ever see one?"

Joel shook his head.

"You put some water—about a pint or a little more—into a container which fits in a copper ball, and then you turn a handle to freeze it. It takes about fifteen minutes to freeze it. I knew some physics once but I can't explain how the thing works—you know better than I do. I remember the first time we made ice with it—the stuff almost scared the life out of my *Mlahis*. They took one touch and then ran for their lives. Imagine never having touched anything cold! It still is a source of wonder to them. They pick up a piece of ice with a sheepish grin and then tear around in circles yelling their lungs out. I don't use it often, but it comes in very handy if one is sick.

"A lady friend of the Bishop's sent us up a set of tea things a year ago last Christmas. There were some tall glasses among them. I didn't know what they were for, but the Americans from Chicago said that they were for iced-tea—so we made iced-tea in honour of their visit. When the Bishop visited me a short time afterward I gave him some. He wouldn't believe it was meant to drink. Said it might give him cramps." The Padre laughed. "I don't believe it did, but he didn't come back to see me for nearly a year."

The missionary turned his attention to his cigar, which had gone out. Long after he stopped talking, it suddenly occurred to Joel that the Bishop was probably the only caller on his list. When he saw that the Padre had lapsed into silence, Joel rose and went over to the rail. He leaned across, looking ahead to where a low mound of black water was turned up by the ship's bow.

"We're under way again," he said over his shoulder.

A beam of light cut obliquely into the rounded top of the wave, making it a living, changing thing, yet fixed in form and space. Suddenly the water broke into a white foaming crest and as quickly melted into its state of fixity. Somewhere a camel sneezed, but in the darkness there was no sign of life. Barely defined against the sky the land slipped by, hardly faster than a man might walk, the horizon rising and falling as barren hills gave way to barren valleys. Desert—where once had been green trees and giant beasts—now shifting, sterile sands where only man might venture in his providence. Desert—the very word meant deserted by life, where life could not live. There were places where life could live—and there was desert. Life could live in the hills, in jungles, in swamps, in plains, in meadows, in lakes and rivers, and in the sea—but there were places in the hills and in the valleys and even in the lakes and in the sea where life could not live—great vacuums of death like the interstellar spaces. They were laid with the curse of death for lack of water, soil, air, or heat. Water, earth, air, and fire—four elements. Joel shuddered; what a horror when they met in disproportion!

I I

JOEL lay back in his deck-chair, his eyes set into the night, his fingers idly stroking the deck beneath him while he puffed on the cigar in the corner of his mouth. He suddenly took the cigar out and examined its ash interestedly.

"The ancients' idea that the world was flat and that if we went too far we'd fall off was not a bad one. Symbolic, in a way. Expressed our limitations. They sensed"—he shrugged his shoulders—"no less than we do, I suppose, the narrow margin in this scheme of things in which we live. We've just been crowded to the narrow edge—crowded between Africa and Arabia until we almost fell off."

The Padre turned his head sideways and studied Joel's face, as though this might help him to understand what he was talking about.

"You mean crowded physically?" he asked.

"Well—crowded physiologically," Joel explained. "You can be crowded in a lot of ways, but they all have the same result in the long run. If you get crowded too much you fall off."

The Padre nodded his head and turned back to examine the ashes of his cigar.

"Yes." He leaned forward to flip the ash into the scupper. "You're always crowded in there." He indicated by a slight movement of his head that he referred to the vast continent of Africa, rather than the meagre sea, behind them. "Crowded one way or another. The margin is a narrow one. I wonder why men go into Africa—when there are so many happy places, glad, joyous, singing—" He glanced at Joel with a look that seemed to say: "Isn't it strange?" or, "Am I not right . . . ?"

Joel shook his head by way of answering generally this general question; then it occurred to him that the way the Padre had put it required something more than this negligent dismissal.

"Well—" He raised his eyebrows and made a gesture that clearly turned the question back upon his companion.

"Oh, I had good reasons." The Padre laughed self-consciously. "But one can't very well put them into words. They are difficult to define and—they run far back into the roots of my life. They are"—he sought a moment for the word—"fundamental. Oh! you know what I mean— the kind of thing that you grow up with, like your language; that is built into you from the very beginning."

Joel was puzzled by this declaration. It somehow did not fit the youthful, active character of the man. Surely he didn't take himself so seriously as to believe that it was a sort of unavoidable destiny—this missionary work. He was not that sort. Why the devil had he gone in for it, anyway? It didn't fit him; he should have been an engineer, or a surgeon, or an archæologist.

Damn it all, Joel thought, you never got below the surface with him. He seemed to be wrapped around by some impregnable armour of silence, like the vacuum around a thermos jar. Once, on a Sunday just out of Mombasa, he had held a morning service on the ship and had come to Joel with a polite: "Would like to have you come." He had the delicacy, the tact, to put it that way, and not to say, "Will you come?" It would have been embarrassing if he had not. From the beginning of the voyage he and Joel had spent most of the time together; they gravitated to each other, for some strange reason, as deck-companions and they found each other's company so agreeable that they just sat together and watched the days go by, talking leisurely and disconnectedly about Africa, England, Prohibition, anything. It would have been embarrassing had he said, "Will you come?" But when he put it indirectly Joel had just said, "Thanks, Padre," and the event had not been mentioned again. Joel's default had not made the slightest difference in their relations. It was swallowed up in that vacuum-like, silent acquiescence that insulated the man. That was one reason why Joel liked him. He was good-humoured, but tactful about it!

Joel wondered why he thought of him as silent, for he was not literally silent—he was, in fact, an easy and intelligent talker. Might it be that there was some deep contentment that pervaded his superficial moods? And yet, contentment was not quite the word, for there was something about him, something in his voice, that suggested discontent, unhappiness, as though he were, or had been, crowded by an oppressive world. But certainly one could not think of him as being crowded in any vulgar sense; he was too well turned-out, too Oxonian, too suave, soigné. No, any crowding here was inside, spirit subtly crowding spirit. The man puzzled him. His whole character belied the superficial inference from his cloth: he was no evangelical fanatic but a man of scholarship, culture, power; a man who viewed the world with an unprejudiced eye and judged it in a reasonable sort of way. He was a man to like, to tie to.

He was a man who should appreciate the unfathomable depths of mysticism, the shallowness of ritual; who should not hold the ignorantly muttered prayers of savages as worth a candle. It was difficult to think of him as teaching savages to pray, or buying their supplications with mingled threats of Hell and promises of Heaven, spreading around himself a shallow sham of power, superiority, beneficence. He was no Glory-to-God man! You simply could not imagine him supplicating, cringing, begging. Rather, you expected to find him suppliant before the mystery of the jungle, searching among the native ways, the old wives' tales and secret stories of myth for a light of understanding to shine upon the savages he had gone out to teach; you expected to find him engaged with the analysis, dissection, reassembling of the obscure life of some barbaric bushman, holding it in his clear vision alongside that of old Greece or Gaul.

But no—he might be these, but, first of all—he was devout. . . . And therein lay the paradox. . . .

Joel wondered again why he had gone in for this sort of thing.

There was something in his voice that suggested regret and disillusion.
. . . "So many happy places, glad, joyous, singing" . . . The forests of
Africa were not happy places. Life was hard, lonely, barren. A man
had to find everything within himself when it was two hundred miles
to the nearest white man, two hundred miles to share a wish, a word,
a memory; two months from friendly face to friendly face. It took a
powerful force to send a man—an intelligent man—into that sort of
life. And this man was, certainly, intelligent. It might have been a
great adventure when he first went out, but he was going back! Going
back again to a round clearing in a Tanganyika forest to be alone
in a rude hut with a meagre pile of books, a rough temple dedicated
to his God, and with his memories—memories of the world, of friends,
of things, joyous, happy things; to be alone with his desires, his aches,
his pains, to be alone with his unutterable loneliness. Was it to take to
his uncomprehending savages some part of himself, some twig of the
spiritual vegetation that grew up in him, rooted in the humus of the
past; some mystic twig of an all-healing herb that was supposed to
bless the recipient with Eternal Life, Salvation? Joel remembered a
parade he had once seen in Mombasa: a string of shiftless, barefoot
blacks dressed in rags and tatters of European clothes had come tramp-
ing down the dusty street one afternoon with a clamour of drums and
bugles. Toward the end of the column a dirty white banner proclaimed: "JESUS SAVES."

It was inconceivable that this man could take that kind of thing
seriously! Joel gave him up as beyond his comprehension.

He suddenly realized that the Padre was staring at him, that they
were staring at each other without acknowledgment, each wondering
what sort of man the other was.

"And you?" the Padre asked without taking his eyes away.

"Oh, my reasons were very simple," said Joel, laughing. "I went to
Africa to—well, to fish. Not for sport, but on a sort of scientific fishing
trip."

The Padre seemed to be waiting for some enlargement on this statement, so Joel added: "I've been there before—two years ago. My wife
and I went to Kisumu, on Lake Victoria, after some of these same fish

and took a number of them home with us. I've just been back to get
more so that I could keep on with my work."

"Oh, I see. For a museum. You are an ichthyologist——"

"No, just a naturalist at——" He named a small college in the
United States.

The Padre acknowledged the information with a slight nod of his
head. "I've heard strange reasons for men going to Africa, but I think
that is the strangest—to come all this way for one fish. Couldn't you
have had them sent to you?"

"No, I had to come and get them. I took them home alive, you see.
I had to have them alive for my purposes. They are peculiar fish.
Lung-fish they are called, because they breathe by means of both
lungs and gills. They live in the rivers and lakes but when the dry
season comes, if they are trapped in the swamps, they dig into the
mud and lie buried until the rains come along and cover the land
with water again. They can live in the hard mud, breathing by means
of their lungs, for months, years—almost in a state of suspended ani-
mation. Starving, waiting, hanging on—crowded," Joel laughed, "as
we were yesterday, by an inexorable Nature."

"They are queer creatures. It's strange I never heard of them. Where
do they live?"

"In Lake Victoria, Lake Albert, the White Nile—you should have
them down your way in Tanganyika. They are found in almost all the
rivers and lakes of Equatorial Africa. There is another species that
lives in the Belgian Congo and a third that lives up in Gambia. Rather
local, spotted distribution. There's a closely related genus in Australia
and another in South America. They live—they always have lived,
I think—only in fresh water, never in the sea. The Australian species
is quite scarce, nearly extinct, in fact. The natives like to eat them
and the Government has had to put them under protection. . . . Government staving off the evil day when they will be crowded out, for
good!

"They once"—Joel turned in his chair, his interest in his subject
drawing him closer to his listener—"were wide-spread over the world.
That was in a geologically remote time when the continents were

fused or connected together. Their fossils have been found in Europe, Asia, Malaya, Australia, North and South America, Africa. Four hundred million years ago they were the cream of life, lords of creation; pioneers in a new way of living, escaping the threat of death that lurks in droughts, stagnant pools, poisoned waters, through breathing air by means of their newly invented lungs. But they have remained almost unchanged through the ages, carrying on in the old way of living until now they are largely crowded out, just a few stragglers hanging on to the very edge of annihilation. Life has gone around them, leaving them behind. They are like living pages out of life's history."

When Joel stopped a feeling of embarrassment came over him. He was irritated by his own loquaciousness. Why should he burst out in a long harangue to a stranger casually inquiring about a thing of interest? Scientific evangelism! That's what it amounted to, and that kind was as bad as any other. He looked over at his companion, wondering what sort of a pushing ass he might think him to be. But the Padre was leaning forward, his chin cupped in his hands, looking out into the night. He had never seen the man until two weeks ago. But the past week—there had been something to throw them together. He had completely forgotten the oppression that he had thought would hang on to him for days. It seemed now unreal, an evil dream dissolving in a wakening moment. He walked over to the rail and looked ahead, searching for the lights of Ismailia that would come up out of the night somewhere to the northwest. The breeze had become stronger, more definite and perceptibly cool. The sandy hills that were moving past seemed to have been piled up by a steam-shovel at regular intervals.

"What do they look like?"

The Padre's voice took him by surprise and a moment intervened before he could reassemble the man and his question. Joel turned around:

"Oh, the fish! . . . They are rather eel-shaped, round and elongated with rope-like fins. They are olive-brown or black above and greyish underneath. Their heads are blunt, like a snake's, with massive jaws and flat teeth designed for crushing snail-shells. The natives say that they can bite a broom-handle in two, but that's probably an exaggeration. However, I'd hate to get my fingers snapped by a big one. There is a mounted specimen in the Nairobi Museum seven feet long. He looks the part of a prehistoric monster! The natives believe that they are a 'cross' between a fish and a crocodile—not a strange association when you see one flopping around on the ground, opening his frightful jaws to take a breath."

"They must be a 'cross' between a fish and some land animal, judging from the way they live; and you say they breathe by means of lungs. Other fishes don't have lungs, do they?"

"The higher fishes did have lungs once; or rather they are descended from archaic forms which did. It was also from those archaic air-breathing fishes that the first land animals came. This lung-fish, though modified in some ways, is the closest surviving remnant of the ancestral stock that gave rise to the modern fishes on the one hand and the terrestrial animals on the other. The fishes have, for the most part, discarded the archaic lung or made it over into an air-tight gas bag or swim-bladder. While the terrestrial animals have kept the lung, and improved upon it."

"Why is he—your lung-fish—so important to you?"

"For two reasons: first, because of the peculiar life he leads. When the dry season comes and the swamplands dry out, he buries himself beneath the mud and engages in a long-time fast. Many animals hibernate in the winter-time when it is cold but the lung-fish goes to sleep in his mud nest during the hottest months of the year. He is imprisoned there until the rains come again and set him free. The mud around him dries as hard as rocks so that he could not, if he wanted it, get anything to eat. So, of course, he has to burn his own tissues for fuel like any other fasting animal, to keep alive. I believe he takes the prize as fasting champion, because he can certainly last for several years. Then, too, he has no water in his earth-bound prison and consequently his kidneys have to stop working. All the poisonous products of his metabolism pile up in his blood and tissues—a condition that would kill all other animals that we know anything about, in a short time. The dry mud around him and the hot dry air that he breathes tend to steal water out of his body, yet for some reason he doesn't dry up himself. In short, he puts himself into an endurance test that no other animal could survive.

"The second reason is that he is the closest form, among the living animals, to the extinct link between the fishes and the first land animals. That splendid creature lies buried in some Devonian sandstone or Carboniferous bed of coal. But the lung-fish, though he has changed a little in his bones and fins, is, we must believe, living in much the same way as did his Devonian ancestors. He shows us something of how the important step from life in the water to life on the land came about. He is, as I said, like a page out of life's history.

"Certainly the first step in the direction of land life was the respiration of air instead of, or in addition to, water. This important step was taken by the fishes long before fins were converted into legs with which to crawl about on land. Some of the earliest fishes, living far back in the Devonian Period, were air-breathers; the convergent lines of evidence from the living and dead records point to this. They had a lung, of sorts, into which they swallowed air and they were enabled by this unique organ to live in pools and rivers when the dry season came and the water disappeared or became foul with rotting animals and plants. They were able to survive when the other fishes were driven out, driven possibly, back into the sea, or into the Beyond. . . . Here is really your connecting link in a bigger sense: a fine new organ, a new power that broadened the organism's way of living, increased its physical freedom, widened its margin of safety. More lowly forms endured, but they were restricted to a narrower field by the changed conditions. The evolution of air-breathing lungs marked an elevation in the stream of life; it had gotten over an obstacle, surmounted it by finding a new way of living."

"Why?"

"Why what?"

"Why did life surmount the obstacle?"

Joel shook his head. "Some say by accident, the accident of mutation and the ultimate survival of the fittest; some say by deliberately adapting itself to get around the obstacle. But I can't tell you why, and I doubt if there is any man who can. We don't, just yet, ask 'why' so much as 'how.' The nature of the rocks in which these fossil forms are buried, red and yellow sandstones devoid of organic matter, shows that they were probably laid down by torrential rivers spreading out at flood-time over vast plains. When the water subsided it left the fish trapped in pools and the pools dried out in the sun and the fish died by the thousands. Perhaps the fish lived along the river banks and in shallow lakes that periodically became dry in the long arid seasons between the rains. In any case it is more than probable that they lived, as the lung-fish does today, in a world that pressed in upon them, that required adjustment. Not only of the individual but of the race. All we can be sure of is that out of that crowding they achieved a new way of living. These straggling survivors, when they rise to the surface of the water to fill their lungs with air, are, in a way, recapitulating the life history of the race written back in the Devonian plains when it was fighting to survive.

"When I went to Africa after these fish it was like going back four hundred million years. Only it was shorter, easier."

The Padre had pulled himself into a position of attention, and was puffing steadily on his cigar while he watched Joel's face.

"Tell me how you got them," he said.

Joel went back to his chair and sat down with his hands between his knees.

"Oh, there was nothing spectacular about it, though it was an interesting experience—for me. You see, the job was of a rather special nature. I wanted to do a lot of chemical work on their blood and tissues, to determine what happened to them while they were asleep in the mud. I wanted to do some experiments with them, to test their kidneys, to compare them with other animals and particularly with ourselves. It was not enough for me to have two or three—I needed dozens of them, some active, some asleep in the mud, asleep one month, three months, six months if possible.

"Of course I had to be prepared to set up a chemical laboratory in the field so I had to take with me all the reagents, the glassware, the delicate instruments that I would need. My wife was prepared to do one part of the job and I another. We planned everything to the last detail—went through every step of the work before we left home. We had only a limited time in which to do the job and a limited grant to finance it. That, naturally, made it somewhat more difficult. It was imperative not to make any mistakes.

"But the hardest part of it all was to know where to get the fish in dried mud. I knew, of course, where they had been found by others, as recorded in the surveys made by biologists in the past. But these records did not tell me whether the fish were plentiful at a particular locality or not, nor did they say much about the local conditions in regard to the dry season, the nearness and extent of the swamplands, and so on. But after going over all the records carefully and after talking to everybody who might be able to help me, I decided to go to Lake Victoria.

"So with all our scientific gear packed in our trunks we set off for Africa, prepared to step in a few weeks from the twentieth century back to the Middle Devonan Period. I really thought about the fish that way, sometimes. They lured me, fascinated me. I wondered how they lived during their long summer sleep, and what they burned for fuel; if they remembered the simple things of life, like swimming, eating, fighting; if they really slept and could be kept asleep when taken out of their mud nest. I wondered why they didn't die of autointoxication while they were buried for months, for years, in the hard earth without water, kidneys paralysed, blood concentrated, life at its lowest ebb. I wondered more things about them than I could have found out in a life-time, more than I had tools to measure.

"But I was prepared to find out what I could about the mystery of their life when I found my fish. That was the first job, and for it I was dependent upon such information as I could pick up after I got to Africa. It was a case of going in the general direction of Lake Victoria and asking our way as we went, until we should find someone who had seen them and could tell us something about the local conditions, here or there.

"As a rule the average man doesn't know the scientific names of the things around him; you have to describe them, but there seemed to be little chance of confusing this fish with any other because of its peculiar life habits. We found men—coffee planters, hunters, engineers experienced in the bush—who had heard of them or seen them. One man told us how the natives dug the fish out of the mud for food; how they would go along the dried water-courses and watch for the blow-holes through which the fish gets air, and how they would push a stick down into every suspicious hole, and if it smelled of fish on withdrawal they would dig up the victim with some mud around him and take him home for safekeeping until they were ready to eat him. The Swahilis, they said, called the fish *samaki ya donga,* 'fish of the dried-up water-courses.' But nobody seemed to know just where they could be found in any abundance; it appeared that you only occasionally, *very occasionally,* ran into one. I began to have visions of spending all our time hunting for the fish instead of doing the chemical work which we had set out to do. One man would insist that we should go to Lake Rudolph, and another that we should go up the Nile into the Sudan, or over into the Belgian Congo. Everybody agreed that the rains had been unusually late and heavy and that it would be very difficult to find the fish in mud just then, anywhere. It seemed that we should have come in January, or last year or the year before. Everybody was more or less guessing, and every guess only served to increase my nervousness.

"I don't need to tell you how big Central Africa is, but you really can't appreciate its size until you start out to find something in it. It is a tremendous target—Abyssinia, Kenya, Tanganyika, Uganda, Congo, Sudan—and you need to aim where you want to land or you practically have to go back and start all over. There is no running from here to there if you have only a few months to spend—when five hundred miles may mean five weeks of *safari.* We were headed for Lake Victoria and we had to keep going in that direction. And that is where we got our fish. I know now that it is probably the best place in all Africa to get them, everything considered, but there was a time when I doubted if they occurred there at all.

"Like all big-game hunters we stopped in Nairobi to assemble our

gear and to get oriented before diving into the blue. You see, as yet I
didn't know whether to take fishing rods along with me, or picks and
shovels. There was a Natural History Museum there and I felt sure
that the people in charge of it would be able to put me on to the right
track. So the first thing I did was to go to the Museum. I had some
difficulty finding it and more difficulty getting in. It consisted of a
small building, hardly larger than one good room, and it was only
after some pounding and knocking about that I stirred up the keeper.
This person turned out to be a ferocious-looking Masai buck; his ears
were adorned with a half-pound of brass and copper pendants, and
his neck was encircled by what appeared at first sight to be a string of
human teeth. I thought that he was part of the collection until he
took me by the arm and led me inside to an open Visitors' Book with
a notice to 'Please Sign Here.' It was also part of his job to see that
the visitor deposited a shilling in a box conveniently placed for that
purpose. He was admirably suited to his responsibilities for I can't
imagine anyone arguing with him about a shilling or anything else.
I tried to find out from him who was the Director of the Museum, but
in answer to my questions he only led me back to the collection box
and pointed to it with a broad grin, so I gave it up as hopeless.

"Nor could I find out from anybody else. Nobody seemed to know
anything about the Museum, except that you had to pay a shilling
admission and that the antelope heads were not nearly so good as
those you could shoot on their *shamba* any morning before breakfast.
There seemed to be a general state of disinterest in the Museum and in
science generally among the planters and tradespeople.

"But it seemed that we ought to find out *something* about our fish
in Nairobi so we plodded around through the dust and made inquiries, asking people if they knew of a fish that breathed by means
of lungs and lived in the dry mud during the hot season. At first they
were very nice to us, but when they saw us a second time they gave
us a queer, sympathetic look, as though they thought that we had had
a touch of the sun. In fact, one man gave me a fatherly talk in the
lobby of the Stanley Hotel. He began by asking me if I had a head-

ache—said that I looked as if I did—and went on to explain how the one thing that one must look out for in Africa is sunstroke. Strangers were particularly sensitive and should keep their sun-helmets on, even when under cover. He had had a friend who had carelessly slept on his helmet and cracked it, and the poor man had fallen dead in the street two days later. He went on in this strain for about fifteen minutes. I lost interest in his pathological monologue and began to think about getting out of Nairobi and on to Lake Victoria, and about getting some gear and a few provisions. I broke in on the gentleman's dissertation on sunstroke to ask where I could buy some canned pork and beans. He told me to go to Safariland, Ltd.

"Safariland, Ltd., is a company—or a British gentleman, to be exact —that specializes in outfitting the *safaris* of big-game hunters. If you want to shoot a pair of big tuskers or to set up an African Wing in the Museum in Weehaucus, Safariland, Ltd., has just what you need. It's a clearing house for baked beans, beds, porters, guns, tents, and so on, as well as for professional hunters who know where to find any kind of game that has ever been seen in Africa. I went around to talk to the proprietor about my modest requirements.

"I told him why I had come to Africa, but he had never seen a lung-fish. He said that he had lived in Nairobi for many years and that he had never even heard of it. I think he was a little offended with me when I insisted that such a thing as a lung-fish lived in Africa; I admit that I felt a little bit foolish when I set my opinion against the heads and what-nots all over the walls. But he was very decent, if sceptical, and he promised to make inquiries right away. He gave me the impression that if it turned out that the lung-fish really lived in Africa, he planned to add it to his advertised list of East African Fauna right away, and get in a stroke ahead of his competitors. He could have special rods and reels, or picks and shovels— whatever one might need for the purpose—in readiness for the next customer.

"As I was about to leave, some remark I made about the States started a new train of thought in his mind. Somebody *had* said something to him about a letter from an American, a letter asking where he could get some fish in Africa. (I had, as a matter of fact, written a letter addressed to the Director of the Natural History Museum at Nairobi, explaining my mission and requesting assistance upon my arrival.) The letter, he went on, had been turned over to the dentist chap.

"I felt a vague sense of uneasiness about the way scientific correspondence was handled in Africa. I had already become self-conscious about my problem and I suspected that people thought I was possessed by a strange obsession which they found amusing, even if pathetic. When I accosted someone to inquire my way I expected a curt 'No, I never heard of any such fish.' Even the 'ricksha boys seemed to look at me a little differently. My abjection became complete when he said that they had turned my letter over to the dentist chap. I couldn't have felt worse had he said the police!

" 'The dentist,' he went on after an interminable interval of staring at the ceiling, 'is secretary to the Kenya and Uganda Scientific Society.' Then he told me his name and where I could find him.

"I looked him up. He was a delightful man! He dentisted in the morning and in the afternoon he retired, unapproachable by any pain, to a sanctuary at the rear of his house where he had built himself a laboratory—a photographic room, a library, a museum: a museum filled, not with human teeth and bridges, but with rare exotic birds and butterflies and monstrous insects; impala, zebra, and waterbuck heads; countless strange and beautiful things out of the heart of Africa, all collected and classified with a purpose.

"Van Wernigen, his name was. I've been told that throughout the length of Kenya and Uganda, that even over in the forests of the Belgian Congo, you hear Van Wernigen's name. They say that out in the depths of the jungle you might come suddenly upon a black tearing madly through the bushes with a butterfly net in his hands, specimen-gathering for *Bwana* Van Wernigen. He went out himself frequently, and always took his vacations in the bush, leaving the Nairobi teeth to ache by themselves; up to Kampala or to the Mountains of the Moon with a string of blacks packing along boxes of pins, formaldehyde, paint brushes, wire cages, note-books. He had painted every bird in Kenya and Uganda, male and female, in their summer and winter plumage!

"When I saw him he was engrossed in the phenomena of mimicry among butterflies. Some butterflies, you know, are not eaten by birds, monkeys, and other animals because of a malodorous or distasteful secretion; other butterflies which are edible secure protection by mimicking the inedible model in coloration and design so closely that only expert examination can detect the difference. Van Wernigen had followed out this process of mimicry within one wide-spread species which mimicked, in different parts of the country, five different inedible models. He showed me the collection of mounted butterflies which he had made to illustrate the development of the pattern in the mimic. At the centre was a primitive butterfly, and radiating from this were five lines leading to five different models, each line made up of butterflies which successively resembled their respective models more and more until the final mimic was almost impossible to distinguish from the model which it imitated. To prove that all these mimics were really one species he had bred them and raised them in captivity. To prove that the mimics really secured immunity by means of their protective colouring he tested them on monkeys. He had a red colobus chained to the front porch which he called the 'testing laboratory.' The monkey loved butterflies but when he was offered an offensive species he would turn his head to one side as much as to say, 'Don't bother me with that thing, it's not fit to eat.' He could tell at a glance that it was inedible. He would reject the mimic in the same way but he would devour its wingless body with relish. Only the appearance of the mimic protected it, you see, for it was really edible. And thus the man worked—he tested everything in nature's own laboratory, he borrowed the eyes of the jungle itself for his work. He collected in every part of Central Africa, mounted the specimens, prepared the wax models of flowers and leaves and assembled them into beautiful and realistic settings—all the time with his eyes on the living animal and its ways, on the mystery and meaning of life.

"Of course, he knew my lung-fish; he knew them by their Latin names, knew where they lived and where to get them. He had once brought several of them home with him and put them into jars filled with mud and let the mud dry out. He had kept them in the hard mud for eighteen months and then watched the fish break out of the mud when the jars were immersed in water. He showed me the jaw-bones of a big lung-fish and we talked about the massive teeth shaped for crushing snail-shells and bivalves. He told me that the best place to collect them was at Kisumu and he gave me introductions to the officials there that proved invaluable. He made only one mistake—he said that I would not have any trouble in getting the fish after I got to Kisumu, the natives there would collect them for me. Let me tell you, I had plenty of trouble. . . .

"But I was full of confidence when I walked out of his house, elated with success, stimulated by the man I had been talking to. I lingered to admire his garden. I would like to live in a place like that—a sort of sophisticated jungle. The house was set at the end of a long drive-way lined with casuarina trees with giant sissals set in between them. Then the trees fell back around the yard which was hedged by hi-biscus bushes bearing big rose-red double blossoms; the yard was cut up by rows of willowy eucalyptus trees and palms into patches of yellow asters, roses, cosmos, and a dozen other flowers. The house stood against a flamboyant in full bloom and a purple bougainvillæa spread across the entire front porch. There was colour everywhere. In every patch of sun there was some gorgeous colour, and in every patch of shade there was dark-green moss or a pale-green fern. There was some sort of little primitive mammal running around the yard, and an evil-tongued parrot scolded the colobus on the front porch. Altogether it was a delightful place. I had never seen the tropics so intimately before and the essence of their rank vitality, their different-ness, seemed to be concentrated in that yard.

"Yes, and the essence of my adventure. I was well pleased with my prospects. I wanted to go back to Safariland, Ltd., and to buy a sub-stantial order of fish-nets and other gear and carry them into the Stanley Hotel over my shoulder as a symbol of my sanity. Fortunately I didn't, or the joke would have been on me. For when I finally got my fish I did not use a fish-net nor even a pick and shovel to dig them out of the mud. I just picked them up off the ground."

III

Joel accepted another cigar from the Padre and nodded his head appreciatively after lighting it; he tried several times to blow a smoke-ring but succeeded only in setting himself to coughing.

"Another miracle?" the Padre asked, smiling and taking a fresh cigar for himself.

"Yes, for me it was," Joel laughed, "for I ultimately came to a point where it seemed that only a miracle could save my little expedition from defeat.

"I supposed that the people around Mombasa and Nairobi had never heard of the lung-fish because the animal did not occur in their immediate neighbourhood. But when I got to Kisumu, where I knew on good authority that the lung-fish did occur, I did not find my informants much more helpful. Of course, the proper thing was to go to the natives for information, especially since I hoped to rely largely upon them for collecting the fish for me. But it was several days before the P.C., who was temporarily acting as interpreter for me, could collect the head men for the necessary *shauri*. Meanwhile, the people of Kisumu took us in hospitably and gave us an empty cottage to live in and to use as a laboratory, and they elected us to a temporary membership in the local Club.

"The industry of your British colonist is remarkable: wherever you find two or more Englishmen gathered together, there you will find a golf course, a tennis court, and one or more clubhouses. The Nyanza Club at Kisumu is a beautiful place, high up on a hill which overlooks the Kavirondo Gulf at the eastern end of Lake Victoria. The hill slopes gently down to the Lake and is dotted here and there with thorn trees, euphorbias, and low bushes. A wide drive lined with gum trees and casuarinas runs along the shore for some distance and then it doubles back along the crest of the hill and into the town proper.

Our own cottage—I still call it ours though we only occupied it for a few weeks—was almost the last one out of town near the end of the hill where the road comes back from the Lake. It was surrounded by frangipani bushes in full bloom, an occasional pink trumpet flower, and wiry euphorbias. From the front yard you looked down the open slope of the hill to the Lake and across to the blue mountains behind Homa Bay. The men at the Club used to joke about being in the Heart of Darkest Africa, but the term sounded absurd when you saw the *Clement Hill* come steaming in from Jinja or when you heard the train whistle from the railway station. The place had its African colour, however; herds of impala came to graze in the short grass around the cottage and crocodiles and hippos were common enough down in the Lake. The hippos trampled down the gardens during the night, searching for lettuce and other tender delicacies. So persistent was the hungry beast in its depredations of the Club's garden that they called him Horace and elected him to Honorary Membership. You frequently encountered Horace while driving along the Lake shore after dark, but you timed your meeting so as not to hurry him across the road; and if you chanced to find a strange, dark object in your *shamba* at night you waved your arms—if it was Horace, he went away. Horace was immune from attack because you simply can't kill a three-ton hippo in a settled community—it is too difficult to shift camp!

"Oh, no! In spite of the steamship and the railway and motor cars we didn't forget that we were in Africa, especially at night. We were far out from the town proper, and after our boys had gone home the fun began. The hyenas prowled around the back porch, knocking over pots and pans, and Horace ambled around in the darkness and sneezed that sneeze of his which sounds like nothing so much as a steam-boiler blowing out its insides; and other nocturnal visitors found ways and means of making strange and unearthly noises right under our windows. If they had only blown that train whistle about nine o'clock at night it would have helped a lot!

"But to come back to the fish. As I said, nobody there seemed to know much about it. They were, of course, very interested and I had to tell them all about the fish while we sat in the Club, how it buried itself in the mud and breathed air, and so on, while we drank each other's health and the success of the expedition. The Club was one of these progressive clubs—each new-comer buys a drink for everybody who is already there and this keeps up until nobody else comes and everybody decides that it's time to go home. If there were many late-comers you might not get home until eleven, but the local cooks were used to this regime and had dinner ready at any hour up to midnight. I used to wonder if they didn't do most of their own sleeping be-tween tea and dinner-time.

"But late in the course of our first evening at the Club the engineer in charge of the P.W.D. came in. He spent most of his time in the bush building bridges and roads and he said that he had frequently heard of the lung-fish and knew just where he could get them, al-though he had never actually seen one. His information, as is fre-quently the case with a layman, appeared to be a bit sketchy but I thought it important to follow up every lead. He said that he knew where he could dig one or more out of the mud and he suggested that we go after them the next day. Of course I was enthusiastic, so we began to make plans and talked about them most of the evening. He wanted to make an early start. He had *jembies* for digging, but he said that we would need some sort of trap to catch the fish in because when it was unearthed it wriggled away over the ground with great rapidity. We finally decided to borrow a washtub from the steward and some string and so on, and planned to rig up a trap in the field. I was feeling pretty cheerful. Old P.W.D. explained again how you located the place where the fish was buried by spotting the blow-holes which can be seen frequently alongside, or even in the middle of the muddy roads.

" 'And you'd be surprised,' he said, 'how those fish love air. I've had four punctures in a week from fish coming up and biting my auto-mobile tires to get at it!'

"Only then did I realize that he had never seen a lung-fish's hole. I had a feeling like falling through space, but I suppose I made some sort of smiling grimace to show my appreciation of the joke.

"But the next day the P.C. got the natives together for a big *shauri*. As soon as he explained to them what I wanted they spoke up and said that they knew the fish. They described it fairly well—as well as you can roughly describe any fish—and said that it buried itself in the mud during the dry season. That was the fish I wanted, I said. They went on to tell how it had 'whiskers' around its mouth by which it suckled its young. I remember how the P.C. wrinkled his forehead and looked up at me at this bit of natural history, but I suggested that we might take a look at this fish, anyway. The description seemed to fit the lung-fish in every respect except the whiskers part of it, and these I ascribed to a misinterpretation of the lung-fish's rope-like fins. So we told the boys to bring us in one of their fish, and the next day I was all primed to have my first lung-fish.

"But the fish turned out to be a common catfish, hence the whiskers. The natives were right about the catfish burying itself in the mud, but it is not a lung-fish. It aerates its blood by means of a spongy tissue rich in capillaries in the mouth—a relatively recent device—and it was not of immediate interest to me.

"So we tried again, getting natives in from all around the neighbouring country. At last we got on to what I felt sure was spoor: it was described as a big fish that slept in the mud and had two rope-like arms in front by which it suckled its young. (The P.C. began to shy away at this, but I held him on.) It was a cross between a fish and a crocodile and there were no females; the father laid the eggs. The fish was called Kamongo. It was a very fierce fish and it would bite you if you came near it. It would even bite you two days after you had cut its head off. 'The *Bwana* must not go near the fish until it was dead,' they said. The P.C. remarked that if I had to wait until two days after the fish died I couldn't work in Kisumu—the Health Officer would object!

"All this was very well, but where could we get this fierce fish?

" 'The *Bwana* can't get it,' they said, 'he has come at the wrong time! The *dongas* are all under water. The *Bwana* must come back in December.'

"That the *dongas* were all under water was clear enough by that time. The rains had been unusually prolonged and, what was more important, Lake Victoria was at the highest point that it had reached for years. There is a cycle in the level of Lake Victoria which runs over a period of about eleven years—it appears to be tied up somehow with sunspots—which shows up in the local water levels far back from the Lake itself. But I didn't know anything about this until I got over there on the ground. Here I ran into serious trouble for the mud was certainly under water, knee-deep, and there wasn't a chance in a million of my finding a lung-fish that had been dried out for even a short period of time. Had those beggars really known they could have told me to come back in five years, at which time I could find vast swamps hard and cracked by the torrid sun that in two or six months might just be emerging from their present flood.

"Since I couldn't wait for the Nile to drain Lake Victoria, I had to give up all immediate hope of studying the fish in æstivation. The best I could do was to make what observations I could on the free-swimming fish, and to try to take some home alive. If I could get them back alive perhaps I could do what Van Wernigen had done, put them into mud and dry them out artificially, so to speak. The plan had its advantages: with the fish once asleep in my laboratory I could exactly control the conditions of their life, such as temperature, humidity, time, and so on, and I could make more leisurely and refined observations upon them than I could ever hope to make in the field.

"But I had still to get the live fish. As yet, I had never seen one.

" 'Where does the fish go,' I asked, 'when the *dongas* are under water?'

"They had several answers to this; one man said that the fish dissolved and was washed away, and another suggested that it dug itself deeper into the mud, but a third and really bright boy pointed out that if I could use a dead fish I could get it at the fish-market.

"Following this pregnant suggestion I inquired at the fish-market and found that Kamongo was occasionally caught by the fishermen at Nanga, a village about five miles along the Lake. It was a hot day, but I went over there that very afternoon with an interpreter to see if I could get them to direct their energies in my behalf.

"They admitted that they caught Kamongo once in a while, but they said that they could not bring them in alive because, in the first place, the fish were very dangerous and had to be killed at once by a blow over the head; and in the second place, if they didn't kill them they would die anyway in a short time! I suggested that I might come out with them and take the fish out of the nets myself. Yes, I could take the fish out of the nets if I wanted to, but I'd never get them back to the shore alive; they wouldn't live after they had been taken out of the water more than a few hours. I said that I would bring a *mtungi* to put water in, and put the fish in the water and take it back to the shore that way. They shook their heads: No, it would die more quickly in a *mtungi* than anywhere else. A Kamongo was the most delicate of all fish and died at once when it was caught. I would either have to use dead Kamongo or else I would have to use some other kind of fish that could be kept alive. This seemed to me to be very strange, but I decided to try my luck with the fish-nets anyway, and promised them a handsome price (as judged by local fish prices) for every Kamongo that I took from them. I arranged to meet them at the place in the Lake where their nets were set at about three o'clock the following morning.

"At last I had come to the end of my trail! All I had to do was to go out in a motor boat in the early hours and take the fish out of the fishermen's nets, put them into tubs or *mtungis* filled with water and bring them in alive to the laboratory. The next morning saw me puff-puffing across the lake toward my rendezvous with the fishermen and my first live lung-fish—or so I thought.

"As I went along I mused on the workings of the native mind. I could see why they believed the lung-fish suckled its young by the two pectoral appendages which were, in spite of their rope-like character, quite obviously fins. And I was beginning to understand why they thought that the animal was a cross between a fish and a crocodile; the more I heard of Kamongo's character the more I appreciated their descriptive, if unbiological, blending. The astonishing statement that there was no female fish I attributed to the peculiar familial arrangements of the lung-fish; the female lays the eggs and then wanders off to more engaging pastimes while the male stays behind and guards the nest. If the water becomes foul, he even stirs himself to the extent of beating it up with his tail to aerate it. I suppose that when the young grow up and are about to leave the nest the old boy eats most of them as a reward for duty faithfully done. Many fish consider this fair play, and Kamongo is a frightful cannibal, anyway— he will eat his aquarium mates if he gets hungry. The business of biting you for two days after decapitation, I learned later, is an exaggeration. The head, when severed from the body, will snap reflexly for several hours and frequently displays rather horrifying gasps of asphyxiation. But that the fish would not live in a tub of water I knew to be an absurdity, for couldn't it live for a year out of water entirely? It certainly wasn't going to die in a tub of water in a couple of hours! The natives had probably just jumped to conclusions in this matter from observing how quickly other fishes die in a limited volume of water.

"But do you know that they were right? I'm blessed if I didn't come to think that those fish were being guarded by some African Malignity determined to keep them from me. Every fish which I took out of those nets kicked about in my tubs for a half-hour or so and then rolled over on its back and died. Some of them even died in my trembling fingers as I disentangled the net from around their squirming bodies! Even the most perfect specimens, without a scratch on them, went the same way! I tell you that I began to be frightened! Frightened by the absurd possibility that I had come ten thousand miles only to look down at those slimy carcasses of dead fish; frightened by the apparent impossibility of ever getting them back alive to America.

"Yes, it was absurd; but the genuineness of my panic comes back to me now as I see myself marching determinedly down to the Lake at the next midnight to try again, my way lighted by a flickering kerosene lantern. I barely noticed the hippos that moved in the bushes along the road or the hyenas that skitted out of my path. I believe that I would have passed a lion face to face with indifference, so great was my absorption in my difficulty. I was certainly possessed by a monomania now. Perhaps it was the intensity of my possession that blinded me to the explanation of my difficulty. But it was as simple as I was blind!

"The word had gone out that I wanted Kamongo, and that I would pay a handsome price to anybody who would bring them to me alive. A few fish had been brought to the cottage by various natives, but they had invariably died within a few hours after I had gotten them. This thing was getting serious, and I was all the more perturbed because it seemed so senseless. I could not reconcile this extreme delicacy with the fact that the fish could live for months in a mud nest. The more I thought about it the more absurd the whole thing became.

"I sat on the front steps with my chin in my hands wondering in a dazed sort of way just what I was going to do next. There didn't seem to be anything to do, except to go back over my same old tracks and try it again. It was the most helpless feeling I've ever had. I saw myself going home and reporting that there seemed to be plenty of lung-fish in Lake Victoria but that you couldn't get them out alive— they died as soon as you looked at them, died of fright, or of some mysterious kind of piscine heart-failure. I was sitting there mooning, with my eyes fixed on the mountains across the Kavirondo Gulf, when my houseboy came tearing up the hill excited with news that he knew would bring me to my feet.

"'*Bwana,* Oworogwada comes! He brings Kamongo, live Kamongo!'

"Oworogwada was a native chief with whom I had held several *shauris*. I got up to look and sure enough the old chief himself was coming leisurely up the grassy slope of the hill. He was dressed in an orange nightgown and he was pulling steadily on a black clay pipe. Even at some distance I could see that he had on all his ceremonial teeth and bones, and that his ears were fringed from top to bottom with the malachite pendants that are passed down from father to son. Clearly, this was a notable occasion! But I didn't see any Kamongo.

"The old man was followed by his eldest son, a strapping buck of thirty-odd who was chewing on the end of some dentifricial root. Bringing up the rear was a grandson, age ten years or thereabouts, with nothing on his body; but on his head was a *mtungi* at least two feet across. In due time the Kamongo was disclosed curled up inside the *mtungi* in about eight inches of water. The fish was nearly five feet long and, with the *mtungi* and water, must have weighed as much as its porter.

"Oworogwada explained that he had found a nest in the swamp-lands and trapped the fellow in a big *basketi*. The job had taken him a couple of days, and of course he was quite set up by his ingenuity and success.

"No less than I. You can imagine my elation! I made haste to transfer the fish to a tub filled with fresh water. I cautiously placed my hands around the massive throat and lifted out my prize, the slime running down off its black body on to my legs and feet. But the beast's mouth was open wide in a terrifying, final gasp! It was rigid with *rigor mortis!*

"As I looked into its gaping maw I broke out in a delirious shout of laughter. I saw at last my own absurdity. The fish had *drowned,* of course! They had drowned in the fishermen's nets, in the shallow tubs, they had drowned on me right and left because they could not get to the precious air. Lung-fish indeed! Drowned beneath the water!

"I have to laugh now when I wonder what the old chief thought of my unexpected reaction. Admittedly these *Bwanas* were strange fellows, always making absurd demands. But my explosion into laughter, coupled with his own consternation at finding the fish dead, must certainly have puzzled him.

"I gave him two shillings for his trouble and I told him to bring me the next one in an old gunny sack which I gave him for the purpose. This request must have seemed to him like outright insanity but he pocketed the shillings and went away in stately procession, followed by the royal heirs.

"Looking back in the light of subsequent discoveries, I wonder that it did not occur to me sooner that these creatures might be entirely dependent upon aerial respiration. As a matter of fact, they cannot live beneath the water for more than a few hours. Their gills are greatly reduced in size, almost vestigial, and even in the water they rise to the surface every fifteen minutes or so to fill their lungs with air. To reach the surface they must be able to bend the forward part of their long bodies, and this had been impossible in the narrow tubs in which the fishermen had put them—if they were not already drowned by being imprisoned in the net below the surface of the water for an indefinite period of time. It's clear enough now, but sometimes we are a long time seeing simple things.

"But the mere explanation of my difficulties did not solve them for me. I still had to find a way to catch the fish without drowning them and, it was clear, I must confine myself to small fish not over a foot or so in length that could move about freely in the tubs and buckets which were all I had to keep them in. Such small fish are not caught by the fishermen's nets because they can slip through the meshes. We had tried a hook and line at several places on the Lake, but without success. We had no fine mesh drag-nets, and it would have taken weeks to make them. The peculiar nature of the fish I wanted rendered useless the local fishing methods, so far as getting them alive was concerned; and in the heart of Africa you can't go out and buy something else when what you have doesn't work. No, it didn't look so easy. But, as it happened, all my difficulties were solved for me at once, and in a most peculiar fashion.

"The cottage in which we were living had, up to a few days before our arrival, been occupied by the Superintendent of the Prison who had vacated it to move into newly completed quarters. I had never met the man but he had often been in my mind because each morning a gang of convicts would pass by our door on the way to the shore where they were cutting out papyrus. The average black looks awesome enough to a new-comer, but thirty or more strapping bucks already convicted of criminal tendencies and guarded only by one or two *askaris* are a sight to instil trepidation. The guard seemed to me to be too light. I could watch the prisoners working on the shore from our front porch; armed with big knives, *jembies,* and ropes they would walk out on to the islands of papyrus that had blown in from across the Gulf and cut off the feathery tops. Then they would cut out big blocks of roots and, working a rope around them, pull them ashore where they burned them. The *askaris* were armed, of course, but they sauntered around in a casual sort of way and I rather looked forward to their getting the job done and moving away from our front yard.

"On the afternoon of the very day that Oworogwada visited us I received a message asking me to come over to the Prison. I must have looked rather haggard when I got there. I had been losing a lot of good sleep collecting dead fish from the Lake, and what with the hot sun and the dust of my walk and with my worrying generally about the thing all the way over I wasn't in any too cheerful a mood. The Superintendent didn't immediately improve it.

"He started off by saying how sorry he was that I couldn't get what I'd come after. The water, he said, was over his cabbage patch and that was very unusual. He suggested that I try such and such a *donga,* that it was usually dry this time of year. But it happened that I had already tried such and such a *donga* and had found the water even deeper than over his precious cabbage patch. He ventured that if I could wait a couple of months his cabbage patch would be dry; he was certain that there were lung-fishes in it because he had seen the boys digging there. I said that I was sorry but I could not wait a couple of months, for I had to be back in America by the first of October. I hoped his cabbages were not ruined by the flood, however. Oh, not likely—they would come along sooner or later. Cabbages grew almost any time in Africa—not that they ever got to be cabbages, properly speaking, not like the cabbages you get at home. . . . But what was I going to do about the lung-fish?

"I told him that I had given up all hope of getting the fish out of dry mud, and that I was trying now to get some small ones alive to take home with me.

"He turned to me with a surprised look and asked: 'Why don't you go and pick some up?'

"For a moment my sight was obscured by a vision of a washtub.

"'Do I need a bucket?' I finally asked him.

" 'Oh, no,' he answered, 'come along.'

"I decided to take a chance. I followed him into his car and we drove back past the cottage and down to the Lake shore where the labour gang was working. He called something in Swahili to a guard and the man brought him a galvanized iron bucket which he passed on to me.

"In it were a half-dozen live lung-fish, kicking around as happy as larks.

" 'They fall out,' he explained, 'when the boys drag the papyrus roots ashore. They usually keep them for dinner but if you want them I'll have them put on your porch. It's funny, isn't it?' he went on; 'I just threw away a barrel of fifty of them when I moved out of the bungalow. My son had kept them there all winter. I'll tell the *askaris* to save them for you tomorrow——'

" 'Thanks,' I said, 'and I'll take these now!'

"I took them back to the cottage and went right to work on them. Within a month I had collected all the lung-fish that I wanted, picked them up literally in my own front yard! The Superintendent kindly kept the labour gang cutting papyrus long after it was really necessary. In fact, I think that he rounded up a few islands just for my special benefit. I remember that man most kindly. I do hope that he had a good crop of cabbages. . . .

"It wasn't a very sporting method of fishing but it served the ends of science. . . .

"Oh, yes, I got them to America all right—carried them all the way out of Kenya, through the Red Sea and across the Atlantic without a single casualty; took them to a modern laboratory and put them to sleep in glass jars, in American mud in which their ancestors had slept countless generations ago. They went to sleep in an incubator which was tenderly guarded by a thermostat and surrounded by test-tubes, gas-analysers, burettes, and colorimeters, just as comfortably as in the Karno plains, unconscious of the change in scenery . . . unconscious that they were part of an experiment. . . ."

"Was your experiment a success?" the Padre asked when Joel gave no sign of going on.

Joel laughed. "Oh, I wasn't thinking so much about my experiment. I was really thinking about Nature's experiment, performed four hundred million years ago when the first Kamongo dug into the mud to avoid desiccation on some arid Devonian plain. My job was merely to watch Nature's experiment and to record the results in my notebook, to observe what life does when it is crowded too near the edge."

"Well, was that experiment a success?"

Joel laughed again, and getting stiffly out of his chair he began to pace up and down the deck with his hands behind him, while his eyes were studying the white dowelled planks beneath his feet.

"In so far as we can see those things, I wouldn't say that it was. He buried himself in the mud, you see, and for most purposes that rather put an end to things. He shut himself up in a prison from which escape hung upon the slenderest thread of accident—that the waters should rise again before he reached the end of his rope. He shut himself up where he had to burn his own tissues for fuel to keep the spark of life in his body; if he didn't die of starvation then the chances were that he would be killed by toxæmia, for he had no water with which to excrete the poisonous products of his own metabolism. If he escaped these hazards he had to go forth on the newly arrived flood and seek food and face his enemies in an emaciated condition, debilitated rather than rested by his long sleep. In any case, he cut down the period of his free physical activity to one-half, perhaps one-third, of his life's span.

"No—when he dived into the mud he dived into a blind alley, into a mode of life that must ultimately end in extinction. The proof of my way of reasoning lies in the fact that he is nearing that end. The marvel is that he has survived this long. His failure is the more pathetic since he had such a brilliant start. This lung of his, which had just come into being, promised to bring him freedom from the old way of living, promised to break the bonds that chained him to a life beneath the water, but it only left him chained alternately beneath the water and the mud. If anything, he was worse off than before.

"In addition to the air-breathing lung, he needed legs to crawl about with, to take him out of the dried-up water-courses and over the land to some place where the water was still standing. His own fins were too feeble, too piscine, for that purpose.

"The legs came, but not to the lung-fish; they came to some air-breathing cousin of his who had stronger bones and muscles in his fins, better raw materials. Can you see the scene: a desiccating swamp-land where Cousin, with his primitive stumps of fin-legs, raises himself out of the hardening mud, laboriously climbs up the bank, and crawls away to some distant green oasis and to freedom—without once looking back at my poor lung-fish, left wallowing helplessly behind, getting ready to dive into his sticky prison, his blind alley?

"Cousin is gone; we have nothing but his footprints—where he walked along the mud which the sun baked hard and the wind covered over—to tell the tale of that experiment. But through him life escaped out of that treacherous swamp to crawl about on land, escaped to a bigger and better way of living, to a greater degree of physical freedom. It escaped to an open road which led on and on. Yes, Cousin was a very successful experiment!

"But my lung-fish bound himself down to a narrower way of living, he reduced his physical freedom when he dived into the mud; he got into a way of living that had no future, into a blind alley. He was an experiment that failed."

Joel took a couple of turns around the cramped deck and then he stopped, half-facing the Padre.

"It's clear enough to us now, when we are looking back upon it, but I wonder, if we had been there half suffocated in that black mud, could we have told which was the blind and which was the open road? . . . I doubt it."

He went off again into his deliberate pacing up and down.

IV

IT was the Padre's turn to become infected with the restlessness that kept Joel moving, and he began to follow his companion around, looking intently at Joel's heels as though he were playing some inane game of stepping in his predecessor's footsteps. Joel stopped to kick a deck-chair out of his path and this let the Padre come abreast with him. The latter gave the chair another push, and then the two men started off in step. The free space was limited, however, by recumbent sleepers who blocked their way, and after a few cramped turns the Padre suggested that they go forward to the bow. "I like the sharp end of a boat," he said; "it gives me an illusion of grandeur." So they moved off in the half-shadows, carefully stepping over the outstretched legs and upturned feet of their fellow-passengers.

The stairway that led down to the forward well-deck presented some difficulty. At its top was one of those gates which by its very nature is supposed to restrain ambitious vagrants: a gate patterned, like the ship's rail, of horizontal iron bars let into somewhat heavier uprights, the whole slung from four protruding hooks which fitted into rings upon the rail-posts. To pass by, you had to lift the gate up and out of the holding-rings and then you were faced with the problem of knowing what to do with it, for you must either take it along with you or else do a sharp turn on the narrow topmost step of the ladder and put it back into its place—which was almost an impossibility. To lay hands upon such a gate made you unpleasantly aware that you were a trespasser. After several attempts to open it, they were forced to climb over the rail and worm themselves on to the steps of the steep ladder.

The forward hatch had been uncovered, preparatory to unloading cargo at Port Said, and the hatch-boards and tarpaulins were piled in rows along the bulwarks. The intervening deck-space was littered with gear and sleeping sailors, and the men had to pick their way carefully to the forecastle through a confusion of shadows. Another steep ladder led up to the forecastle-deck; here they stumbled over steam-pipes and anchor-chains until at last they came into the bow. Three steps ascended from the forecastle-deck to a shallow bracket set into the bow; the bracket afforded a comfortable place to stand or sit, and it was sheltered by the bulwarks where they rose high above the hawse-pipes so that by leaning over one could look down at the prow cutting through the black water. A large searchlight fixed upon the bow illuminated the sides of the canal and the water ahead.

The ship was just turning through the curve of Lake Timsah, and the lights of Ismailia sparkled on the west. She seemed to be making greater speed in the open water and her bow moved up and down with a slight but exuberant motion. The stars, instead of sliding from side to side as they do when viewed from a rolling ship, appeared to rise and fall like a canopy fitfully inflated by the wind. The illusion was emphasized by the reflection from the water of the searchlight, the radiance of which was alternately concentrated and scattered by a low procession of rounded waves.

Leaning over the bulwark it seemed to Joel that he was looking down upon a pit in the bottom of which a moving stream of water was splitting itself against a rock. There was nothing along the vertical prow to give it its proper dimensions. It was hard to believe that just below Cape Guardafui seas had swept across that bow and shattered themselves against the windlasses and ventilators behind. But out there in the Indian Ocean the monsoon had had three thousand miles of fairway in which to stir the water up, while here there was only a small lake and a little wisp from some Aegean gale that, having spent itself on the broad Mediterranean, now swung eastward to die above the Desert of Arabia.

"I wish that were Port Said," Joel said.

The Padre did not answer him. His back was turned to Joel, and the latter fell to musing on the freedom that now lay but a few hours ahead. He was anxious to stretch his legs on land after his long imprisonment. He had visions of himself climbing down the ship's ladder into an Arab boat, climbing out upon the float and up the steps at the landing wharf. He saw himself going through the streets, still brightly lighted by the open shops and cafés in spite of the late hour, pushing off the eternal guides and pedlars as he found his way to a table on the sidewalk.

Curious beggars, those pedlars, they never seemed to sleep. They were always on the spot whenever a ship came in, any hour of the day or night. They boarded her before the anchor was down, swarming

up her sides on grappling poles for all the world like a band of bloody
pirates. They pushed into every recess and sat squat-legged on the
deck while they spread out their wares in a neat array: all the junk
in the world—picture postcards, glass beads, amber beads, stone beads,
Turkish paste ("good for the stomach, mister!"), ivory elephants in a
procession of grandfather to great-grandson—all the junk in the
world, half of it made in Birmingham or Manchester and all of it
priced at ten times its real value (if any). But all of it, the bustle and
noise and confusion, was fascinating with novelty. It beat upon the
senses with the refreshing vigour of a showerbath! If the robbers didn't
get your money on the ship there was another horde waiting to
pester you when you stepped ashore, or to hover near your table on the
sidewalk trying to engage you in a bartering contest.

And the dirty little Arab tricksters with their abracadabra of "gilly-
gilly-gilly"; for twopence they'll "gilly-gilly" a baby chick or a
tumbler of water out of a mysterious nowhere, and for a shilling they
will "gilly-gilly" snakes or coloured balls in and out of boxes for half
an hour, while you sit at a table on the sidewalk in the early morning
hours and drink long, cold drinks of lime and gin, encouraging your
thirst with peanuts, chips, cheese, sandwiches—you and the tourist
from Oklahoma and the diamond merchant from Antwerp and the
dancing-girl from Paris and the Russian outcast and the P.C. going
home on leave—while the polyglot of Said dins in your ears. Said—
where every beggar in the streets is a facile linguist and every coin in
the world is legal tender—where the ships of the East pause for a few
short hours to coal or oil, and pay their Suez Canal fees.

The residents of Port Said walk up and down the breakwater past
M. de Lesseps' statue and watch the ships go by. They pride themselves on being able to identify the funnel-markings on every steamship line in the world and to name its nationality. The last is not so
difficult since more than fifty per cent of them fly the Union Jack.
The big and little ships come and go like blood corpuscles carrying the
raw materials to feed a thousand industries, or their finished products
to be metabolized by a civilized world; ships from Japan with silk,
pottery, matches, toys; and from China with eggs, beans, millet, cot-

ton, peanuts, more silk, and firecrackers; from Singapore and Penang with rubber, tin, copra, gums, and rice; and from Siam and Burma with teakwood with which to build more ships; from Colombo and Bombay with tea, coconut oil, jute, cotton, gunny-cloth, opium, and mail for the people back home; from Java and Sumatra with sugar, rubber, rice, and oil; and from South and East Africa with corn, wool, hides, diamonds, gold, ivory, sisal, cloves, and more coffee and tea—and back again laden with steel, machinery, railway engines, bicycles, automobiles, gramophones, cinema films, chemicals, high explosives, aeroplanes, guns; all the commerce between a billion people in the awakening East and a half-billion in mechanical Europe; between a restless, overcrowded East, eager to learn new ways, and an overcrowded Europe, eager to teach.

Thirty million tons of ships pass through the Canal each year, and more than half of them sail under one flag. In fact, more than half the ships of the world sail under that flag, and nine-tenths of them move under the ægis of two men who play them against each other like the pieces of a gigantic game of draughts. . . . M. de Lesseps was almost as far from seeing the consequences of his digging in the sand as was old King Necho who started the first canal four thousand years ago.

And the digging was far from finished, Joel noticed from an occasional suction-dredge along the bank. Here and there a track had been laid down so that the sand could be pulled by patient donkeys back into the desert. It was clear that the digging would never be over until the sand stopped blowing.

Joel tried to make out the hills where they rolled away into the desert on either side, but all that he could decipher were the outlines of those close to the shore. He gave it up with a shrug, thinking that they all looked alike anyway—a desolate monotony of shifting sand. Sand so fine that you have to look closely to see the minute black and white and red grains of it. It is stirred up by the wind and peppered against your face or twirled into whirling dervishes that skim joyously across the desert. It is piled up around your ankles in flowing stream-lines when you watch it, and when the wind is through with it, it is left in little ripples and big waves marching across the open spaces or in smooth, rounded hills, crescent-shaped as though their lee-sides had been scooped out with a big tablespoon. When the wind is through with it there are buried beneath it things which may never see the light again, plants and animals and the works of man. You can push your hand down into its soft substance to the elbow, to the shoulder, and not find the bottom. . . .

But the sand had not always been there—only recently a vast sea had covered this very land. The sea bottom had risen slowly until the Red Sea was separated from the Mediterranean; and the River Nile, carrying mud from the highlands of Abyssinia, had built out its great Delta to make the land of Egypt. The new land had become covered with a green forest of cycads, giant ferns, and equisetums, and peopled by bizarre animals; the steam-shovels while digging the Canal had unearthed their bones as they had fallen where they died, long before the sand had come. The sand was only a mantle of dust that had settled upon the earth during a quiet moment; upon an earth so sensitive that it sinks and rises with every tide or heavy rain, an earth so big that wrinkles upon its crust relatively less than the lines upon an orange could plunge the peak of Everest as far below the water as the deepest oceanic depth; an earth so restless that, in its ups and downs, cycle after cycle of life had swept across it—first below the sea for corals, worms, and trilobites and then above the sea for giant ferns and scorpions; then down again for armoured fishes and more worms and feathery sea-stars, then up for cryptogamous trees and reptiles—or perhaps only to be desert for a time before it plunged below the sea again. The broken, jagged hills, formed where the faulted crust pushed up through the Arabian sand, showed the record of that restlessness in layer after layer of limestones, sandstones, coal-beds, clays, marls, shales; if all the layers which have been washed away by wind and rain were still in place they would stand, perhaps, higher than the Himalayas. While the River Nile, which has flowed throughout the Time of Man, has laid down a mere hundred feet of mud. . . . Now the sand lay like a mantle over this buried past, covering alike the tracks of prehistoric monsters and the deserted temples of man. Man—who was always trying to conquer Nature, as though that were possible. He had dug a half-dozen canals in this very sand and, sooner or later, Nature had filled them up again. In the great panorama of time, permanence was but little more assured to man than to his footprints in the dust of that desert. . . .

Would he, Joel wondered, turn out to be a blind alley, too? The human species had already so over-populated the earth that competition and jealousy among its own numbers had led it to devise better and better means of self-destruction. Would its rapid evolution be accompanied by an equally rapid descent and extinction? Perhaps, and then the sand could blow back leisurely and cover the iron and mortar even as it had covered the stone temples of four thousand years ago—and, beneath them, the forests and swamps of prehistoric times.

v

A SUDDEN movement by the Padre made Joel look up. The Padre sat down cross-legged on the floor, resting his back against the bulwark.

"What's the matter, are you cold?" Joel asked him.

"No, no, I'm not cold. . . . Look here, I'm not satisfied with that explanation you put on your lung-fish. You called him an experiment that failed, a blind alley. Don't you think you are doing him an injustice?"

Joel did not know what to say, so he put his hands in his pockets, wrinkled his brows, and stared at his feet.

"What I mean is, I don't like this blind alley sort of thing. I don't care about your lung-fish—I never heard of him until you told me about him—but he seems to stand for a lot, doesn't he?

"I liked him immensely when you told me how he or his ancestors had been choked in the stagnant pools when the water dried up, and how through him life invented a new way of living, which widened its scope and increased its possibilities, by breathing air instead of water. He was magnificent then, a pioneer through which life had escaped from a threatening difficulty. But dash it all, man, when you leave him behind in the mud, when you call him a futile experiment, it seems like outright desertion! Doesn't he deserve something better than that?"

Joel laughed—not that he meant to give the Padre offence, but he began to see what was bothering him, to sense his perplexity over a Nature that could play such scurvy tricks.

"It means a great deal to me. I'm lost in seeing just how he fits into my scheme of things. I must interpret him—your lung-fish wallowing in the mud—and I don't like to see him called a futile experiment."

The Padre's expression, "I'm lost," brought back to Joel's mind another occasion when he had used the same words. It had been on an evening just out of Mombasa when they had been talking about the stars, the galaxies of stars that swing through the heavens at incomprehensible distances and incomprehensible speeds. "I get lost," he had said, "when I think of the magnitude of creation."

And there had been yet another time when Joel had lent him a recent best-seller. He had sat all day with his eyes glued to the pages of the novel, absorbed in its tale of passionate though unconventional love. He had handed it back with a smiling shake of his head and some cryptic remark about "modern moral confusion." Had he been lost in an emotional conflict stirred up by the book's carnal realism? . . . "Glad, happy places"—there it was again. Joel was beginning to suspect that after five years of Africa this man, who must have set out with such a high purpose, was beginning to challenge its wisdom. It seemed to Joel that his expression was more than rhetorical; it spoke of a doubt nibbling away at the roots of his faith in himself, in the universe, in the Ultimate Goodness of Things.

Now he was saying: "Evolution has always appealed to me. I can't understand why some people are thrown into such a panic about it. The Church, of course, being conservative, would stave it off as long as possible just as the medieval churchmen fought off the newer knowledge of astronomy. But we are not so near-sighted today. Anyway, to me this picture of life coming up to difficulties and surmounting them is magnificent! If the old Biblical poets had had the facts that we have they would have made equally magnificent poetry about them. But, somehow, it doesn't seem right to mar its magnificent character by putting in futile mistakes and deserting the failures, now does it?"

"It may mar its magnificence for you, Padre, but it is a cold, hard fact. My lung-fish is not the only mistake that has been made in evolution. The road is littered with them. I think that perhaps you see evolution as a concerted movement on the part of life toward some exalted and predetermined goal, some far-off crowning pinnacle. But all the evidence is against such a view.

"There is no goal to the evolution of life, there is no maintained direction. Its progression simply follows a haphazard course more or less directed by its environment at the moment. The whole progressive idea is purely an illusion that comes from looking at only one part of life's history. The only time when we can properly speak of evolution as being upward is in those instances where the theatre of life's activity has been enlarged, where some new acquisition or way of living permits the animal to move about more freely and independently within the circumscriptions of its environment. The evolution of lungs was upward in this sense, and so was the evolution of legs with which to crawl about the land and of wings with which to fly, and of warm-bloodedness to keep the animal warm and active throughout the winter. But all of these changes are upward only in relation to the particular time and conditions of life under which the animals which shared them lived. They are not always upward in the long run for they may actually prove to be a handicap under new conditions, or in relation to other evolutionary developments.

"Take the evolution of wings by the birds for example: in spite of its immediate value and its brilliant promise it was a limited advance, for looking backward we can see that the birds have sacrificed their forelimbs to a restricted purpose and thereby cut themselves off from the tremendous power that these members might otherwise have acquired. To soar through the air appears to be full of poetic promise, but from the point of view of man with his two marvellous creative hands, a bird's life is only a little better than that of a lung-fish. Wings are, from that point of view, a blind alley and it does not seem possible that the birds can ever escape from it to a better way of living. Some day they may go under like the lung-fish because they chose the wrong road.

"The course of evolution is full of monstrous and absurd beasts so erratically fashioned that they proved to be their own undoing. Animals have repeatedly gone off in the direction of specializing some part of themselves until they have reduced the thing to futile absurdity. Some of the dinosaurs got bigger and bigger until their size became an outright handicap; the elephant, the hippopotamus, the gorilla are going the same way. The tusks, the horns, the teeth, the jaws on many animals have become so specialized that they bind these animals down to living a very limited kind of life. Many adaptations start out by being useful but end up through excessive development in being a disadvantage. It is so common to find excessive specialization just preceding the extermination of a race that one comes to associate them together, and to accept the one as a sign of senescence presaging the other. The highly specialized animal is reaching the end of his blind alley.

"Then, too, the new inventions of one day may be carelessly thrown away in the next: the lung that was so precious to the Devonian fishes is not needed in the stable waters of today and so most fishes have discarded it entirely, or converted it into an airtight swim-bladder. But should the world become arid again, these fishes, at least on the continents, would find themselves back where they were in the Devonian, suffocating in the mud and unable to save themselves. The legs that first purchased freedom on the land have been discarded by many animals because, right now, they can get along without them. The whales have gone back into an aquatic prison and undone the work of two hundred million years; now they are no better off, except for being warm-blooded, than the average fish so far behind them on the evolutionary road. Animals have thrown away their eyes, their teeth, their bones, their power of movement, even their power to live a free and independent life! The whole realm of parasites, which are drawn from almost every branch of the vegetable and animal kingdoms, is a story of this degeneration.

"No, evolution is not all upward. It is only life flowing on through new forms, trying new ways of living, experimenting on an inconceivably varied scale. And for no purpose and with no meaning except that it wants to go on living. As we look back through the ages we can see that the circle of organic freedom has widened here or narrowed there as one branch or another has enjoyed new freedom in its separate time and place; but the upward phases are but infrequent, marked eruptions above the common level of flux and change. A line connecting them would zigzag along first one branch and then another. There is no sustained movement toward a special end, only an occasional carrying-over by some minor branch of the gains of one era to the potential victors of the next. It is this occasional and essentially haphazard carrying-over that has led to the increased freedom of the higher animals—the fishes, the amphibians, the reptiles, the birds, the mammals—and not a maintained, progressive movement. The only purpose of evolution is that life shall go on living in spite of all the obstacles that tend to put it down.

"Right there is its cardinal, most important feature: the stream of life tends always to persist, to carry on; except that now and then, for reasons that we do not understand, it changes its course into some new way of living. It gets around obstacles by diversifying itself. It is out of the fact that it has changed its way of living so many times— and met so many obstacles—that it has come to be so diversified, that some branches of the stream have come into such great freedom, and that other branches have come only into blind alleys. But if it could speak it could truthfully say, 'I am what the obstacles that I have met have made me.'

"The quickened moments of evolution almost always coincide with great geological upheavals and climatic change. The climate of the earth has oscillated between extremes of heat and cold, of aridity and humidity. It is because of these oscillations that life has been moulded into the swift-swimming fish, the air-breathing amphibian, the arid-living reptile, the warm-blooded bird and mammal, and into dexterous, quick-witted man. The story of life is the story of a vast battle between its wish to go on living and its ever-changing, infinitely complex environment.

"We don't know yet how life comes to change its way of living; whether it is by responsive and more or less permanent adaptations, or by the spontaneous variations in its way of living that we call mutations. But in either case Darwin's scimitar of selection, to mix the metaphor, still trims the stream and permits only some branches to flow freely on, while in time it cuts the others off; in either case the final animal, be it bird or beast or worm, is incidental—merely one of the many products which have been carved from this mutable organic stream. And in either case blind alleys are inevitable."

The Padre studied the floor between his feet for several minutes. When he looked up his face was wrinkled by perplexed interrogation.

"You mean that man is nothing more than one of the incidental products of this stream of life?"

"Certainly," Joel answered. "There is no evidence that evolution was intended solely to produce him. He is but one of its many products, not so much higher or lower than the rest, as just—more free. Nor is he the last—the stream of life has long since flowed on past him. He is neither so recent a product as the horse nor so highly specialized, in respect to the general characters of the common mammalian stem, as the sea-cow."

The Padre interrupted:

"But just a minute—when you come to man you must admit that there is something that resides in him, and in him alone, that sets him apart from all the rest of the animal world. Something unique, more valuable, more precious. I grant you the evolution of man's mortal frame, but you must grant me that he is set apart from this stream of life that has produced him by some Spirit; by some quality that savours of Divinity, a spark of Divinity put into him along the road from beast to man. I don't know how I know it, but I know it's there! When I look at the infinite stars, at the infinitesimal atoms, when I look back over the course of your stream of life, then I am surest of myself. It is my special Inspiration. It makes me lift up my head in joy, in faith!"

Joel pondered over the Padre's remark. The force, the very tone of his voice carried his meaning better than his words. He was revealing himself now, disclosing the faith that was in him; a faith in a Spirit that transcended the mortal frame. He was not going to give it up easily, if at all, for to forfeit it was to let himself down into a pit of darkness in which there was no hope, only the chaos of a foul creation, the emptiness of a mortal flesh, both destined to become putrid with decay. His faith was in a Spirit that illumined the world and man with meaning, with an ultimate value and with a personal significance. His faith was in a Spirit that transcended all experience, all reality, to have its being in some Perfection for which the finite world was but a means to a greater end, a vessel to hold for a short day an infinitely more precious content. That faith had been bred into him and nurtured into strength and still more strength. Was it so strong that it must swing an entire universe around his head and bring it into some special orientation with himself that was contrary to all fact? If so, the internal luminescence of it would blind him to its artificial nature; if not, then the truth would surely find its weakness out.

He did not like to be called a beast, Joel saw. . . . Was man a beast? The Church had long ago said yes. Cursed by original sin, born in corruption, how could he be saved except by Redemption? The doctrine of Infant Damnation and the hope of Salvation were the answers which the Holy Fathers had sent back. In the old Jewish legend man was fallen from Grace; then a Saviour held down a hand to the grave to lift him back to his High Estate. . . .

It was man's cry against the terrifying world about him, against the awfulness of nature, against the futility of life.

"No, Padre, we are only beasts. . . . It's strange how we consider ourselves the centre of the universe. The old boys used to think that the sun went around the earth, that the stars went around the earth, that everything went around the earth. They had difficulties making their geocentric system jibe with the observed movements of the heavenly bodies, so they got around their difficulties by compounding these movements out of cycles and epicycles and epi-epicycles. Copernicus showed them how simple it was, but when he took his figures to them they talked some metaphysical nonsense about the Perfect Nature of a Circle! Galileo made a telescope and found some irregularities on the Moon which he said were mountains, and some satellites around Jupiter which he said confirmed the Copernican theory; but he was damned for a heretic because everybody knew that the Moon must be a Perfect Body, and the Copernican doctrine had already been pronounced contrary to the Best Belief.

"Copernicus and Galileo and Newton did finally get us out of that metaphysical morass; but, you know, they didn't do much for us in a spiritual way. We still think that we are the centre of the universe; we still cling to a life-centred and a man-centred philosophy that is as artificial as the geocentric astronomy of the Middle Ages. We look upon the peculiar fact that the earth is placed a bit off-centre among the stars as due, perhaps, to some fanciful whim of the Creator.

"When we look about us we say, 'What a magnificent universe this is we live in! Aren't we important?' Every time a new star is discovered or a few million miles are added to the stellar spaces we expand accordingly. We see the universe around us as a frame for ourselves, and the bigger the frame the bigger the picture!

"It is man's colossal conceit! And when he sees that it does not jibe with the cold, hard facts of life and the universe around him, he rationalizes himself out of his insuperable difficulties by talking about the Redemption of the Spirit. . . .

"We are beasts, right along with the other flesh-and-blood beasts, one branch of the stream of life. We have not all the pages of the record, but we have enough of it to read the story: an unbroken stream from beast to man, life flowing on from one beast to another, changing its ways of living, getting around obstacles, first beast, then less beast, then more man. A beast more erect, with a larger cranium, less hair, shorter appendix, higher nose-bridge, higher forehead, sharper wits. Right there is the difference that sets him farthest apart from the other animals—his brain. There is his own unique and priceless specialty, a mass of nerve cells developed beyond any parallel in the animal king-

dom! He has gone in for specializing that particular organ in preference to teeth or skin or bones. But the difference which it makes is not
fundamental—it is only one of degree. . . .

"One wonders what terrific environmental pressure or what happy
accident started that brain of his on its race to leave every other
brain behind. There is no doubt that his hands have played a large
part in its extraordinary development. If there is anything divine in
man, it is that his front paws were liberated at some remote time to
the freedom which lets them clutch, carry, feel, measure, compare! Or
it is the happy accident that drove him to use them in that manner.
Perhaps he was driven by some emergency, some crowding danger
that threatened his existence to use first one and then both paws, trying, shaping, making, doing, feeling; and his paws became hands
and his brain was forced to grow to care for this vast wealth of
sensory and motor experience; and as his brain grew his hands were
there to serve it, whereupon they brought it new knowledge . . . and
so the cycle sped on, faster and faster, until his brain grew into the
colossal, complex organ which it is. All his art, his science, his philosophy, all his variegated activity must go back to these"—Joel held
out his hands before him and wiggled his fingers in slow rhythms—
"and to the fortunate combination of circumstances that permitted
him, or forced him, through manual experience and manual experiment, to develop his wits.

"One imagines that perhaps he lived in a forest extending far north
into the plateaux of Asia, a semi-tropical forest with a steady climate
the year round. He walked more or less upright with the aid of his
hands and lived by picking berries or fruits from the bushes or trees.
He had a family life of sorts, keeping his young with him so that they
had an opportunity to learn by example some of the cunning acquired by their elders. But Nature began to drive—the air grew colder
and food grew scarcer and he was forced to leave his familiar forests
and to migrate into open grasslands where he had to walk unaided
by his hands. Perhaps there were no fruits or berries or sheltering trees
and he had to tear up the grasses and grub among their roots for food,
and to pile the stems about him to keep off the wind at night. Travel

has a broadening influence: when he got hungry and his berries and fruits were gone he learned to catch the little field-mice that hid among the roots. He learned to kill the field-mice with a stick as they scurried out beneath his fumbling paws. He learned how to throw stones at them and how to match his wits against their cunning. Field-mice are fleet creatures and it takes quickness and dexterity to catch them. But our man had the advantage of standing on his hind legs, and of being able to pick up a stick or a stone in his forepaws. And there was always the family; his children were by him and they had the invaluable opportunity to learn in a few days what he had found out by months or years of experience.

"Oh, that's just a picture! We don't know yet just how it happened, but some day we will. Our vision is obscured by distance, but it is penetrating that mist as Galileo's did when he first saw the mountains on the Moon through his hand-made telescope.

"But we can be sure that it is by these hands and the brain above them that man has come into his vast freedom. He has literally taken the world with them, both because he had them to use and because he had to use them. . . .

"But is the cycle of brains and hands coming to an end? Animals appear to evolve so far and then to stop. Man has changed very little in the past twenty thousand years, except in some minor details of hair and teeth. After the marked physical changes that transformed him from his pre-human ancestors, his bodily evolution appears to have slowed down, or to have stopped completely. It is doubtful if his intellectual evolution has not stopped in the same way. Of course, he has been accumulating, year after year, a greater store of knowledge which has given him a greater command of Nature and himself. But is this enough? The accumulation of knowledge is a different thing from the capacity to use it, and there are many who claim that, in this respect, modern man is already a degenerate creature. One has only to look at his mental inertia, his destructive wars, his economic instability, his innate prejudice, his blind subservience to religion, his stupid politics, his dead resistance to changing his way of living, to wonder if he has reached his own blind alley. . . . Someone has cynically said that one of the marvels of Nature is the resistance which the human brain offers to the introduction of knowledge. One wonders that it got as far it did. For it works by repetitional rutting, and it sticks to its ruts until it is forcibly ejected. Its first concern is always with itself, and its greatest achievement is the profuse invention of labour-saving devices. Its highest aspiration is a Heaven where there are no clothes to put on, and no exercise more strenuous than playing a harp! It is, like every other manifestation of life, intrinsically conservative; it travels in a straight line until it is forcibly deflected from its course. It appears to be headed for the same fate that overtook the dinosaurs, too specialized in one direction and too rigid in form and function to meet the dangers of another day.

"Right now we have the run of things because our hands and our wits can work for us. But let some new set of environmental conditions arise: let there come some new and devastating plague, or let the earth grow cold or hot or humid—all within the range of reason—and would our hands and wits suffice us? Perhaps . . .

"Oh, yes, by our standards we are very superior creatures! But it is probable that the mighty dinosaurs who lorded it over the Jurassic forests felt the same way as they uprooted the cycads and equisetums and trampled upon the little timid mammals that scurried among their roots. Someone has suggested that the dinosaurs were exterminated because these little mammals ate up all the dinosaur eggs! In any case, the dinosaurs are gone and a biped descendant of the creatures they despised now reigns. . . .

"It is very difficult to see ahead: I boast about these hands of ours, but how can I know that in gaining them we have not cut ourselves off from some powerful sense that is not yet evolved, a sense that could penetrate the mysteries of Nature that perplex us and lift us right out of this world and into another as lungs lifted the Devonian fishes on to the land? A sense that, perhaps, is even now being evolved from the rudimentary forelimbs of some primitive mammal in an obscure corner of Africa? Absurd? . . . The birds cut themselves off from hands by taking wings. . . . Man has been a rational creature for only a few thousand years, while the flow of life by evolution must be measured

in hundreds of millions! Life may be breaking out through some obscure stream right now into a superior kind of animal, a superior way
of living, and we would never know it!

"No, Padre. By the standards of the vast river of life that has
produced us we are but a super-intelligent mammal momentarily over-
running the globe and setting all manner of things upon it into whirling, confusing motions; creating our own criteria of superiority, creating our own far-off Divine Events, our own Divinities—to serve our
ends."

V I

THE Padre rose and, resting his arms upon the bulwarks, remained
silent as though contemplating the beauty of the night. His back was
turned toward Joel, who noted again his excellent physique. His broad
flat shoulders were like those of some idealized sculpture and the
profile of his half-turned head might have been a marble statue seen in
the faint starlight. Joel thought about him as a specimen of the tall,
broad-shouldered, long-headed type that had been bred within recent
times out of the Anglo-Saxon stock. He seemed wrapped up in his
own thoughts, so Joel kept silent. He wondered if he had offended
him; he certainly had not meant to. There were certain facts from
which all reasoning, all belief, must start. The essential thing was to
have all the facts in hand, then each man could take his own interpretation. The Padre was not the kind of man to shudder at these facts,
or to be easily shaken from his self-appointed course.

Joel got up and noted that the ship was again moving along the
narrow Canal which stretched away into the darkness like a black
ribbon. Occasionally they passed a dredge tied up for the night, or a
few trees near a fresh-water well, but mostly there was only desert and
that black ribbon stretching away, illuminated right ahead by the
searchlight fixed upon the bow.

Once they passed close to one of the signal stations whose duty it is
to marshal into orderly procession the ships that pass from sea to sea.
This one was a small white house set so close to the water's edge that

it came into the glare of the bow-light. One could look down upon its red-tiled roof from the towering ship. A few date-palms and a small patch of grass around it afforded relief from the monotony of sand. A light, which from afar Joel had mistaken for a star, was swinging from a pole rigged like a ship's mast and set close to the water. Joel wondered what determined the right of way, for, when two ships passed, one had to tie up to the shore. He had heard that warships took precedence over everything else, and then ships bearing petrol or explosives. The latter were obviously a danger to the Canal, but it was very annoying to be on a supposedly fast mail-liner and to be shouldered aside by every oil-tramp that came along. The passage through the Canal took long enough, for that matter—from twelve hours upward according to the amount of traffic. No ship was allowed to proceed faster than six miles an hour. They had to proceed with "extreme caution," and, moreover, the wash at any greater speed would raise havoc with the sandy shore. The infernal sand was always caving in, and on either side there was a never-ending stream coming out of Arabia or Africa to keep up the supply. Two billowing seas of sandy desert. Here and there was a close-set picket fence, running parallel with the Canal, which had been set up to keep the sand back.

You were always either fighting inanimate Nature, Joel thought, or you were fighting other kinds of life. Fighting not because you wanted to, but because you had to, to keep alive! Life fighting for life against the wind, the sand, the water, against every other living thing. That was the only purpose that one could find in any living thing—that was the first law of animate Nature—life fighting for life. . . .

Joel tried to reconstruct a scene against the darkness of the night: there is a big tree too large to encircle with your arms, a smooth, grey-green tree that runs up four or five times your height before it disappears into a dense roof of leaves. At its base it has great sloping buttresses that hold it upright in the soft soil; they remind you of the ribs left in a bank of earth worn down by rain-water. You can stand in the angle between two buttresses which come up to your shoulder, and lean with your back against the tree between them. When you close your hand over their rounded edges they are like the arms of a great chair. The bark is cool and hard and covered with crisp grey lichens which scrape off beneath your fingers. Those buttresses—their slope, their rounded edges, their thickness between your fingers, suggest some living thing frozen into temporary immobility.

Leaning back against the tree you can look up at the green roof above you. It is a dense mat of branches and leaves intricately tangled and interwoven, so dense that the light just filters through it. That is why it is so dark around you. But when you look closer you see that those leaves are not the leaves of your tree but the leaves of plants that are growing upon its branches, countless creeping, climbing plants that hang down in a twisted, tangled canopy, plants that have climbed up and up to get the light. Behind your back is the stalk of one of them, a stalk nearly as big as your wrist that twists upon itself like a corkscrew as it runs up the trunk to disappear into the tangle of leaves. The stalk does not appear to be fastened to the trunk but you cannot budge it, you cannot pull it away far enough to slip your fingers under it. Beside it is another creeper-stalk, a small brown stem that zigzags back and forth in sharp angles up the trunk; at every zigzag it puts out a filament which ends in a little brown pad. When you tear the stalk away the filaments break off, leaving the pads adhering to the bark.

You cannot see the branches of your tree at all, so dense are the plants hanging from them. Some of them, born of a seed lodged in a crack and wanting soil, drop their aerial roots down to the ground where they dig themselves into the earth. The roots twist and turn as they come down and wind themselves around everything they touch, like snakes; and they dig themselves into the earth so far that you cannot pull them out, no matter how hard you try.

But some of the plants over your head seem to be growing out of the trunk of the tree itself. High up, there is a green fern which has a mass of brown roots adhering to the bark, and which spreads out its big fronds into a fan that is wider than a man's reach. The fronds have an intricate lace-like pattern that is everywhere the same except at the tips where a fuzzy grey bud is uncurling itself in an opening spiral. They seem to go on uncurling and uncurling—there is not one frond that is not uncurling at the tip. The pale-green fern is lovely against the dark-green leaves above it. Next to it on a dead branch there is a gigantic plant—a mass of stems and leaves that must weigh five hundred pounds. It is an orchid from which there drops through the shadows a shower of pale-pink flowers, hundreds and hundreds of them, strung along a slender stem alternately with pale-green, heart-shaped leaves. It is a marvel that so large a plant can hang on to the smooth, hard bark. Back in a recess there is another flower, a white waxy blossom with a golden centre; as your eyes take in its shadowy features you discover a big dragonfly whose almost invisible wings are faintly outlined against a curving petal. The white blossom is growing upon a swinging root that is itself hanging from your tree. . . . One thing growing upon another, hanging on. . . . There is no wind and everything is perfectly still . . . and everything is silent; there is not a sound except your own heart beating in your ears.

Right beside your face there is a flat green rope which hangs down from above; its edges are armed with spikes as long as your finger and sharpened on both sides, sharpened like a razor. If you were to move your head against it, it would cut a deep gash in your cheek. All around you there are swinging stems armed with sharp thorns. Even the leaves on the bushes have saw-tooth edges—everything is armed! You are surrounded by a wall of trees, giant ferns, and bushes that are bound into a solid mass by creepers that climb in and out, and everything has a cruel, cutting edge. You are imprisoned by a vicious vegetation through which no soft-skinned animal could make its way . . . and you are standing in water, for the moss beneath your feet has let you down until the green, scummy liquid has crept up around your ankles. There is treacherous green moss everywhere and there is not a dry place to which you can move—unless you pull yourself up against the buttresses of your tree and hang on. . . . It is hot, insufferably hot; so hot that the sweat runs down your face and the stifling air makes you sick and faint.

There is a sound in the dense bushes—they rustle as they are pushed aside and the twigs lying on the ground snap as they are crushed underfoot by some heavy animal. A small blunt head is thrust upward into an open space—it has round, shiny eyes and black holes where there should be ears—but it is lowered again quickly as the animal comes on toward the clearing. Behind the head is an incredibly long neck and a massive body from which the tail tapers off and runs back thirty or forty feet where it drags upon the ground. . . . You have seen that animal before, somewhere. . . . It comes on through the bushes with a slow, lumbering step, and with its head held low so as to dodge the branches; and every few steps it raises its head in a quick darting movement to look about it. Once it opens its mouth slightly and you see a red, sharply pointed tongue move up and down between its lips. When the beast reaches the clearing around your tree it straightens up and the head and neck tower to twice the height of your body. It takes a quick look to either side and, after a moment of immobility, it begins to nibble at the leaves around your head. Suddenly it shifts its weight and turns sidewise in its ardour to reach some tender shoot, and as the massive tail moves around through a half-circle the bushes and small trees are bent over and crushed as though they were fragile flowers. The beast rises slightly on its hind legs, throwing its tremendous weight on to its thick tail, and rests its fore-limbs lightly against a nearby buttress. The legs are short and stumpy and sheathed in loose folds of skin and the toes are armed with sharp claws. You can see now that the skin is covered with scales which make a faint design of diamonds, like the skin of a snake, and as the big neck moves from side to side the diamonds become stretched and twisted and the scales make a faint sound like the rustle of dry paper. You lay your hand upon the shoulder nearest you and it is cold . . . very cold. . . .

The Padre's voice suddenly broke in upon Joel's reverie.

"But that would be a denial of all our spiritual values, if we are only beasts, only better than the rest by a modicum of intelligence."

Joel's eyes lingered for a moment on the undulating sand-hills: no, that was an anachronism, he thought, for that beast had been extinct a long time before those flower-bearing plants had been evolved. He looked around. The Padre was still leaning on the bulwark, his back turned toward Joel, and he turned his head slightly as he went on speaking.

"Look here—when the cave-man first drew a crude picture of a mammoth upon the wall of his cave he was giving expression to some impulse, some emergent or ascendant force that was more than the simple sum of his experience. He was at that moment different from his ancestors—something had been born, put into him!

"It is the same with his concept of Divinity, his striving for some ideal far above himself. This concept of Divinity has hovered about him, run through the fabric of his life, ever since we have had a record of his thoughts. I admit that it is variously coloured by his local time and nature, but it is always there, and its persistence must have some significance.

"You must admit that it is from his spiritual sense that man has gotten the best that is in him. Through it there has come to him his moral consciousness—man's special blessing. Through it there has been revealed to him a special knowledge; there are more spiritual values in the simple teachings of Jesus than in all the accumulated experiences of mankind before him, spiritual truths that were so far advanced of His time that after two thousand years we are still studying them, emulating them; but not improving upon them. There is nothing bestial about the Golden Rule!

"I'll take your science as a record of the flesh, but you cannot take away from me my inner being, my bit of personal inspiration, that turns itself toward a spiritual standard that is far above me—like a magnet toward an unseen Pole." The Padre turned abruptly. "In that I am a man and not a beast!"

Several moments passed before Joel made any answer. Then he shook his head: "Your cave-man," he said, "is the key to the whole question. Without him we would be lost, but with him we can find our way. You have to understand that brain of his."

Joel had taken a metal key-ring out of his pocket and he was turning it between his fingers in an absent-minded way. His eyes rested on this trinket as he went on speaking:

"His brain worked in a quite simple fashion. On one side, so to

speak, there was a storehouse where he could keep the sensory pictures
—sights, smells, sounds, touch—of the world about him, and on the
other side there was a delivery room where he could send out orders
to his muscles for action; in the middle there was a clearing-house
where he could sort everything out and size it up. All his life this
brain of his was busy collecting sensory information in the one side,
correlating that information in the central clearing-house, and acting
upon the final product in the other. When he saw a mango, he ate it;
when he saw a stick, he passed it by; but when he saw a mammoth,
he ran!

"But there was yet another part to his brain, a fourth part which
we can call his emotional sounding-board. It was just as important as
the other three. Whenever any sensory picture came to his brain it
passed, on its way to the clearing-house, across this sounding-board
where it evoked some typical emotional reaction which was itself delivered to the clearing-house simultaneously with the original sensory
picture. Thus the final sensory image consisted of a picture of the object coloured by the man's emotional reaction to that object. The
mango evoked in him a sensation of delight mingled, perhaps, with
hunger pains and a desire to have it; the stick produced no emotional
response, while the mammoth filled him with awe and fear. He did
not see hunger pains in the mango or awe and fear in the mammoth
—these sensations were born entirely within him by resonance from
his emotional sounding-board at the base of his brain. Yet, to him, they
were just as real and just as much a part of the picture as the colour
and size of the mango or the length of the mammoth's tusks.

"That sounding-board was a very old part of his brain. The general
pattern of it had been laid down in his ancestors back in bygone ages.
So, also, had its motor connexions, and for this reason the general
emotional pattern and the typical emotional responses were much the
same in all men, and relatively invariable. But the specific connexions
between the sounding-board and the sensory paths to his brain were
mostly left unattached, so that each man was free to plug them in with
the sensory pictures from the world about him according to his individual experience. As his experience widened, more and more objects

came to evoke some typical emotional response, and he came to classify the world more or less in terms of his emotional reactions: good things and bad things, pleasant and unpleasant, beautiful and ugly, indifferent and awful.

"That sounding-board played a very important part in his life. Its purpose was to reinforce the cold sensory image, to make it more vivid and to give it some personal, sensual colour; to give outside things a purpose, a meaning in his eyes. To meet his need it put delight in the mango; to meet his danger it put awe in the mammoth. It made the world significant—for himself.

"On the other hand it did things for him which thinking could not do. It was capable of calling forth in moments of anger or fright reserves of energy from his heart and tired muscles that his brain could never command. In emergencies when life was threatened it took charge of his brain even against his will and sent his body into quick action which he himself could not afterward understand. In a primitive way its pattern was laid down in such a manner as to safeguard him individually, and to safeguard the race, from annihilation. Secondarily, it was the driving force that motivated his every move and directed his conduct every hour. It was the real spirit of his life.

"It sent him out to find a mate, dark or fair, brown eyes or blue. It set him to catching animals that he might clothe and feed her, and to guarding her from the dangers that beset them both. It built up his family, his tribal life, his inter-tribal warfare. It set him to watching the world around him with curious eyes, and to feeling, wondering, thinking. . . .

"Such was the nature of your cave-man's brain when he first saw a mammoth.

"Probably his experience with these creatures was such that when he saw one of them he was filled with fear: his breath stopped, his heart beat faster and thumped against his chest, his pulse throbbed in his temples, his knees shook under him, his mouth went dry, and he broke out in a cold sweat. But as soon as he recovered he ran back to his cave where he began to think about the awful creature, trying to fit it into its proper place in his life. . . . Little by little it slipped into the background of his thoughts, but he never really forgot it because its image seemed to lurk in the shadows and to hide around corners, and the memory of it, and of his fear, guided his footsteps through the dark jungles and coloured his fireside tales.

"Then there came a day when, while scratching around with a sharp pointed rock, he accidentally put some lines together so that they looked like a mammoth. The trick filled him with excitement, so he tried it again and again until he had a presentable picture. Perhaps it took him five thousand years, or perhaps it only took him five minutes, but in either case he was merely extending the combinations within his brain by varying the association paths between its sensory and motor connexions. When he transposed the imagery of his senses into a crude picture of the original he was only sublimating his experience into a new form of behaviour—drawing instead of running. The one was perhaps more effete, but it was, no more inspired. And his emotional stimulus was behind both of them.

"Ultimately he began to draw other kinds of pictures. There were many mammoths in his life: birth, death, misfortune, hope and despair, thunder and lightning—things that played just as large a part in his life as real mammoths had ever played, and about which he knew even less. He could not draw them upon the wall of his cave because they had no lineal character, but as his artistic ability improved he learned to draw abstract conceptions of them, interpretations, explanations. These imaginary pictures were rougher, cruder even, than his scratches on stone, because that sounding-board of his exaggerated or distorted everything; its incessant rumbling made it difficult for him to see things clearly or to think about them straight. When he thought about the world at all he had to interpret not only its own complex features but also this maze of joy, sorrow, fear, hope, despair, desire, anger, love, awe, through which he saw it. In order to think along the shortest distance in a straight line he had first to penetrate his own emotional confusion. He had to stop to think—he had to stop the rumble of that archaic sounding-board which had come down to him through the ages, in order to hear his own thoughts. The trouble was, he did not often do it. From the beginning he felt first, and thought afterwards. . . .

"Primitive man was born in a dark jungle of supernaturalism, and only little by little has he built himself a home in the sunny fields of reality. I admit that he found some magnificent spiritual values, as you call them, while he was lost in that supernatural jungle, but I deny that they were the fruit of its vegetation. They were, like the jungle itself, the fruit of his own imagination.

"Possibly the greatest of these is his discovery of himself—of self-appraisal. But there is nothing of Inspiration or Revelation in it; it is merely a new mode of cerebration, like drawing the picture of the mammoth, or like arithmetic, logic, or relativity. Man's appreciation of the Golden Rule came by experience, contemplation, and discovery, just as did his appreciation of the laws of gravity. The one waited for a Jesus to formulate it in words and the other waited for a Newton. The spiritual appreciation of Jesus far transcended that of the men about him, but so did the physical appreciation of Newton. There was behind each a vast accumulation of experience waiting for an interpreter. . . . And behind each there was the cave-man's emotional urge.

"When you lay claim to a personal inspiration that turns you toward a spiritual goal, it is not an inspiration at all, but an expiration from that emotional sounding-board of yours modulated by your nativity, your culture, your experience. When the passive and indifferent wind of living plays upon you, you are set into reverberation and give out a certain tune. There are many different kinds of men in the world, as many different kinds as there are mothers to bear them and experiences to make them, and in the same wind each gives out a different tune.

"For that old sounding-board of man's has not lost any of its vibrant quality with time; and it still furnishes him with most of his driving power to go through life. He has learned, a little, how to put his will upon its chords, how to still its reverberations so that he can think; but, being what he is, he needs, he must have emotional exercise lest his spirit atrophy and fade away. Now that he no longer gets it from a cave-man's life he turns to other sources—to music, drama, literature, and art. He loves it—he loves to have that sounding-board struck into reverberation, to have it pounded upon until its music jingles in his ears and tingles in his toes—and it is well that he should if for no other reason than that through this exercise he will come into a better understanding of himself. As yet, however, he is still your cave-man, squatting on his haunches and bewitched by his picture on the wall. . . . The Sacred Soul of Man—the Devil that lives in the mammoth! He would have awakened to the absurdity of it long ago were it not for his emotional confusion; he still cannot see himself except through the raptures of his body! But perhaps as time goes on he will learn the nature of those raptures, and his vision of himself will clear.

"But he is old enough now to throw away his Inspiration, Revelation, Special Providence, and all the rest of his cave-man's pictures, and to put himself back into his proper place in Nature, back among the beasts, the birds, the flowers. He is old enough to see himself as he really is—a mammal among mammals, fighting the same fight as all the rest. He is old enough to know that in the years to come he may be crowded out like the prehistoric monsters of the past, while life breaks out in some ascendant form that is better fitted to survive. . . .

"If he wishes to know where life begins and ends, then he must study it, see how it works and what it is. Perhaps the perfect knowledge will not come to him until he has evolved some superhuman sense, some novel way of living; or perhaps it waits only for the discovery of some new mode of cerebration, like your picture-boy. Or it may never come to him, for the stream of life may shift to some other bed before that time, and leave him a blind alley."

VII

Joel tossed the key-ring with which he was playing into the air, and thrust it back into his pocket. He turned to the bulwark and leaned over to watch the series of smooth waves that marched alongside at the foot of the steep prow.

"What a pessimist you are, Joel!"

The Padre squirmed himself into a more comfortable position, half on his back.

"You *are* discouraging. But I still think there is some loophole in your mechanistic doctrine through which I can escape to a more satisfying philosophy. Life and evolution must have some meaning for me as well as for you, but as you interpret it, it is meaningless.

"Even if I grant that my emotional instincts are—what shall I say, animalistic reactions?—and therefore unworthy of an ultimate appeal I still am not satisfied on the grounds of pure reason with your explanation of things. Beyond the realm of the phenomena which we can see and measure, behind the whole process of evolution and within the warm pulse of life itself, there lingers an Unknown which neither you nor I nor any man can ever fully comprehend. You as a scientist have your attention fixed upon the known while I, being what my sounding-board has made me, would turn my eyes toward that more distant horizon.

"I cannot remain content with a philosophy that is out of step with life; I want to go along with life and understand it, to live as much of it as I can. The scientific spirit is one aspect of life which has proved its worth, both pragmatically and intellectually—yes, and æsthetically, too. There is grandeur and beauty in your scientific saga as in the Psalms of David—I love them both. I am a man of two parts: a man of faith and a man of action. It is not enough for me to say, 'God made it thus'; for I must always ask myself, 'Do I see it as God made it?' So I would step closer and obtain a nearer vision of the Unseen by treading the path of reason, by walking along with you. . . .

"At night, after the African drum which does duty for a church bell has rolled out its summons to prayers, I ponder on it; when the village is safely asleep under the heavy-eyed and misty stars and there is no sound except the incessant whirring of cicadas or the occasional bark of a stray ape up to some mischief in the maize, I walk among the acacias with evolution in one hand and astronomy in the other. I am lost, not in a web of emotional confusion, but in the sheer tangle of my reason trying to put them all together and to make them fit into a coherent whole. I go from a theory of Special Creation to one of Evolution without finding any that satisfies me, and without finding a God Who is compatible with either. . . . What you say about man is true, he is a beast; and life is filled each day, as throughout its evolution, with pitfalls, with blind alleys. The bitter cruelty of man, the hardness of his lot, his hapless fate, are difficult to reconcile with the smooth orbits of the stars, the geometry of a crystal. Life alone seems to be devoid of order. Only in us is God incomprehensible . . . but surely He has not so hidden His countenance that we cannot obtain some little light to guide our steps. . . . I do not ask to know the ultimate beginnings and the ultimate end of life, but only how to find the open road. . . . Which way, O Life, shall I turn now?"

"I cannot help you." Joel turned back from the water. "Isn't it said that you can only find God by faith alone? . . . Modern science cannot take you any nearer your unseen horizon than could the science of ancient Greece or Babylonia. Some scientists think that it can, but they are only fooling themselves. Scientific knowledge comprises the world of the known and the knowable, and hypotheses based upon the known are scientific hypotheses; the validity of science and its hypotheses rest upon the proof by correspondence with reality. Beyond these there is only the great vacuity of the unknown, and science cannot stop you, and fundamentally is not interested, if you as a man of faith or as a philosopher wish to jump off into that vacuity; except to say that there is nothing in history to indicate that you will accomplish anything by doing so. . . . Special Creation is as good a doctrine to jump into as any other, for all those who would instil something into matter in order to make life are only Special Creationists squeezed out of shape by trying to square themselves with experience. Whenever they come to a tempting gap in our knowledge—whether it be vital spirits and animal heat or the limitations of physical measurement— they put their fingers on it and say: 'Here is God.' At heart, what they want to do is to put into the Universe *purpose* where there is only *process;* to put plan *before* the event rather than *after.* They want to mark the sparrow's fall, not by the Laws of Chance, but by the Hand of God. So they peer out past the outlying ramparts of science to discover if there is a Deity hovering near; not realizing, when they find

Him, that either He must devour them or they must devour Him—either they must post a sign toward science saying, 'Here is where you get off!' or they must be prepared to amputate a slice off their Deity at any future time and to graft it on to the body of verifiable knowledge. . . . No, you can never find God by walking with me. . . . When you start back for your temple in the jungle you should leave your biology at home. For life is a phenomenon of Nature and the more we dig into natural law the more we find of the laws of chance."

The Padre shook his head, and held up a hand as though to stop Joel from saying more.

"No, Joel—I see it now, you contradict yourself! You say that life is a phenomenon of Nature; yet life has risen in spite of Nature, it has risen above her until it over-rides her, uses her, dominates her. . . . You can't do that with a *part* of Nature; it's contrary to the laws of chance! You talk about life flowing on through new forms, trying to keep alive; and yet you do not know what life is, this life that you say flows on through bird and beast and man! You biologists talk about protoplasm as the 'physical basis of life,' yet it seems to me that it is only the machinery by which life carries on this business of living. You take the animal to pieces and try to find life hidden away in the single cell, or in its proteins, or in its enzymes, or in its chromosomes; or you put it all back together again and say that life is the delicate organization of the cell, or the organization of innumerable cells into a complex organism. But it seems to me that you are only chasing life from pillar to post. For where can you find any of the cardinal features of life in that slimy protoplasmic jelly? Can its enzymes or its chromosomes explain the insurgence of life that has carried it over obstacle after obstacle in its evolution? Is there anything in the nucleus or the cytoplasm to account for the sentience, or the self-concern, or whatever you want to call it, that every living animal shows to a greater or lesser degree?

"Perhaps it is true that we cannot see ourselves clearly because of our emotional confusion, but we should certainly be able to see an amœba without prejudice! Yet your protoplasm does not tell you why an amœba grows, why it reproduces itself, why it is so nicely adapted to its environment, or why it goes on being an amœba instead of turning suddenly into something else! Oh, I know that you can give a reasonable account of *how* these things occur, in long physical and chemical terms; but you never say a word about *why,* as though the *why* of an amœba were not infinitely more important than its *how!* I cannot avoid the suspicion that there is *something* within even an amœba that *wants* to live and that *knows* how to go about living, and that it simply uses the amœba as a material means of doing so. . . . The lowest creature tries to keep on living—it is always bucking death, seeking ways to avoid destruction. All living things are for ever pushing forward. . . . Life is different from the rest of the universe because it is for ever warming up, while the universe is for ever cooling off, running down.

"No, there is something wrong with your picture. There is something missing from it; something that supplies a will-to-live and that centralizes, integrates, directs the complex process of living, even in an amœba. Something that is determined to buck the current, even—yes, even if it gets itself into blind alleys! That is why I said that you don't know what life is—you only know *how* it lives, and there is a big difference between the two."

Joel turned back to the yellow, fan-shaped beam that cut sharply through the surrounding blackness and illuminated the water and the sandy shore ahead. It seemed to possess some tangible golden substance which it sprayed like paint over the landscape, and as it crept forward at a steady pace the formless shadows which it engulfed became stones, or posts, or eerie masses of machinery that were sharply defined in scintillating radiance. He straightened up and ran his hands along the cold iron edge of the bulwark.

"No, we don't know what life is, but we must find out what it is from how it works. I admit, so far as protoplasm is concerned, that there may be something wrong with the picture. But it will straighten itself out in time. . . . I sometimes wonder if we don't look at life, at protoplasm, in the wrong way. I wonder if we do not see it backwards, upside down, wrong side out! Perhaps that complex slimy jelly in the cell is not really the 'physical basis of life,' as Huxley called it, but merely a pile of driftwood, a mantle of debris thrown up around the centre where life is. If so, it only obscures the living centre from our view. We would have to tear the jelly away, as you tear away the slime from around a spit-bug, to find the living focus at its heart."

The Padre squatted back on the floor and thrust his hands into his coat-pockets.

"Are you going over to a dualistic theory of mind and matter?" he asked, looking up at Joel with an amused smile.

"No," Joel answered, "nothing like that. I remain a mechanist. I am only going consistently back along the course of mechanistic evolution. We have asked ourselves, Did the reptile exist before the mammal, the invertebrate before the vertebrate, the protozoan before the metazoan; why not ask, Did not life exist before the mantle of flesh in which we now find it clothed? I was thinking that perhaps it did. I was thinking—if I may indulge in a scientific fantasy—that at the heart of that gelatinous blob of protoplasm there may be something utterly primitive and simple—something, say, like a whirlpool."

"Heavens!" the Padre interjected. "Isn't protoplasm complex enough for you without putting a whirlpool inside it?"

Joel shrugged his shoulders. "That's the trouble—it's too complex. It has the complexity of a multitude of effects that can issue from a single source. I was looking for the source, something that is simplicity itself. That is why I chose a whirlpool—a whirlpool of sunlight, if you wish, or, if you prefer, call it an eddy in the Second Law of Thermodynamics."

The Padre laughed. "I'm worse off now than I was before."

Joel flashed a smile at his companion, then jumped down from the bracket and paced back and forth along its edge.

"What I mean is"—he stopped suddenly to make a gesture with his hand—"did you ever have among your toys a gyroscope? Do you remember, when the wheel was spinning rapidly, how the thing felt in your hand? How it resisted you when you tried to turn it over, pushing back against your fingers with such uncanny power? And when it was forcibly laid on its side, how it straightened itself up at once? Well, life is something like that. . . .

"It's a crude analogy, but try to imagine a flowing river and note where it strikes against a sandbar of just the right shape." Joel pointed his fingers at the Padre's feet and began to make rapid, circular motions. "Part of the water is deflected from its course and thrown into a whirling motion. That whirlpool is a dynamic entity, a thing apart from the smoothly flowing river in which it has its being."

He waved his hand toward the brilliant stars above them.

"Now turn from the river of water to the universe around us: you say the universe is running down. I would put it another way—I would say that we live in a vast river of free energy that tends to flow from a high level to a lower one. And when you pursue your inquiry to the last physical and chemical analysis you find that the living organism is a self-perpetuating arrangement of matter engaged in absorbing, storing, and spending again a little of this energy. For its short span of life, it seems to swim against the major stream.

"It seems to me that life is to this river of energy what the whirlpool is to the flowing water; that much as the whirlpool's extent and direction are born of the sandbars and shallows, so the nature of the living organism is born of some sandbar that has turned this other river into a local eddy. I venture to think that life is an inevitable consequence of sunlight striking upon the dust and being deflected into a special motion, just as the whirlpool is the inevitable consequence of water striking upon the sandbar."

Several minutes passed before the Padre spoke. The silence was broken only by the notes of the ship's bell striking the hour, and the lower tones of the forecastle bell echoing back a few seconds later.

"But life has a purpose, it has power and knowledge—there must be something to it beside a mere spin of energy like a whirling dervish in the wind——"

"Right!" Joel interrupted him. "That is just why I called it a whirlpool. . . . A whirlpool, you see, when once set in motion tends always to continue in that motion, and it opposes destruction with an almost intelligent resistance. If friction wears the whirlpool down, then the river speeds it up again so that it is always whirling, whirling. It has a will to live that is born of its momentum. And it has power, borrowed from the river, to resist invasion or deflection from its course. And because of its gyroscopic nature it has knowledge, for it tends always to right itself if it is pushed out of a position of equilibrium.

"So it is with life: for life's purpose is to keep on living although at every hand its environment tends to arrest it; its power is the force with which it opposes the destructive forces that tend to put it down; and its knowledge is the sentience by which it selects from the world about it those means and conditions best suited to its ends.

"Life is like a whirlpool in many ways. . . . When once set a-going it spins on and on. It is not self-sustained because its energy is but borrowed from the river, being constantly renewed upstream and discharged below. If you deprive it of the energy or destroy the material matrix in which it spins, it dies. If friction draws upon its energy and slows it down, it restores itself by drawing upon the river. In that tendency to spin on for ever there is life's purpose—to go on living. . . . So long as the sunlight flows, the whirlpool is charged with power, for the energy which is turned into it can reappear in any form. It can appear as force to resist invasion or deflection from its course, or it can be used to batter the material which it encounters into new shapes and sizes. Or it can appear as heat. . . . But most important, the whirlpool is intelligent for, like the gyroscope, it is endowed by its dynamic nature with direction, with discrimination toward the world about it, and with the knowledge necessary to select from the world those states which best promote its being. When it is disturbed it automatically reacts to bring itself back into a balanced state, into a condition of well-being. It is that dynamic balance which is life's sentience; it is the reaction, when that balance is upset, that is life's activity. . . . And to a certain extent, the whirlpool is adaptive, for, when some contact with the world about it acts as a stress upon its being, that stress sets up an opposing strain which permits it to endure. When the stress is removed the internal strain restores the system to its original condition, and perfect readaptation to the original state is assured. . . .

"Here are the cardinal features of life, born of the momentum of a whirlpool: a will to live, power to live, intelligence to live, and adaptiveness to tide it over minor dangers. There is no cell, there is no protoplasmic jelly, yet life is on its way. Before it is ever clothed in that jelly it knows what it wants, it has the power to get what it wants, and it is willing to give way a little in order to get it! And all that it wants is to go on living!"

"Then what is the protoplasmic jelly for?"

"It is not *for* anything. It is a waste product, a pile of debris. . . . To paraphrase an old law of physiology, life never acts, but only reacts. The flesh of life is not an action, but a reaction—a by-product of the random encounters of the whirlpool with the world about it. I said that all that a whirlpool wants is to go on whirling . . . but our whirlpool in the sunlight is surrounded by an environment that by nature opposes its immortal instinct, an environment that presses in upon it at every hand and tends to choke it up. It must do battle with that environment every second of its existence, matching its momentum against whatever obstacles it meets. But with good luck, the battle may be drawn out through all eternity, while the whirlpool cries, 'Won't die!' and environment cries, 'Must die!' . . . *'Won't die!—Must die!—Won't die!—Must die!'* . . . There is the pulse of life that beats every second—there is the pulse by which life itself is to beat its way up the long course of evolution—and the first protoplasmic cell was the first beat of that pulse, it was born of the first battle!

"See how the logs and branches floating in the water chance to come upon the whirlpool in the river and are picked up and hurled about: so molecules of matter float by chance against our whirlpool in the sunlight where they are momentarily caught up in the vortex of its activity and hurled about until they are broken and rearranged and at last shot out at the periphery. The battle is on between the whirlpool and its environment; and it is thick fighting, for everywhere there are molecules to besiege it, and every one of them, be it ever so little, saps something of the whirlpool's strength. The immediate outcome of this battle hangs upon the chance nature of these encounters, for it might happen that some of the molecules would break the sandbar to pieces, or clog the whirlpool up or otherwise impair its action, but it actually happens that they rarely do, that most of them are the kind of molecules that can be tossed about by the whirlpool, one way or another, and so it wins the first round by sheer good luck, and escapes to go on whirling . . . but, ironically, only to find itself surrounded by the enemy from the rear!

"I said that the energy of the whirlpool's spin can be deflected and spent in any way in which energy can be spent. If the molecules that strike it escape unchanged, then the energy which they steal will be dissipated as heat. But if these molecules happen to be reactive, then the stolen energy can be locked up in them by the synthesis of new substances.

"The whirlpool in the water throws its matter toward the shore; the whirlpool in the sunlight automatically becomes a spinning-wheel which spins the drifting matter into complex organic compounds before it throws them out around its edges. Some of these compounds are only slightly diffusible, so they pile up around the whirlpool, adhering together, molecule to molecule, forming a jelly which is pushed out and out as far as the whirlpool can push. . . . Thus is your protoplasmic mantle spun and you have a cell. This cell is an extraordinarily complex mass—the organic chemist hasn't unravelled it yet, and the physical chemist is jolly well lost in the intricacies of its potentials and surface tensions; but who ever saw a junk pile that wasn't a bewildering conglomeration? Its internal and external features have become greatly modified during the course of evolution . . . but in our primordial organism it has no special appropriateness—it is both good and bad.

"It has some features, for example, which may help our would-be immortal whirlpool to go on spinning. Every particle of it is equilibrated with every other, and with the active centre by the chemical and physical forces that have spun and pushed it outward, so that, if it is pressed upon at any point, the impulse is transmitted throughout, and the answering forces from within are carried back. In this way the sentience of the whirlpool is transmuted into sensibility, and its power into action at the periphery of the protoplasmic mass. This mantle of flesh also tends to guard the whirlpool from the buffeting of a rude world, and thus contributes to its immortality by keeping off its enemy, environment. If the mantle is bruised, then the pressure from within forces fresh materials into the hole and the whirlpool automatically spins more stuff to take its place, and the wound heals. And since energy is stored up in its organic compounds, these can be used to keep the whirlpool going in the dark.

"But it is also in the nature of this chance mantle that it is a handicap. Its very thickness tends to shut out the sunlight, for one thing; and, for another, its mass is an encumbrance to the whirlpool's freedom to move from one place or position to another. But these are less important than the mere presence of the mantle itself, because by its very nature it tends to pull the whirlpool down. As the pile of debris grows bigger the centre spins more slowly, until it all but dies.

"But let us see how a whirlpool dies—you can watch the process in your bathtub, or in a whirlwind or a waterspout. Viewed from the side, a symmetrical whirlpool looks like two cones meeting at their points. So long as the whirlpool is going at full speed these points adhere together, but as the whirlpool slows down they pull apart so that there is only half a whirlpool above and half a whirlpool below, separated by a more or less inactive region in the middle. As the pile of debris around our whirlpool of sunlight increases in size, the whirlpool is retarded until it breaks into two parts; in the centre the forces which push out the protoplasmic jelly are diminished, and this jelly, falling back through instability and disintegration, shrinks into the cell—and itself divides into two parts—into two equal daughter cells each having one-half a whirlpool. But in the matter of whirlpools a part is as good as a whole, and, as soon as the retarding effect is removed, the missing halves restore themselves and, from the chance encounters with the drifting matter around them, begin to throw up new piles of protoplasmic jelly, continuing until they themselves, choked down again and dying, divide; thus one cell into two, two into four, four into eight, *ad infinitum*. So the whirlpool escapes from the pile of debris which accumulates around its edges by dividing and starting over. . . .

"It is, by the simple laws of chance, impossible for a single whirlpool to last for ever because sooner or later some accident would inevitably destroy it. But by division and multiplication of its numbers its chances of survival are also multiplied; and so our would-be immortal whirl-pool escapes the threat of death that lurks in the laws of chance even while it is escaping the threat of death that lurks in the accumulation of debris around it. . . .

"Now it has won three battles, it has made three steps along the road of evolution, it is three paces nearer to realizing its innermost wish for immortality. It has escaped the threat of death that lurks in its random encounters with environment; it has escaped the threat of death that lurks in the debris piled up as a result of these encounters, and it has escaped the threat of death that lurks in the very laws of chance by multiplying itself into a large number of individuals. It has won its battle with only its will-to-live, its limited power, its limited intelli-gence, and a limited amount of adaptiveness. . . . And it has become an organism that grows spontaneously to a fixed size and shape, and that heals itself after injury; it has a delicate physical and chemical perception of the world about it and the necessary intelligence to in-terpret the information which it gets in relation to its own well-being; it has power, deflected from the river of sunlight, to gain its ends, and power stored away in fuel for those hours when the river is not flow-ing; it has a specific nature that is fixed, but it has also a limited degree of adaptiveness to unfavourable conditions. It undergoes spontaneous and perfect division when it reaches maturity, and thus tends to mul-tiply itself in numbers and to spread into all the habitable parts of the earth. And it has a will-to-live that carries it on and on!

"It is spun out of matter by the deflection of the sunlight stream into a local channel: that is why I called life an eddy in the Second Law of Thermodynamics—which, stated in one way, says that free energy al-ways tends to flow from a high level to a lower one. Life tends to ac-cumulate energy for its own ends; but there is nothing unique about life in this respect—every hydro-electric power plant does the same thing. I called it a gyroscopic whirlpool to give it a conservative but dynamic character; but there is nothing unique about life in this re-spect, either—because every mobile system in equilibrium is conserva-tive and reacts so as to diminish any change."

Joel laughed as he added: "And because I am tired of talking about enzymes and catalysts—they appear to be, after all, only part of the junk pile. . . .

"We need not worry just yet about the complexity of the sandbar upon which our whirlpool spins; for in these days our ideas of matter, like real sandbars, are shifting overnight. I do not know the details of its structure, or of the motion within it; but it is not out of these so much as out of the simple fact that there is something spinning, spinning, that the essential characters of life come.

"There may be several different kinds of life—perhaps the green plants and the animals, the sulphur bacteria, the filterable viruses, and many other kinds of living things have each had a different origin, or perhaps they are only different habits of the same life-stream. But they are all just local eddies in the river of energy that flows around them.

"Neither do I know how and why life changes its way of living. By most people the raw materials of evolution are held to be spontaneous mutations, though there are some who would include, one way or another, the acquired characters or adaptations of the individual. This question has not been answered from observation and no hypothesis can answer it. If I were given the chance to ask a single question of some Omniscience about the finite world, I think that would be it. But, however evolution comes about, it must obviously be in our whirlpool that the mutation or permanent adaptations occur—alterations in its character that change its nature by the slightest bit. Perhaps they follow from some long-continued strain, or perhaps they arise spontaneously and according to the laws of chance even as atoms sometimes blow to pieces for no apparent reason. But that life does change its way of living is incontestable. . . . And since the earth is not all habitable, nor even much of it, the living stream is beset at every hand by danger, by an environment that presses in upon it and crowds it until it all but dies. It is this continuous battle between environment and the mutant organic stream that we see in evolution. While life was being carried forward by its own momentum, its way of living was carved by that battle with environment into the vegetable and animal kingdoms. But in each new plant or animal the whirlpool that is at the heart of every cell spins on with gyroscopic fixity until its direction is again abruptly altered by a slight quantum of variation, by a new mutation. . . .

"The apparent complexity of the higher animals tends to obscure life's real simplicity, for out of its long history it has acquired a manifold design.

"There have come to be cells which, though dividing, yet remain together in delicate balance to make a multicellular organism. These cells have come, through the potentialities of the mother cell, to be differentiated into a body of highly specialized parts—skin, muscles, nerves, glands, receptors, bones—so that by this division of physiological labour the efficiency of each is increased; but these cells have no powers or properties that are not inherent in the fundamental plan.

"During this evolution into a body of specialized parts it has come to pass that certain cells have been set aside to carry on the stream of life —the germ cells—by beginning anew and spinning another body. Perhaps this is because the great specialization of the body cells renders them unfit to serve a genetic role, and perhaps there is an advantage to be gained by putting the germ cells away where they will not be bruised by a rude world. But it is thus that death finally came about. The lower animals that multiply by division are immortal for, as someone has said, you cannot speak of death where there is nothing left to bury. But the flesh of the higher animals is too specialized, this pile of debris is too cumbersome, to be of further use; so after it has matured and been given an opportunity to pass on the seed of life, it is thrown aside. And the whirlpool escapes through the germ cell, to fight another battle. . . .

"It has come about that organisms have learned to draw the energy to keep their whirlpools going not directly from the sunlight but from the dead, enriched substance of other organisms; until the fisherman lives upon fish which live upon crustaceans which live upon infusorians which live upon diatoms, while only the diatoms still live directly in the sunlight stream. Life has gained, perhaps, its greatest freedom by this cannibalistic habit, but it has not changed its nature for, fisherman or diatom, it is still sunlight spinning within the cell.

"It has come about that the natural forces of that primordial organism are made manifest in ways that are variegated beyond belief;

"Until life lives in bodies that are big and small, in bodies that are born from a spore, from an egg, or from a mother's womb; in bodies that last a week, a month, or threescore years and ten; in bodies that are of two sexes or only one; in bodies that have long noses, short noses, or no noses at all;

"Until life has broken itself into hundreds of thousands of species and has spread itself into the depths of the ocean, the heights of the mountains, the air, into caverns, coal-mines, icebergs, hot springs;

"Until the scorpion has poison on the tip of its tail and the cobra poison at the roots of its fangs; until the flower has honey in its heart and the bee honey in its comb;

"Until the spider revels in the shadows and the bird in the sunshine and the biologist in all of them!

"Yes, life has spun itself into a web that is infinitely complex with interrelations, interdependencies—but it makes no difference; these, like the first protoplasmic mantle, are but products of that battle between the spinning sunlight and its environment, the battle that we call evolution. In all that time life has not changed its real nature by the slightest bit. It is still in every cell a whirlpool whose momentum is its will-to-live—the insurgence of life; its dynamic force is its power—the vitality of life; its gyroscopic nature is the intelligence that selects from the world about it those particles and circumstances which best promote its being—the sentience of life. It is the same sunlight spinning the same matter in all of us—in you and me, the bird, the tree, the worm, the diatom; only the life-habit of the whirlpool, the number of whirlpools in our bodies, and the intricate pattern of their arrangement are in each of us a little different. . . .

"One should not be surprised that there is a remarkable 'fitness' between life and the world it lives in, for the fitness of the living organism to its environment and the fitness of environment to the living organism are as the fit between a die and its mould, between the whirlpool and the river bed. . . . What we should note is that the fit is neither perfect nor permanent, because environment is not constant in its character for a fleeting instant; it changes with every breeze and sound, with every light and shadow. The battle is never finished and the pulse of life beats on . . . *Won't die!—Must die!—Won't die!— Must die!* . . . It throbs anew each second into the substance of its flesh, into its healing, its reproduction, its rhythms, its activities, its further evolution—into its innermost wish. . . . Life has come a long way in its journey from the first sandbar in the sunlight to the poet singing about a little child lying upon his back:

> Over his head were the maple buds,
> And over the tree was the moon,
> And over the moon were the starry studs
> That drop from the Angels' shoon.

But that is only sunlight answering back to starlight in rhythms across great gulfs of time and space, and with a sentience hardly less than these in measure. . . . But still it is not intelligent enough to keep itself out of blind alleys—of mud or philosophy, or of speculating about its own nature!"

Joel laughed and shook his head. "No, I do not know what life is. But I think that it is something like that; like a whirlpool stirred up in the dust by sunlight that, spinning on and on, of its own momentum presses always against its environment where the blind alleys are cut off and the rest escapes through different ways of spinning."

VIII

"It is a beautiful idea!" The Padre looked up at Joel and smiled.

"Beautiful!" Joel stepped up on the bracket and glowered down at him. He folded his arms in an attitude of belligerent scorn. "Beautiful? How can you call it beautiful? Then you don't see it! Look at it again—see that whirlpool in the river that drowns the bodies of men. . . . See that whirlpool in the sunlight that vomits its refuse around its edge, pushing it farther and farther away until it can push no more! That flesh is but the excrement accumulated around the spinning vortex; the whole body of life, its tissue, its bone, its nerves are but waste products that would have been gotten rid of by the whirlpool if it could, and failing that have been disposed of in the way least offensive to its activity. The lovely features of that flesh have been moulded by being thrown haphazardly against the world! The *beautiful* temple of flesh, indeed!

"It is only choking refuse, aching for immortality with an ache that is naught but the shriek of a brake on a wheel! Its first birth was an escape from an accident, and its continued existence from hour to hour, from generation to generation, from race to race, is but a succession of escapes from a succession of new accidents—dodging the death to which it is doomed when the sun stops shining; and even if the sun shines for ever, life will stop first, for the doom of death was laid upon it at the moment of its birth—it lives only until the last momentum meets the last inertia—until the last accident! Is an accident *beautiful?*

"Its spinning heart lives by taking the easiest way, the one least likely to inconvenience it! The warmth of its body is but a result of friction! Its very sense and perception are but mere echoes of the fact that it wants to be let alone! The power—the glorious power of life!—is stolen out of its heart against its innermost wish, and is given up only that it may stop a further theft! Life's vitality, its activity, its whole evolution are but the remonstrance of that whirlpool against being disturbed from its eternal motion—its eternal, eternal momentum! Is momentum *beautiful?*

"I said that there is no goal to evolution except that life shall go on living, that there is no maintained direction except the one in which life is already moving. I should say that there is nothing but a long-drawn-out battle between matter and motion, and a battlefield strewn with debris. . . . Damn it all! Can you find anything in that picture to call it *beautiful?*"

"Yes," the Padre answered promptly, "I can . . . if one individual can see and hear and talk to another, and if they can make each other smile . . . then force has met force agreeably and to their mutual benefit—for life travels faster in co-operation than otherwise, doesn't it?"

He looked up, laughing. "There must be something wrong with your theory, Joel, because we start with two mutually repellent whirlpools that want to be let alone and in the end have them coming together to their mutual acceleration."

"Yes," Joel answered, laughing himself now. "But only because that is the mutually easiest way!

"I'm sorry," he went on; "I was afraid—I only wanted you to see life as it is for its own sake, and be prepared to take the consequences; and not for some anthropomorphic idea of what is or is not beautiful."

"Why?"

"Because the idea that just because we find a thing pretty, it's good, or true, or has any significance whatever beyond the eye of the beholder, has done immeasurable harm. We must learn to put our wills upon the strings of that sounding-board when we want to think, so that we can see the mammoth and not our fear or our delight in it."

The Padre looked up at Joel with a quizzical smile and suddenly broke into a loud laugh.

"I'm glad to know you were afraid," he said.

But Joel did not get the drift of his remark. He moved to stretch his cramped arms and legs and was surprised to see that the ship had come into Port Said and was moving slowly down the channel to an anchorage. He had no idea what time it was, but he guessed that it must be close to morning. So they were at Said at last! A feeling of intense relief mingled with revulsion swept over him. He loathed the sea— he'd never get into a ship again! Why on earth should anyone put himself into that prison except out of sheer necessity? After incarceration on a boat for two weeks you loathed everything connected with it; the mere gestures of civility became a painful bore; you knew every face, everything it had to say, every thought behind its eyes, every cravat it chose to wear. Why, on God's earth, did that Frenchman pick out a pink one with yellow fleurs-de-lis if it was to be the only one he had? And why did they choose to paint the dining-salon with red parrots and purple monkeys when you had to look at them three times a day for fourteen days? Who invented the damnable deck-chairs that broke your back and cut your legs off above the knees and why do

French colonials have twelve children? And why is one of them always cross-eyed?

Joel shrugged his shoulders. There seemed to be no passageway through the maze of dark forms that rode at anchor in the coaling-basins and along the channel. Their masts and spars and lines made an intricate web of black against the faintly luminous sky. There were big ships and little ships, some with their deck-lights burning and some shrouded in darkness except for the riding-lights fixed upon the mast-stays. Joel could make out the names of a few of them as the light from the *Dumbea* passed across their overhanging sterns or their pointed bows—*Razmak:* now by her marks she was a P. and O. boat, and she'd be coming in from India; *Hakosaki Maru:* she'd be from the land of cherry blossoms and temples lacquered in blue and red and gold; she'd have called at Shanghai, near the mouth of the Yangtse in the valley of which lives one-tenth of the world's population, and again at the old pirates' harbour of Hong Kong where the mountains of China drop abruptly into the sea; *Llanstephan Castle:* she'd be going down the East Coast to South Africa and she'd call at Mombasa, Zanzibar, and Dar-es-Salaam; *Finisterre:* now she'd be a bug-ridden tramp knocking about Heaven knows where or what for—she didn't look as if she could ride out a heavy sea!

New ships and old ships, made fast stem and stern to buoys anchored in parallel lines along the Canal. Ships asleep, and soiled as all ships soil when they come into port, to lie passive and unresisting while coolies swarm over them like ants to steal away their cargo or dump baskets of filthy coal into their hatches. But ships sleeping lightly, apt to wake up at any moment and with a long blast on the whistle shove off to sea. Tomorrow they would be riding along the blue horizon with their decks scoured down to clean white wood and their brass newly gleaming in the morning sun, proudly throwing off a crested wave on either side. But now they lay sleeping quietly, dark hulks against the sky, while lighters and small craft crowded into their darker shadows like flotsam lodged against a rock. Silent ships, asleep; there was some magic locked up in their sombre masses that, if released, would spring forth with life and meaning. . . .

Above the masts and funnels great lamps covered by conical reflectors illuminated the coaling-basins and the sides of the Canal. Behind them only gloomy, cubical shadows marked the streets where they ran back into the Arab quarter. The scene, with its suggestion of mechanism here and there, was strangely like a modernistic stage-setting. A plume of steam escaping from a nearby vessel waved slowly from side to side as the breeze played with it. It was illuminated from above into faintly phosphorescent rings and spirals that vanished into thin air.

Once a searchlight shoved its ghostly finger through the night and moved it with incredible speed here and there in crazy paths, lighting up for brief instants bits of ship's gear, spidery coaling-towers, giant derricks; it rested for a moment on the grey-clad figure of a sailor stretched face upward on a deck; the man rolled over and the luminous finger shot downwards to the black water, revealing a boat being poled by an Arab in a banded gown; then it shot across more black water to come to rest pointing down along a ship's ladder into a dory waiting for its passenger. The passenger turned out to be a portly man in baggy white clothes, with a briefcase under his arm and a red fez on his head. He chose to descend the ladder backwards and he stopped every few steps to look up and gesticulate an emphatic farewell to some invisible person above him. He had hardly reached the dory when the searchlight was abruptly switched off.

Almost as if this were a signal, a gramophone on the deck which he had left began to play a dance tune. Joel stiffened slightly with attention: the tune had merry notes that were syncopated into delicate crescendos; it seemed to spin a web of sound upon the still night air. It caught his pulse and breathing in its measures and forced them into its own rhythm with a sharp sense of pain. He shut his eyes and gave himself up to the enchantment of its glad melody, letting it beat upon his ears as though he could drink a song to satisfy a thirst. He was no longer tired, for the music welled up in him, filling his aching muscles with new life even while he was intent upon its sharp impact with his brain. . . . They came, those notes, in a sequence that was inevitable; foreordained, one followed another into the waiting expectancy of time, and were one missing their sequence would be incomplete, like

an unfinished thought, or a sentence with a word left out. . . . Silver
notes, jingling in wild rhythms with coppery notes pounding in slow
measures down below. Silver notes, dancing against the eardrums, trying to get in, but always just outside. . . . If one could only let them
in instead of leaving them to patter painfully against the eardrums—
the big notes got in and reverberated between your ribs, but damn it
all, the little notes bounced off and hurt . . . dancing notes that fell
across the sky like golden sparks slanting over velvet blackness. . . .

"What's the matter?" Joel looked at the Padre, who was shaking
him violently by the shoulder.

"How long have you been asleep, man?"

"I wasn't asleep! I was watching the sparks falling——"

"Sparks? Where have you seen any sparks?"

Joel looked up but there was only a grey muggy mist, so he joined
sheepishly in the Padre's laughter. He saw that sailors were moving
about on the deck behind him, unwinding ropes and letting steam
noisily into the windlasses. An officer came up the forecastle-ladder;
after a brief glance at the two men standing in the bow, he muttered
an injunction to a sailor and moved to the back edge of the deck where
he stood as though waiting for a signal.

The ship drifted slowly past her neighbours, some of which were so
close that one could have talked in a quiet voice across the intervening
space. Here and there a man leaned out to watch them indifferently, or
raised his hand in a friendly gesture. Joel suddenly realized that he was
cold and a violent shiver made him turn up his collar and button his
coat. He heard a bell sound on the bridge and someone call, "Let go!"
The officer echoed, "Let go!" The starboard windlass creaked as a
sailor released the brake around the windlass-drum and metal grated
on metal beneath their feet where the anchor-chain moved forward a
little. Then the chain moved again and began to run out with such a
screeching, crashing, roaring noise that the men had to cover their
ears. When it was over, Joel recalled that he had not heard the anchor
hit the water; he had expected it to make a great splash but it was
completely lost in the ear-splitting thunder of that mad chain. He
turned to the Padre with a shrug, relieved to be again in silence.

"At last! There was a time when I thought that we would never get here! We've sat up a long time to get that drink. Come on——"

The Padre stopped him with a hand upon his arm.

"Wait a minute. . . . If you put me back among the beasts, what becomes of my life—has it no goal, no purpose?"

Joel looked for a moment at the Padre's hand, which had closed into a tight grip over his arm. He studied the long brown fingers, which held him with an arresting tension as the words echoed in his ears: "Has it no goal, no purpose? Purpose?" . . . The fingers relaxed, and Joel turned away to lean again upon the bulwark. A boat was moving slowly out from the shadow of the bow, pulling an enormous hawser to a buoy. Making her fast! How good it was, after the open sea, to be bound again to something permanent, resting from the unceasing voyaging onward and onward across trackless wastes, through time and space—how good it was, if it were only to rest and voyage again. . . . He rubbed his hand over his forehead and straightened up.

"Must we for ever be like children, seeking purpose in the fall of the rain, in the sweep of the wind, in the strike of the lightning! Why must we always seek it in ourselves? . . . No, your life has no more purpose than that of any other beast. . . . It has no purpose except as you choose to give it one. I give you, in the very nature of life itself, in the momentum that keeps it spinning on its course, an unquenchable instinct for self-determination—if you wish to call it that; and in the flesh which life accumulates around itself I give you the capacity to learn by experience and to test your knowledge by experiment. Is that not enough? . . . But I cannot give you any personal, predetermined significance. You are only a branch of the stream that is flowing on, resisting the world about it, trying——"

"There it is!" the Padre interrupted. He was smiling, his eyes fixed upon the faint colours of the morning sky. ". . . trying different ways of living, in order to keep alive! Perhaps in my obscure corner of Africa I am an experiment, too. Perhaps"—he pressed Joel's arm with a friendly gesture as he moved away—"well, anyway I hope I don't turn out to be a blind alley! Come along—you have sat up long enough to get that drink. You've earned it!"

Joel watched the priest with a puzzled frown as he walked across the deck. His resounding footsteps seemed to echo some familiar phrase, and Joel stopped to listen; but it was not until they had died away that his memory captured it. He chuckled to himself—it was the pulse of life, it had escaped again!

AN AFTERWORD ON
"KAMONGO"

THOSE whose trade is the putting of words down on paper undergo, from time to time, the wholesomely abashing experience of discovering that men with whom writing is only an avocation can teach them a trick or two. Thus this John W. Thomason, Jr., whose superb drawings adorn the pages of his own sinewy and beautiful prose, is primarily devoted to the profession of arms and had thereby—at last accounts—achieved a majority in the United States Marine Corps. Then no mere author has a better English style than that jolly medico, Dr. Logan Clendening, who, when he takes his pen in hand in the library of his modest Kansas City home—his house is called Roaring Toilet—can write an entire physiology or a comprehensive history of medicine without once lapsing into the horrid jargon of the consulting-room, unless you count an occasional infatuated surrender to the sheer hypnosis of such a medicated word as, let us say, borborygmi.

Surely in this distinguished group we must include Homer W. Smith, the biologist, who, in the course of his meditative exploration into the human kidney, its tricks and its manners, went to East Africa in quest of some lung-fish and came back with this unique and winning fable called *Kamongo*. It was written aboard ship and probably owed its actual appearance on paper to his wife's skepticism. Indeed, she made so bold as to take up his airy wager of five hundred dollars that not merely would he write the book but that it would then be bought by the first publisher who saw it. Mrs. Smith just won the bet. *Kamongo* was bought by the second publisher who saw it.

For the kamongo which Dr. Smith brought back to New York in November 1931, an adequate shelter of mud was arranged in his laboratory at Bellevue Hospital. Of the forty-eight which thus went into retirement on Armistice Day of that year, ten were still there at last accounts and doing, it was supposed, as well as could be expected. All the rest—save one—had died in exile at varying intervals, either in the mud or after their inquisitive custodian had awakened them from their long siesta. The single exception had, in October 1935, lived a year after his emergence from the mud. It is true he was looking poorly. His weight had dwindled by more than sixty per cent, but then he had had nothing to eat for four years—an abstention which seems pretty drastic to anyone who feels heroic if he merely omits that second helping to Brown Betty. It was not Dr. Smith's intention, however, to wait until this fast had proved lethal. Rather he was planning to intervene benevolently in the nick of time, first feeding his charge a light luncheon of ground beef-heart and then working him up by degrees to a debauch of worms and snails.

As for the other martyrs to science—not the first unconsulted creatures to be captured in Africa and, for our convenience, brought in shackles to the land of the free—even they did not pass away without first yielding up many fascinating facts about uræmia. And while here, of course, they enjoyed free of charge certain blessings of civilization for which our neurasthenic matrons have to pay through the nose. I mean something more than the mud baths. Why, the ailing lung-fish were accorded the soothing privilege of having their basal metabolism taken every day.

A. W.

THE
BAR SINISTER

by

RICHARD
HARDING
DAVIS

THE BAR SINISTER

I

THE Master was walking most unsteady, his legs tripping each other. After the fifth or sixth round, my legs often go the same way.

But even when the Master's legs bend and twist a bit, you mustn't think he can't reach you. Indeed, that is the time he kicks most frequent. So I kept behind him in the shadow, or ran in the middle of the street. He stopped at many public houses with swinging doors, those doors that are cut so high from the sidewalk that you can look in under them, and see if the Master is inside. At night, when I peep beneath them, the man at the counter will see me first and say, "Here's the Kid, Jerry, come to take you home. Get a move on you"; and the Master will stumble out and follow me. It's lucky for us I'm so white, for, no matter how dark the night, he can always see me ahead, just out of reach of his boot. At night the Master certainly does see most amazing. Sometimes he sees two or four of me, and walks in a circle, so that I have to take him by the leg of his trousers and lead him into the right road. One night, when he was very nasty-tempered and I was coaxing him along, two men passed us, and one of them says, "Look at that brute!" and the other asks, "Which?" and they both laugh. The Master he cursed them good and proper.

But this night, whenever we stopped at a public house, the Master's pals left it and went on with us to the next. They spoke quite civil to me, and when the Master tried a flying kick, they gives him a shove. "Do you want us to lose our money?" says the pals.

I had had nothing to eat for a day and a night, and just before we set out the Master gives me a wash under the hydrant. Whenever I am locked up until all the slop-pans in our alley are empty, and

603

made to take a bath, and the Master's pals speak civil and feel my ribs, I know something is going to happen. And that night, when every time they see a policeman under a lamp-post, they dodged across the street, and when at the last one of them picked me up and hid me under his jacket, I began to tremble; for I knew what it meant. It meant that I was to fight again for the Master.

I don't fight because I like fighting. I fight because if I didn't the other dog would find my throat, and the Master would lose his stakes, and I would be very sorry for him, and ashamed. Dogs can pass me and I can pass dogs, and I'd never pick a fight with none of them. When I see two dogs standing on their hind legs in the streets, clawing each other's ears, and snapping for each other's windpipes, or howling and swearing and rolling in the mud, I feel sorry they should act so, and pretend not to notice. If he'd let me, I'd like to pass the time of day with every dog I meet. But there's something about me that no nice dog can abide. When I trot up to nice dogs, nodding and grinning, to make friends, they always tell me to be off. "Go to the devil!" they bark at me. "Get out!" And when I walk away they shout "Mongrel!" and "Gutter-dog!" and sometimes, after my back is turned, they rush me. I could kill most of them with three shakes, breaking the backbone of the little ones and squeezing the throat of the big ones. But what's the good? They *are* nice dogs; that's why I try to make up to them: and, though it's not for them to say it, I *am* a street-dog, and if I try to push into the company of my betters, I suppose it's their right to teach me my place.

Of course they don't know I'm the best fighting bull-terrier of my weight in Montreal. That's why it wouldn't be fair for me to take notice of what they shout. They don't know that if I once locked my jaws on them I'd carry away whatever I touched. The night I fought Kelley's White Rat, I wouldn't loosen up until the Master made a noose in my leash and strangled me; and, as for that Ottawa dog, if the handlers hadn't thrown red pepper down my nose I *never* would have let go of him. I don't think the handlers treated me quite right that time, but maybe they didn't know the Ottawa dog was dead. I did.

I learned my fighting from my mother when I was very young. We slept in a lumber-yard on the river-front, and by day hunted for food along the wharves. When we got it, the other tramp-dogs would try to take it off us, and then it was wonderful to see mother fly at them and drive them away. All I know of fighting I learned from mother, watching her picking the ash-heaps for me when I was too little to fight for myself. No one ever was so good to me as mother. When it snowed and the ice was in the St. Lawrence, she used to hunt alone, and bring me back new bones, and she'd sit and laugh to see me try-ing to swallow 'em whole. I was just a puppy then; my teeth was falling out. When I was able to fight we kept the whole river-range to ourselves. I had the genuine long "punishing" jaw, so mother said, and there wasn't a man or a dog that dared worry us. Those were happy days, those were; and we lived well, share and share alike, and when we wanted a bit of fun, we chased the fat old wharf-rats! My, how they would squeal!

Then the trouble came. It was no trouble to me. I was too young to care then. But mother took it so to heart that she grew ailing, and wouldn't go abroad with me by day. It was the same old scandal that they're always bringing up against me. I was so young then that I didn't know. I couldn't see any difference between mother—and other mothers.

But one day a pack of curs we drove off snarled back some new names at her, and mother dropped her head and ran, just as though they had whipped us. After that she wouldn't go out with me except in the dark, and one day she went away and never came back, and, though I hunted for her in every court and alley and back street of Montreal, I never found her.

One night, a month after mother ran away, I asked Guardian, the old blind mastiff, whose Master is the night watchman on our slip, what it all meant. And he told me.

"Every dog in Montreal knows," he says, "except you; and every Master knows. So I think it's time you knew."

Then he tells me that my father, who had treated mother so bad, was a great and noble gentleman from London. "Your father had twenty-two registered ancestors, had your father," old Guardian says, "and in him was the best bull-terrier blood of England, the most ancientest, the most royal; the winning 'blue-ribbon' blood, that breeds champions. He had sleepy pink eyes and thin pink lips, and he was as white all over as his own white teeth, and under his white skin you could see his muscles, hard and smooth, like the links of a steel chain. When your father stood still, and tipped his nose in the air, it was just as though he was saying, 'Oh, yes, you common dogs and men, you may well stare. It must be a rare treat for you colonials to see real English royalty.' He certainly was pleased with hisself, was your father. He looked just as proud and haughty as one of them stone dogs in Victoria Park—them as is cut out of white marble. And you're like him," says the old mastiff—"by that, of course, meaning you're white, same as him. That's the only likeness. But, you see, the trouble is, Kid—well, you see, Kid, the trouble is—your mother——"

"That will do," I said, for then I understood without his telling me, and I got up and walked away, holding my head and tail high in the air.

But I was, oh, so miserable, and I wanted to see mother that very minute, and tell her that I didn't care.

Mother is what I am, a street-dog; there's no royal blood in mother's veins, nor is she like that father of mine, nor—and that's the worst— she's not even like me. For while I, when I'm washed for a fight, am as white as clean snow, she—and this is our trouble—she, my mother, is a black-and-tan.

When mother hid herself from me, I was twelve months old and able to take care of myself, and as, after mother left me, the wharves were never the same, I moved uptown and met the Master. Before he came, lots of other men-folks had tried to make up to me, and to whistle me home. But they either tried patting me or coaxing me with a piece of meat; so I didn't take to 'em. But one day the Master pulled me out of a street-fight by the hind legs, and kicked me good.

"You want to fight, do you?" says he. "I'll give you all the *fighting* you want!" he says, and he kicks me again. So I knew he was my

Master, and I followed him home. Since that day I've pulled off many fights for him, and they've brought dogs from all over the province to have a go at me; but up to that night none, under thirty pounds, had ever downed me.

But that night, so soon as they carried me into the ring, I saw the dog was overweight, and that I was no match for him. It was asking too much of a puppy. The Master should have known I couldn't do it. Not that I mean to blame the Master, for when sober, which he some-times was,—though not, as you might say, his habit,—he was most kind to me, and let me out to find food, if I could get it, and only kicked me when I didn't pick him up at night and lead him home.

But kicks will stiffen the muscles, and starving a dog so as to get him ugly-tempered for a fight may make him nasty, but it's weakening to his insides, and it causes the legs to wobble.

The ring was in a hall back of a public house. There was a red-hot whitewashed stove in one corner, and the ring in the other. I lay in the Master's lap, wrapped in my blanket, and, spite of the stove, shivering awful; but I always shiver before a fight: I can't help gettin' excited. While the men-folks were a-flashing their money and taking their last drink at the bar, a little Irish groom in gaiters came up to me and give me the back of his hand to smell, and scratched me behind the ears.

"You poor little pup," says he; "you haven't no show," he says. "That brute in the tap-room he'll eat your heart out."

"That's what *you* think," says the Master, snarling. "I'll lay you a quid the Kid chews him up."

The groom he shook his head, but kept looking at me so sorry-like that I begun to get a bit sad myself. He seemed like he couldn't bear to leave off a-patting of me, and he says, speaking low just like he would to a man-folk, "Well, good luck to you, little pup," which I thought so civil of him that I reached up and licked his hand. I don't do that to many men. And the Master he knew I didn't, and took on dreadful.

"What 'ave you got on the back of your hand?" says he, jumping up.

"Soap!" says the groom, quick as a rat. "That's more than you've got on yours. Do you want to smell of it?" and he sticks his fist under the Master's nose. But the pals pushed in between 'em.

"He tried to poison the Kid!" shouts the Master.

"Oh, one fight at a time," says the referee. "Get into the ring, Jerry. We're waiting." So we went into the ring.

I never could just remember what did happen in that ring. He give me no time to spring. He fell on me like a horse. I couldn't keep my feet against him, and though, as I saw, he could get his hold when he liked, he wanted to chew me over a bit first. I was wondering if they'd be able to pry him off me, when, in the third round, he took his hold; and I begun to drown, just as I did when I fell into the river off the Red C slip. He closed deeper and deeper on my throat, and everything went black and red and bursting; and then, when I were sure I were dead, the handlers pulled him off, and the Master gave me a kick that brought me to. But I couldn't move none, or even wink, both eyes being shut with lumps.

"He's a cur!" yells the Master, "a sneaking, cowardly cur! He lost the fight for me," says he, "because he's a —— —— —— cowardly cur." And he kicks me again in the lower ribs, so that I go sliding across the sawdust. "There's gratitude fer yer," yells the Master. "I've fed that dog, and nussed that dog and housed him like a prince; and now he puts his tail between his legs and sells me out, he does. He's a coward! I've done with him, I am. I'd sell him for a pipeful of tobacco." He picked me up by the tail, and swung me for the men-folks to see. "Does any gentleman here want to buy a dog," he says, "to make into sausage-meat?" he says. "That's all he's good for."

Then I heard the little Irish groom say, "I'll give you ten bob for the dog."

And another voice says, "Ah, don't you do it; the dog's same as dead—mebbe he is dead."

"Ten shillings!" says the Master, and his voice sobers a bit; "make it two pounds and he's yours."

But the pals rushed in again.

"Don't you be a fool, Jerry," they say. "You'll be sorry for this when you're sober. The Kid's worth a fiver."

One of my eyes was not so swelled up as the other, and as I hung by my tail, I opened it, and saw one of the pals take the groom by the shoulder.

"You ought to give 'im five pounds for that dog, mate," he says; "that's no ordinary dog. That dog's got good blood in him, that dog has. Why, his father—that very dog's father——"

I thought he never would go on. He waited like he wanted to be sure the groom was listening.

"That very dog's father," says the pal, "is Regent Royal, son of Champion Regent Monarch, champion bull-terrier of England for four years."

I was sore, and torn, and chewed most awful, but what the pal said sounded so fine that I wanted to wag my tail, only couldn't, owing to my hanging from it.

But the Master calls out: "Yes, his father was Regent Royal; who's saying he wasn't? but the pup's a cowardly cur, that's what his pup is. And why? I'll tell you why: because his mother was a black-and-tan street-dog, that's why!"

I don't see how I got the strength, but, someway, I threw myself out of the Master's grip and fell at his feet, and turned over and fastened all my teeth in his ankle, just across the bone.

When I woke, after the pals had kicked me off him, I was in the smoking-car of a railroad-train, lying in the lap of the little groom, and he was rubbing my open wounds with a greasy yellow stuff, exquisite to the smell and most agreeable to lick off.

11

"Well, what's your name—Nolan? Well, Nolan, these references are satisfactory," said the young gentleman my new Master called "Mr. Wyndham, sir." "I'll take you on as second man. You can begin today."

My new Master shuffled his feet and put his finger to his forehead. "Thank you, sir," says he. Then he choked like he had swallowed a fish-bone. "I have a little dawg, sir," says he.

"You can't keep him," says "Mr. Wyndham, sir," very short.

" 'E's only a puppy, sir," says my new Master; " 'e wouldn't go outside the stables, sir."

"It's not that," says "Mr. Wyndham, sir." "I have a large kennel of very fine dogs; they're the best of their breed in America. I don't allow strange dogs on the premises."

The Master shakes his head, and motions me with his cap, and I crept out from behind the door. "I'm sorry, sir," says the Master. "Then, I can't take the place. I can't get along without the dawg, sir."

"Mr. Wyndham, sir," looked at me that fierce that I guessed he was going to whip me, so I turned over on my back and begged with my legs and tail.

"Why, you beat him!" says "Mr. Wyndham, sir," very stern.

"No fear!" the Master says, getting very red. "The party I bought him off taught him that. He never learnt that from me!" He picked me up in his arms, and to show "Mr. Wyndham, sir," how well I loved the Master, I bit his chin and hands.

"Mr. Wyndham, sir," turned over the letters the Master had given him. "Well, these references certainly are very strong," he says. "I guess I'll let the dog stay. Only see you keep him away from the kennels—or you'll both go."

"Thank you, sir," says the Master, grinning like a cat when she's safe behind the area railing.

"He's not a bad bull-terrier," says "Mr. Wyndham, sir," feeling my head. "Not that I know much about the smooth-coated breeds. My dogs are St. Bernards." He stopped patting me and held up my nose. "What's the matter with his ears?" he says. "They're chewed to pieces. Is this a fighting dog?" he asks, quick and rough-like.

I could have laughed. If he hadn't been holding my nose, I certainly would have had a good grin at him. Me the best under thirty pounds in the Province of Quebec, and him asking if I was a fighting dog! I ran to the Master and hung down my head modest-like, waiting for him to tell my list of battles; but the Master he coughs in his cap most painful. "Fightin' dawg, sir!" he cries. "Lor' bless you, sir, the Kid don't know the word. 'E's just a puppy, sir, same as you see; a pet dog, so to speak. 'E's a regular old lady's lap-dog, the Kid is."

"Well, you keep him away from my St. Bernards," says "Mr. Wyndham, sir," "or they might make a mouthful of him."

"Yes, sir; that they might," says the Master. But when we gets outside he slaps his knee and laughs inside hisself, and winks at me most sociable.

The Master's new home was in the country, in a province they called Long Island. There was a high stone wall about his home with big iron gates to it, same as Godfrey's brewery; and there was a house with five red roofs; and the stables, where I lived, was cleaner than the aërated bakery-shop. And then there was the kennels; but they was like nothing else in this world that ever I see. For the first days I couldn't sleep of nights for fear someone would catch me lying in such a cleaned-up place, and would chase me out of it; and when I did fall to sleep I'd dream I was back in the old Master's attic, shivering under the rusty stove, which never had no coals in it, with the Master flat on his back on the cold floor, with his clothes on. And I'd wake up scared and whimpering, and find myself on the new Master's cot with his hand on the quilt beside me; and I'd see the glow of the big stove, and hear the high-quality horses below-stairs stamping in their straw-lined boxes, and I'd snoop the sweet smell of hay and harness-soap and go to sleep again.

The stables was my jail, so the Master said, but I don't ask no better home than that jail.

"Now, Kid," says he, sitting on the top of a bucket upside down, "you've got to understand this. When I whistle it means you're not to go out of this 'ere yard. These stables is your jail. If you leave 'em I'll have to leave 'em too, and over the seas, in the County Mayo, an old mother will 'ave to leave her bit of a cottage. For two pounds I must be sending her every month, or she'll have naught to eat, nor no thatch over 'er head. I can't lose my place, Kid, so see you don't lose it for me. You must keep away from the kennels," says he; "they're not for the likes of you. The kennels are for the quality. I wouldn't take a litter of them woolly dogs for one wag of your tail, Kid, but for all that they are your betters, same as the gentry up in the big house are my betters. I know my place and keep away from the gentry, and you keep away from the champions."

So I never goes out of the stables. All day I just lay in the sun on the stone flags, licking my jaws, and watching the grooms wash down the carriages, and the only care I had was to see they didn't get gay and turn the hose on me. There wasn't even a single rat to plague me. Such stables I never did see.

"Nolan," says the head groom, "some day that dog of yours will give you the slip. You can't keep a street-dog tied up all his life. It's against his natur'." The head groom is a nice old gentleman, but he doesn't know everything. Just as though I'd been a street-dog because I liked it! As if I'd rather poke for my vittles in ash-heaps than have 'em handed me in a wash-basin, and would sooner bite and fight than be polite and sociable. If I'd had mother there I couldn't have asked for nothing more. But I'd think of her snooping in the gutters, or freezing of nights under the bridges, or, what's worst of all, running through the hot streets with her tongue down, so wild and crazy for a drink that the people would shout "mad dog" at her and stone her. Water's so good that I don't blame the men-folks for locking it up inside their houses; but when the hot days come, I think they might remember that those are the dog-days, and leave a little water outside in a trough, like they do for the horses. Then we wouldn't go mad, and the policemen wouldn't shoot us. I had so much of everything I wanted that it made me think a lot of the days when I hadn't nothing, and if I could have given what I had to mother, as she used to share with me, I'd have been the happiest dog in the land. Not that I wasn't happy then, and most grateful to the Master, too, and if I'd only minded him, the trouble wouldn't have come again.

But one day the coachman says that the little lady they called Miss Dorothy had come back from school, and that same morning she runs over to the stables to pat her ponies, and she sees me.

"Oh, what a nice little, white little dog!" said she. "Whose little dog are you?" says she.

"That's my dog, miss," says the Master. " 'Is name is Kid." And I ran up to her most polite, and licks her fingers, for I never see so pretty and kind a lady.

"You must come with me and call on my new puppies," says she, picking me up in her arms and starting off with me.

"Oh, but please, miss," cries Nolan, "Mr. Wyndham give orders that the Kid's not to go to the kennels."

"That'll be all right," says the little lady; "they're my kennels too. And the puppies will like to play with him."

You wouldn't believe me if I was to tell you of the style of them quality-dogs. If I hadn't seen it myself I wouldn't have believed it neither. The Viceroy of Canada don't live no better. There was forty of them, but each one had his own house and a yard—most exclusive —and a cot and a drinking-basin all to hisself. They had servants standing round waiting to feed 'em when they was hungry, and valets to wash 'em; and they had their hair combed and brushed like the grooms must when they go out on the box. Even the puppies had overcoats with their names on 'em in blue letters, and the name of each of those they called champions was painted up fine over his front door just like it was a public house or a veterinary's. They were the biggest St. Bernards I ever did see. I could have walked under them if they'd have let me. But they were very proud and haughty dogs, and looked only once at me, and then sniffed in the air. The little lady's own dog was an old gentleman bull-dog. He'd come along with us, and when he notices how taken aback I was with all I see, 'e turned quite kind and affable and showed me about.

"Jimmy Jocks," Miss Dorothy called him, but, owing to his weight, he walked most dignified and slow, waddling like a duck, as you might say, and looked much too proud and handsome for such a silly name.

"That's the runway, and that's the trophy-house," says he to me, "and that over there is the hospital, where you have to go if you get distemper, and the vet gives you beastly medicine."

"And which of these is your 'ouse, sir?" asks I, wishing to be respectful. But he looked that hurt and haughty. "I don't live in the kennels," says he, most contemptuous. "I am a house-dog. I sleep in Miss Dorothy's room. And at lunch I'm let in with the family, if the visitors don't mind. They 'most always do, but they're too polite to say so. Besides," says he, smiling most condescending, "visitors are always afraid of me. It's because I'm so ugly," says he. "I suppose," says he, screwing up his wrinkles and speaking very slow and impressive, "I suppose I'm the ugliest bull-dog in America"; and as he seemed to be so pleased to think hisself so, I said, "Yes, sir; you certainly are the ugliest ever I see," at which he nodded his head most approving.

"But I couldn't hurt 'em, as you say," he goes on, though I hadn't said nothing like that, being too polite. "I'm too old," he says; "I haven't any teeth. The last time one of those grizzly bears," said he, glaring at the big St. Bernards, "took a hold of me, he nearly was my death," says he. I thought his eyes would pop out of his head, he seemed so wrought up about it. "He rolled me around in the dirt, he did," says Jimmy Jocks, "an' I couldn't get up. It was low," says Jimmy Jocks, making a face like he had a bad taste in his mouth. "Low, that's what I call it—bad form, you understand, young man, not done in my set—and—and low." He growled 'way down in his stomach, and puffed hisself out, panting and blowing like he had been on a run.

"I'm not a street fighter," he says, scowling at a St. Bernard marked "Champion." "And when my rheumatism is not troubling me," he says, "I endeavor to be civil to all dogs, so long as they are gentlemen."

"Yes, sir," said I, for even to me he had been most affable.

At this we had come to a little house off by itself, and Jimmy Jocks invites me in. "This is their trophy-room," he says, "where they keep their prizes. Mine," he says, rather grand-like, "are on the sideboard." Not knowing what a sideboard might be, I said, "Indeed, sir, that must be very gratifying." But he only wrinkled up his chops as much as to say, "It is my right."

The trophy-room was as wonderful as any public house I ever see. On the walls was pictures of nothing but beautiful St. Bernard dogs, and rows and rows of blue and red and yellow ribbons; and when I asked Jimmy Jocks why they was so many more of blue than of the others, he laughs and says, "Because these kennels always win." And there was many shining cups on the shelves, which Jimmy Jocks told me were prizes won by the champions.

"Now, sir, might I ask you, sir," says I, "wot is a champion?"

At that he panted and breathed so hard I thought he would bust hisself. "My dear young friend!" says he, "wherever have you been educated? A champion is a—a champion," he says. "He must win nine blue ribbons in the 'open' class. You follow me—that is—against all comers. Then he has the title before his name, and they put his photograph in the sporting papers. You know, of course, that *I* am a champion," says he. "I am Champion Woodstock Wizard III, and the two other Woodstock Wizards, my father and uncle, were both champions."

"But I thought your name was Jimmy Jocks," I said.

He laughs right out at that.

"That's my kennel name, not my registered name," he says. "Why, certainly you know that every dog has two names. Now, for instance, what's your registered name and number?" says he.

"I've got only one name," I says. "Just Kid."

Woodstock Wizard puffs at that and wrinkles up his forehead and pops out his eyes.

"Who are your people?" says he. "Where is your home?"

"At the stable, sir," I said. "My Master is the second groom."

At that Woodstock Wizard III looks at me for quite a bit without winking, and stares all around the room over my head.

"Oh, well," says he at last, "you're a very civil young dog," says he, "and I blame no one for what he can't help," which I thought most fair and liberal. "And I have known many bull-terriers that were champions," says he, "though as a rule they mostly run with fire-engines and to fighting. For me, I wouldn't care to run through the streets after a hose-cart, nor to fight," says he: "but each to his taste."

I could not help thinking that if Woodstock Wizard III tried to follow a fire-engine he would die of apoplexy, and seeing he'd lost his teeth, it was lucky he had no taste for fighting; but, after his being so condescending, I didn't say nothing.

"Anyway," says he, "every smooth-coated dog is better than any hairy old camel like those St. Bernards, and if ever you're hungry down at the stables, young man, come up to the house and I'll give you a bone. I can't eat them myself, but I bury them around the garden from force of habit and in case a friend should drop in. Ah, I see my mistress coming," he says, "and I bid you good day. I regret," he says, "that our different social position prevents our meeting frequent, for you're a worthy young dog with a proper respect for your betters, and in this country there's precious few of them have that." Then he waddles off, leaving me alone and very sad, for he was the first dog in many days that had spoke to me. But since he showed, seeing that I was a stable-dog, he didn't want my company, I waited for him to get well away. It was not a cheerful place to wait, the trophy-house. The pictures of the champions seemed to scowl at me, and ask what right such as I had even to admire them, and the blue and gold ribbons and the silver cups made me very miserable. I had never won no blue ribbons or silver cups, only stakes for the old Master to spend in the publics; and I hadn't won them for being a beautiful high-quality dog, but just for fighting—which, of course, as Woodstock Wizard III says, is low. So I started for the stables, with my head down and my tail between my legs, feeling sorry I had ever left the Master. But I had more reason to be sorry before I got back to him.

The trophy-house was quite a bit from the kennels, and as I left it I see Miss Dorothy and Woodstock Wizard III walking back toward them, and, also, that a big St. Bernard, his name was Champion Red Elfberg, had broke his chain and was running their way. When he reaches old Jimmy Jocks he lets out a roar like a grain-steamer in a fog, and he makes three leaps for him. Old Jimmy Jocks was about a fourth his size; but he plants his feet and curves his back, and his hair goes up around his neck like a collar. But he never had no show at no time, for the grizzly bear, as Jimmy Jocks had called him, lights on old Jimmy's back and tries to break it, and old Jimmy Jocks snaps his gums and claws the grass, panting and groaning awful. But he can't do nothing, and the grizzly bear just rolls him under him, biting and tearing cruel. The odds was all that Woodstock Wizard III was going to be killed; I had fought enough to see that: but not knowing the rules of the game among champions, I didn't like to interfere between two gentlemen who might be settling a private affair, and, as it were, take it as presuming of me. So I stood by, though I was shaking terrible, and holding myself in like I was on a leash. But at that Woodstock Wizard III, who was underneath, sees me through the dust, and calls very faint, "Help, you!" he says. "Take him in the hind leg," he says. "He's murdering me," he says. And then the little Miss Dorothy, who was crying, and calling to the kennel-men, catches at the Red Elfberg's hind legs to pull him off, and the brute, keeping his front pats well in Jimmy's stomach, turns his big head and snaps at her. So that was all I asked for, thank you. I went up under him. It was really nothing. He stood so high that I had only to take off about three feet from him and come in from the side, and my long "punishing jaw," as mother was always talking about, locked on his woolly throat, and my back teeth met. I couldn't shake him, but I shook myself, and every time I shook myself there was thirty pounds of weight tore at his windpipes. I couldn't see nothing for his long hair, but I heard Jimmy Jocks puffing and blowing on one side, and munching the brute's leg with his old gums. Jimmy was an old sport that day, was Jimmy, or Woodstock Wizard III, as I should say. When the Red Elfberg was out and down I had to run, or those kennel-men would have had my life. They chased me right into the stables; and from under the hay I watched the head groom take down a carriage-whip and order them to the right about. Luckily Master and the young grooms were out, or that day there'd have been fighting for everybody.

Well, it nearly did for me and the Master. "Mr. Wyndham, sir," comes raging to the stables. I'd half killed his best prize-winner, he says, and had oughter be shot, and he gives the Master his notice. But Miss Dorothy she follows him, and says it was his Red Elfberg what began the fight, and that I'd saved Jimmy's life, and that old Jimmy Jocks was worth more to her than all the St. Bernards in the Swiss mountains—wherever they may be. And that I was her champion, any-way. Then she cried over me most beautiful, and over Jimmy Jocks, too, who was that tied up in bandages he couldn't even waddle. So when he heard that side of it, "Mr. Wyndham, sir," told us that if Nolan put me on a chain we could stay. So it came out all right for everybody but me. I was glad the Master kept his place, but I'd never worn a chain before, and it disheartened me. But that was the least of it. For the quality-dogs couldn't forgive my whipping their champion, and they came to the fence between the kennels and the stables, and laughed through the bars, barking most cruel words at me. I couldn't understand how they found it out, but they knew. After the fight Jimmy Jocks was most condescending to me, and he said the grooms had boasted to the kennel-men that I was a son of Regent Royal, and that when the kennel-men asked who was my mother they had had to tell them that too. Perhaps that was the way of it, but, however, the scandal got out, and every one of the quality-dogs knew that I was a street-dog and the son of a black-and-tan.

"These misalliances will occur," said Jimmy Jocks, in his old-fashioned way; "but no well-bred dog," says he, looking most scornful at the St. Bernards, who were howling behind the palings, "would refer to your misfortune before you, certainly not cast it in your face. I myself remember your father's father, when he made his début at the Crystal Palace. He took four blue ribbons and three specials."

But no sooner than Jimmy would leave me the St. Bernards would take to howling again, insulting mother and insulting me. And when I tore at my chain, they, seeing they were safe, would howl the more. It was never the same after that; the laughs and the jeers cut into my heart, and the chain bore heavy on my spirit. I was so sad that some-times I wished I was back in the gutter again, where no one was better than me, and some nights I wished I was dead. If it hadn't been for the Master being so kind, and that it would have looked like I was blaming mother, I would have twisted my leash and hanged myself.

About a month after my fight, the word was passed through the kennels that the New York Show was coming, and such goings on as followed I never did see. If each of them had been matched to fight for a thousand pounds and the gate, they couldn't have trained more conscientious. But perhaps that's just my envy. The kennel-men rubbed 'em and scrubbed 'em, and trims their hair and curls and combs it, and some dogs they fatted and some they starved. No one talked of nothing but the Show, and the chances "our kennels" had against the other kennels, and if this one of our champions would win over that one, and whether them as hoped to be champions had better show in the "open" or the "limit" class, and whether this dog would beat his own dad, or whether his little puppy sister couldn't beat the two of 'em. Even the grooms had their money up, and day or night you heard nothing but praises of "our" dogs, until I, being so far out of it, couldn't have felt meaner if I had been running the streets with a can to my tail. I knew shows were not for such as me, and so all day I lay stretched at the end of my chain, pretending I was asleep, and only too glad that they had something so important to think of that they could leave me alone.

But one day, before the Show opened, Miss Dorothy came to the stables with "Mr. Wyndham, sir," and seeing me chained up and so miserable, she takes me in her arms.

"You poor little tyke!" says she. "It's cruel to tie him up so; he's eating his heart out, Nolan," she says. "I don't know nothing about bull-terriers," says she, "but I think Kid's got good points," says she, "and you ought to show him. Jimmy Jocks has three legs on the Rensselaer Cup now, and I'm going to show him this time, so that he can get the fourth; and, if you wish, I'll enter your dog too. How would you like that, Kid?" says she. "How would you like to see the most beautiful dogs in the world? Maybe you'd meet a pal or two," says she. "It would cheer you up, wouldn't it, Kid?" says she. But I was so upset I could only wag my tail most violent. "He says it would!" says she, though, being that excited, I hadn't said nothing.

So "Mr. Wyndham, sir," laughs, and takes out a piece of blue paper and sits down at the head groom's table.

"What's the name of the father of your dog, Nolan?" says he. And Nolan says: "The man I got him off told me he was a son of Champion Regent Royal, sir. But it don't seem likely, does it?" says Nolan.

"It does not!" says "Mr. Wyndham, sir," short-like.

"Aren't you sure, Nolan?" says Miss Dorothy.

"No, miss," says the Master.

"Sire unknown," says "Mr. Wyndham, sir," and writes it down.

"Date of birth?" asks "Mr. Wyndham, sir."

"I—I—unknown, sir," says Nolan. And "Mr. Wyndham, sir," writes it down.

"Breeder?" says "Mr. Wyndham, sir."

"Unknown," says Nolan, getting very red around the jaws, and I drops my head and tail. And "Mr. Wyndham, sir," writes that down.

"Mother's name?" says "Mr. Wyndam, sir."

"She was a—unknown," says the Master. And I licks his hand.

"Dam unknown," says "Mr. Wyndam, sir," and writes it down. Then he takes the paper and reads out loud: " 'Sire unknown, dam unknown, breeder unknown, date of birth unknown.' You'd better call him the 'Great Unknown,' " says he. "Who's paying his entrance fee?"

"I am," says Miss Dorothy.

Two weeks after we all got on a train for New York, Jimmy Jocks and me following Nolan in the smoking-car, and twenty-two of the St. Bernards in boxes and crates and on chains and leashes. Such a barking and howling I never did hear; and when they sees me going, too, they laughs fit to kill.

"Wot is this—a circus?" says the railroad man.

But I had no heart in it. I hated to go. I knew I was no "show" dog, even though Miss Dorothy and the Master did their best to keep me from shaming them. For before we set out Miss Dorothy brings a man from town who scrubbed and rubbed me, and sandpapered my tail, which hurt most awful, and shaved my ears with the Master's razor, so you could 'most see clear through 'em, and sprinkles me over with pipe-clay, till I shines like a Tommy's cross-belts.

"Upon my word!" says Jimmy Jocks when he first sees me. "Wot a swell you are! You're the image of your grand-dad when he made his début at the Crystal Palace. He took four firsts and three specials." But I knew he was only trying to throw heart into me. They might scrub, and they might rub, and they might pipe-clay, but they couldn't pipe-clay the insides of me, and they was black-and-tan.

Then we came to a garden, which it was not, but the biggest hall in the world. Inside there was lines of benches a few miles long, and on them sat every dog in America. If all the dog-snatchers in Montreal had worked night and day for a year, they couldn't have caught so many dogs. And they was all shouting and barking and howling so vicious that my heart stopped beating. For at first I thought they was all enraged at my presuming to intrude. But after I got in my place they kept at it just the same, barking at every dog as he come in: daring him to fight, and ordering him out, and asking him what breed of dog he thought he was, anyway. Jimmy Jocks was chained just behind me, and he said he never see so fine a show. "That's a hot class you're in, my lad," he says, looking over into my street, where there were thirty bull-terriers. They was all as white as cream, and each so beautiful that if I could have broke my chain I would have run all the way home and hid myself under the horse-trough.

All night long they talked and sang, and passed greetings with old pals, and the homesick puppies howled dismal. Them that couldn't sleep wouldn't let no others sleep, and all the electric lights burned in the roof, and in my eyes. I could hear Jimmy Jocks snoring peaceful, but I could only doze by jerks, and when I dozed I dreamed horrible. All the dogs in the hall seemed coming at me for daring to intrude, with their jaws red and open, and their eyes blazing like the lights in the roof. "You're a street-dog! Get out, you street-dog!" they yells. And as they drives me out, the pipe-clay drops off me, and they laugh and shriek; and when I looks down I see that I have turned into a black-and-tan.

They was most awful dreams, and next morning, when Miss Dorothy comes and gives me water in a pan, I begs and begs her to take me home; but she can't understand. "How well Kid is!" she says. And when I jumps into the Master's arms and pulls to break my chain, he says, "If he knew all as he had against him, miss, he wouldn't be so gay." And from a book they reads out the names of the beautiful high-bred terriers which I have got to meet. And I can't make 'em understand that I only want to run away and hide myself where no one will see me.

Then suddenly men comes hurrying down our street and begins to brush the beautiful bull-terriers; and the Master rubs me with a towel so excited that his hands trembles awful, and Miss Dorothy tweaks my ears between her gloves, so that the blood runs to 'em, and they turn pink and stand up straight and sharp.

"Now, then, Nolan," says she, her voice shaking just like his fingers, "keep his head up—and never let the judge lose sight of him." When I hears that my legs breaks under me, for I knows all about judges. Twice the old Master goes up before the judge for fighting me with other dogs, and the judge promises him if he ever does it again he'll chain him up in jail. I knew he'd find me out. A judge can't be fooled by no pipe-clay. He can see right through you, and he reads your insides.

The judging-ring, which is where the judge holds out, was so like a fighting-pit that when I come in it, and find six other dogs there, I springs into position, so that when they lets us go I can defend myself. But the Master smooths down my hair and whispers, "Hold 'ard, Kid, hold 'ard. This ain't a fight," says he. "Look your prettiest," he whispers. "Please, Kid, look your prettiest"; and he pulls my leash so tight that I can't touch my pats to the sawdust, and my nose goes up in the air. There was millions of people a-watching us from the railings, and three of our kennel-men, too, making fun of the Master and me, and Miss Dorothy with her chin just reaching to the rail, and her eyes so big that I thought she was a-going to cry. It was awful to think that when the judge stood up and exposed me, all those people, and Miss Dorothy, would be there to see me driven from the Show.

The judge he was a fierce-looking man with specs on his nose, and a red beard. When I first come in he didn't see me, owing to my being too quick for him and dodging behind the Master. But when the Master drags me round and I pulls at the sawdust to keep back, the judge looks at us careless-like, and then stops and glares through his specs, and I knew it was all up with me.

"Are there any more?" asks the judge to the gentleman at the gate, but never taking his specs from me.

The man at the gate looks in his book. "Seven in the novice class," says he. "They're all here. You can go ahead," and he shuts the gate.

The judge he doesn't hesitate a moment. He just waves his hand toward the corner of the ring. "Take him away," he says to the Master, "over there, and keep him away"; and he turns and looks most solemn at the six beautiful bull-terriers. I don't know how I crawled to that corner. I wanted to scratch under the sawdust and dig myself a grave. The kennel-men they slapped the rail with their hands and laughed at the Master like they would fall over. They pointed at me in the corner, and their sides just shaked. But little Miss Dorothy she presses her lips tight against the rail, and I see tears rolling from her eyes. The Master he hangs his head like he had been whipped. I felt most sorry for him than all. He was so red, and he was letting on not to see the kennel-men, and blinking his eyes. If the judge had ordered me right out it wouldn't have disgraced us so, but it was keeping me there while he was judging the high-bred dogs that hurt so hard. With all those people staring, too. And his doing it so quick, without no doubt nor questions. You can't fool the judges. They see inside you.

But he couldn't make up his mind about them high-bred dogs. He scowls at 'em, and he glares at 'em, first with his head on the one side and then on the other. And he feels of 'em, and orders 'em to run about. And Nolan leans against the rails, with his head hung down, and pats me. And Miss Dorothy comes over beside him, but don't say nothing, only wipes her eye with her finger. A man on the other side of the rail he says to the Master, "The judge don't like your dog?"

"No," says the Master.

"Have you ever shown him before?" says the man.

"No," says the Master, "and I'll never show him again. He's my dog," says the Master, "and he suits me! And I don't care what no judges think." And when he says them kind words, I licks his hand most grateful.

The judge had two of the six dogs on a little platform in the middle of the ring, and he had chased the four other dogs into the corners, where they was licking their chops, and letting on they didn't care, same as Nolan was.

The two dogs on the platform was so beautiful that the judge his-self couldn't tell which was the best of 'em, even when he stoops down and holds their heads together. But at last he gives a sigh, and brushes the sawdust off his knees, and goes to the table in the ring, where there was a man keeping score, and heaps and heaps of blue and gold and red and yellow ribbons. And the judge picks up a bunch of 'em and walks to the two gentlemen who was holding the beautiful dogs, and he says to each, "What's his number?" and he hands each gentle-man a ribbon. And then he turned sharp and comes straight at the Master.

"What's his number?" says the judge. And Master was so scared that he couldn't make no answer.

But Miss Dorothy claps her hands and cries out like she was laugh-ing, "Three twenty-six," and the judge writes it down and shoves Master the blue ribbon.

I bit the Master, and I jumps and bit Miss Dorothy, and I waggled so hard that the Master couldn't hold me. When I get to the gate Miss Dorothy snatches me up and kisses me between the ears, right before millions of people, and they both hold me so tight that I didn't know which of them was carrying of me. But one thing I knew, for I listened hard, as it was the judge hisself as said it.

"Did you see that puppy I gave first to?" says the judge to the gentleman at the gate.

"I did. He was a bit out of his class," says the gate gentleman.

"He certainly was!" says the judge, and they both laughed.

But I didn't care. They couldn't hurt me then, not with Nolan hold-ing the blue ribbon and Miss Dorothy hugging my ears, and the kennel-men sneaking away, each looking like he'd been caught with his nose under the lid of the slop-can.

We sat down together, and we all three just talked as fast as we could. They was so pleased that I couldn't help feeling proud myself, and I barked and leaped about so gay that all the bull-terriers in our street stretched on their chains and howled at me.

"Just look at him!" says one of those I had beat. "What's he giving hisself airs about?"

"Because he's got one blue ribbon!" says another of 'em. "Why, when I was a puppy I used to eat 'em, and if that judge could ever learn to know a toy from a mastiff, I'd have had this one."

But Jimmy Jocks he leaned over from his bench and says, "Well done, Kid. Didn't I tell you so?" What he 'ad told me was that I might get a "commended," but I didn't remind him.

"Didn't I tell you," says Jimmy Jocks, "that I saw your grandfather make his début at the Crystal——"

"Yes, sir, you did, sir," says I, for I have no love for the men of my family.

A gentleman with a showing-leash around his neck comes up just then and looks at me very critical. "Nice dog you've got, Miss Wyndham," says he; "would you care to sell him?"

"He's not my dog," says Miss Dorothy, holding me tight. "I wish he were."

"He's not for sale, sir," says the Master, and I was *that* glad.

"Oh, he's yours, is he?" says the gentleman, looking hard at Nolan. "Well, I'll give you a hundred dollars for him," says he, careless-like.

"Thank you, sir; he's not for sale," says Nolan, but his eyes get very big. The gentleman he walked away; but I watches him, and he talks to a man in a golf-cap, and by and by the man comes along our street, looking at all the dogs, and stops in front of me.

"This your dog?" says he to Nolan. "Pity he's so leggy," says he. "If he had a good tail, and a longer stop, and his ears were set higher, he'd be a good dog. As he is, I'll give you fifty dollars for him."

But, before the Master could speak, Miss Dorothy laughs and says: "You're Mr. Polk's kennel-man, I believe. Well, you tell Mr. Polk from me that the dog's not for sale now any more than he was five minutes ago, and that when he is, he'll have to bid against me for him."

The man looks foolish at that, but he turns to Nolan quick-like. "I'll give you three hundred for him," he says.

"Oh, indeed!" whispers Miss Dorothy, like she was talking to herself. "That's it, is it?" And she turns and looks at me just as though she had never seen me before. Nolan he was a-gaping, too, with his mouth open. But he holds me tight.

"He's not for sale," he growls, like he was frightened; and the man looks black and walks away.

"Why, Nolan!" cries Miss Dorothy, "Mr. Polk knows more about bull-terriers than any amateur in America. What can he mean? Why, Kid is no more than a puppy! Three hundred dollars for a puppy!"

"And he ain't no thoroughbred, neither!" cries the Master. "He's 'Unknown,' ain't he? Kid can't help it, of course, but his mother, miss——"

I dropped my head. I couldn't bear he should tell Miss Dorothy. I couldn't bear she should know I had stolen my blue ribbon.

But the Master never told, for at that a gentleman runs up, calling, "Three twenty-six, three twenty-six!" And Miss Dorothy says, "Here he is; what is it?"

"The Winners' class," says the gentleman. "Hurry, please; the judge is waiting for him."

Nolan tries to get me off the chain on to a showing-leash, but he shakes so, he only chokes me. "What is it, miss?" he says. "What is it?"

"The Winners' class," says Miss Dorothy. "The judge wants him with the winners of the other classes—to decide which is the best. It's only a form," says she. "He has the champions against him now."

"Yes," says the gentleman, as he hurries us to the ring. "I'm afraid it's only a form for your dog, but the judge wants all the winners, puppy class even."

We had got to the gate, and the gentleman there was writing down my number.

"Who won the open?" asks Miss Dorothy.

"Oh, who would?" laughs the gentleman. "The old champion, of course. He's won for three years now. There he is. Isn't he wonderful?" says he; and he points to a dog that's standing proud and haughty on the platform in the middle of the ring.

I never see so beautiful a dog—so fine and clean and noble, so white like he had rolled hisself in flour, holding his nose up and his eyes shut, same as though no one was worth looking at. Aside of him we other dogs, even though we had a blue ribbon apiece, seemed like lumps of mud. He was a royal gentleman, a king, he was. His master didn't have to hold his head with no leash. He held it hisself, standing as still as an iron dog on a lawn, like he knew all the people was looking at him. And so they was, and no one around the ring pointed at no other dog but him.

"Oh, what a picture!" cried Miss Dorothy. "He's like a marble figure by a great artist—one who loved dogs. Who is he?" says she, looking in her book. "I don't keep up with terriers."

"Oh, you know him," says the gentleman. "He is the champion of champions, Regent Royal."

The Master's face went red.

"And this is Regent Royal's son," cries he, and he pulls me quick into the ring, and plants me on the platform next my father.

I trembled so that I near fell. My legs twisted like a leash. But my father he never looked at me. He only smiled the same sleepy smile, and he still kept his eyes half shut, like as no one, no, not even his own son, was worth his lookin' at.

The judge he didn't let me stay beside my father, but, one by one, he placed the other dogs next to him and measured and felt and pulled at them. And each one he put down, but he never put my father down. And then he comes over and picks up me and sets me back on the platform, shoulder to shoulder with the Champion Regent Royal, and goes down on his knees, and looks into our eyes.

The gentleman with my father he laughs, and says to the judge, "Thinking of keeping us here all day, John?" But the judge he doesn't hear him, and goes behind us and runs his hand down my side, and holds back my ears, and takes my jaws between his fingers. The crowd around the ring is very deep now, and nobody says nothing. The gentleman at the score-table, he is leaning forward, with his elbows on his knees and his eyes very wide, and the gentleman at the gate is whispering quick to Miss Dorothy, who has turned white. I stood as stiff as stone. I didn't even breathe. But out of the corner of my eye I could see my father licking his pink chops, and yawning just a little, like he was bored.

The judge he had stopped looking fierce and was looking solemn. Something inside him seemed a-troubling him awful. The more he stares at us now, the more solemn he gets, and when he touches us he does it gentle, like he was patting us. For a long time he kneels in the sawdust, looking at my father and at me, and no one around the ring says nothing to nobody.

Then the judge takes a breath and touches me sudden. "It's his," he says. But he lays his hand just as quick on my father. "I'm sorry," says he.

The gentleman holding my father cries:

"Do you mean to tell me——"

And the judge he answers, "I mean the other is the better dog." He takes my father's head between his hands and looks down at him most sorrowful. "The king is dead," says he. "Long live the king! Good-by, Regent," he says.

The crowd around the railings clapped their hands, and some laughed scornful, and everyone talks fast, and I start for the gate, so dizzy that I can't see my way. But my father pushes in front of me, walking very daintily, and smiling sleepy, same as he had just been waked, with his head high and his eyes shut, looking at nobody.

So that is how I "came by my inheritance," as Miss Dorothy calls it; and just for that, though I couldn't feel where I was any different, the crowd follows me to my bench, and pats me, and coos at me, like I was a baby in a baby-carriage. And the handlers have to hold 'em back so that the gentlemen from the papers can make pictures of me, and Nolan walks me up and down so proud, and the men shake their heads and says, "He certainly is the true type, he is!" And the pretty ladies ask Miss Dorothy, who sits beside me letting me lick her gloves to show the crowd what friends we is, "Aren't you afraid he'll bite you?" And Jimmy Jocks calls to me, "Didn't I tell you so? I always knew you were one of us. Blood will out, Kid; blood will out. I saw your grandfather," says he, "make his début at the Crystal Palace. But he was never the dog you are!"

After that, if I could have asked for it, there was nothing I couldn't get. You might have thought I was a snow-dog, and they was afeard I'd melt. If I wet my pats, Nolan gave me a hot bath and chained me to the stove; if I couldn't eat my food, being stuffed full by the cook,— for I am a house-dog now, and let in to lunch, whether there is visitors or not,—Nolan would run to bring the vet. It was all tommy rot, as Jimmy says, but meant most kind. I couldn't scratch myself comfortable, without Nolan giving me nasty drinks, and rubbing me outside till it burnt awful; and I wasn't let to eat bones for fear of spoiling my "beautiful" mouth, what mother used to call my "punishing jaw"; and my food was cooked special on a gas-stove; and Miss Dorothy gives me an overcoat, cut very stylish like the champions', to wear when we goes out carriage-driving.

After the next Show, where I takes three blue ribbons, four silver cups, two medals, and brings home forty-five dollars for Nolan, they gives me a "registered" name, same as Jimmy's. Miss Dorothy wanted to call me "Regent Heir Apparent"; but I was *that* glad when Nolan says, "No; Kid don't owe nothing to his father, only to you and hisself. So, if you please, miss, we'll call him Wyndham Kid." And so they did, and you can see it on my overcoat in blue letters, and painted top of my kennel. It was all too hard to understand. For days I just sat and wondered if I was really me, and how it all came about, and why everybody was so kind. But oh, it was so good they was, for if they hadn't been I'd never have got the thing I most wished after. But, because they was kind, and not liking to deny me nothing, they gave it me, and it was more to me than anything in the world.

It came about one day when we was out driving. We was in the cart they calls the dog-cart because it's the one Miss Dorothy keeps to take Jimmy and me for an airing. Nolan was up behind, and me, in my new overcoat, was sitting beside Miss Dorothy. I was admiring the view, and thinking how good it was to have a horse pull you about so that you needn't get yourself splashed and have to be washed, when I hears a dog calling loud for help, and I pricks up my ears and looks over the horse's head. And I sees something that makes me tremble down to my toes. In the road before us three big dogs was chasing a little old lady-dog. She had a string to her tail, where some boys had tied a can, and she was dirty with mud and ashes, and torn most awful. She was too far done up to get away, and too old to help herself, but she was making a fight for her life, snapping her old gums savage, and dying game. All this I see in a wink, and then the three dogs pinned her down, and I can't stand it no longer, and clears the wheel and lands in the road on my head. It was my stylish overcoat done that, and I cursed it proper, but I gets my pats again quick, and makes a rush for the fighting. Behind me I hear Miss Dorothy cry: "They'll kill that old dog. Wait, take my whip. Beat them off her! The Kid can take care of himself"; and I hear Nolan fall into the road, and the horse come to a stop. The old lady-dog was down, and the three was eating her vicious; but as I come up, scattering the pebbles, she hears, and thinking it's one more of them, she lifts her head, and my heart breaks open like someone had sunk his teeth in it. For, under the ashes and the dirt and the blood, I can see who it is, and I know that my mother has come back to me.

I gives a yell that throws them three dogs off their legs.

"Mother!" I cries. "I'm the Kid," I cries. "I'm coming to you. Mother, I'm coming!"

And I shoots over her at the throat of the big dog, and the other two they sinks their teeth into that stylish overcoat and tears it off me, and that sets me free, and I lets them have it. I never had so fine a fight as that! What with mother being there to see, and not having been let to mix up in no fights since I become a prize-winner, it just naturally did me good, and it wasn't three shakes before I had 'em yelping. Quick as a wink, mother she jumps in to help me, and I just laughed to see her. It was so like old times. And Nolan he made me laugh, too. He was like a hen on a bank, shaking the butt of his whip, but not daring to cut in for fear of hitting me.

"Stop it, Kid," he says, "stop it. Do you want to be all torn up?" says he. "Think of the Boston show," says he. "Think of Chicago. Think of Danbury. Don't you never want to be a champion?" How was I to think of all them places when I had three dogs to cut up at the same time? But in a minute two of 'em begs for mercy, and mother and me lets 'em run away. The big one he ain't able to run away. Then mother and me we dances and jumps, and barks and laughs, and bites each other and rolls each other in the road. There never was two dogs so happy as we. And Nolan he whistles and calls and begs me to come to him; but I just laugh and play larks with mother.

"Now, you come with me," says I, "to my new home, and never try to run away again." And I shows her our house with the five red roofs, set on the top of the hill. But mother trembles awful, and says: "They'd never let me in such a place. Does the Viceroy live there, Kid?" says she. And I laugh at her. "No; I do," I says. "And if they won't let you live there, too, you and me will go back to the streets together, for we must never be parted no more." So we trots up the hill side by side, with Nolan trying to catch me, and Miss Dorothy laughing at him from the cart.

"The Kid's made friends with the poor old dog," says she. "Maybe he knew her long ago when he ran the streets himself. Put her in here beside me, and see if he doesn't follow."

So when I hears that I tells mother to go with Nolan and sit in the cart; but she says no—that she'd soil the pretty lady's frock; but I tells her to do as I say, and so Nolan lifts her, trembling still, into the cart, and I runs alongside, barking joyful.

When we drives into the stables I takes mother to my kennel, and tells her to go inside it and make herself at home. "Oh, but he won't let me!" says she.

"Who won't let you?" says I, keeping my eye on Nolan, and growling a bit nasty, just to show I was meaning to have my way.

"Why, Wyndham Kid," says she, looking up at the name on my kennel.

"But I'm Wyndham Kid!" says I.

"You!" cries mother. "You! Is my little Kid the great Wyndham Kid the dogs all talk about?" And at that, she being very old, and sick, and nervous, as mothers are, just drops down in the straw and weeps bitter.

Well, there ain't much more than that to tell. Miss Dorothy she settled it.

"If the Kid wants the poor old thing in the stables," says she, "let her stay.

"You see," says she, "she's a black-and-tan, and his mother was a black-and-tan, and maybe that's what makes Kid feel so friendly toward her," says she.

"Indeed, for me," says Nolan, "she can have the best there is. I'd never drive out no dog that asks for a crust nor a shelter," he says. "But what will Mr. Wyndham do?"

"He'll do what I say," says Miss Dorothy, "and if I say she's to stay, she will stay, and I say—she's to stay!"

And so mother and Nolan and me found a home. Mother was scared at first—not being used to kind people; but she was so gentle and loving that the grooms got fonder of her than of me, and tried to make me jealous by patting of her and giving her the pick of the vittles. But that was the wrong way to hurt my feelings. That's all, I think. Mother is so happy here that I tell her we ought to call it the Happy Hunting Grounds, because no one hunts you, and there is nothing to hunt; it just all comes to you. And so we live in peace, mother sleeping all day in the sun, or behind the stove in the head groom's office, being fed twice a day regular by Nolan, and all the day by the other grooms most irregular. And as for me, I go hurrying around the country to the bench-shows, winning money and cups for Nolan, and taking the blue ribbons away from father.

AN AFTERWORD ON
"THE BAR SINISTER"

AT Christmas and Easter time, the managing editors of the
New York dailies vanish into storm-cellars to hide
from all the Harvard, Yale, and Princeton seniors who
plan, in the fall, to take up journalism in a big way. Your old-
timer is especially infuriated by these latter-day postulants for
holy orders because they all aspire to become either columnists
or, at least, dramatic critics. None of them seems interested in
contributing to, understanding, or even reading that part of a
newspaper which makes it one. It was not so in the era which
lasted from the storming of San Juan Hill until the gray November morning in 1918 when the order to cease firing went out by
wireless from the high Eiffel Tower in Paris—that fast receding
period which, to the discomfort of the recently senescent, is already referred to as the good old days. Then a would-be journalist asked nothing better than to be a reporter, a roving spectator
of current history, a news-man on assignment. He would expect
to attend wars and shipwrecks and coronations, with occasional
breathing spells to be spent breakfasting under the gay, striped
awnings of the Vienna Bakery or nodding to George Ade at a
first-night at the Empire. Then, when he had seen all there
was to see and grown too old for such junketing about the
world—that is, when he was thirty or more—he would settle
down at some little place in the Berkshires and write fiction.
In other words, all newcomers to Park Row in those days had it

in mind to be as much as possible like Richard Harding Davis.

You have only to look at the Gibson drawings of the late nineties to see how handsome a fellow Davis was. This footnote is written by one who can testify that he was also brave and loyal and enormously kind. Among his contemporaries still cluttering up the earth, there must be many who will feel a little pang at the heart and hear—hanging like perfume in the air—the jaunty old tune about the Yama Yama Man when they note that *The Bar Sinister* was last copyrighted in the name of Bessie McCoy Davis.

This story was first published in *Scribner's Magazine* in 1902 and was based on a fairly well-documented legend that the prize-winning bull-terrier of that day, Edgewood Cold Steel, had been sired of a humble black-and-tan by the unguarded champion, Lord Minto, and was the only white puppy in a litter of black-and-tans. Whether Davis's telling of the tale be good or not, I could not say. I have known it too long and been too fond of it to be any longer a judge.

A. W.

THE WHISTLERS' ROOM

by

PAUL ALVERDES

TRANSLATED FROM THE GERMAN
BY
BASIL CREIGHTON

DEDICATED TO

HANS CAROSSA

THE WHISTLERS' ROOM

I

THE large room with the wide terrace in front and the view over the park and fields and a glimpse of the Rhine in the distance beneath a brown cloud of smoke was known throughout the hospital as the Whistlers' Room. It was named after the three soldiers who had been shot in the throat and awaited their recovery there. They had been there a long while; some said since the first year of the war. The stretcher-bearers who were the first to bandage them under fire in the shelter of ruined houses or in dugouts roofed over with planks and turf, pronounced on them a sentence of speedy death. But in defiance of all precedent and expectation they came through, for the time at any rate.

The process of healing, however, overshot its mark, for the bullet holes were covered over on the inner side of the windpipe by new flesh in such thick rolls and weals that the air passage was speedily blocked, and a new channel had to be made to meet this unforeseen threat of suffocation. So the surgeon's knife cut a small hole in the neck below the old wound, which was causing a more and more impassable block. At this point a tube was sunk into the windpipe, and the air then passed freely in and out of the lungs.

The tube was a small silver pipe of the length and thickness of the little finger. At its outer end there was a small shield, fixed at right angles, not larger than the identity disk that everyone at the front wore next his skin. The purpose of it was to prevent the tube slipping into the gullet; and to prevent it falling out, there was a white tape passing through two eyeholes in the shield and secured behind round the neck by a double slip knot. In itself, however, the pipe was of two parts, closely fitted together, the innermost of which was held in its place by a tiny winged screw. Three times a day it was pulled out by two small handles to be cleaned, for since they could not breathe through the nostrils, the tubes had become, as it were, the whistlers' noses. And when they were not actually bedridden they gladly cleaned them for themselves with the little round brush provided for that purpose.

After it was cleaned, the entrance of the tube had at once to be protected against dust and flies by a clean curtain. This was about the size of the hand and rectangular in form. It was cut from a thick roll of white muslin and attached to the tape with pins. It recalled the clerical band that forms part of the official garb of evangelical clergymen. Thus it was that the whistlers, with their spotless white between chin and chest, had always a ceremonial air. They were well aware of it. There was something of this in their whole bearing, and gladly they changed their bibs and tuckers several times a day for cleaner and whiter ones. When they breathed quickly or laughed, a soft piping note, like the squeaking of mice, came from the silver mouth. Hence they were called the neck whistlers, or simply the whistlers.

Talking, after being for a long while practically dumb, gave them great trouble at first, and they were glad to avoid it, particularly before strangers. When they wished to speak they had to close the mouth of the pipe with the tip of the finger. Then a thread-like stream of air found its way upwards through the throat and played on the vocal cords, or what remained of them, and they, very unwillingly roused from their torpor, emitted no more than a painful wheezing and croaking.

It was not, however, for their cracked notes that the whistlers blushed, but for this to-do with lifting their bibs and feeling with their fingers for their secret mouthpiece. This predicament they tried to disguise by every means. Were a stranger to address them on the roads through the park, or in the wide passages and halls of the great building, where in bad weather they sometimes took their walks, they usually forebore returning on immediate answer. They looked in meditation down at their toes, or with head courteously inclined and raised eyebrows, gazed into the face of him who accosted them as though earnestly seeking within themselves for a suitable response. Meanwhile, quite without any particular object, they put up a hand to their breasts and after a moment proceeded as though to dally with a shirt button that might be concealed beneath the white pinafore. After this they began to talk and sometimes, if they gained sufficient confidence, their first silence might be exchanged for a cheerful loquacity. It was as though they wished to show that in the very understandable and, indeed, most everyday matter of being hoarse, they were not any different from other men. Why they did this they could not themselves have said, and they did not speak of it to each other. Yet they all behaved as though sworn to secrecy by oath, and when a fourth was added to the group, he, from the very first, did likewise.

It was just the same, moreover, with the others in the room upstairs who had lost an arm or a leg. They felt no shyness at being seen by strangers with an empty sleeve or a trouser leg dangling loose and empty; indeed some of them vaunted their docked limbs and even went so far as to instil a kind of veneration, in those who had come off more lightly, by a display of their sad stumps. Yet the scraping and creaking of the sometimes not very successful appliances with which they had to learn to walk again caused them acute embarrassment before strangers. At once they came to a stop and tried to disguise the grasp for the lever that enabled them to fix the artificial joint by catching or pulling at their trousers, or by any other apparently trivial movement. They never displayed an unclothed false hand or foot, and at night when they undressed for bed they concealed the arm they had screwed off by hanging the coat over it, or the leg by leaving it carefully in a corner inside the trouser. For they were always afraid of being surprised by outsiders, and would have liked best always to be by themselves.

Sometimes, however, visitors from outside came to distribute gifts—to the whistlers, as well, in their room. They made presents of wine, fruit and cakes, and especially of all kinds of scent with which the whistlers gladly and copiously besprinkled themselves. It is true that their sense of smell was for the time in abeyance, but they were all the more gratified to feel that they carried a pleasant aroma about with them. For all that, these occasions of munificence did not long continue. Too often the visitors came to a hasty conclusion that he who could not utter a sound, or only in a treble voice, must necessarily be stone deaf as well, and they proceeded to shout at the whistlers without mercy, and some even pulled out notebooks and wrote in enormous letters what they might just as well have said. Or they tried from the very outset to make themselves intelligible by gestures of the most exaggerated description. For the whistlers this was a gross insult. The defect which they had now adopted as a peculiarity of their own seemed to them in a sense a merit, and no longer really a defect at all. But the one that was thus falsely laid to their door wounded them to the quick. And so, no sooner had the unknown visitor entered at one door, than they took flight by another. But if they were caught in bed they pretended to be asleep, or put their fingers warningly to their lips, shook their heads with a pretence of regret, and enjoined upon the intruders an alarmed and guilty retreat.

Among themselves the whistlers held lively and intimate talks. They could do so easily in a wordless clucking speech that, in default of a stream of air to make words with, they formed by means of their lips and tongues and teeth. Their powers of comprehension had arrived at such a pitch that in the night, when lights were out and when there was no help from gestures of the hands, the three held long talks from bed to bed. It sounded like the incessant clucking and splashing in a water-butt under the changing quick patter of heavy drops. For the low fever that seldom left the whistlers, or the influence of drugs administered for their healing, kept them often long awake. They never talked of a future and seldom of a past before the war. But of their last day at the front and of the exact circumstances in which they were wounded they never tired of giving vivid and stirring accounts, and with such leisure for recollection there was always more and more to add, and sometimes, indeed, an entirely new story was evolved and told for the first time. But not one of them showed any surprise at that.

I I

THERE was one thing, however, to be told of the eldest of the three that could not be varied, and this was that a shell splinter had smashed his jaws and his larynx. His name was Pointner, and he was a peasant's son from Bavaria. He had been in the whistlers' room for over a year, and his case was the worst of the three. A poison had infected his blood, and slowly, almost imperceptibly, his condition became hopeless. He often had to be in bed, with a high temperature, and then there was little he could be tempted to eat. Though well grown and well nourished when he left home, he was now as lank as a young boy. But nothing vexed him so much as when some of the convalescents from other wards picked him up like a child in their arms and offered to carry him about. A dark flush came into his cheeks, and he spat and scratched in rage and hit out unsparingly on all sides with his fever-wasted hands. He was ashamed of weighing so little. Nobody who saw him now would have guessed that he had been a butcher by trade, a master of all the secrets of the slaughter-house and an adept at making sausages. To be sure, his time for that was over.

Perhaps Pointner had been once of a hot-blooded and even truculent disposition. On the cupboard beside his bed, in a highly decorated frame of silver metal, he had a photograph of himself as a reservist. This frame was composed of two gnarled oak trees, whose branches, through which ran broad scrolls bearing inscriptions, were gathered together along the top and bore the crown of a princely house. At their base, amid the mighty roots, was entwined a bunch of all kinds of swords, flags, rifles, and cavalry lances. Between the oaks, however, reservist Pointner was to be seen, his cap, beneath which a so-called *Sechserlocke* protruded, set jauntily over one ear, and two fingers of the right hand stuck between the buttons of his tunic. In his left was jauntily held a cane bound with a plaited band from which depended a knot. His jaw was unusually strong and prominent, and this gave an aggressive turn to his short stature and the amiable expression of the upper part of his face. "Reserve now has rest," was written on the photograph, and it was lightly tinted in bright colours. Nevertheless reserve had not had rest and the aggressive jaw had disappeared, a small boneless and retreating chin taking its place. It gave his face, with the always slightly parted lips and the white gleam of the upper teeth—which had escaped unscathed—beneath the straw-coloured moustache, a childlike and weak expression. And indeed the alteration in Pointner was more and more marked, though the old hot blood still sometimes came uppermost and made him dangerous.

Pointner had been wounded in one of the first fights with the English, and after that had lain for a week or two in a field hospital. From there one morning he found his way, in the midst of a crowd of lightly wounded cases, and quite contrary to regulations, into an emergency hospital train and got back to Germany. He was clothed in a long-skirted hospital garment of blue and white striped wool, with felt slippers on his feet. On his head he wore a plundered English sniper's cap, which he had brought with him on the stretcher into the field hospital and had never surrendered. Speechless as he was, with face and neck bandaged up to the eyes, and with no papers either, he was taken for an English prisoner throughout the journey and treated as such. Even the memory of this threw him into a rage. Certainly, the simplest thing would have been to cast away the khaki cap, but to this he could not bring himself. Rather than that he remained a Britisher despite himself, passed over unwelcomed and unbeflowered, and left to one side in his stretcher shedding tears of rage. It was not till later that he succeeded in making himself understood.

Nevertheless, in spite of peremptory orders, he still kept the cap safely in a lower shelf of the cupboard which served as the retreat for a different article. Now and then when neither doctor nor nurse was expected to come in, he took it out. With care he polished the badge and the chin strap till they shone, and had a long look at it, turning it about meanwhile in his delicate hands, where the whites of the nails were turning from snow white to a bluish tinge.

III

KOLLIN, the second whistler, was a volunteer and Prussian pioneer. He had round and very bright blue eyes, set close together in a thin long face, and a hooked nose that increased its air of fearlessness. Kollin suffered keenly under his disability, for he was ambitious and had set his heart on promotion. He often examined his wound with despairing impatience in a little pocket-mirror, and angrily shook his head when compelled to find that there was no alteration to be seen. Many a morning after dreaming that he was cured, he woke to find himself entirely recovered and free from his disfigurement. He seemed to breathe freely again in the normal way, and got up at once to prove it to his comrades with his eyes shining. But it did not last long. Even before the doctor's visit he had to admit that his breath began to fail him, and that everything was as before.

Kollin's passion was numbers and number games. In warm weather, too, he sat all day long outside on the terrace with Pointner, bent over the chessboard and surrounded by a group of silent spectators. He hung a long while over each move, and as he hovered with slightly trembling hands over the board, he seemed to be cogitating a second game in the recesses of his mind. Now and again he made notes on a piece of paper. Pointner, whose moves were made with rapidity and who loved to rap down his pieces with a smart report, looked out meanwhile over the park as though bored and indifferent. He made himself acquainted with the alteration on the board without more than a lightning glance over his shoulder, but all the same his flushed cheeks grew darker as the threat of checkmate drew nearer and nearer. He still, however, made a few more moves with a hand so light it seemed as if they followed of themselves, and a disdainful and superior gesture made it very clear that reservist Pointner was not to be caught so simply. He would have dearly liked now and then to whistle a tune just to show that he had every reason to be content, but he was no more able to whistle than the other whistlers. At least he could purse up his lips to show that he meant to, and produce a tiny sound that recalled the cheery chirp of a finch. Even while he did so he was already avoiding the eyes of the onlookers, and they were unable to hide their glee any longer over the progress of the game. Suddenly, when Kollin was about to draw the noose tighter and turn his careful preparations into leisurely triumph, he broke out. With short round movements from the wrist, like the pats of a cat, he sent the pieces flying in all directions. At the same time, reddening with anger and shame, he got up with a final contemptuous gesture to signify he would have no more of it, pulled his cap down over his fair hair, and stumped off into the park without looking around. Kollin smiled grimly and shrugged his shoulders. Then he gathered up the chessmen and put them back as they were, in order to demonstrate to the onlookers that the inevitable progress of the game could not have ended otherwise than in his own conclusive victory. But usually they, too, had lost interest and gone away one after another, leaving Kollin alone with his aggrieved reflections. Pulling out his notebook, he wrote down exactly how the game had gone. "White," he wrote, and then in brackets "Reservist Pointner gives up." After his death there was found among his papers an exact account of every game played in the whistlers' room. In the course of two years he had played fifteen hundred and eighty-nine games, and of these he had won seven hundred and one. The rest had been broken off by his opponent in desperate straits.

After a game had been broken off in this way, the next morning, at the latest, Pointner always set out the chessboard before breakfast had even been brought in, and sat waiting in silence beside it. Kollin meanwhile went on reading an old newspaper, but soon he was unable to endure the pleasures of anticipation or to attend to what he read, and laying the paper aside he silently took his seat at the board. Sometimes on such mornings Pointner prevailed on himself to sit out his defeat.

I V

The third whistler, a boy of seventeen, was called Benjamin. He had been christened so in a field hospital close up to the line on the west front. One October morning, just as it was getting light, a so-called char-à-banc arrived there. It was a vehicle with two long benches opposite each other, the whole enclosed within a square covering of grey tent-cloth that came closely down on all sides. As could be seen, it belonged to a Westphalian battery which had been put out of action the day before.

For a moment nothing stirred. Then a man without a tunic, in mud-caked breeches, climbed down backwards and very circumspectly out of the caravan. Last came his left arm, bent up to the level of his chest in a superfluously large and makeshift splint. "Vice-Quartermaster Joseph," he reported to the doctor who at that moment came out of the entrance with sleeves rolled up and a brown rubber apron over his white overalls. "Vice-Quartermaster Joseph, of such-and-such a regiment, with eleven severely wounded men of his battery."

These eleven sat dazed and fevered, or hung rather, with sunken heads, since there was no room to lie, along both benches inside the char-à-banc. Some clung fast to each other, and none moved when the covering was thrown back and the bearers came up with stretchers. One after another they were carried out. The last was a boy who, as he was carried in, his blood-stained coat on the arms of an immense Army Medical Corps non-commissioned officer, suddenly cheered up and tried to say something. Meanwhile he described wide circles with his hands across the sky which now began to show its cloudless blue, and raised his eyebrows and blew out his cheeks; he seemed, too, to wish to convey certain numbers. But not a sound proceeded from his throat. "To be sure," said the doctor in a fine quiet voice, laying a finger gently under his chin, "to be sure, it is Joseph and his brethren, and you must certainly be Benjamin. I'll put you all together in the best ward we have."

None the less they were no sooner in their beds than they began dying. On the very same day five of Joseph's brethren were wound in the sheets they could warm no longer and carried out. But the boy was called Benjamin thereafter.

And next it seemed that he, too, would never get back to Germany. The doctor forbade him meat or drink. But during the night, the house in which they were was set on fire by a shell from a long-range gun, and Benjamin, who lay under a blanket on his palliasse, was strapped on a stretcher and taken out naked—for the unexpected stream of wounded that day had exhausted the supply of nightshirts. In this manner he reached another house, but owing to the disorder that followed upon the sudden shelling and the outbreak of fire, the prohibition did not catch him up even on the next day. Thirst tortured him, and with raised hands he begged a cup of the soup that was being taken round to the rest of the room. He had scarcely attempted to swallow a sip of it before he felt as though someone gripped him by the throat with both hands. In horror he sprang right up out of bed and tore his mouth open as far as it would go. But do as he might—throwing his head about on all sides with his chest convulsively distended, and striking out at last with arms and shoulders as though swimming in the water, and turning wildly round and round where he stood—he could not succeed in inhaling the least breath of air. Finally, while his comrades shouted for help, he raged over and over on his bed without uttering a sound, and then rising once more to his feet fell forward senseless.

Often he told the whistlers in later days how he stormed death with all the strength of his soul and actually reached his goal. There, at a stroke, he had lost all desire for breath, and hovering without weight in the void, had felt light and airy as he never felt before in his whole life. At the same time music rang out in a melody that he could never convey, but certainly no musician in the world could ever hit on notes like those. After that, he would conclude, he might well say it was good to die. The whistlers listened with earnest faces and nodded their heads; they did not doubt it. To anyone else Benjamin never said a word of all this, nor of all that he still had to go through in that hospital.

He was awakened by sudden merciless pain. At once the music ceased and his agony returned, but just as he tried to renew his struggles the cool air streamed like water into his lungs. He began to breathe once more, and once more felt that he had weight and was lying on his back, and this, too, he felt as a happiness.

Later he was told that the doctor happened to be on his way to visit other cases near by, and hurrying in at the cries for help, arrived in the nick of time to catch Benjamin in his arms. As he had not his case of instruments with him, he had pierced Benjamin's throat with his pocket knife.

After this Benjamin began to recover very quickly. But it seemed that his being still had a hankering for the experience that had already cost so dear. One morning, not long afterwards, just as the doctor, attended by his orderlies, was carefully cleaning the wound, the artery on the left side of the throat burst, as though it had been too long dammed, and shot the blood in a crimson arch out of his mouth. The artery had been severed by a bullet, but a piece of sinewy flesh which had likewise been shot through had clapped itself like a piece of plaster over the torn artery and for the time arrested the flow of blood.

Benjamin was beyond all terror as the hot torrent surged over his hands as he put them up in astonishment to catch it. He looked into the doctor's face. Then he felt himself bent down backwards, and while his head hung down over the edge of the table the knife began burrowing for the artery in his extended throat. Meanwhile, at every beat of the heart, the blood was forced up like a pulsing fountain and fell back on his face, blinding his eyes with a gleaming scarlet veil. But the effect was to make him feel more and more light-headed, and the faint click of the needle, as he was stitched up, made an almost cheerful impression on him. It sounded like the clicking of knitting needles and caused him no pain. Then it ceased and the blood, too, came to a stop. A sponge was passed lightly over his eyes. He was slowly raised up and saw before him the doctor's white face, bespattered with blood right to the roots of his beard. He held an instrument of shining steel in his hand, and playfully pinched Benjamin's nose with it. "Well," he said quietly, "there you are again, my son."

Towards midday, however, Benjamin began to be very much afraid. He held his eyes wide open, yet he was unable to read the name-plate at the head of the bed opposite, though it was quite near and inscribed with large white letters on a black ground. He took this as a warning of death. Pulling his sheet over his head he prayed with hands together. After that he wept for a long while. Towards evening he felt slightly better. He wrote on a piece of paper, asking if he would ever get better, and gave it to the orderly when he came with a drink for him. The orderly made no answer, but only put his hand silently behind his back and the cup to his lips. It was a mixture of champagne, red wine, sugar and beaten egg.

v

FIVE weeks later he was driven through the park in a cab and stopped in front of the building in which was the whistlers' room. On his head he had a cap without a badge, and was clothed in a tattered tunic that was far too big for him. It had been given him for his journey to Germany. In addition he wore trousers of brown corduroy with red piping. There were flowers in his buttonhole. He smelt very strongly of eau-de-Cologne, and he felt a little uneasy over it. As he refused the cigars that the ladies pressed upon him in the station and also could not eat or drink, they insisted at least upon refreshing his face with sponges dipped in eau-de-Cologne. He did not like to resist, and as he was dumb and had to sit for half an hour with the other wounded soldiers in a long row on the platform till the cabs came, this refreshment was repeated time after time by one lady after another.

It was Backhuhn who opened the door for him and helped him to alight. Backhuhn was a Silesian grenadier. A crossing shot had taken off his nose, and the doctors were in the process of making him a new one by a recently devised method. To this end they had to start by grafting on the spot a few pieces of his own flesh with the skin and hair belonging to it. This superstructure had been incorporated most satisfactorily, and even beyond expectation, as they said, but in the meantime it was painful to look at, for it was as big as his two fists and towered up far beyond his forehead. In form and colour it resembled a fowl prepared for the oven, and hence the noseless grenadier had been given the name Backhuhn, or the roasting fowl. He was delighted with the name, for he was proud of the pains the doctor took over him, and wore his disfigurement as though it were a sort of decoration. From time to time he underwent a surgical operation, and the design was brought nearer to completion by stages that were often scarcely appreciable. Between whiles he was allowed to go about as he pleased.

Backhuhn loved to slip up behind the servant girls of the clinic and to cover their eyes with his hands. Then he asked them who it was, and if they could not guess, he turned them swiftly about. "Do you like me? Can you bear me?" he asked them in his gurgling voice and grinned in their faces.

Often they cried out in horror, threw up their hands and ran away. He, however, was delighted and sprang after them with uncouth gestures, and, in spite of everything, they all got fond of him by degrees, for he was very big and tall, and he tried to make himself agreeable whenever he found an opportunity by his immense strength, which was quite unimpaired.

For a long while it was one of his privileges to greet new arrivals and conduct them in or help to carry them. He could not understand it at all when at last he had to be stopped, for he confidently expected the best results from the sight he presented, and never neglected to make them a little speech bearing thereon.

"Look at me, comrade," he said on this occasion to Benjamin, as he lifted him from the carriage. "I had no nose left, not as much as that, my boy, but now it's all right. They give you back here whatever you've lost."

Benjamin was glad to have someone to help him along, for he could only walk with difficulty, and in this way he reached the bathroom where all newcomers were first taken.

He felt embarrassed when he caught sight of two nurses in long washing aprons with their sleeves rolled up, who were apparently waiting for him. For he had never known what it was to be given helplessly over to the hands of women for all that he needed to have done to him. Also he was suddenly conscious that his whole body was caked with dirt and dried blood. He had been brought in in mud-soaked clothing and, among so many severely wounded and dying cases, no one had had time to give him more than a hasty cleaning up. He was glad now he had not resisted the plentiful sprinklings of eau-de-Cologne on his arrival at the station and expected every minute to see a bath orderly come along to relieve the nurses. But when these two put him on a chair and without ceremony began to undress him, a blush of shame overspread his face. At the same time he had the most intense longing to explain the pickle they would find him in. He kept fast hold of his trousers with both hands when the younger of the two tried to pull them from his legs, and began addressing her in his voiceless fashion. Unfortunately she could not understand him, and no more could the other when, at his increasing signs of embarrassment, she held her ear close to his lips. Meanwhile they were not at all discouraged and made various joking guesses at his meaning, but to each he replied with despairing gestures. At length they assured him that they understood him and skipped laughing out of the room and came back again pushing in front of them a chair on wheels with a lid on its box-shaped seat. Benjamin turned away and shook his head; he was almost in tears. After that he let himself be undressed and hoisted into the tub without another word. They buckled a kind of chest-strap round him, like those that children learn to walk with, so that he should not fall this way and that, and then soaped and washed him, talking all the time and laughing at his weight. They put their warm hands pityingly round his poor little arms, as they called them, and counted the vertebræ of his spine and each of his ribs with the tips of their fingers. Benjamin, however, for very confusion made no response. Obediently he held out arms and legs and bent his back to be scrubbed just as they required of him and gave himself up to them like a dumb animal. After that they enveloped him in a warmed shirt, and putting him on a wheeled stretcher took him down the long corridor to the whistlers' room. Kollin and Pointner were waiting for him at the open door, and Benjamin saw with delight that they, too, like him, had tubes in their necks.

V I

THE whistlers loved one another; not that they would have admitted it to themselves or displayed their feelings to each other. But every time, as often happened, one of them was wheeled away on a stretcher to submit to the knife and forceps of the surgeon, the two who remained could play no game and hold no talk. Instead they busied themselves on the floor with one thing and another, each by himself, and went again and again, as though for no particular reason, as far as the big swing doors that separated the corridor from the operating theatre. At last the stretcher came trundling back, looking like a white model of a mountain. Now there was an arc light over the recumbent figure, a kind of wooden tunnel with many lamps inside, whose purpose was to warm the patient during his return. They walked along beside him as though at a christening, or, indeed, at a funeral. They cautiously lifted the cloth from his face that protected it from the draught and nodded and winked as though to say: "We three know what it is, and no one else does but us." And the returning one, in spite of his pain, nodded back.

At that time the doctor was doing his best to widen by degrees the whistlers' natural air channel so that one day they would be able to breathe without pipes. It was done by repeated insertions of sharp spoons and tongs, and at last by pushing in long nickel rods and forcing them past the constricted passage of the throat. The process was, in fact, exactly the same as stretching gloves with glove stretchers, and since it had to be carried out without an anæsthetic, it caused the whistlers the most acute pain. For it seemed that Nature wished to protect from further interference what had once been torn without her consent. The places where the wound had healed became tougher; they hardened like the bones of young children and resisted the least alteration with fierce pain.

The whistlers sat, during this procedure, three in a row on a long bench, wrapped in white sheets up to the chin, as though they were going to be shaved. They held the long bent tube whose end projected from the mouth firmly in one hand, for owing to its smooth surface and the wild convulsions into which the gullet was thrown by the effort to get rid of it, it was impossible to hold it with the teeth alone. With the other hand they drummed on their knees, at the same time passing the third finger without ceasing over the thumb. For they had a positive longing to give vent to their pain in one way or another; sometimes, too, they stamped violently with their feet. But the longer they kept the tube in the gullet, the longer time there was for their endurance to assert its influence and to accustom the tissues more radically to the new condition. So the doctor said, and so, too, the nurses; nor were the whistlers behindhand, till at last, from pride, they prolonged the healing torture of their own free will. One morning, while she stood at the disposal of the doctor when he was putting in the tubes, the operation sister said that they were curious to see which of the whistlers was bravest and could hold out the longest. Now the word "brave" in reality meant singularly little to the whistlers. It went without saying, or at any rate they had had enough of it. Nevertheless, from then onwards, they sat side by side without a movement, merely groaning softly, and with stolen glances measured themselves against each other, till their hands trembled and the sweat trickled in streams down their foreheads. Then Pointner and Benjamin usually snatched their tubes out at the same moment, while Kollin sat on a moment longer, though he allowed not a sign of triumph to escape him. Nevertheless, Pointner sometimes showed his annoyance. He tapped his forehead lightly in disdain and rolled his eyes upwards—a favourite gesture of his. The next day, however, he would exert all his strength to come off the victor.

The whistlers were devoted to their doctor with all their hearts, and held him in secret wonder and veneration, although they never spoke of him among themselves except with the kind of tolerance extended to a chum, and made no end of fun over many of his peculiarities. Although he could not be more than a few years older than Pointner and Kollin, they always called him the "old 'un," and when he joked with them in his jolly and at the same time merciless way, or even praised them for their pluck, they smiled and cast down their eyes and were so overcome with pride that they did not know what to say. Then, as soon as ever he was out of the room, replies of the utmost wit and familiarity occurred to them, and they bragged before the others of all they might so easily have said.

The "old 'un," Doctor Quint, as his name really was, always came in a blinding white medical overall which gave off an odor of powerful disinfectants and strong vinegar; beneath it could be seen the creased trousers of an English suit. He wore bright silk socks and shining patent-leather shoes. He liked bright red ties, and preferred that colour to any other because, as he said, it was a red rag to all priests. Owing to a certain refractory attitude that he had in official matters and his unconcealed contempt for the military hierarchy, he was not in the good books of the superior officers in control of the clinic, but as he was exceptionally gifted and spent all his great energy to the point of exhaustion in the service of the sick and wounded, nothing further had come of several very carefully formulated reports in his disfavour. He had a small white face, very broad shoulders and well-knit frame, and all the sisters and nurses blushed when he went along the corridors with quick elastic steps, his hands sunk in the pockets of his overall. His eyes were large and dark and fiery, but they were set at an angle to each other and for this reason it was his habit to conceal one of them with the concave eyeglass which he used in his examinations. He was seldom seen without it in any part of the clinic. It was very much of the shape and circumference of a small saucer, and was kept in position by a leather band round the forehead. In the middle of it, just large enough to spy through, was a small aperture which had, as well, the effect of concentrating the light.

When he sat in front of a wounded man with this instrument, it seemed that while his spy-glass eye was busied in scrutiny and diagnosis, the other roved sideways into the distance, as though he were already meditating new methods of healing, and this the whistlers firmly believed to be the case. For this reason, as though by tacit agreement, they never made fun of his eyes, and it was their dearest wish to look one day through this spy-glass with the light directed into it. What they expected to see, when this great moment came, stirred their imaginations to a great pitch.

Doctor Quint had the strength of a giant. To keep himself fit, it was his practice to wrestle with enormous weights, lifting them on high and to make a sport of handling great iron bowls and disks of a terrifying circumference. He took pleasure in displaying these feats of strength to the whistlers before operating on them. While the nurses were still busy strapping Kollin to the operating-table, he suddenly grasped the heavy iron surgical chair that stood in the same room and held it up in his outstretched arm.

"Do that, Pioneer," he said impressively after a moment, looking down upon him over his shoulders. Kollin, who had just been made fast with the knee-strap, smiled with astonishment. Even though he was not at the moment in a position to take up the challenge, yet the invitation to do so cheered him to the utmost, and he made up his mind to attempt it with another chair as a preliminary as soon as ever he had the opportunity. After that he submitted himself quietly to the knife with boundless confidence.

The compass of Doctor Quint's voice answered to these exhibitions of strength. As a rule he did not speak unusually loud, but occasionally it amused him to throw the nurses into alarm and consternation by suddenly giving vent to a sort of trumpeting over his work. Often while they were still sitting over their breakfast in their room, the whistlers heard him in the far distant treatment-rooms shouting at the top of his voice for a *Hohlnadel* or a *Speischüssel*. Then they raised their heads and listened with delight and nodded knowingly to each other. As a rule Doctor Quint appeared not long after in the passage outside the door, winking out of the corners of his eyes and strolling along with a man, who had just been operated on, resting like a doll in his arms, while the nurses, half pleased and half upset, wheeled the stretcher along in the rear. He chose the heaviest and stoutest among all the lot of wounded for this manœuvre, and then laid them carefully in their beds wrapped in their blankets and still in the deep sleep of the anæsthetic.

Nevertheless, he hated any shouting on the part of others. There was not the least occasion for whimpering and shouting, he informed his patients before a painful operation without an anæsthetic. He begged them to forbear, with the assurance that, taken as a whole, the affair would be perfectly painless. He granted that one bad moment could not be avoided. Of this he would give warning and then they might roar. As a rule after this the victims sat quietly without making a sound, till he suddenly threw knife and forceps into the basin, pulled the spy-glass from his eye, and, with a look over his shoulders at the next man, announced that it was over. But not everyone was altogether satisfied. Many had been waiting for the promised moment when they might emit the terrific howl that they had been storing up.

But to the whistlers he said: "Shout Pointner! Shout, Bombardier!" and holding them around the shoulders in a tight embrace pressed down the agonizing rod with relentless force past the scars in their throats, and they loved him for it.

VII

ONE morning, not long after his arrival, Benjamin went for a walk through the halls and corridors of the hospital. At that time he was still quite voiceless. He wished to visit a comrade with whom he had been at school. On his way he mistook the door and found himself in the ward of the blind. They sat in a green half-light on their beds or on chairs, many with bandages as in blind-man's buff, and all with faces slightly raised in the always-listening attitude peculiar to them.

"Well, comrade, who are you? and what have you got?" Sergeant

Wichtermann said after a moment, from a wheel-chair by a window. Sergeant Wichtermann had got the whole burst of a bomb in front of Arras. Nevertheless he was not killed, for, as he said, he had a strong constitution. He was blind. Both legs and one arm had been shot away; his remaining arm had but two fingers. In these he held a long pipe.

Benjamin was very much frightened. He drummed at once with his hand on the door behind him, so as to give at least a token of his presence, and at the same time he looked anxiously around, in the hope of discovering a man with one eye who would be able to explain why he preserved so unfitting a silence in the ward of the blind. But there was not one to be seen.

"Well," Wichtermann growled, "can't you open your mouth? Are you making fools of us?" "I'll soon put him in tune," promised another, getting down from his bed in a rage and showing his fists. A well-aimed slipper came hurtling through the air and struck the door close behind Benjamin's head. Benjamin delayed his departure no longer.

By good fortune he found Landwehrmann Ferge, whom he knew already, just outside the door. Ferge was a good-natured Thuringian with a pasty-coloured moustache on his sallow face, but he was not well received among his fellows. It must be explained that he bore an evil nickname. A bullet had gone right through his seat and torn the bowel. In order to give this very susceptible organ time to heal, the doctors had made for him another temporary orifice in the region of his hip, and this unfortunately was always open. For this reason Ferge was forced to wear on his naked skin, under his shirt, a large india-rubber bag. This condemned him to a lonely existence and doubled and tripled the bitterness of his peculiar plight. For Ferge all his life long had had a passion for card play—that is for watching others play with an interest all the keener because his stinginess prevented him taking a hand himself. In former days this had been his favourite Sunday pastime, and now he might have whiled away entire months in the indulgence of this passion. For everywhere, indoors and out in the garden, the halt and the maimed sat in threes and fours and played sheepshead, skat and doublehead, and on quiet days there was a murmur and thunder, gentle and fascinating, from behind every door, of the trumps that were slapped down upon the tables. But his comrades drove him off because of his smell, and so he wandered about in the park in the open air, longing for the day when his shame and torment would be removed from him.

Hence he was now cheered to the heart when at last someone had need of him. He took Benjamin back among the blind and explained to them in a short address how it came about that he had been dumb. The blind were immediately reconciled. They came round him eagerly, and each in turn touched his silver mouthpiece and held their hands in front of the warm stream of air that issued from it. Even Sergeant Wichtermann had himself wheeled up in his chair, and with his two fingers made a precise investigation of the tube, saying all the while: "I understand, I understand."

"The doctors make everything you need," he said at length very jovially. "One gets a new mouth and another a new backside. But after all it's not the right one, except that you're more easily known by it, Comrade Ferge." At that everyone laughed uproariously. But Ferge sadly and silently withdrew and took his evil smell with him.

After this the whistlers often visited the blind to play draughts or chess with them. For this the blind had chessmen half of which were furnished with little round tops of lead. These were not simply placed on the board, but fixed in it with little pegs so that the groping fingers should not upset them. On these occasions Deuster, an army medical corporal, always greeted the whistlers with a finished imitation of their croaking manner of speech, to the delight of all, the whistlers included. Deuster was very small and red-haired. His face and hands were thickly covered with freckles. He had lost his sight while bringing in one of the enemy who lay wounded on the wire in front of the trench. The cries of this man were so lamentable that they got on everybody's nerves in the trench and set them jangling, till at last, as Deuster said, it was more than a man could bear.

Pointner was particularly fond of him and was always as pleased to see him as if he were a new discovery, for he was the only one among the blind who was now and then to be beaten at draughts or chess. They saw everything as they had it in their own minds, and the opponent had scarcely made his move before their hands flitted over the board to ascertain his intentions and then replied at once in accordance with the well-thought-out plan to which they clung meanwhile in their darkness with undeviating purpose. Deuster alone, who loved to chatter, sometimes made gross blunders whereat Pointner was so beside himself with joy and delight that he jumped up and, skipping behind his chair, threw his arms affectionately around the neck of his conquered opponent. "Blind man of Hess," he said to him, and admonished him like a father to keep his eyes in his fingers next time.

It was the custom in the hospital for the patients to chaff each other over their infirmities; they found a certain consolation in it. Fusileer Kulka, for example, from what was then the province of Posen, who for a time occupied the spare bed in the whistlers' room, rarely spoke to them without pressing his finger to an imaginary tube and rattling in his throat. He could only speak broken German, but he delighted in recounting in his sing-song voice how he came to lose his leg. He was lying in the open with his company, after it had swarmed out in an engagement with Siberian infantry, when a bullet ripped his left cheek and passed out through his ear. At that Fusileer Kulka unstrapped his pack and got out a little mirror that he kept in it. He just wanted to see how he looked, for he had a bride at home. While taking a leisurely survey, he must have exposed himself too far, for a machine gunner got his range and shot him twelve times in the left leg. Now he had one of leather and steel.

The whistlers took him between them when he practised walking with it outside their room. Kollin on his right, Benjamin on his left, they tottered with earnest demeanour up and down the corridor. The whistlers, too, now appeared to have false legs. Just as Kulka did, they hoisted one shoulder and hip to the fore at every step, at the same time sinking a little on one side. When it came to turning about however, Benjamin, by choice, got into great difficulties. He hopped helplessly on one leg where he stood and tried in vain to steady himself with the false one. Finally he fell at full length, and then, raising his stick, he began to chastise the refractory leg with it. At that Fusileer Kulka laughed so immoderately that the tears ran down his cheeks and he threatened to fall over backwards in earnest. This happened outside the door of the blind, and instantly the army medical corporal, Deuster, came groping his way out and desired to know what the joke might be, for he was always eager to join in a laugh and forever on the look-out for an opportunity.

On a later occasion he went for a walk with Benjamin in the park. Some days before he had been with the others to a fine concert. Never in his life, he confessed, had he ever known anything so beautiful. From that day he had made up his mind to become a musician as soon as he was released from hospital, though he could not play any instrument and would first have to learn. He had been a worker in a cloth factory.

"Comrade," he said in an ecstasy, standing still after he had exposed his project, "it comes from within. It is all inside one. He who has it in him, can—" Suddenly he stopped as though he no longer knew what he had been going to say, or had himself abruptly lost belief in it. He lifted his face and fixed it on Benjamin's. He blinked his hollow eyes without ceasing, and the corners of his mouth began to twitch. But Benjamin knew no more than he what to say. So he took him by the arm and led him, now dumb, back to the room of the blind.

VIII

FUSILEER KULKA had been released and sent home and the year had once more passed into summer, when one morning the volunteer Jäger, Fürlein, made his appearance in the whistlers' room. Still clothed in his green uniform, just as he had been sent to them by Doctor Quint, he stood among the whistlers and laboriously expounded the situation in which he found himself.

He had not been wounded, but from a cause that so far could not be explained, had suddenly lost his voice and found it an effort to produce even a hoarse whisper. At dawn, after a night under canvas, he had just crept out of his tent to pass on an order. Then he found this change in himself, and even with the air, as he said, he had had difficulty from then onwards. Even now he could sometimes scarcely breathe, and on such occasions an anxious expression came over his face and he hastily removed the clumsy shooting spectacles from his nose as though this would bring him relief.

The faces of the whistlers, however, cleared at once. With cheering and consoling nods, as though they knew all about it long ago and were in secret possession of chosen remedies for this very case, they corroborated all that he could say, and Pointner with long deliberation felt his lean neck with his supple fingers, while with a composed expression he stared past him into a corner. Fürlein, meanwhile, glanced shyly at the white bibs that surrounded him—from beneath which a slender cheeping and rustling sounded from time to time. Finally they all clapped him on the shoulder and told him to cheer up. "The old 'un will soon see to it," they said, and looked meaningly at one another. Then they conducted him to his bed, and Kollin went hastily to the cupboard and returned with one of the striped linen garments such as they all wore.

Fürlein's condition seemed to grow worse during the following days; more and more frequently he had to struggle with slight attacks of suffocation, and sometimes even swallowing gave him trouble. But Doctor Quint did nothing with him for the time being. He was going to wait a bit longer, he said, with an impenetrable expression. The whistlers, however, had already decided that Fürlein was destined to be one of them. Kollin, on the very first day, had suggested to the operation nurse, whom he helped in cleaning the instruments, that she should see to it, and quickly, that the Jäger got his tube, and she had declined abruptly to have anything to do with it. Now they tried Fürlein. The three of them gathered in the evening at his bedside and began talking to him intimately, kindly and also a little patronizingly. It was as though they had a rare favour to bestow. Fürlein, who had been in secret fear of something like this, plaintively shook his head.

Gradually, however, the whistlers, who had set their hearts on it, won his confidence, though at the cost of indefatigable efforts, and persuaded him to look at their tubes with a mixture of curiosity and aversion. He was still heartily afraid of the operation, but at the same time he began to put his trust in it, and his impatience became more and more apparent. After it was over he would be entirely at his ease with it. He actually looked forward to that time, he assured them with a helpless smile. The whistlers enthusiastically concurred. Did they not breathe more freely and easily than ever, perhaps, in their lives? No one could have any notion who was not himself a whistler. Kollin raised his bib, drew a deep breath and exhaled it again with a triumphant air, while he fanned to and fro with his hand in front of the little opening. Benjamin, for his part, did not know how to say enough for the undisturbed sleep he could enjoy at any hour. As a prompt demonstration he got into bed in his clothes and covered himself up to his neck. He put the large pillow over his face till nothing was to be seen of him. But through a little gap between the bed clothes and the pillow he breathed in at his tube, and Fürlein looked with all his eyes at this marvellous phenomenon that had so uncanny a fascination for him.

His days were happy now. He began to learn, as they called it, and drew out the inner tubes from the whistlers' necks and cleaned them. Or he cut out new bibs for them and neatly pinned them on. And the whistlers made him returns. He was permitted to be the first to read the paper; many a choice morsel to which the kitchen maids gave them a secret priority was allotted him, and they poured him out a double allowance of the beer or wine which occasionally found its way to their room by the channel of private munificence.

At length early one summer morning, before seven o'clock, Fürlein was taken to the operating theatre, and the whistlers, much elated, conducted him a part of the way. But against all expectation, he came back after a quarter of an hour while they were still busily employed making his bed ready and putting the blocks under its feet at the lower end, for those who were operated upon in the neck had to lie at first with their heads lower than their feet, in case the blood ran into the ramifications of the windpipe. Fürlein came back, not on the wheeled stretcher, but on his feet as he had gone, and he had not, either, any bandage on his neck. Doctor Quint had sent a strong electric current through his throat and suddenly ordered him to shout. Immediately Jäger Fürlein uttered a loud shout, and now he could speak and breathe again as of old. He explained all this to the whistlers with downcast eyes, and they heard him without making a sound. He had a fine rousing voice. That much it was easy to hear, though he took great pains to damp it down.

"It's all for the best, comrade," said Fürlein at last to each one of the circle round him, and held out his hand. The whistlers slowly recovered themselves and with forced smiles offered their congratulations. After that they betook themselves, all three, to the park for their rest in the open air. Fürlein in any case could not accompany them, for he was to be sent at once to his unit at the base and had to pack up his effects. Also there was the pretext of having his papers put in order. When they came in again at mid-day, the Jäger was no longer there. He had gone without saying good-bye, and the whistlers readily understood. But they never spoke of him any more.

I X

In the third autumn of the war, however, a fourth comrade was added to the whistlers in earnest. One afternoon Sister Emily, a red-cheeked Valkyrie of uncertain age, came in and laid a heap of clean clothes on the fourth bed that since Fürlein's departure had stood unmade in the corner.

"Early tomorrow there's a new whistler coming, and a real one this time," she said in her robust tones, as she turned down the sheet over the heavy blanket, "and—what d'you think?—it's an English prisoner."

The whistlers pricked up their ears and shook their heads. Pointner noisily pushed back his chair and laid down his spoon. "No," he said loudly, and the other two showed their indignation in their faces.

"It's not a bit of use," said Sister Emily emphatically, and shook up the pillow. "He has been shot through the throat like you, and there's nowhere else for him to go for treatment. So you must just put up with him."

Herewith she pulled a piece of chalk out of the pocket of her apron and wrote on the nameplate at the head of the empty bed. "Harry Flint" could now be read on it, and below, where in other cases a man's rank was stated—"Englishman." Pointner still signified his distaste with one or two gestures of his hands, and brought the coffee jug threateningly down on the table. Then he rammed his cap down on one side and went out into the garden, spitting with rage like a cat.

The next morning when the whistlers were sitting over their breakfast, the door slowly opened and there entered a round-faced boy with large brown eyes and thick blue-black hair. In his hand he held a small bundle about the size of a head of cabbage. He wore the blue and white striped linen hospital uniform, and over it a kind of bicycling cape. On his head was an utterly washed-out cap of the same material and far too small for him. It was Harry Flint, in German, Heine Kieselstein, or simply Kiesel, of the Gloucesters. He stood blushing in the doorway, and, putting his hand to his cap by way of greeting, made something like a slight bow at the same time. After that he remained fixed in an appealing attitude, his hands laid one over the other at the level of his waist, and looked fixedly at the three whistlers with a mixture of shame, pride, and fear.

The whistlers did not appear to see him. Each looked straight in front of him over his cup, and so contrived to avoid the eyes of the others. After a while Harry once more saluted, and his eyes began to fill with tears. Pointner sat mouthing a large piece of soaked bread with a long knife in his hand, and at this he jerked the knife over his shoulder in the direction of the vacant bed. Harry Flint betook himself there at once and sat down gingerly on the edge of it, as though he desired to show that he made the least possible claim on the air space of the room. Directly afterwards the whistlers got up all together for a walk in the garden, and left the rifleman to himself without deigning to cast him a glance.

When they came back again at mid-day they found Harry sweeping out the room with a broom and shovel that he had found for himself.

It was now apparent that he wore his tube in his neck without any protective covering and secured only by a thin cord. It looked as though he had a large metal button or a screw stuck in the front of his throat. Kollin shook his head and went up to him, and leading him by the sleeve to the cupboard at his bedside, took a clean piece of muslin out of the drawer and pinned it carefully and neatly under his chin. Harry, who had stood without a movement, took a small looking-glass from his pocket and looked at himself with delight. Then he rummaged in his bundle and produced a stick of chocolate and offered it to Kollin. Kollin gave it a passing glance and quietly shook his head. Harry bit his lip and turned away.

At this time food was scarce in Germany, and white bread, cake, meat, and imported fruit had vanished. Harry, however, had no lack of them. Soon after his arrival a large parcel of otherwise unprocurable food came for him from an English Prisoners of War Committee in Switzerland, and regularly every third and fourth day came another. Harry handed it all around in the friendliest way—smoked bacon, wurst in cans, butter in tin tubes, cakes with nuts and almonds, and white bread with brown and shining crust. But though the whistlers had long forgotten their hatred of Great Britain they obstinately refused to touch even a morsel of it.

It was not always their loss. For sometimes the parcels were a long time on the road, and then there was a dangerous hissing and effervescing when Harry stuck in the can-opener. The meat smelled like bad cheese, and the bread was not to be cut with any knife. This put the whistlers in the best of moods. They surrounded the table on which Harry had spread his treasures, and in the mixture of German and English that had become meanwhile the common whistler lingo, passed the severest criticisms on England and English products. "Stinkflesh!" they croaked, and showed their disgust by holding their noses. This was always a disconcerting moment for Harry. He could not admit that Britain presented a Briton with bad fare. With indignant eyes he soaked his bread in his soup and rubbed salt in the putrid meat. And then he swallowed it all down, and patting his stomach endeavoured to show by his face how much he enjoyed it.

Often, however, he turned pale, hurried out and vomited long and painfully for the honour of Great Britain.

The originator of the common German-English whistler language was Benjamin. After he had overcome his first modesty he brought forward his grammar-school English and initiated Harry into the usages and rules of the hospital, and in particular of the whistlers' room. He instructed him also in the art of speaking, or rather croaking, by stopping the mouth of the tube with the finger-tip, and began to teach him a little German. Harry was a quick pupil, and soon transformed himself from the dumb and constrained foreigner into a friend who was always ready for a talk. The whistlers got to be very fond of him.

One day he confided to Benjamin that he was married. A war marriage, he called it. He was twenty and Mrs. Flint of Gloucester a little over sixteen. Benjamin had often found him seated on his bed in the act, apparently, of smelling, or indeed tasting, a sheet of note paper, and had been at a loss for the explanation. And now Harry revealed it. Mrs. Flint was allowed by the censorship to send no more than four sides of note paper to her prisoner husband every week. But writing was no easy task for her; she had, as Harry confessed, first to set about learning how to do it. For this reason each letter contained no more than one or two laboured sentences, traced in large letters on lines previously ruled out. The remaining space, three and a half sides, was covered with small neatly formed crosses. Each one of them, Harry explained, betokened a kiss of wedded love. Harry loyally responded to each. Even in the darkness of the night his lips often met those of his far-distant wife on the paper. Benjamin, whose bed was opposite his, could hear the rustling folds and the sighs of the prisoner. Once he got up and groped his way across to console him with a joke. But Harry quickly pulled the bedclothes over his head because his face was wet with tears.

x

NOT long after, as winter drew on, Pointner became bedridden. His heart began to feel the strain of the poison that circled in his veins. Yet he was very happy at that time. He lay in bed quietly and without pain and read until far into the night. True, he had soon finished the love and murder stories in the library, but to make up for it, a thick volume containing the complete fairy tales of the brothers Grimm, that Benjamin had taken out one day, became his inseparable companion. Over and over again he read with a blissful smile the stories of the Golden Bird, of Florinda and Yoringal, of Rapunzel, of the Blue Light, and the little man with a glow, although he knew them now by heart; and Benjamin marvelled over him, while Kollin sadly shook his head. Sometimes he laughed silently to himself and laid the book for a while in his lap, but not for a moment letting it out of his hands; or he beckoned Benjamin to him and laying his finger on the title of the story handed him the book without a word. Lying quietly on his side he watched his expression closely, and when Benjamin smiled his whole face lit up; then he sat up and croaked:

> *"Als hinaus*
> *Nach des Herrn Korbes seinem Haus."*

or

> *"Sind wir nicht Knaben glatt und fein,*
> *Was wollen wir länger Schuster sein?"*

then lay back again, waved his head to and fro and shook with laughter.

Often when the other two had gone for a walk, Harry Flint sat for hours by his bed and took care of him. He cleaned his tube, put a clean bib under his chin, gave him a drink, and pulled his bedclothes straight; or else he just sat still and communicated to him something of his own vitality by his mere presence. It went so far that Pointner did not even persist in refusing the cakes of white flour from Great Britain. Harry soaked them in milk and gave them to him in a spoon.

It happened this way. One morning there had been an unexpected inspection of the drawers of the bedside cupboards, and in each one the Sister found a broken packet of beautiful English butter-scotch. She took a piece of it and exclaimed how good it was. But the whistlers went very red, and Harry Flint went reddest of all and hastily left the room, for he had gone at night to each one's bed, one day to Benjamin's, the next to Kollin's, and last to Pointner's and given a packet to each of them in turn. Thereupon the whistlers could hold out no longer, and each thought he was the only one who secretly beneath his bedclothes nibbled at the honour of the Fatherland. From that morning they assisted Harry quite openly to demolish the white bread and the admirable wurst. It relieved Harry too, for he could now openly confess when the bacon was bad or the butter rancid, and was no longer under the necessity of making himself ill.

One day, when the two were alone together, Pointner took his English cap out of its hiding place and put it on Harry's head. Harry stood motionless with head erect and beamed with delight. It was his dearest wish to possess this cap. Among the various buildings of the hospital, which in peace time was a State clinic, there were some devoted to patients from the civil population. They wore the same patient's uniform as the soldiers except for the military caps, and this distinction was so punctiliously preserved that a soldier-patient was seldom seen without his cap. When occasion demanded they had them on their heads even in bed. Harry, too, was a soldier, but he was no longer in possession of an English cap, and as he could not wear a German one, he was compelled to go about bareheaded, or else in that little boy's cap of linen, and to let himself be taken for a civilian patient. He suffered the more because nearly all the civilians of his age and height were at that time in the skin clinic, which was called the Ritterburg, and were given as wide a berth as possible.

Even the soldiers who had to have temporary quarters there, were left during that time to themselves. Moreover it was there that the so-called Ritter *fräulein*—women of ill-fame from the town—were subjected to compulsory cure. They were not permitted to leave the floor assigned to them except on rare occasions, though it was said that they swung their cavaliers up to their rooms at night by means of ropes of twisted sheets. However the rest might enjoy these tales and find in them an inexhaustible topic of conversation, not one of them would have anything to do with the building or its occupants, let alone being mistaken for one of them.

The trouble was that Pointner could not bring himself to part with his trophy. But he allowed Harry to wear it now and then when no one was about. There was nothing then that Harry more eagerly desired than to be taken by surprise with the cap on his head. But no sooner was a step heard outside than Pointner whipped it away and hid it under the clothes. He promised him, however, that he would leave him the cap at his death. He gave Harry his hand on it, and Harry grasped it in token of acceptance and stood at attention with a solemn and ceremonial air. It was soon to come true.

X I

BEFORE that, however, Benjamin himself had to go to the Ritterburg. One day, to his horror, he discovered inexplicable and painful symptoms on his body. But from shame he could not confide to anybody the state he was in; he kept silence in the desperate hope that the malady would pass over of itself, and that one morning he would wake up healed and cleansed as though it had all been a dream. But the pain only got worse, and loathsome spots began to spread all over his body. At last there was nothing for it but to tell Herr Mauch all about it—perhaps he would be able to help him without Doctor Quint and the Sister needing to know anything about it.

Herr Mauch, as he was called, a grey-haired and moustached Landsturm man, was the orderly of the department. It was his duty to perform the heavier bodily labours. He stood by when patients were moved from one bed to another or bathed. He washed the dead and conveyed them into the cellar, where a post-mortem was sometimes carried out. Also he went to and fro with the commode when required, and had charge of the various vessels that ministered to necessities. He was the first to appear every morning, making a jovial entry in each room with a clinking wire basket in which he collected the glass bottles, making very knowing comments the while. He wore a peakless service cap with the Landwehr cross on the badge, and an old pair of service trousers, also the regulation canvas tunic and a large apron. He laid great stress on being a military personage, although the source of his never-failing good spirits was in having, as he said, got hold of a fine job that protected him from being called up and sent to the front. For this reason he carried out every part of his duties with the utmost precision.

He was none the less frank in his admiration of his wounded companions-in-arms, and loved to address them as "old soldiers" or even as "corporal." There was nothing he delighted in more than the most bloodthirsty adventures from the battles on all fronts, and only these could sometimes delay him on his round with the bottle-basket. A wounded soldier was often disposed to talk at early dawn, and then he would set down his receptacle for a moment and spur the narrator on with enthusiastic exclamations and encouraging questions as to the fierce slaughter of one enemy after another. "On, on to battle! For battle we are born! For battle are we ready!" he hummed with a defiant look while he collected the rest of the bottles and betook himself to the next room. The few civilian patients, on the other hand, who now and then came under his care, he treated with scorn. "To you," he used to say when one of them addressed him as Mauch, "to a shirker like you I am Herr Mauch!" Hence the soldiers, too, always called him Herr Mauch, though they addressed him familiarly with "thou."

His usual haunt was the bath-house of the station. Here he looked after all his various utensils in a mess of soda and soapsuds, cleaned boots, made sundry lists and held himself in readiness in case he was needed. For the most part, he sat upon his perambulatory chair, the seat of which was upholstered with an air cushion. Here he carried on a secret traffic in surplus bottles of beer, as he called them, from the hospital stores, for he stole like a crow. On occasion a leave certificate was to be had through him, and indeed all kinds of bartering was transacted.

"God damn me!" said Herr Mauch with jovial astonishment, when Benjamin, with trembling hands, had undone his clothes. Then he put down his cup. "God damn me, Corporal, you've got the Turkish music." By this he referred to the severest form of venereal disease. "How on earth did you get that?"

Benjamin knew no more than he did. He had never been with a woman in his life. "Help me, Herr Mauch," he pleaded in a voice that almost failed him, and nearly fell backwards over the edge of the bath he was sitting on. But Herr Mauch could do nothing of the sort. No, he couldn't help him there, he said. It must be reported to Doctor Quint, otherwise it would end in the other fellows getting it too.

Benjamin staggered out. As he knew of no other place where he could be undisturbed, he shut himself in a closet and stood squeezed in a corner, his eyes dry, while his teeth chattered and shudders shook his whole frame. Whatever else had happened to him and around him had been within his comprehension and he had accepted it. But now he had come to the end. He resolved to die.

When he had actually pulled out the tube from his neck so that the little opening in which it was placed might speedily close up, he was aware of a soft chirping sound above him, and looking up over the top of the partition wall that separated the one compartment from the next, he saw the anxious face of Harry Flint of Gloucester. A moment later the door was forced, and Herr Mauch rushed in, crying aloud, and hauled him out. Harry had seen Benjamin vanish, and noticed his tottering steps and distraught expression. And when Benjamin did not return within a reasonable time, he stole softly into the neighbouring compartment, climbed upon the window ledge, and from there looked down over the partition.

Doctor Quint, to whom Herr Mauch had meanwhile reported the matter, was even paler than usual. The first thing he did was to take hold of the half-unconscious Benjamin and insert a new tube with considerable force through the opening, which was indeed already closing up. Then he pulled the spy-glass from his forehead and examined Benjamin's spots through a powerful microscope, and at once his face became more and more serene. "Scabies," he then said quietly. "Lesions, a perfectly normal case of lesions, my boy. You must go straight across to the Ritterburg. In three days you'll be clean again."

Tears fell fast down Benjamin's cheeks. His chin worked convulsively to and fro; he was shaken with violent sobs and he laughed for joy. Doctor Quint turned about on his revolving stool. "Idiot!" he bellowed in a terrible voice. "Blockhead! Child-murderer! I'll have you court-martialled and shot." But Herr Mauch had already bolted through the door.

Thus it was that Benjamin got to the Ritterburg without being allowed, owing to the risk of infection, to return to his comrades first.

There an experienced hand smeared him at once from head to foot with a corrosive ointment of a greenish colour. The shirt, too, that was given him to put on, was green, and the cotton gloves as well. Even the beds were green from the ointment, and the very wall paper of the room into which he was taken. For this reason it was called the hunters' room and its occupants the hunters. There were half a dozen of them there together.

The oldest of them was a white-haired tramp who hated doctors. His bed was next to Benjamin's. "They're liars," he informed him, and gratefully ate Benjamin's rations, for Benjamin ate nothing the whole time he had to stay in the hunters' room. "It is all rubbish they tell us about the little animals. It is in the blood, deep in the blood, and it comes out as the trees come out. Why should I get it otherwise every spring? But sometimes it stays till the autumn. Then it is against nature and something has to be done to check it."

Benjamin scarcely listened to him. He looked down through the window into the yellowing garden of the Ritterburg. It was strictly shut off from the park, where anybody could walk about. There, in the midst of a bevy of Ritterburg *Fräulein,* was a yellow-skinned fellow with black hair gleaming in the pale mid-day sunlight. He was called the Legionary, for he was a deserter from the Foreign Legion, who had got back through the lines to Germany. He had a wild face, beautiful and adventurous, and Benjamin began to lose himself in dreams of the amazing experiences that he seemed to be telling the girls around him.

XII

NOT long after Benjamin's return to the whistlers' room, Doctor Quint performed on him and Harry what he hoped would prove the final and decisive operation, and they had to lie in bed in great pain and with high fever. Kollin, the only one now left on his legs, entered on dreary days. Since Benjamin's arrival card games had taken their place beside the ever-beloved chess in the daily life of the whistlers, games that three or four could play. The excitement and the scoring they involved, and also the passionate discussion after the game was over, as to how everything should have been, or might have been if this trump had been held back or that trick had been taken, had all been the keenest joy for Kollin. It comforted him for his disappointment at always being a loser at cards, for he played a clever and cunning game, but in this as in all else he had no luck.

Now, however, the luck suddenly turned in his favour. Sitting alone at the table, he shuffled and dealt to himself and two imaginary partners with the utmost precision. Then he turned his hand up and, sure enough, he had the game all in his hands, untakable solos and grands with all the aces and jacks as well. Time after time he jumped up, with the cards spread in his hand, and hurried over to Pointner's and Benjamin's beds to show them the incontestable evidence of victory and luck. Pointner, who had suddenly begun to sink and could seldom now read his fairy tales, only waved a hand feebly and turned away, and Benjamin looked at him through a daze of narcotics, with fevered, gleaming eyes, but did not know him. At last Kollin reported to Doctor Quint and begged him to do with him as with the two others, for they were his comrades. But Doctor Quint could not risk it yet in his case, and had to console him by holding out hopes for the future.

Thus passed monotonous days. Outside it snowed on and on, and sometimes a regimental band took up its position before the windows on a patch from which the snow had been shovelled, and played the usual rousing tunes.

Harry Flint always showed the liveliest pleasure when at the close "Hail to thee in conqueror's wreath" was played, for it had the same tune as the hymn in which God is implored to save the gracious King of Great Britain. He sat up in bed, and putting on a ceremonial and dignified expression, beat time with his finger.

Sometimes Sergeant Wichtermann had himself wheeled in on his chair and discussed the military situation with Kollin. He was very confident and prognosticated a speedy victory. He would then contemplate taking part, from a carriage, in his regiment's triumphal return. Harry, meanwhile, pricked up his ears and sadly shook his head, but Kollin, too, who sat carving a set of chessmen that he intended as a present to Pointner, looked grave. He got up and took from his drawer a paper on which he had worked out in figures a statement of all the allied and enemy forces. He began to read it carefully while he followed the rows of figures with his finger. There, for him, lay the answer to this question.

Harry and Benjamin had not been long on their feet again, with the hope that they might soon be quit of their tubes, when Pointner's end came. Often he lay unconscious, and slowly, without ceasing, turned his head this way and that, as though he were always wondering about something. His face had become small and peaceful like the face of a child, and his eyes, when he opened them, were always a deeper and deeper blue. But he opened them seldom now, and when he did, the other whistlers collected at once around his bed and joked with him, and he smiled and looked tenderly at them.

One morning early, when they were all still in bed, they heard him getting restless. He was rattling violently at the cupboard by his bed, and a glass fell with a crash to the floor. They made a light, and there sat Pointner upright in bed holding out the English cap to Harry. Harry jumped up and ran across in bare feet to prop him up, but Pointner had already sunk slowly back. His eyes were fixed on the ceiling, and he did not move again.

He was buried in the little soldiers' cemetery behind the park. In the first row behind the coffin walked the three whistlers, for even Harry Flint, by the special intercession of Doctor Quint, was permitted, as an exception (so they called it), to go too. He wore the English cap for the first time.

Immediately behind them walked Herr Mauch. He had girded on a bayonet, and had also procured a helmet which, being too big for him, fell sideways on his head at every step. On his arm he had the army medical corporal, Deuster, beside whom went Backhuhn, whose nose was now very nearly completed. The band played the Comrades' Song, and Herr Mauch sobbed aloud into his helmet, which he held before his moustache. Benjamin and Harry Flint were shaking too and looked, with drawn faces, to the ground. Kollin alone kept a calm face and dry eyes, but when his turn came to step in front of the heap of earth and scatter some of it into the grave, he put the spade aside and threw on the coffin the chessmen that he had brought with him in his overcoat pocket.

A few weeks later he was wheeled into the operating theatre on a stretcher. The final critical operation was now to be put to the test in his case too. But Benjamin and Harry waited in vain for his return. When they saw him again, he was dead behind the white folding screen in Herr Mauch's bath-house, where, when there was time, it was the practice to convey the dying, for it had been found that the sight of a dying man often had a dangerous influence on the others and drew them in his train.

And then the day came when Doctor Quint drew the silver pipes from the necks of the two survivors. The little mouth above the breast closed in one night, and they could now breathe almost like other people.

"No longer whistlers," Harry whispered. But they did not venture to show their joy. Arm in arm they walked along the garden paths and sighed deeply.

One morning, when they were both lying on their beds, sleeping in their clothes, Herr Mauch came in with a sheaf of papers under his arm. "Get up, Harry Flint," he called. "Get ready—sharp! You've been exchanged and are going home. You must be dressed in half an hour. There's still time to catch today's train to Rotterdam." Therewith he threw a bundle of clothes on the bed. Harry slowly sat up and stared across in consternation at Benjamin. "No," he said. "No. Not going away. Staying here." Only by degrees he began to understand. Slowly a gleam lit up in his eyes, and try as he might he could not hide it. With trembling hands he pulled off his hospital uniform and put on the khaki one. It came from the disinfecting room and was faded and little more than rags.

Then he sat down on his bed with his hands laid one over the other, and his bundle at his feet, just as he had sat the first time on the day of his arrival. Again and again he looked at Benjamin and Benjamin looked at him. They did not know what to say and became more and more embarrassed. When Herr Mauch knocked on the door, they both stood up at the same time and blushed crimson. Then they stepped out quickly between the beds, met in a clumsy embrace, and kissed each other.

AN AFTERWORD ON
"THE WHISTLERS' ROOM"

WHEN the German poet and novelist, Carossa, turned fifty years in 1928, there was published in Leipzig a volume called *Buch des Dankes für Hans Carossa,* to which twenty-six authors contributed, among them Hugo von Hofmannsthal, D. H. Lawrence, and Stefan Zweig. "Die Pfeiferstube" was the contribution made by a young Munich journalist named Paul Alverdes. Thereafter his story was issued separately, not only in Germany but in England and America, where it enlisted the impassioned enthusiasm of such wildly unlike drumbeaters as Charles MacArthur and James Hilton.

When the Nazis came into power and began purging the library of all unmanly and devitalizing influences, *Die Pfeiferstube* was committed to the flames in the famous Munich bonfire, but this seems to have been an unauthorized and purely local gesture by some ardent muddlehead, who doubtless had the Alverdes work confused with the abhorrent *Im Westen Nichts Neues,* of which the author had already gone into exile. Unlike Remarque, Alverdes, as far as can be judged from a distance, appears to have experienced no spiritual or social difficulty in adjusting himself to the complicated task of functioning as a journalist in Adolf Hitler's Germany.

The Whistlers' Room—a noble and compassionate story—seems to me one of the great records of the World War. As in the case of the incomparable *Paths of Glory*—though to a lesser extent, surely—it is painful reading. Some have found it unbearably so and put the book down unfinished. You can have no quarrel with such readers, but you would, I think, be justified in tearing them limb from limb if, when next our statesmen get us into war and the bands begin to play, you were to catch these same sensitive creatures cheering their silly and unimperiled heads off, while their younger neighbors file down the street on the way to the waiting transports.

A. W.

CARDINAL MANNING

by

LYTTON STRACHEY

WITH A FOREWORD BY
REBECCA WEST

A FOREWORD ON
LYTTON STRACHEY

BY REBECCA WEST

GILES LYTTON STRACHEY was born fifty years ago
into a family which has been influential for so long that
it has become a clan within the governing class. It has
been known in the West Country since the fourteenth century,
and for the last few centuries has had for headquarters a little
fortified manor house in Somerset, which a Strachey who was the
first secretary to the Colony of Virginia acquired with a well-
portioned wife. It has flourished ever since, so that there are now
a large number of soldiers, politicians, scholars, and writers, who,
if they resemble each other in no other particular, are all Stracheys
and have the family faculty of continuance in positions of authority. Lytton Strachey was born in the very centre of this family, not,
as might have been supposed, of some remoter branch that had
grown far beyond the manor confines and leaned out into the
wilder airs. He was the son of Sir Richard Strachey, a capable
and devoted Indian administrator, and a pillar of the British Empire. His much older cousin, John St. Loe Strachey, was the
ebullient and beloved editor of *The Spectator,* the weekly which
made propaganda for the subtle and intellectual type of Toryism
developed by Lord Milner and Lord Cromer. But the presence of
the iconoclastic author of *Eminent Victorians* in this nest of Con-
servatism must not be put down simply as a sport, as an example
of the inveterate disposition observable in the wind of the spirit

to blow where it listeth. The children of St. Loe Strachey could look back over their shoulders at what was doubtless once their forward cousin Lytton, for one of them, Mrs. Williams-Ellis, is the author of *Volcano,* the most passionate apologia for Bolshevist Russia yet written in England, and the other, John Strachey, recently left the Mosley Party because it was insufficiently revolutionary.[1] The work of Lytton Strachey was, indeed, an illustration of the steady movement of the English governing class toward the left wing of political thought.

His career, so far as the public knew it, began late. At Cambridge he became a well-known figure, as he was bound to do, if only because of the endearing oddity of his physique. He had the oblong and wry-necked character of some of Giotto's figures; his beard, which was like an extension of his personality in the direction of doubt, seemed to be cut with square edges. For some reason his pallor was comic, perhaps because it was so excessive that it might well have been paint assumed by an actor about to give a performance as a lackadaisical grotesque. But from his eyes, blindish behind strong spectacles, proceeded a benevolent regard; his exquisite hands proclaimed him a creature from a fine mould; and he moved with a deer-like grace which spoke of shyness and friendliness. One could not help smiling at him, as Henry Lamb smiled at him in his celebrated portrait of him which hangs in the Tate Gallery in London, but if one had any sensibility at all one would know that this was a person to be honoured. He had also a voice, a thin glass tube of a voice, which would have been delicious had it been the vehicle of nonsense, which was incredibly entrancing when one realized that it transmitted instead learning, wit and moral passion. Because of these things, and because of certain merits of character which his intimates will doubtless partly disclose to us in the future, he was a well-known figure in

[1] Miss West's essay was published on February 7, 1932.—ED.

English social life of the more intellectual type, long before his thirty-second year, when he published *Landmarks in French Literature*.

That book is not among those of his works which the public keeps on reading year after year, and Mr. Desmond MacCarthy has dismissed it as "only a little text-book of enthusiastic critical clichés, well arranged, useful to pupil and teacher." But that judgment errs on the sides of both harshness and leniency. Literature would show a fairer front were it possible to describe with any sort of justice the exquisitely turned phrases which can be found on every page of this book, as "critical clichés." The sentences, pure as a cadenza played by an inspired flautist, in which Lytton Strachey delivers the matter of a Molière or a Marivaux comedy, are of a sort that has never been sold at two a penny in any market. There, as in all his work, Lytton Strachey did English prose a service by trying to write with the kind of shining readability which is the particular glory of the French. But, on the other hand, one may legitimately doubt whether *Landmarks in French Literature* could be really very useful to pupils and teachers. For as one gets further and further into the volume one has to admit to a growing sense of dissatisfaction. There is much to satisfy. How like living men his Villon, his Bossuet, his Saint-Simon, his André Chenier, walk across the page! But how poor his Pascal, how incomplete his Voltaire! So much nonsense has been written on both sides of the Atlantic about Rousseau that one must feel grateful to Lytton Strachey for remaining in full possession of his senses when dealing with the subject; but we are still forced to exclaim at his inadequacy. The cause for this inadequacy leaps to the eye. The *Contrat Social* means nothing to him; his comments on it are perfunctory and ill informed. The *Confessions* mean a great deal to him; there he is sensitive and penetrating. In fact, he has wanted to talk about Rousseau without mentioning the state, just as he has wanted to talk about Voltaire without mentioning Leibnitz, and just as he has wanted to talk about Pascal without mentioning the Jansenists and Port-Royal. He has failed with these great men just because they are great men, because they gathered up into themselves the intellectual life of their times, and could only be fully discussed in relation to certain clearly formulated ideas. He revealed it as the dominant element of his character, which was to determine the nature of all his future work, that, although by endowment he was an intellectual, he was interested not in ideas but in personalities. There lay his weakness and his strength.

Some time passed before the publication of his first mature book, which was also to be his first success: *Eminent Victorians*. He spent four years of it in adding a new occupation to the repertory of the Strachey family: he was a conscientious objector. Though his piping sense and wit made him the terror of the boards for examining conscientious objectors, these years must have been a severe ordeal, for his repudiation of sadism was unsupported by membership of any political body with internationalist sympathies. But it showed an undaunted audacity that he should come before the public very soon after with a book which consisted of nothing more nor less than allegations of hypocrisy and violence against four of the most venerated figures of the hierarchy which the nineteenth century had imposed on England. He approached Cardinal Manning, who was so superbly one of the real right people that he could even bring the Church of Rome into Protestant England and explain that she was not, as had been erroneously believed, the Whore of Babylon, but something more in the nature of foreign royalty, looked long into his handsome face, and accused him of devilish ambition. With a deflating finger he prodded the rounded waistcoat of Dr. Arnold, sacrosanct founder of the sacrosanct public school system in its sacrosanct present form, father of Matthew Arnold, and grandfather of Mrs. Humphry Ward, and named him a pompous and superstitious ignoramus whose inability to conceive one single valid idea regarding education led him to support customs which did much to make the young gentlemen of England brainless oafs and bullies. Gently overthrowing the bland plaster effigy which had long been installed in the heart of the English under the name of "The Lady of the Lamp," he exposed Florence Nightingale as a tyrannous and impassioned fanatic. And Chinese Gordon, the Victorian Galahad, the shedding of whose pure blood so many old ladies held as an eternal reproach against Gladstone, was whisked out of sainthood and recatalogued as a genius, and one that fully availed itself of the licence to be a lunatic which is popularly accorded it, and was at times a little tipsy too. The book was an orgy of iconoclasm, and it brought him instant fame, of which some part will, almost certainly, be lasting.

That fame was very largely a delighted response to his style, which he had developed to a formidable pitch of effectiveness. A proof of its extreme formidability may be found in the essay on Cardinal Manning, where the author is negligent enough to tell us twice with the same inflection of irony that the Pope's private secretary, Monsignor Talbot, was suddenly obliged to abandon a very promising set of intrigues by a disorder which necessitated removal to a private asylum at Passy. This trifling negligence is positively shocking to the reader; he feels as if the author is as naïve as a yokel who, wanting to frighten a friend out of his skin by progressive alarms, lets off a pistol by his ear twice in one evening; and it may never occur to him that those authors are few and far between whose ironical inflections are so registered by the nerves that the repetition seems an anticlimax. This effectiveness is not mechanical. It is the outward and visible sign of validity in argument; and if at times, as in certain passages of the essay on Gordon, it is baroque in character, there has not yet been any ordinance passed that there shall be no more cakes and ale. But the real secret of the power of *Eminent Victorians* to evoke extreme liking and loathing lies deeper than this. It lies in his preference for personalities over ideas, and in the cause that lay below that.

The indifference to ideas was, indeed, something of a blot on the book. It accounted for certain passages concerning religion in the essay on Cardinal Manning in which Lytton Strachey can hardly contain his amusement at those who show relief at having found what they think to be the means of salvation, or distress at having lost their faith. These passages make his admirers compare him to Gibbon, but the comparison is not happy; for whereas Gibbon smiled scornfully when men held beliefs that were absurd and degrading. Lytton Strachey smiled gently when men held any beliefs at all. One must count it as a deficiency in him that the universal tendency of men to symbolize their experience in religious terms seemed to him a whim which could be mocked away by sense and wit. But he more than atoned for that deficiency by the enormous gift he made us in restoring life to the nineteenth-century great. It is falsely supposed that his usefulness lay in his exposure of their imperfections; though that was indeed a service which was needed, considering how England was gagged by the legend of their perfection. Only a year or so before the war the editor of a great newspaper famous for its liberal opinions summarily dismissed a reviewer who had reasonably enough remarked that most modern readers found it difficult to understand the reputation for universal wisdom which had hedged about George Eliot and Herbert Spencer in their time; and he answered all protests by shaking his head and saying grimly, "A fellow who could write that can't be sound."

That sort of thing was not respect for tradition, it was an

imbecile amalgam of ancestor worship and fetishism; and in so far as Lytton Strachey brought it nearer an end we must be grateful to him. But it must not be forgotten that he exposed the imperfections of the great only because imperfection is the characteristic quality of personality. He was plucking from life the disguises under which it hides what its enemies call its shame, and its friends know to be its glory; its failure to comply with the standards of excellence devised by living creatures. He was denying that there were such beings as Victorians, these legendary automatic machines which, the right coin of moral and religious teaching having been dropped into them, produced the right insipid sweetmeat of good works; he was affirming that there were human beings who lived in the time of Queen Victoria and were exactly like the human beings who have lived in the time of any other King or Queen, a fusion of magnificence and meanness. He was denying that the Strachey family had any existence save as a convenient figment of the conventional mind; he was affirming that there were a large number of individuals called Strachey who were of the identical substance as the men they governed. He was denying that Papa and Mamma were the passionless and infallible shells they pretended to be when the nursery was looking; he was affirming that the peccant flesh of the offspring was the same as that which had begotten and borne it. There are, indeed, half a dozen ways of stating his denial and affirmation; but they all amount to a confession of faith that if an age fails to comply with the standards of excellence devised by its creatures, it is because those standards are the inadequate results of imperfect comprehension. If he smashed the sham personalities that had been built round the Victorians to render them completely pleasing to the standards of their age, it was not out of malice. It was because he believed that the real personality behind, simply by virtue of its reality, was infinitely more pleasing.

It was by the passion of this assertion that Lytton Strachey's work made its mark on his times, and by its essential truth that it will survive. The objective truth of that volume has been questioned. Without doubt Strachey suffered from that disposition to make tendentious use of his material which is so much the besetting sin of historians that it is doubtful whether anybody would ever become a historian if he were not liable to it. Those who are curious on the point can turn to the passage in Mr. Arnold Lunn's *Roman Converts,* where he compares Lytton Strachey's essay on Cardinal Manning with its sources, and detects certain extravagances. But it should also be noted that his view of Florence Nightingale has been completely justified by the work founded on hitherto inaccessible private papers which has recently been published by Miss I. B. O'Malley and which presents a vehement character much more like that depicted in *Eminent Victorians* than the starched and merciful nincompoop of popular legend; and attempts to criticize other parts of his work have been so unsuccessful that one may concede it as proven that the sum total of his findings shows a handsome balance on the side of the certain.

Nobody has questioned that such was the case with his *Queen Victoria,* though that was marred by signs of an impropriety which came to a ranker growth in *Elizabeth and Essex,* the only great popular success he ever enjoyed, the only book of his which his admirers could wish unwritten. There was something painfully like a Freudian obsession; something very different from the required attitude of an artist to his subject, in Lytton Strachey's fascinated and repelled dilations on the amorous anthropophagies of these crowned women, in Queen Victoria's daily, nightly erosions on the vitality of the Prince Consort, on Queen Elizabeth's suction of her favorites' marrow bones. Titianesque as *Elizabeth and Essex* was in sweep and colour, it broke too flagrantly the rule that a work of art must never be an obvious compensation for the deficiencies of its author's existence. It was too plainly the revenge taken by the suppressed romantic elements in a character committed by a majority vote to a cool and classical way of living, and it had the turgid and disconcerting quality of adolescent dreams that have been dreamed too long. One may guess that future readers will put it aside to turn back to *Eminent Victorians;* to *Books and Characters,* which, if the chapters on Voltaire are dullish because they lead the author toward the realm of ideas where he was never quite at home, is delightful for such pages as describe his relish for that self-unveiling of a gorgeous and sombre personality, the style of Sir Thomas Browne; and to that last miscellany, *Portraits in Miniature,* in which his genius for understanding and delineating his fellow-countrymen came to such a flowering that it is intolerable to think the plant is now uprooted. There he depicted some of the freakish folk who, ever since the days of freakish Gloriana, have given the English governing classes that character of eccentricity which they have never lost, and which has puzzled and shocked so many foreign observers, even including your Henry Adams. His wit was beautifully developed to the task; he could compress a heavy load of meaning into a light phrase, and represent the special quality of an enraged scholar by saying that the great Bentley "treated his opponents as if they had been corrupt readings in an old manuscript." And that his wit was held in its true course by a proper preference for life over death, for love over hate, for beauty over squalor, was exposed in the chapter on Walpole's friend, Mary Berry. In the dying fall of that essay, where he quotes the old woman's lament over a dream that had deluded her slumber with the idea that she was not infirm and alone and barren, one looks into the inner chamber of Lytton Strachey's nature and sees that, like all of us, he judged the world by what was within himself. He loved personality because his own personality was lovable, and one is amazed by the revealed harmony and simplicity. His real possession of those qualities was, indeed, the secret of the disconcerting effect he exercised on a world that is not so harmonious nor so simple as it believes itself. When a year or two ago, some young bloods organized an exhibition of daubs made blindfold, under the pretence that they were the works of a brilliant young artist, great play was made by the press with the news that Lytton Strachey had purchased two of the paintings. Here, it was announced, was sophistication falling over itself, a palate so refined that it had become perverse and insensitive. Yet the truth, which had been piped to a companion as they passed round the gallery, was very different. "And does this poor young man really think he can paint! Oh, poor young man! Poor young man! If his pictures are cheap one must buy one! Oh, poor young man, one must buy two! Oh, poor, poor young man—" The episode should be remembered by all those who, envious of brilliance, try to find mean interpretations for the work and life of Lytton Strachey.

CARDINAL MANNING

HENRY EDWARD MANNING was born in 1807 and died in 1892. His life was extraordinary in many ways, but its interest for the modern inquirer depends mainly upon two considerations—the light which his career throws upon the spirit of his age, and the psychological problems suggested by his inner history. He belonged to that class of eminent ecclesiastics—and it is by no means a small class—who have been distinguished less for saintliness and learning than for practical ability. Had he lived in the Middle Ages he would certainly have been neither a Francis nor an Aquinas, but he might have been an Innocent. As it was, born in the England of the Nineteenth Century, growing up in the very seed-time of modern progress, coming to maturity with the first onrush of Liberalism, and living long enough to witness the victories of Science and Democracy, he yet, by a strange concatenation of circumstances, seemed almost to revive in his own person that long line of diplomatic and administrative clerics which, one would have thought, had come to an end with Cardinal Wolsey. In Manning, so it appeared, the Middle Ages lived again. The tall gaunt figure, with the face of smiling asceticism, the robes, and the biretta, as it passed in triumph from High Mass at the Oratory to philanthropic gatherings at Exeter Hall, from Strike Committees at the Docks to Mayfair drawing-rooms where fashionable ladies knelt to the Prince of the Church, certainly bore witness to a singular condition of affairs. What had happened? Had a dominating character imposed itself upon a hostile environment? Or was the Nineteenth Century, after all, not so hostile? Was there something in it, scientific and progressive as it was, which went out to welcome the representative of ancient tradition and uncompromising faith? Had it perhaps, a place in its heart for such as Manning—a soft place, one might almost say? Or, on the other hand, was it he who had been supple and yielding? he who had won by art what he would never have won by force, and who had managed, so to speak, to be one of the leaders of the procession less through merit than through a superior faculty for gliding adroitly to the front rank? And, in any case, by what odd chances, what shifts and struggles, what combinations of circumstance and character had this old man come to be where he was? Such questions are easier to ask than to answer; but it may be instructive, and even amusing, to look a little more closely into the complexities of so curious a story.

I

UNDOUBTEDLY, what is most obviously striking in the history of Manning's career is the persistent strength of his innate characteristics. Through all the changes of his fortunes the powerful spirit of the man worked on undismayed. It was as if the Fates had laid a wager that they would daunt him, and in the end they lost their bet.

His father was a rich West India merchant, a governor of the Bank of England, a Member of Parliament, who drove into town every day from his country seat in a coach and four, and was content with nothing short of a bishop for the christening of his children. Little Henry, like the rest, had his bishop; but he was obliged to wait for him—for as long as eighteen months. In those days, and even a generation later, as Keble bears witness, there was great laxity in regard to the early baptism of children. The delay has been noted by Manning's biographer as the first stumbling-block in the spiritual life of the future Cardinal: but he surmounted it with success.

His father was more careful in other ways.

"His refinement and delicacy of mind were such [wrote Manning long afterwards] that I never heard out of his mouth a word which might not have been spoken in the presence of the most pure and sensitive,— except [he adds] on one occasion. He was then forced by others to repeat a Negro story which, though free from all evil *de sexu,* was indelicate. He did it with great resistance. His example gave me a hatred of all such talk."

The family lived in an atmosphere of Evangelical piety. One day the little boy came in from the farmyard, and his mother asked him whether he had seen the peacock. "I said yes, and the nurse said no, and my mother made me kneel down and beg God to forgive me for not speaking the truth." At the age of four the child was told by a cousin of the age of six that "God had a book in which He wrote down everything we did wrong. This so terrified me for days that I remember being found by my mother sitting under a kind of writing-table in great fear. I never forgot this at any time in my life," the Cardinal tells us, "and it has been a great grace to me." When he was nine years old he "devoured the Apocalypse; and I never all through my life forgot the 'lake that burneth with fire and brimstone.' That verse has kept with me like an audible voice through all my life, and through worlds of danger in my youth."

At Harrow the worlds of danger were already around him; but yet he listened to the audible voice. "At school and college I never failed to say my prayers, so far as memory serves me, even for a day." And he underwent another religious experience: he read Paley's *Evidences*. "I took in the whole argument," wrote Manning, when he was over seventy, "and I thank God that nothing has ever shaken it." Yet on the whole he led the unspiritual life of an ordinary schoolboy. We have glimpses of him as a handsome lad, playing cricket, or strutting about in tasselled Hessian top-boots. And on one occasion at least he gave proof of a certain dexterity of conduct which deserved to be remembered. He went out of bounds, and a master, riding by and seeing him on the other side of a field, tied his horse to a gate, and ran after him. The astute youth outran the master, fetched a circle, reached the gate, jumped on to the horse's back, and rode off. For this he was very properly chastised; but of what use was chastisement? No whipping, however severe, could have eradicated from little Henry's mind a quality at least as firmly planted in it as his fear of Hell and his belief in the arguments of Paley.

It had been his father's wish that Manning should go into the Church; but the thought disgusted him; and when he reached Oxford, his tastes, his ambitions, his successes at the Union, all seemed to mark him out for a political career. He was a year junior to Samuel Wilberforce, and a year senior to Gladstone. In those days the Union was the recruiting-ground for young politicians; Ministers came down from London to listen to the debates; and a few years later the Duke of Newcastle gave Gladstone a pocket borough on the strength of his speech at the Union against the Reform Bill. To those three young men, indeed, the whole world lay open. Were they not rich, well-connected, and endowed with an infinite capacity for making speeches? The event justified the highest expectations of their friends; for the least distinguished of the three died a bishop. The only danger lay in another direction.

"Watch, my dear Samuel [wrote the elder Wilberforce to his son], watch with jealousy whether you find yourself unduly solicitous about acquitting yourself; whether you are too much chagrined when you fail, or are puffed up by your success. Undue solicitude about popular estimation is a weakness against which all real Christians must guard with the most jealous watchfulness. The more you can retain the impression of your being surrounded by a cloud of witnesses of the invisible world, to use the Scripture phrase, the more you will be armed against this besetting sin."

But suddenly it seemed as if such a warning could, after all, have very little relevance to Manning; for, on his leaving Oxford, the brimming cup was dashed from his lips. He was already beginning to dream of himself in the House of Commons, the solitary advocate of some great cause whose triumph was to be eventually brought about by his extraordinary efforts, when his father was declared a bankrupt, and all his hopes of a political career came to an end for ever.

It was at this time that Manning became intimate with a pious lady, the sister of one of his College friends, whom he used to describe as his Spiritual Mother. He made her his confidante; and one day, as they walked together in the shrubbery, he revealed the bitterness of the disappointment into which his father's failure had plunged him. She tried to cheer him, and then she added that there were higher aims open to him which he had not considered. "What do you mean?" he asked. "The kingdom of Heaven," she answered; "heavenly ambitions are not closed against you." The young man listened, was silent, and said at last that he did not know but she was right. She suggested reading the Bible together; and they accordingly did so during the whole of that vacation, every morning after breakfast. Yet, in spite of these devotional exercises, and in spite of a voluminous correspondence on religious subjects with his Spiritual Mother, Manning still continued to indulge in secular hopes. He entered the Colonial Office as a supernumerary clerk, and it was only when the offer of a Merton Fellowship seemed to depend upon his taking orders that his heavenly ambitions began to assume a definite shape. Just then he fell in love with Miss Deffell, whose father would have nothing to say to a young man without prospects, and forbade him the house. It was only too true; what *were* the prospects of a supernumerary clerk in the Colonial Office? Manning went to Oxford and took orders. He was elected to the Merton Fellowship, and obtained through the influence of the Wilberforces a curacy in Sussex. At the last moment he almost drew back. "I think the whole step has been too precipitate," he wrote to his brother-in-law. "I have rather allowed the instance of my friends, and the allurements of an agreeable curacy in many respects, to get the better of my sober judgment." His vast ambitions, his dream of public service, of honours, and of power, was all this to end in a little country curacy "agreeable in many respects"? But there was nothing for it; the deed was done; and the Fates had apparently succeeded very effectively in getting rid of Manning. All he could do was to make the best of a bad business. Accordingly, in the first place, he decided that he had received a call from God *"ad veritatem et ad seipsum"*; and, in the second, forgetting Miss Deffell, he married his rector's daughter. Within a few months the rector died, and Manning stepped into his shoes: and at least it could be said that the shoes were not uncomfortable. For the next seven years he fulfilled the functions of a country clergyman. He was energetic and devout; he was polite and handsome; his fame grew in the diocese. At last he began to be spoken of as the probable successor to the old Archdeacon of Chichester. When Mrs. Manning prematurely died, he was at first inconsolable, but he found relief in the distraction of redoubled work. How could he have guessed that one day he would come to number that loss among "God's special mercies"? Yet so it was to be. In after years, the memory of his wife seemed to be blotted from his mind; he never spoke of her; every letter, every record, of his married life he destroyed; and when word was sent to him that her grave was falling into ruin: "It is best so," the Cardinal answered; "let it be. Time effaces all things." But, when the grave was yet fresh, the young Rector would sit beside it, day after day, writing his sermons.

I I

In the meantime a series of events was taking place in another part of England, which was to have a no less profound effect upon Manning's history than the merciful removal of his wife. In the same year in which he took up his Sussex curacy, the *Tracts for the Times* had begun to appear at Oxford. The "Oxford Movement," in fact, had started on its course. The phrase is still familiar; but its meaning has become somewhat obscured both by the lapse of time and the intrinsic ambiguity of the subjects connected with it. Let us borrow for a moment the wings of Historic Imagination, and, hovering lightly over the Oxford of the thirties, take a rapid bird's-eye view.

For many generations the Church of England had slept the sleep of the . . . comfortable. The sullen murmurings of dissent, the loud battle-cry of Revolution, had hardly disturbed her slumbers. Portly divines subscribed with a sigh or a smile to the Thirty-Nine Articles, sank quietly into easy livings, rode gaily to hounds of a morning as gentlemen should, and, as gentlemen should, carried their two bottles of an evening. To be in the Church was in fact simply to pursue one of those professions which Nature and Society had decided were proper to gentlemen and gentlemen alone. The fervours of piety, the zeal of

Apostolic charity, the enthusiasm of self-renunciation—these things were all very well in their way—and in their place; but their place was certainly not the Church of England. Gentlemen were neither fervid nor zealous, and above all they were not enthusiastic. There were, it was true, occasionally to be found within the Church some straitlaced parsons of the high Tory school who looked back with regret to the days of Laud or talked of the Apostolical Succession; and there were groups of square-toed Evangelicals who were earnest over the Atonement, confessed to a personal love of Jesus Christ, and seemed to have arranged the whole of their lives, down to the minutest details of act and speech, with reference to Eternity. But such extremes were the rare exceptions. The great bulk of the clergy walked calmly along the smooth road of ordinary duty. They kept an eye on the poor of the parish, and they conducted the Sunday Services in a becoming manner; for the rest, they differed neither outwardly nor inwardly from the great bulk of the laity, to whom the Church was a useful organization for the maintenance of Religion, as by law established.

The awakening came at last, however, and it was a rude one. The liberal principles of the French Revolution, checked at first in the terrors of reaction, began to make way in England. Rationalists lifted up their heads; Bentham and the Mills propounded Utilitarianism; the Reform Bill was passed; and there were rumours abroad of disestablishment. Even Churchmen seemed to have caught the infection. Dr. Whately was so bold as to assert that, in the interpretation of Scripture, different opinions might be permitted upon matters of doubt; and Dr. Arnold drew up a disquieting scheme for allowing Dissenters into the Church, though it is true that he did not go quite so far as to contemplate the admission of Unitarians.

At this time there was living in a country parish a young clergyman of the name of John Keble. He had gone to Oxford at the age of fifteen, where, after a successful academic career, he had been made a fellow of Oriel. He had then returned to his father's parish and taken up the duties of a curate. He had a thorough knowledge of the contents of the Prayer-Book, the ways of a Common Room, the conjugations of the Greek Irregular Verbs, and the small jests of a country parsonage; and the defects of his experience in other directions were replaced by a zeal and a piety which were soon to prove themselves equal, and more than equal, to whatever calls might be made upon them. The superabundance of his piety overflowed into verse; and the holy simplicity of the *Christian Year* carried his name into the remotest lodging-houses of England. As for his zeal, however, it needed another outlet. Looking forth upon the doings of his fellowmen through his rectory windows in Gloucestershire, Keble felt his whole soul shaken with loathing, anger, and dread. Infidelity was stalking through the land; authority was laughed at; the hideous doctrines of Democracy were being openly preached. Worse still, if possible, the Church herself was ignorant and lukewarm;` she had forgotten the mysteries of the sacraments, she had lost faith in the Apostolical Succession, she was no longer interested in the Early Fathers, and she submitted herself to the control of a secular legislature, the members of which were not even bound to profess belief in the Atonement. In the face of such enormities what could Keble do? He was ready to do anything, but he was a simple and an unambitious man, and his wrath would in all probability have consumed itself unappeased within him had he not chanced to come into contact, at the critical moment, with a spirit more excitable and daring than his own.

Hurrell Froude, one of Keble's pupils, was a clever young man to whom had fallen a rather larger share of self-assurance and intolerance than even clever young men usually possess. What was singular about him, however, was not so much his temper as his tastes. The sort of ardour which impels more normal youths to haunt Music Halls and fall in love with actresses took the form, in Froude's case, of a romantic devotion to the Deity and an intense interest in the state of his own soul. He was obsessed by the ideals of saintliness, and convinced of the supreme importance of not eating too much. He kept a diary, in which he recorded his delinquencies, and they were many. "I cannot say much for myself today," he writes on September 29, 1826 (he was twenty-three years old). "I did not read the Psalms and Second Lesson after breakfast, which I had neglected to do before, though I had plenty of time on my hands. Would have liked to be thought adventurous for a scramble I had at the Devil's Bridge. Looked with greediness to see if there was a goose on the table for dinner; and though what I ate was of the plainest sort, and I took no variety, yet even this was partly the effect of accident, and I certainly rather exceeded in quantity, as I was muzzy and sleepy after dinner." "I allowed myself to be disgusted with ——'s pomposity," he writes a little later; "also smiled at an allusion in the Lessons to abstemiousness in eating. I hope not from pride or vanity, but mistrust; it certainly was unintentional." And again, "As to my meals, I can say that I was always careful to see that no one else would take a thing before I served myself; and I believe as to the kind of my food, a bit of cold endings of a dab at breakfast, and a scrap of mackerel at dinner, are the only things that diverged from the strict rule of simplicity." "I am obliged to confess," he notes, "that in my intercourse with the Supreme Being, I am become more and more sluggish." And then he exclaims: "Thine eye trieth my inward parts, and knoweth my thoughts . . . O that my ways were made so direct that I might keep Thy statutes. I will walk in Thy Commandments when Thou hast set my heart at liberty."

Such were the preoccupations of this young man. Perhaps they would have been different if he had had a little less of what Newman describes as his "high severe idea of the intrinsic excellence of Virginity"; but it is useless to speculate. Naturally enough the fierce and burning zeal of Keble had a profound effect upon his mind. The two became intimate friends, and Froude, eagerly seizing upon the doctrines of the elder man, saw to it that they had as full a measure of controversial notoriety as an Oxford common room could afford. He plunged the metaphysical mysteries of the Holy Catholic Church into the atmosphere of party politics. Surprised Doctors of Divinity found themselves suddenly faced with strange questions which had never entered their heads before. Was the Church of England, or was it not, a part of the Church Catholic? If it was, were not the Reformers of the Sixteenth Century renegades? Was not the participation of the Body and Blood of Christ essential to the maintenance of Christian life and hope in each individual? Were Timothy and Titus bishops? Or were they not? If they were, did it not follow that the power of administering the Holy Eucharist was the attribute of a sacred order founded by Christ Himself? Did not the Fathers refer to the tradition of the Church as to something independent of the written word, and sufficient to refute heresy, even alone? Was it not therefore God's unwritten word? And did it not demand the same reverence from us as the Scriptures, and for exactly the same reason—*because it was His word?* The Doctors of Divinity were aghast at such questions, which seemed to lead they hardly knew whither; and they found it difficult to think of very apposite answers. But Hurrell Froude supplied the answers himself readily enough. All Oxford, all England, should know the truth. The time was out of joint, and he was only too delighted to have been born to set it right.

But, after all, something more was needed than even the excitement of Froude combined with the conviction of Keble to ruffle seriously the vast calm waters of Christian thought; and it so happened that that thing was not wanting: it was the genius of John Henry Newman. If Newman had never lived, or if his father, when the gig came round on the fatal morning, still undecided between the two Universities, had chanced to turn the horse's head in the direction of Cambridge, who can doubt that the Oxford Movement would have flickered out its little flame unobserved in the Common Room of Oriel? And how different, too, would have been the fate of Newman himself! He was a child of the Romantic Revival, a creature of emotion and of memory, a dreamer whose secret spirit dwelt apart in delectable mountains, an artist whose subtle senses caught, like a shower in the sunshine, the impalpable rainbow of the immaterial world. In other times, under other skies, his days would have been more fortunate. He might have helped to weave the garland of Meleager, or to mix the *lapis lazuli* of Fra Angelico, or to chase the delicate truth in the shade of an Athenian *palæstra,* or his hands might have fashioned those ethereal faces that smile in the niches of Chartres. Even in his own age he might, at Cambridge, whose cloisters have ever been consecrated to poetry and common sense, have followed quietly in Gray's footsteps and brought into flower those seeds of inspiration which now lie embedded amid the faded devotion of the *Lyra Apostolica*. At Oxford, he was doomed. He could not withstand the last enchantment of the Middle Age. It was in vain that he plunged into the pages of Gibbon or communed for long hours with Beethoven over his beloved violin. The air was thick with clerical sanctity, heavy with the odours of tradition and the soft warmth of spiritual authority; his friendship with Hurrell Froude did the rest. All that was weakest in him hurried him onward, and all that was strongest in him too. His curious and vaulting imagination began to construct vast philosophical fabrics out of the writings of ancient monks, and to dally with visions of angelic visitations and the efficacy of the oil of St. Walburga; his emotional nature became absorbed in the partisan passions of a University clique; and his subtle intellect concerned itself more and more exclusively with the dialectical splitting of dogmatical hairs. His future course was marked out for him all too clearly; and yet by a singular chance the true nature of the man was to emerge triumphant in the end. If Newman had died at the age of sixty, today he would have been already forgotten, save by a few ecclesiastical historians; but he lived to write his *Apologia,* and to reach immortality, neither as a thinker nor as a theologian, but as an artist who has embalmed the poignant history of an intensely human spirit in the magical spices of words.

When Froude succeeded in impregnating Newman with the ideas of Keble, the Oxford Movement began. The original and remarkable characteristic of these three men was that they took the Christian Religion *au pied de la lettre.* This had not been done in England for centuries. When they declared every Sunday that they believed in the Holy Catholic Church, they meant it. When they repeated the Athanasian Creed, they meant it. Even when they subscribed to the Thirty-Nine Articles, they meant it—or at least they thought they did. Now such a state of mind was dangerous—more dangerous, indeed, than they at first realized. They had started with the innocent assumption that the Christian Religion was contained in the doctrines of the Church of England; but the more they examined into this matter, the more difficult and dubious it became. The Church of England bore everywhere upon it the signs of human imperfection; it was the outcome of revolution and of compromise, of the exigencies of politicians and the caprices of princes, of the prejudices of theologians and the necessities of the State. How had it happened that this piece of patchwork had become the receptacle for the august and infinite mysteries of the Christian Faith? This was the problem with which Newman and his friends found themselves confronted. Other men might, and apparently did, see nothing very strange in such a situation; but other men saw in Christianity itself scarcely more than a convenient and respectable appendage to existence, by which a sound system of morals was inculcated, and through which one might hope to attain to everlasting bliss. To Newman and Keble it was otherwise. They saw a transcendent manifestation of Divine power, flowing down elaborate and immense through the ages; a consecrated priesthood, stretching back, through the mystic symbol of the laying on of hands, to the very Godhead; a whole universe of spiritual beings brought into communion with the Eternal by means of wafers; a great mass of metaphysical doctrines, at once incomprehensible and of incalculable import, laid down with infinite certitude; they saw the supernatural everywhere and at all times, a living force, floating invisible in angels, inspiring saints, and investing with miraculous properties the commonest material things. No wonder that they found such a spectacle hard to bring into line with the institution which had been evolved from the divorce of Henry VIII., the intrigues of Elizabethan parliaments, and the Revolution of 1688. They did, no doubt, soon satisfy themselves that they had succeeded in this apparently hopeless task; but the conclusions which they came to in order to do so were decidedly startling.

The Church of England, they declared, was indeed the one true Church, but she had been under an eclipse since the Reformation—in fact, since she had begun to exist. She had, it is true, escaped the corruptions of Rome; but she had become enslaved by the secular power, and degraded by the false doctrines of Protestantism. The Christian Religion was still preserved intact by the English priesthood, but it was preserved, as it were, unconsciously—a priceless deposit, handed down blindly from generation to generation, and subsisting less by the will of man than through the ordinance of God as expressed in the mysterious virtue of the Sacraments. Christianity, in short, had become entangled in a series of unfortunate circumstances from which it was the plain duty of Newman and his friends to rescue it forthwith. What was curious was that this task had been reserved, in so marked a manner, for them. Some of the divines of the seventeenth century had, perhaps, been vouchsafed glimpses of the truth; but they were glimpses and nothing more. No, the waters of the true Faith had dived underground at the Reformation, and they were waiting for the wand of Newman to strike the rock before they should burst forth once more into the light of day. The whole matter, no doubt, was Providential—what other explanation could there be?

The first step, it was clear, was to purge the Church of her shams and her errors. The Reformers must be exposed; the yoke of the secular power must be thrown off; dogma must be reinstated in its old pre-eminence; and Christians must be reminded of what they had apparently forgotten—the presence of the supernatural in daily life. "It would be a gain to this country," Keble observed, "were it vastly more superstitious, more bigoted, more gloomy, more fierce in its religion, than at present it shows itself to be." "The only good I know of Cranmer," said Hurrell Froude, "was that he burnt well." Newman preached, and soon the new views began to spread. Among the earliest of the converts was Dr. Pusey, a man of wealth and learning, a professor, a canon of Christ Church, who had, it was rumoured, been to Germany. Then the *Tracts for the Times* were started under Newman's editorship, and the Movement was launched upon the world.

The Tracts were written "with the hope of rousing members of our Church to comprehend her alarming position . . . as a man might give notice of a fire or inundation, to startle all who heard him." They may be said to have succeeded in their object, for the sensation which they caused among clergymen throughout the country was extreme. They dealt with a great variety of questions, but the underlying intention of all of them was to attack the accepted doctrines and practices of the Church of England. Dr. Pusey wrote learnedly on Baptismal Regeneration; he also wrote on Fasting. His treatment of the latter subject met with considerable disapproval, which surprised the Doctor. "I was not prepared," he said, "for people questioning, even in the abstract, the duty of fasting; I thought serious-minded persons at least supposed they practised fasting in some way or other. I assumed the duty to be acknowledged and thought it only undervalued." We live and learn, even though we have been to Germany.

Other tracts discussed the Holy Catholic Church, the Clergy, and the Liturgy. One treated of the question "whether a clergyman of the Church of England be now bound to have morning and evening prayers daily in his parish church?" Another pointed out the "Indications of a superintending Providence in the preservation of the Prayer-Book and in the changes which it has undergone." Another consisted of a collection of "Advent Sermons on Antichrist." Keble wrote a long and elaborate tract "On the Mysticism attributed to the Early Fathers of the Church," in which he expressed his opinions upon a large number of curious matters.

"According to men's usual way of talking [he wrote] it would be called an accidental circumstance that there were *five* loaves, not more nor less, in the store of Our Lord and His disciples wherewith to provide the miraculous feast. But the ancient interpreters treat it as designed and providential, in this surely not erring: and their conjecture is that it represents the sacrifice of the whole world of sense, and especially of the Old Dispensation, which, being outward and visible, might be called the dispensation of the senses, to the FATHER of our LORD JESUS CHRIST, to be a pledge and means of communion with Him according to the terms of the new or evangelical law. This idea they arrive at by considering the number five, the number of the senses, as the mystical opponent of the visible and sensible universe: τὰ αἰσθητὰ as distinguished from τὰ νοητά. Origen lays down the rule in express terms. 'The number five,' he says, 'frequently, nay almost always, is taken for the five senses.'"

In another passage, Keble deals with an even more recondite question. He quotes the teaching of St. Barnabas that "Abraham, who first gave men circumcision, did thereby perform a spiritual and typical action, looking forward to the Son." St. Barnabas's argument is as follows: Abraham circumcised of his house men to the number of 318. Why 318? Observe first the 18, then the 300. Of the two letters which stand for 18, 10 is represented by I, 8 by H. "Thou hast here," says St. Barnabas, "the word of Jesus." As for the 300, "the Cross is represented by Tau, and the letter Tau represents that number." Unfortunately, however, St. Barnabas's premise was of doubtful validity, as the Rev. Mr. Maitland pointed out, in a pamphlet impugning the conclusions of the Tract.

"The simple fact is [he wrote] that when Abraham pursued Chedorlaomer 'he armed his trained servants, *born in his own house,* three hundred and eighteen.' When, more than thirteen (according to the common chronology, fifteen) years after, he circumcised 'all the men of his house, *born in the house,* and *bought with money* of the stranger,' and, in fact, every male who was as much as eight days old, we are not told what the number amounted to. Shall we suppose (just for the sake of the interpretation) that Abraham's family had so dwindled in the interval as that now all the males of his household, trained men, slaves, and children, equalled only and exactly the number of his warriors 15 years before?"

The question seems difficult to answer, but Keble had, as a matter of fact, forestalled the argument in the following passage, which had apparently escaped the notice of the Rev. Mr. Maitland.

"Now whether the facts were really so or not (if it were, it was surely by special providence), that Abraham's household at the time of the circumcision was exactly the same number as before; still the argument of St. Barnabas will stand. As thus: circumcision had from the beginning a reference to our SAVIOUR, as in other respects, so in this; that the mystical number, which is the cypher of Jesus crucified, was the number of the first circumcised household in the strength of which

Abraham prevailed against the powers of the world. So St. Clement of Alexandria, as cited by Fell."

And Keble supports his contention through ten pages of close print, with references to Aristeas, St. Augustine, St. Jerome, and Dr. Whitby.

Writings of this kind could not fail of their effect. Pious youths in Oxford were carried away by them, and began to flock around the standard of Newman. Newman himself became a party chief, encouraging, organizing, persuading. His long black figure, swiftly passing through the streets, was pointed at with awe; his sermons were crowded; his words repeated from mouth to mouth. "Credo in Newmannum" became a common catchword. Jokes were made about the Church of England, and practices, unknown for centuries, began to be revived. Young men fasted and did penance, recited the hours of the Roman Breviary, and confessed their sins to Dr. Pusey. Nor was the movement confined to Oxford; it spread in widening circles through the parishes of England; the dormant devotion of the country was suddenly aroused. The new strange notion of taking Christianity literally was delightful to earnest minds; but it was also alarming. Really to mean every word you said, when you repeated the Athanasian Creed! How wonderful! And what enticing and mysterious vistas burst upon the view! But then, those vistas, where were they leading to? Supposing—oh heavens!—supposing after all they were to lead to——!

III

In due course the Tracts made their appearance at the remote Rectory in Sussex. Manning was some years younger than Newman, and the two men had only met occasionally at the University; but now, through common friends, a closer relationship began to grow up between them. It was only to be expected that Newman should be anxious to enroll the rising young Rector among his followers; and on Manning's side there were many causes which impelled him to accept the overtures from Oxford.

He was a man of a serious and vigorous temperament, to whom it was inevitable that the bold, high principles of the Movement should strongly appeal. There was also an element in his mind—that element which had terrified him in his childhood with Apocalyptic visions, and urged him in his youth to Bible readings after breakfast—which now brought him under the spell of the Oxford theories of sacramental mysticism. And besides, the Movement offered another attraction; it imputed an extraordinary, a transcendent merit to the profession which Manning himself pursued. The cleric was not as his lay brethren; he was a creature apart, chosen by Divine will and sanctified by Divine mysteries. It was a relief to find, when one had supposed that one was nothing but a clergyman, that one might, after all, be something else—one might be a priest.

Accordingly, Manning shook off his early Evangelical convictions, started an active correspondence with Newman, and was soon working for the new cause. He collected quotations, and began to translate the works of Optatus for Dr. Pusey. He wrote an article on Justin for the *British Critic,* Newman's magazine. He published a sermon on Faith, with notes and appendices, which was condemned by an evangelical bishop, and fiercely attacked by no less a person than the celebrated Mr. Bowdler. "The sermon," said Mr. Bowdler, in a book which he devoted to the subject, "was bad enough, but the appendix was abominable." At the same time he was busy asserting the independence of the Church of England, opposing secular education, and bringing out pamphlets against the Ecclesiastical Commission, which had been appointed by Parliament to report on Church Property. Then we find him in the role of a spiritual director of souls. Ladies met him by stealth in his church, and made their confessions. Over one case—that of a lady, who found herself drifting towards Rome—he consulted Newman. Newman advised him to "enlarge upon the doctrine of 1 Cor. vii";—

"also I think you must press on her the prospect of *benefiting* the poor Church, through which she has her baptism, by stopping in it. Does she not care for the souls of all around her, steeped and stifled in Protestantism? How will she best care for them: by indulging her own feelings in the communion of Rome, or in denying herself, and staying in sackcloth and ashes to do them good?"

Whether these arguments were successful does not appear.

For several years after his wife's death Manning was occupied with these new activities, while his relations with Newman developed into what was apparently a warm friendship. "And now *vive valeque,* my dear Manning," we find Newman writing in a letter dated "in festo S. Car. 1838," "as wishes and prays yours affectionately John H. Newman." But, as time went on, the situation became more complicated. Tractarianism began to arouse the hostility, not only of the evangelical, but of the moderate churchmen, who could not help perceiving, in the ever deepening "catholicism" of the Oxford party, the dread approaches of Rome. The *Record* newspaper—an influential Evangelical journal—took up the matter, and sniffed Popery in every direction; it spoke of certain clergymen as "tainted"; and after that, Manning seemed to pass those clergymen by. The fact that Manning found it wise to conduct his confessional ministrations in secret was in itself highly significant. It was necessary to be careful, and Manning was very careful indeed. The neighbouring Archdeacon, Mr. Hare, was a low churchman; Manning made friends with him, as warmly, it seemed, as he had made friends with Newman. He corresponded with him, asked his advice about the books he should read, and discussed questions of Theology—"As to Gal. vi. 15, *we cannot differ.* . . . With a man who reads and reasons I can have no controversy; and you do both." Archdeacon Hare was pleased, but soon a rumour reached him, which was, to say the least of it, upsetting. Manning had been removing the high pews from a church in Brighton, and putting in open benches in their place. Everyone knew what that meant; everyone knew that a high pew was one of the bulwarks of Protestantism, and that an open bench had upon it the taint of Rome. But Manning hastened to explain.

"My dear friend [he wrote] I did not exchange pews for open benches, but got the pews (the same in number) moved from the nave of the church to the walls of the side aisles, so that the whole church has a regular arrangement of open benches, which (irregularly) existed before . . . I am not today quite well, so farewell, with much regard— Yours ever, H. E. M."

Archdeacon Hare was reassured.

It was important that he should be, for the Archdeacon of Chichester was growing very old, and Hare's influence might be exceedingly useful when a vacancy occurred. So, indeed, it fell out. A new bishop, Dr. Shuttleworth, was appointed to the See, and the old Archdeacon took the opportunity of retiring. Manning was obviously marked out as his successor, but the new bishop happened to be a low churchman, an aggressive low churchman, who went so far as to parody the Tractarian fashion of using Saints' days for the dating of letters by writing "The Palace, washing day," at the beginning of his. And—what was equally serious—his views were shared by Mrs. Shuttleworth, who had already decided that the pushing young Rector was "tainted." But at the critical moment Archdeacon Hare came to the rescue; he persuaded the Bishop that Manning was safe; and the appointment was accordingly made—behind Mrs. Shuttleworth's back. She was furious, but it was too late; Manning was an Archdeacon. All the lady could do, to indicate her disapprobation, was to put a copy of Mr. Bowdler's book in a conspicuous position on the drawing-room table, when he came to pay his respects at the Palace.

Among the letters of congratulation which Manning received was one from Mr. Gladstone, with whom he had remained on terms of close friendship since their days together at Oxford.

"I rejoice [Mr. Gladstone wrote] on your account personally: but more for the sake of the Church. All my brothers-in-law are here and scarcely less delighted than I am. With great glee am I about to write your new address; but the occasion really calls for higher sentiments; and sure am I that you are one of the men to whom it is especially given to develop the solution of that great problem—how all our minor distractions are to be either abandoned, absorbed, or harmonized, through the might of the great principle of communion in the body of Christ."

Manning was an Archdeacon; but he was not yet out of the wood. His relations with the Tractarians had leaked out, and the *Record* was beginning to be suspicious. If Mrs. Shuttleworth's opinion of him were to become general, it would certainly be a grave matter. Nobody could wish to live and die a mere Archdeacon. And then, at that very moment, an event occurred which made it imperative to take a definite step, one way or the other. That event was the publication of Tract No. 90.

For some time it had been obvious to every impartial onlooker that Newman was slipping down an inclined plane at the bottom of which lay one thing, and one thing only—the Roman Catholic Church. What was surprising was the length of time which he was taking to reach the inevitable destination. Years passed before he came to realize that his grandiose edifice of a Church Universal would crumble to pieces if one of its foundation stones was to be an amatory intrigue of Henry VIII. But at last he began to see that terrible monarch glowering at him wherever he turned his eyes. First he tried to exorcise the spectre with the rolling periods of the Caroline divines; but it only strutted the more truculently. Then in despair he plunged into the writings of the early Fathers, and sought to discover some way out of his difficulties in the complicated labyrinth of ecclesiastical history. After months spent in the study of the Monophysite heresy, the alarming conclusion began to force itself upon him that the Church of England was perhaps in schism. Eventually he read an article by a Roman Catholic on St. Augustine and the Donatists, which seemed to put the matter beyond doubt. St. Augustine, in the fifth century, had pointed out that the Donatists were heretics because the Bishop of Rome had said so. The argument was crushing; it rang in Newman's ears for days and nights; and, though he continued to linger on in agony for six years more, he never could discover any reply to it. All he could hope to do was to persuade himself and anyone else who liked to listen to him that the holding of Anglican orders was not inconsistent with a belief in the whole cycle of Roman doctrine, as laid down at the Council of Trent. In this way he supposed that he could at once avoid the deadly sin of heresy and conscientiously remain a clergyman in the Church of England; and with this end in view he composed Tract No. 90.

The object of the Tract was to prove that there was nothing in the Thirty-Nine Articles incompatible with the creed of the Roman Church. Newman pointed out, for instance, that it was generally supposed that the Articles condemned the doctrine of Purgatory; but they did not; they merely condemned the *Romish* doctrine of Purgatory; and *Romish,* clearly, was not the same thing as *Roman*. Hence it followed that believers in the Roman doctrine of Purgatory might subscribe the Articles with a good conscience. Similarly, the Articles condemned "the sacrifice of the masses," but they did *not* condemn "the sacrifice of the Mass." Thus the Mass might be lawfully celebrated in English Churches. Newman took the trouble to examine the Articles in detail from this point of view, and the conclusion he came to in every case supported his contention in a singular manner.

The Tract produced an immense sensation, for it seemed to be a deadly and treacherous blow aimed at the very heart of the Church of England. Deadly it certainly was, but it was not so treacherous as at first sight appeared. The members of the English Church had ingenuously imagined up to that moment that it was possible to contain in a frame of words the subtle essence of their complicated doctrinal system, involving the mysteries of the Eternal and the Infinite on the one hand, and the elaborate adjustments of temporal government on the other. They did not understand that verbal definitions in such a case will only perform their functions so long as there is no dispute about the matters which they are intended to define: that is to say, so long as there is no need for them. For generations this had been the case with the Thirty-Nine Articles. Their drift was clear enough; and nobody bothered over their exact meaning. But directly someone found it important to give them a new and untraditional interpretation, it appeared that they were a mass of ambiguity, and might be twisted into meaning very nearly anything that anybody liked. Steady-going churchmen were appalled and outraged when they saw Newman, in

Tract No. 90, performing this operation. But, after all, he was only taking the Church of England at its word. And indeed, since Newman showed the way, the operation has become so exceedingly common that the most steady-going churchman hardly raises an eyebrow at it now.

At the time, however, Newman's treatment of the Articles seemed to display not only a perverted supersubtlety of intellect, but a temper of mind that was fundamentally dishonest. It was then that he first began to be assailed by those charges of untruthfulness which reached their culmination more than twenty years later in the celebrated controversy with Charles Kingsley, which led to the writing of the *Apologia*. The controversy was not a very fruitful one, chiefly because Kingsley could no more understand the nature of Newman's intelligence than a subaltern in a line regiment can understand a Brahmin of Benares. Kingsley was a stout Protestant, whose hatred of Popery was, at bottom, simply ethical—an honest, instinctive horror of the practices of priestcraft and the habits of superstition; and it was only natural that he should see in those innumerable delicate distinctions which Newman was perpetually drawing, and which he himself had not only never thought of, but could not even grasp, simply another manifestation of the inherent falsehood of Rome. But, in reality, no one, in one sense of the word, was more truthful than Newman. The idea of deceit would have been abhorrent to him; and indeed it was owing to his very desire to explain what he had in his mind exactly and completely, with all the refinements of which his subtle brain was capable, that persons such as Kingsley were puzzled into thinking him dishonest. Unfortunately, however, the possibilities of truth and falsehood depend upon other things besides sincerity. A man may be of a scrupulous and impeccable honesty, and yet his respect for the truth— it cannot be denied—may be insufficient. He may be, like the lunatic, the lover, and the poet, "of imagination all compact"; he may be blessed, or cursed, with one of those "seething brains," one of those "shaping fantasies" that "apprehend more than cool reason ever comprehends"; he may be by nature incapable of sifting evidence, or by predilection simply indisposed to do so. "When we were there," wrote

Newman in a letter to a friend after his conversion, describing a visit to Naples, and the miraculous circumstances connected with the liquefaction of St. Januarius's blood,

"the feast of St. Gennaro was coming on, and the Jesuits were eager for us to stop—they have the utmost confidence in the miracle—and were the more eager because many Catholics, till they have seen it, doubt it. Our father director here tells us that before he went to Naples he did not believe it. That is, they have vague ideas of natural means, exaggeration, etc., not of course imputing fraud. They say conversions often take place in consequence. It is exposed for the Octave, and the miracle continues—it is not simple liquefaction, but sometimes it swells, sometimes boils, sometimes melts—no one can tell what is going to take place. They say it is quite overcoming—and people cannot help crying to see it. I understand that Sir H. Davy attended every day, and it was this extreme variety of the phenomenon which convinced him that nothing physical would account for it. Yet there is this remarkable fact, that liquefactions of blood are common at Naples —and unless it is irreverent to the Great Author of Miracles to be obstinate in the inquiry, the question certainly rises whether there is something in the air. (Mind, I don't believe there is—and, speaking humbly, and without having seen it, think it a true miracle—but I am arguing.) We *saw* the blood of St. Patrizia, half liquid; *i.e.* liquefying, on her feast day. St. John Baptist's blood sometimes liquefies on the 29th of August, and did when we were at Naples, but we had not time to go to the church. We saw the liquid blood of an Oratorian Father, a good man, but not a saint, who died two centuries ago, I think; and we saw the liquid blood of Da Ponte, the great and Holy Jesuit, who, I suppose, was almost a saint. But these instances do not account for liquefaction on certain days, if this is the case. But the most strange phenomenon is what happens at Ravello, a village or town above Amalfi. There is the blood of St. Pantaloon. It is in a vessel amid the stonework of the Altar—it is not touched—but on his feast in June it liquefies. And more, there is an excommunication against those who bring portions of the True Cross into the Church. Why? Because the blood liquefies, whenever it is brought. A person I know, not knowing the prohibition, brought in a portion—and the Priest suddenly said, who showed the blood, 'Who has got the Holy Cross about him?' I tell you what was told me by a grave and religious man. It is a curious coincidence that in telling this to our Father Director here, he said, 'Why, we have a portion of St. Pantaloon's blood at the Chiesa Nuova, and it is always liquid.'"

After leaving Naples, Newman visited Loreto, and inspected the house of the Holy Family, which, as is known to the faithful, was transported thither, in three hops, from Palestine.

"I went to Loreto [he wrote] with a simple faith, believing what I still more believed when I saw it. I have no doubt now. If you ask me why I believe, it is because *everyone* believes it at Rome; cautious as they are and sceptical about some other things. *I have no antecedent difficulty in the matter.* He who floated the Ark on the surges of a worldwide sea, and enclosed in it all living things, who has hidden the terrestrial paradise, who said that faith might move mountains, who sustained thousands for forty years in a sterile wilderness, who transported Elias and keeps him hidden till the end, could do this wonder also."

Here, whatever else there may be, there is certainly no trace of a desire to deceive. Could a state of mind, in fact, be revealed with more absolute transparency?

When Newman was a child he "wished that he could believe the Arabian Nights were true." When he came to be a man, his wish seems to have been granted.

Tract No. 90 was officially condemned by the authorities at Oxford, and in the hubbub that followed the contending parties closed their ranks; henceforward any compromise between the friends and the enemies of the Movement was impossible. Archdeacon Manning was in too conspicuous a position to be able to remain silent; he was obliged to declare himself, and he did not hesitate. In an archidiaconal charge, delivered within a few months of his appointment, he firmly

repudiated the Tractarians. But the repudiation was not deemed sufficient, and a year later he repeated it with greater emphasis. Still,
however, the horrid rumours were afloat. The *Record* began to investi-
gate matters, and its vigilance was soon rewarded by an alarming discovery: the sacrament had been administered in Chichester Cathedral
on a week-day, and "Archdeacon Manning, one of the most noted and
determined of the Tractarians, had acted a conspicuous part on the
occasion." It was clear that the only way of silencing these malevolent
whispers was by some public demonstration whose import nobody
could doubt. The annual sermon preached on Guy Fawkes Day before
the University of Oxford seemed to offer the very opportunity that
Manning required. He seized it; got himself appointed preacher; and
delivered from the pulpit of St. Mary's a virulently Protestant harangue.
This time there could indeed be no doubt about the matter: Manning
had shouted "No Popery!" in the very citadel of the Movement, and
everyone, including Newman, recognized that he had finally cut himself off from his old friends. Everyone, that is to say, except the Archdeacon himself. On the day after the sermon, Manning walked out to
the neighbouring village of Littlemore, where Newman was now living in retirement with a few chosen disciples, in the hope of being
able to give a satisfactory explanation of what he had done. But he
was disappointed; for when, after an awkward interval, one of the
disciples appeared at the door, he was informed that Mr. Newman was
not at home.

    With his retirement to Littlemore, Newman had entered upon the
final period of his Anglican career. Even he could no longer help perceiving that the end was now only a matter of time. His progress was
hastened in an agitating manner by the indiscreet activity of one of
his proselytes, W. G. Ward, a young man who combined an extraordinary aptitude for *a priori* reasoning with a passionate devotion to
Opéra Bouffe. It was difficult, in fact, to decide whether the inner
nature of Ward was more truly expressing itself when he was firing
off some train of scholastic paradoxes on the Eucharist or when he
was trilling the airs of Figaro and plunging through the hilarious
roulades of the *Largo al Factotum*. Even Dr. Pusey could not be quite

sure, though he was Ward's spiritual director. On one occasion his young penitent came to him, and confessed that a vow which he had taken to abstain from music during Lent was beginning to affect his health. Could Dr. Pusey see his way to releasing him from the vow? The Doctor decided that a little sacred music would not be amiss. Ward was all gratitude, and that night a party was arranged in a friend's rooms. The concert began with the solemn harmonies of Handel, which were followed by the holy strains of the "O Salutaris" of Cherubini. Then came the elevation and the pomp of "Possenti Numi" from the Magic Flute. But, alas! there lies much danger in Mozart. The page was turned, and there was the delicious duet between Papageno and Papagena. Flesh and blood could not resist that; then song followed song, the music waxed faster and lighter, until at last Ward burst into the intoxicating merriment of the *Largo al Factotum*. When it was over a faint but persistent knocking made itself heard upon the wall; and it was only then that the company remembered that the rooms next door were Dr. Pusey's.

The same *entraînement* which carried Ward away when he sat down to a piano possessed him whenever he embarked on a religious discussion. "The thing that was utterly abhorrent to him," said one of his friends, "was to stop short." Given the premises, he would follow out their implications with the mercilessness of a medieval monk, and when he had reached the last limits of argument be ready to maintain whatever propositions he might find there with his dying breath. He had the extreme innocence of a child and a mathematician. Captivated by the glittering eye of Newman, he swallowed whole the supernatural conception of the universe which Newman had evolved, accepted it as a fundamental premise, and began at once to deduce from it whatsoever there might be to be deduced. His very first deductions included irrefutable proofs of (1) God's particular providence for individuals; (2) the real efficacy of intercessory prayer; (3) the reality of our communion with the saints departed; (4) the constant presence and assistance of the angels of God. Later on he explained mathematically the importance of the Ember Days. "Who can tell," he added, "the degree of blessing lost to us in this land by neglecting, as we alone of Christian Churches do neglect, these holy days?" He then proceeded to convict the Reformers, not only of rebellion, but "—for my own part I see not how we can avoid adding—of perjury." Every day his arguments became more extreme, more rigorously exact, and more distressing to his master. Newman was in the position of a cautious commander-in-chief being hurried into an engagement against his will by a dashing cavalry officer. Ward forced him forward step by step towards—no! he could not bear it; he shuddered and drew back. But it was of no avail. In vain did Keble and Pusey wring their hands and stretch forth their pleading arms to their now vanishing brother. The fatal moment was fast approaching. Ward at last published a devastating book in which he proved conclusively by a series of syllogisms that the only proper course for the Church of England was to repent in sackcloth and ashes her separation from the Communion of Rome. The reckless author was deprived of his degree by an outraged University, and a few weeks later was received into the Catholic Church.

Newman, in a kind of despair, had flung himself into the labours of historical compilation. His views of history had changed since the days when as an undergraduate he had feasted on the worldly pages of Gibbon.

"Revealed religion [he now thought] furnishes facts to other sciences, which those sciences, left to themselves, would never reach. Thus, in the science of history, the preservation of our race in Noah's ark is an historical fact, which history never would arrive at without revelation."

With these principles to guide him, he plunged with his disciples into a prolonged study of the English Saints. Biographies soon appeared of St. Bega, St. Adamnan, St. Gundleus, St. Guthlake, Brother Drithelm, St. Amphibalus, St. Wulstan, St. Ebba, St. Neot, St. Ninian, and Cunibert the Hermit. Their austerities, their virginity, and their miraculous powers were described in detail. The public learnt with astonishment that St. Ninian had turned a staff into a tree, that St. German had stopped a cock from crowing, and that a child had been raised from the dead to convert St. Helier. The series has subsequently been continued by a more modern writer whose relation of the history of

the blessed St. Maël contains, perhaps, even more matter for edifica-
tion than Newman's biographies. At the time, indeed, those works
caused considerable scandal. Clergymen denounced them in pamphlets. St. Cuthbert was described by his biographer as having "carried
the jealousy of women, characteristic of all the saints, to an extraordinary pitch." An example was given: whenever he held a spiritual
conversation with St. Ebba, he was careful to spend the ensuing hours
of darkness "in prayer, up to his neck in water."

"Persons who invent such tales [wrote one indignant commentator]
cast very grave and just suspicions on the purity of their own minds.
And young persons, who talk and think in this way, are in extreme
danger of falling into sinful habits. As to the volumes before us, the
authors have, in their fanatical panegyrics of virginity, made use of
language downright profane."

One of the disciples at Littlemore was James Anthony Froude, the
younger brother of Hurrell, and it fell to his lot to be responsible for
the biography of St. Neot. While he was composing it, he began to
feel some qualms. Saints who lighted fires with icicles, changed bandits into wolves, and floated across the Irish Channel on altar-stones,
produced a disturbing effect on his historical conscience. But he had
promised his services to Newman, and he determined to carry through the
work in the spirit in which he had begun it. He did so; but he thought
it proper to add the following sentence by way of conclusion: "This is
all, and indeed rather more than all, that is known to men of the
blessed St. Neot; but not more than is known to the angels in heaven."

Meanwhile the English Roman Catholics were growing impatient;
was the great conversion never coming, for which they had prayed so
fervently and so long? Dr. Wiseman, at the head of them, was watching and waiting with special eagerness. His hand was held out under
the ripening fruit; the delicious morsel seemed to be trembling on its
stalk; and yet it did not fall. At last, unable to bear the suspense any
longer, he dispatched to Littlemore Father Smith, an old pupil of
Newman's, who had lately joined the Roman communion, with in-

structions that he should do his best, under cover of a simple visit of friendship, to discover how the land lay. Father Smith was received somewhat coldly, and the conversation ran entirely on topics which had nothing to do with religion. When the company separated before dinner, he was beginning to think that his errand had been useless; but on their reassembling he suddenly noticed that Newman had changed his trousers and that the colour of the pair which he was now wearing was grey. At the earliest moment, the emissary rushed back post-haste to Dr. Wiseman. "All is well," he exclaimed; "Newman no longer considers that he is in Anglican orders." "Praise be to God!" answered Dr. Wiseman. "But how do you know?" Father Smith described what he had seen. "Oh, is that all? My dear father, how can you be so foolish?" But Father Smith was not to be shaken. "I know the man," he said, "and I know what it means. Newman will come, and he will come soon."

And Father Smith was right. A few weeks later, Newman suddenly slipped off to a priest, and all was over. Perhaps he would have hesitated longer still, if he could have foreseen how he was to pass the next thirty years of his unfortunate existence; but the future was hidden, and all that was certain was that the past had gone for ever, and that his eyes would rest no more upon the snapdragons of Trinity. The Oxford Movement was now ended. The University breathed such a sigh of relief as usually follows the difficult expulsion of a hard piece of matter from a living organism, and actually began to attend to education. As for the Church of England, she had tasted blood, and it was clear that she would never again be content with a vegetable diet. Her clergy, however, maintained their reputation for judicious compromise, for they followed Newman up to the very point beyond which his conclusions were logical, and, while they intoned, confessed, swung incense, and burnt candles with the exhilaration of converts, they yet managed to do so with a subtle *nuance* which showed that they had nothing to do with Rome. Various individuals underwent more violent changes. Several had preceded Newman into the Roman fold; among others an unhappy Mr. Sibthorpe, who subsequently changed his mind, and returned to the Church of his fathers, and then —perhaps it was only natural—changed his mind again. Many more followed Newman, and Dr. Wiseman was particularly pleased by the conversion of a Mr. Morris, who, as he said, was "the author of the essay, which won the prize, on the best method of proving Christianity to the Hindoos." Hurrell Froude had died before Newman had read the fatal article on St. Augustine; but his brother, James Anthony, together with Arthur Clough, the poet, went through an experience which was more distressing in those days than it has since become; they lost their faith. With this difference, however, that while in Froude's case the loss of his faith turned out to be rather like the loss of a heavy portmanteau, which one afterwards discovers to have been full of old rags and brickbats, Clough was made so uneasy by the loss of his that he went on looking for it everywhere as long as he lived; but somehow he never could find it. On the other hand, Keble and Pusey continued for the rest of their lives to dance in an exemplary manner upon the tight-rope of High Anglicanism; in such an exemplary manner, indeed, that the tight-rope has its dancers still.

I V

MANNING was now thirty-eight, and it was clear that he was the rising man in the Church of England. He had many powerful connexions: he was the brother-in-law of Samuel Wilberforce, who had lately been made a bishop; he was a close friend of Mr. Gladstone, who was a Cabinet Minister; and he was becoming well known in the influential circles of society in London. His talent for affairs was recognized not only in the Church, but in the world at large, and he busied himself with matters of such varied scope as National Education, the administration of the Poor Law, and the Employment of Women. Mr. Gladstone kept up an intimate correspondence with him on these and on other subjects, mingling in his letters the details of practical statesmanship with the speculations of a religious thinker.

"Sir James Graham [he wrote in a discussion of the bastardy clauses of the Poor Law] is much pleased with the tone of your two communications. He is disposed, without putting an end to the application of the workhouse test against the mother, to make the remedy against the putative father 'real and effective' for expenses incurred in the workhouse. I am not enough acquainted to know whether it would be advisable to go further. You have not proposed it; and I am disposed to believe that only with a revived and improved discipline in the Church can we hope for any generally effective check upon lawless lust. I agree with you *eminently* [he writes, in a later letter] in your doctrine of *filtration*. But it sometimes occurs to me, though the question may seem a strange one, how far was the Reformation, but especially the Continental Reformation, designed by God, in the region of final causes, for that purification of the Roman Church which it has actually realized?"

In his archdeaconry, Manning lived to the full the active life of a country clergyman. His slim, athletic figure was seen everywhere—in the streets of Chichester, or on the lawns of the neighbouring rectories, or galloping over the downs in breeches and gaiters, or cutting brilliant figures on the ice. He was an excellent judge of horseflesh, and the pair of greys which drew his hooded phaeton so swiftly through the lanes were the admiration of the county. His features were already beginning to assume their ascetic caste, but the spirit of youth had not yet fled from them, so that he seemed to combine the attractions of dignity and grace. He was a good talker, a sympathetic listener, a man who understood the difficult art of preserving all the vigour of a manly character and yet never giving offence. No wonder that his sermons were crowded, no wonder that his spiritual advice was sought for eagerly by an ever-growing crowd of penitents, no wonder that men would say, when his name was mentioned, "Oh, Manning! No power on earth can keep *him* from a bishopric!"

Such was the fair outward seeming of the Archdeacon's life; but the inward reality was different. The more active, the more fortunate, the more full of happy promise his existence became, the more persistently was his secret imagination haunted by a dreadful vision—the lake that burneth for ever with brimstone and fire. The temptations of the Evil One are many, Manning knew; and he knew also that, for him at least, the most subtle and terrible of all temptations was the temptation of worldly success. He tried to reassure himself, but it was in vain. He committed his thoughts to a diary, weighing scrupulously his every motive, examining with relentless searchings into the depths of his heart. Perhaps, after all, his longings for preferment were merely legitimate hopes for "an elevation into a sphere of higher usefulness." But no, there was something more than that. "I do feel pleasure," he noted, "in honour, precedence, elevation, the society of great people, and all this is very shameful and mean." After Newman's conversion, he almost convinced himself that his "visions of an ecclesiastical future" were justified by the *role* that he would play as a "healer of the breach in the Church of England." Mr. Gladstone agreed with him; but there was One higher than Mr. Gladstone, and did He agree?

"I am pierced by anxious thoughts. God knows what my desires have been and are, and why they are crossed. . . . I am flattering myself with a fancy about depth and reality. . . . The great question is: Is God enough for you *now?* And if you are as now, even to the end of life, will it suffice you? . . . Certainly I would rather choose to be stayed on God, than to be in the thrones of the world and the Church. Nothing else will go into Eternity."

In a moment of ambition, he had applied for the Readership of Lincoln's Inn, but, owing chiefly to the hostile influence of the *Record,* the appointment had gone elsewhere. A little later, a more important position was offered to him—the office of sub-almoner to the Queen, which had just been vacated by the Archbishop of York, and was almost certain to lead to a mitre. The offer threw Manning into an agony of self-examination. He drew up elaborate tables, after the manner of Robinson Crusoe, with the reasons for and against his acceptance of the post:—

For.	*Against.*
1. That it comes unsought.	1. Not therefore to be accepted. Such things are trials as well as leadings.
2. That it is honourable.	2. Being what I am, ought I not therefore to decline it—
	(1) as humiliation;
	(2) as revenge on myself for Lincoln's Inn;
	(3) as a testimony?

And so on. He found in the end ten "negative reasons," with no affirmative ones to balance them, and, after a week's deliberation, he rejected the offer.

But peace of mind was as far off from him as ever. First the bitter thought came to him that "in all this Satan tells me I am doing it to be thought mortified and holy"; and then he was obsessed by the still bitterer feelings of ineradicable disappointment and regret. He had lost a great opportunity, and it brought him small comfort to consider that "in the region of counsels, self-chastisement, humiliation, self-discipline, penance, and of the Cross" he had perhaps done right.

The crisis passed, but it was succeeded by a fiercer one. Manning was taken seriously ill, and became convinced that he might die at any moment. The entries in his diary grew more elaborate than ever; his remorse for the past, his resolutions for the future, his protestations of submission to the will of God, filled page after page of parallel columns, headings and sub-headings, numbered clauses, and analytical tables. "How do I feel about Death?" he wrote.

"Certainly great fear—
   1. Because of the uncertainty of our state before God.
   2. Because of the consciousness—
      (1) of great sins past,
      (2) of great sinfulness,
      (3) of most shallow repentance.
What shall I do?

He decided to mortify himself, to read St. Thomas Aquinas, and to make his "night prayers forty instead of thirty minutes." He determined during Lent "to use no pleasant bread (except on Sundays and feasts) such as cake and sweetmeat"; but he added the proviso "I do not include plain biscuits." Opposite this entry appears the word *"kept."* And yet his backslidings were many. Looking back over a single week, he was obliged to register "petulance twice" and "complacent visions." He heard his curate being commended for bringing so many souls to God during Lent, and he "could not bear it"; but the remorse was terrible: "I abhorred myself on the spot, and looked upward for help." He made out list upon list of the Almighty's special mercies towards him, and they included his creation, his regeneration, and (No. 5)

"the preservation of my life six times to my knowledge—
  (1) In illness at the age of nine.
  (2) In the water.
  (3) By a runaway horse at Oxford.
  (4) By the same.
  (5) By falling nearly through the ceiling of a church.
  (6) Again by a fall of a horse. And I know not how often in shooting, riding, etc."

At last he became convalescent; but the spiritual experiences of those agitated weeks left an indelible mark upon his mind, and prepared the way for the great change which was to follow.

For he had other doubts besides those which held him in torment as to his own salvation; he was in doubt about the whole framework of his faith. Newman's conversion, he found, had meant something more to him than he had at first realized. It had seemed to come as a call to the redoubling of his Anglican activities; but supposing, in reality, it were a call towards something very different—towards an abandonment of those activities altogether? It might be a "trial," or again it might be a "leading"; how was he to judge? Already, before his illness, these doubts had begun to take possession of his mind.

"I am conscious to myself [he wrote in his Dairy] of an extensively changed feeling towards the Church of Rome . . . The Church of England seems to me to be diseased:—1. *Organically* (six sub-headings). 2. *Functionally* (seven sub-headings) . . . Wherever it seems healthy it approximates the system of Rome."

Then thoughts of the Virgin Mary suddenly began to assail him—

"(1) If John the Baptist were sanctified from the womb, how much more the B.V.!

(2) If Enoch and Elijah were exempted from death, why not the B.V. from sin?

(3) It is a strange way of loving the Son to slight the mother!"

The arguments seemed irresistible, and a few weeks later the following entry occurs—

"Strange thoughts have visited me:

(1) I have felt that the Episcopate of the Church of England is secularized and bound down beyond hope. . . .

(6) I feel as if a light had fallen upon me. My feeling about the Roman Church is not intellectual. I have intellectual difficulties, but the great moral difficulties seem melting.

(7) Something keeps rising and saying, 'You will end in the Roman Church.'"

He noted altogether twenty-five of these "strange thoughts." His mind hovered anxiously round—

"(1) The Incarnation,

(2) The Real Presence,

    i. Regeneration,

    ii. Eucharist,

and (3) The Exaltation of S. M. and Saints."

His twenty-second strange thought was as follows:—"How do I know where I may be two years hence? Where was Newman five years ago?"

It was significant, but hardly surprising, that, after his illness, Manning should have chosen to recuperate in Rome. He spent several months there, and his Diary during the whole of that period is concerned entirely with detailed descriptions of churches, ceremonies, and relics, and with minute accounts of conversations with priests and nuns. There is not a single reference either to the objects of art or to the antiquities of the place; but another omission was still more remarkable. Manning had a long interview with Pius IX., and his only record of it is contained in the bald statement: "Audience today at the Vatican." Precisely what passed on that occasion never transpired; all that is known is that His Holiness expressed considerable surprise on learning from the Archdeacon that the chalice was used in the Anglican Church in the administration of Communion. "What!" he exclaimed, "is the same chalice made use of by everyone?" "I remember the pain I felt," said Manning, long afterwards, "at seeing how unknown we were to the Vicar of Jesus Christ. It made me feel our isolation."

On his return to England, he took up once more the work in his Archdeaconry with what appetite he might. Ravaged by doubt, distracted by speculation, he yet managed to maintain an outward presence of unshaken calm. His only confidant was Robert Wilberforce, to whom, for the next two years, he poured forth in a series of letters, headed, *"Under the Seal"* to indicate that they contained the secrets of the confessional, the whole history of his spiritual perturbations. The irony of his position was singular; for during the whole of this time Manning was himself holding back from the Church of Rome a host of hesitating penitents by means of arguments which he was at the very moment denouncing as fallacious to his own confessor. But what else could he do? When he received, for instance, a letter such as the following from an agitated lady, what was he to say?

"My dear Father in Christ,

". . . I am sure you would pity me and like to help me, if you knew the unhappy, unsettled state my mind is in, and the misery of being *entirely, wherever I am,* with those who look upon joining the Church of Rome as the most awful 'fall' conceivable to anyone, and are devoid of the smallest *comprehension* of how any enlightened person can do it. . . . My old Evangelical friends, with all my deep, deep love for them, do not succeed in shaking me in the least. . . .

"My brother has just published a book called *Regeneration,* which all my friends are reading and highly extolling; it has a very contrary effect to what he would desire *on my mind.* I can read and understand it all in an altogether different sense, and the facts which he quotes about the articles as drawn up in 1536, and again in 1552, and of the Irish articles of 1615 and 1634, *startle* and *shake* me about the Reformed Church in England far more than anything else, and have done ever since I first saw them in Mr. Maskell's pamphlet (as quoted from Mr. Dodsworth's).

"I do hope you have sometimes time and thought to pray for me still. Mr. Galton's letters long ago grew into short formal notes, which hurt me and annoyed me particularly, and I never answered his last, so, literally, I have no one to say things to and get help from, which in one sense is a comfort, when my convictions seem to be leading me *on* and *on* and gaining strength in spite of all the dreariness of my lot.

"Do you know I can't help being very anxious and unhappy about poor Sister Harriet. I am afraid of her *going out of her mind.* She comforts herself by an occasional outpouring of everything to me, and I had a letter this morning. . . . She says Sister May has promised the Vicar never to talk to her or allow her to talk on the subject with her, and I doubt whether this can be good for her, because though she has lost her faith, she says, in the Church of England, yet she never thinks of what she could have faith in, and resolutely without enquiring into the question determines not to be a Roman Catholic, so that really you see she is allowing her mind to run adrift, and yet perfectly powerless.

"Forgive my troubling you with this letter, and believe me to be always your faithful, grateful and affectionate daughter,

"EMMA RYLE.

"P.S. I wish I could see you once more so very much."

How was Manning, a director of souls, and a clergyman of the Church of England, to reply that in sober truth there was very little to choose between the state of mind of Sister Emma, or even of Sister

Harriet, and his own? The dilemma was a grievous one: when a soldier finds himself fighting for a cause in which he has lost faith, it is treachery to stop, and it is treachery to go on.

At last, in the seclusion of his library, Manning turned in an agony to those old writings which had provided Newman with so much instruction and assistance; perhaps the Fathers would do something for him as well. He ransacked the pages of St. Cyprian and St. Cyril; he went through the complete works of St. Optatus and St. Leo; he explored the vast treatises of Tertullian and Justin Martyr. He had a lamp put into his phaeton, so that he might lose no time during his long winter drives. There he sat, searching St. Chrysostom for some mitigation of his anguish, while he sped along between the hedges to distant sufferers, to whom he duly administered the sacraments according to the rites of the English Church. He hurried back to commit to his Diary the analysis of his reflections, and to describe, under the mystic formula of secrecy, the intricate workings of his conscience to Robert Wilberforce. But, alas! he was no Newman; and even the fourteen folios of St. Augustine himself, strange to say, gave him very little help.

The final propulsion was to come from an entirely different quarter. In November, 1847, the Reverend Mr. Gorham was presented by the Lord Chancellor to the living of Bramford Speke in the diocese of Exeter. The Bishop, Dr. Phillpotts, was a High Churchman, and he had reason to believe that Mr. Gorham held evangelical opinions; he therefore subjected him to an examination on doctrine, which took the form partly of a verbal interrogatory, lasting thirty-eight hours, and partly of a series of one hundred and forty-nine written questions. At the end of the examination he came to the conclusion that Mr. Gorham held heretical views on the subject of Baptismal Regeneration, and he therefore refused to institute. Mr. Gorham thereupon took proceedings against the Bishop in the Court of Arches. He lost his case; and he then appealed to the Judicial Committee of the Privy Council.

The questions at issue were taken very seriously by a large number of persons. In the first place, there was the question of Baptismal Regeneration itself. This is by no means an easy one to disentangle; but it may be noted that the doctrine of Baptism includes (1) God's intention, that is to say, His purpose in electing certain persons to eternal life—an abstruse and greatly controverted subject, upon which the Church of England abstains from strict definition; (2) God's action, whether by means of sacraments or otherwise—concerning which the Church of England maintains the efficacy of sacraments, but does not formally deny that grace may be given by other means, repentance and faith being present; and (3) the question whether sacramental grace is given instrumentally, by and at the moment of the act of baptism, or in consequence of an act of prevenient grace rendering the receiver worthy—that is to say, whether sacramental grace in baptism is given absolutely or conditionally: it was over his last question that the dispute raged hottest in the Gorham Case. The High Church party, represented by Dr. Phillpotts, asserted that the mere act of baptism conferred regeneration upon the recipient and washed away his original sin. To this the Evangelicals, headed by Mr. Gorham, replied that, according to the Articles, regeneration would not follow unless baptism was *rightly* received. What, then, was the meaning of "rightly"? Clearly it implied not merely lawful administration, but worthy reception; worthiness, therefore, is the essence of the sacrament; and worthiness means faith and repentance. Now, two propositions were accepted by both parties—that all infants are born in original sin, and that original sin is washed away by baptism. But how could both these propositions be true, argued Mr. Gorham, if it was *also* true that faith and repentance were necessary before baptism could come into operation at all? How could an infant in arms be said to be in a state of faith and repentance? How, therefore, could its original sin be washed away by baptism? And yet, as everyone agreed, washed away it was. The only solution of the difficulty lay in the doctrine of prevenient grace; and Mr. Gorham maintained that unless God performed an act of prevenient grace by which the infant was endowed with faith and repentance, no act of baptism could be effectual; though to whom, and under what conditions, prevenient grace was given, Mr. Gorham confessed himself unable to decide. The light thrown by the Bible upon the whole matter seemed somewhat dubious, for whereas the baptism of St. Peter's disciples at Jerusalem and St. Philip's at Samaria was followed by the gift of the Spirit, in the case of Cornelius the sacrament succeeded the gift. St. Paul also was baptized; and as for the language of St. John iii. 5; Rom. vi. 3, 4; 1 Peter iii. 21, it admits of more than one interpretation. There could, however, be no doubt that the Church of England assented to Dr. Phillpotts' opinion; the question was whether or not she excluded Mr. Gorham's. If it was decided that she did, it was clear that henceforward there would be very little peace for Evangelicals within her fold.

But there was another issue, even more fundamental than that of Baptismal Regeneration itself, involved in the Gorham trial. An Act passed in 1833 had constituted the Judicial Committee of the Privy Council the supreme court of appeal for such cases; and this Committee was a body composed entirely of laymen. It was thus obvious that the Royal Supremacy was still a fact, and that a collection of lawyers appointed by the Crown had the legal right to formulate the religious doctrine of the Church of England. In 1850 their judgment was delivered; they reversed the decision of the Court of Arches, and upheld the position of Mr. Gorham. Whether his views were theologically correct or not, they said, was not their business; it was their business to decide whether the opinions under consideration were contrary or repugnant to the doctrine of the Church of England as enjoined upon the clergy by its Articles, Formularies, and Rubrics; and they had come to the conclusion that they were not. The judgment still holds good; and to this day a clergyman of the Church of England is quite at liberty to believe that Regeneration does not invariably take place when an infant is baptized.

The blow fell upon no one with greater violence than upon Manning. Not only was the supreme efficacy of the sign of the cross upon a baby's forehead one of his favourite doctrines, but up to that moment he had been convinced that the Royal Supremacy was a mere accident—a temporary usurpation—which left the spiritual dominion of the Church essentially untouched. But now the horrid reality rose up before him, crowned and triumphant; it was all too clear that an Act of Parliament, passed by Jews, Roman Catholics, and dissenters, was the ultimate authority which decided upon the momentous niceties of the Anglican faith. Mr. Gladstone, also, was deeply perturbed. It was absolutely necessary, he wrote, to "rescue and defend the conscience of the Church from the present hideous system." An agitation was set on foot, and several influential Anglicans, with Manning at their head, drew up and signed a formal protest against the Gorham judgment. Mr. Gladstone, however, proposed another method of procedure: precipitate action, he declared, must be avoided at all costs, and he elaborated a scheme for securing procrastination, by which a covenant was to bind all those who believed that an article of the creed had been abolished by Act of Parliament to take no steps in any direction, nor to announce their intention of doing so, until a given space of time had elapsed. Mr. Gladstone was hopeful that some good might come of this—though indeed he could not be sure. "Among others," he wrote to Manning, "I have consulted Robert Wilberforce and Wegg-Prosser, and they seemed inclined to favour my proposal. It might, perhaps, have kept back Lord Fielding. But he is like a cork."

The proposal was certainly not favoured by Manning. Protests and procrastinations, approving Wegg-Prossers and cork-like Lord Fieldings—all this was feeding the wind and folly; the time for action had come.

"I can no longer continue [he wrote to Robert Wilberforce] under oath and subscription binding me to the Royal Supremacy in Ecclesiastical causes, being convinced:—

(1) That it is a violation of the Divine Office of the Church.
(2) That it has involved the Church of England in a seperation from the universal Church, which separation I cannot clear of the character of schism.
(3) That it has thereby suspended and prevented the functions of the Church of England."

It was in vain that Robert Wilberforce pleaded, in vain that Mr. Gladstone urged upon his mind the significance of John iii. 8.[1]

1 "The wind bloweth where it listeth, and thou hearest the sound thereof, but canst not tell whence it cometh, and whither it goeth: so is everyone that is born of the Spirit."

"I admit [Mr. Gladstone wrote] that the words might in some way be satisfied by supposing our Lord simply to mean 'the facts of nature are unintelligible, therefore be not afraid if revealed truths be likewise beyond the compass of the understanding'; but this seems to me a meagre meaning."

Such considerations could hold him no longer, and Manning executed the resignation of his office and benefice before a public notary. Soon afterwards, in the little chapel off Buckingham Palace Road, kneeling beside Mr. Gladstone, he worshipped for the last time as an Anglican. Thirty years later the Cardinal told how, just before the Communion service commenced, he turned to his friend with the words:

"'I can no longer take the Communion in the Church of England.' I rose up and laying my hand on Mr. Gladstone's shoulder, said 'Come.' It was the parting of the ways. Mr. Gladstone remained; and I went my way. Mr. Gladstone still remains where I left him."

On April 6, 1851, the final step was taken: Manning was received into the Roman Catholic Church. Now at last, after the long struggle, his mind was at rest.

"I know what you mean [he wrote to Robert Wilberforce] by saying that one sometimes feels as if all this might turn out to be only another 'Land of Shadows.' I have felt it in time past, but not now. The θεολογία from Nice to St. Thomas Aquinas, and the undivided unity suffused throughout the world, of which the Cathedra Petri is the centre,—now 1800 years old, mightier in every power now than ever, in intellect, in science, in separation from the world; and purer too, refined by 300 years of conflict with the modern infidel civilization— all this is a fact more solid than the earth."

v

WHEN Manning joined the Church of Rome he acted under the combined impulse of the two dominating forces in his nature. His preoccupation with the supernatural might, alone, have been satisfied within the fold of the Anglican communion; and so might his preoccupation with himself: the one might have found vent in the elaborations of High Church ritual, and the other in the activities of a bishopric. But the two together could not be quieted so easily. The Church of England is a commodious institution; she is very anxious to please; but, somehow or other, she has never managed to supply a happy home to superstitious egotists. "What an escape for my poor soul!" Manning is said to have exclaimed when, shortly after his conversion, a mitre was going a-begging. But, in truth, Manning's "poor soul" had scented nobler quarry. To one of his temperament, how was it possible, when once the choice was plainly put, to hesitate for a moment between the respectable dignity of an English bishop, harnessed by the secular power, with the Gorham judgment as a bit between his teeth, and the illimitable pretensions of the humblest priest of Rome?

For the moment, however, it seemed as if the Fates had at last been successful in their little game of shunting Manning. The splendid career which he had so laboriously built up from the small beginnings of his Sussex curacy was shattered—and shattered by the inevitable operation of his own essential needs. He was over forty, and he had been put back once more to the very bottom rung of the ladder—a middle-aged neophyte with, so far as could be seen, no special claim to the attention of his new superiors. The example of Newman, a far more illustrious convert, was hardly reassuring: he had been relegated to a complete obscurity, in which he was to remain until extreme old age. Why should there be anything better in store for Manning? Yet it so happened that within fourteen years of his conversion Manning was Archbishop of Westminster and the supreme ruler of the Roman Catholic community in England. This time the Fates gave up the unequal struggle; they paid over their stakes in despair, and retired from the game.

Nevertheless it is difficult to feel quite sure that Manning's plunge was as hazardous as it appeared. Certainly he was not a man who was likely to forget to look before he leaped, nor one who, if he happened to know that there was a mattress spread to receive him, would leap with less conviction. In the light of after-events, one would be glad to know what precisely passed at that mysterious interview of his with the Pope, three years before his conversion. It is at least possible that the authorities in Rome had their eye on Manning; they may well have felt that the Archdeacon of Chichester would be a great catch. What did Pio Nono say? It is easy to imagine the persuasive innocence of his Italian voice. "Ah, dear Signor Manning, why don't you come over to us? Do you suppose that we should not look after you?"

At any rate, when he did go over, Manning *was* looked after very thoroughly. There was, it is true, a momentary embarrassment at the outset: it was only with the greatest difficulty that he could bring himself to abandon his faith in the validity of Anglican Orders, in which he believed "with a consciousness stronger than all reasoning." He was convinced that he was still a priest. When the Rev. Mr. Tierney, who had received him into the Roman Catholic communion, assured him that this was not the case, he was filled with dismay and mortification. After a five hours' discussion, he started to his feet in a rage. "Then, Mr. Tierney," he exclaimed, "you think me insincere." The bitter draught was swallowed at last, and, after that, all went smoothly. Manning hastened to Rome, and was immediately placed by the Pope in the highly select *Accademia Ecclesiastica,* commonly known as the "nursery of Cardinals," for the purpose of completing his theological studies. When the course was finished, he continued, by the Pope's special request, to spend six months of every year in Rome, where he preached to the English visitors, became acquainted with the great personages of the Papal court, and enjoyed the privilege of constant interviews with the Holy Father. At the same time he was able to make himself useful in London, where Cardinal Wiseman, the newly-created Archbishop of Westminster, was seeking to reanimate the Roman Catholic community. Manning was not only extremely popular in the pulpit and in the confessional; he was not only highly efficient as a gleaner of souls—and of souls who moved in the best society; he also possessed a familiarity with official persons and official ways, which was invaluable. When the question arose of the appointment of Catholic chaplains in the Crimea during the war, it was Manning who approached the Minister, interviewed the Permanent Secretary, and finally succeeded in obtaining all that was required. When a special Reformatory for Catholic children was proposed, Manning carried through the negotiations with the Government. When an attempt was made to remove Catholic children from the Workhouses, Manning was again indispensable. No wonder Cardinal Wiseman soon determined to find some occupation of special importance for the energetic convert. He had long wished to establish a congregation of secular priests in London particularly devoted to his service, and the opportunity for the experiment had clearly now arisen. The order of the Oblates of St. Charles was founded in Bayswater, and Manning was put at its head. Unfortunately no portion of the body of St. Charles could be obtained for the new community, but two relics of his blood were brought over to Bayswater from Milan. Almost at the same time the Pope signified his appreciation of Manning's efforts by appointing him Provost of the Chapter of Westminster—a position which placed him at the head of the Canons of the diocese.

This double promotion was the signal for the outbreak of an extraordinary intestine struggle, which raged without intermission for the next seven years, and was only to end with the accession of Manning to the Archbishopric. The condition of the Roman Catholic community in England was at that time a singular one. On the one hand the old repressive laws of the seventeenth century had been repealed by liberal legislation, and on the other a large new body of distinguished converts had entered the Roman Church as a result of the Oxford Movement. It was evident that there was a "boom" in English Catholicism, and, in 1850, Pius IX. recognized the fact by dividing up the whole of England into dioceses, and placing Wiseman at the head of them as Archbishop of Westminster. Wiseman's encyclical, dated "from without the Flaminian Gate," in which he announced the new departure, was greeted in England by a storm of indignation, culminating in the famous and furibund letter of Lord John Russell, then Prime Minister, against the insolence of the "Papal Aggression." Though the particular point against which the outcry was raised— the English territorial titles of the new Roman bishops—was an insignificant one, the instinct of Lord John and of the English people was in reality sound enough. Wiseman's installation did mean, in fact, a new move in the Papal game; it meant an advance, if not an aggression—a quickening in England of the long dormant energies of the Roman Church. That Church has never had the reputation of being an institution to be trifled with; and, in those days, the Pope was still ruling as a temporal Prince over the fairest provinces of Italy. Surely, if the images of Guy Fawkes had not been garnished, on that fifth of November, with triple crowns, it would have been a very poor compliment to His Holiness.

But it was not only the honest Protestants of England who had cause to dread the arrival of the new Cardinal Archbishop; there was a party among the Catholics themselves who viewed his installation with alarm and disgust. The families in which the Catholic tradition had been handed down uninterruptedly since the days of Elizabeth, which had known the pains of exile and of martyrdom, and which clung together, an alien and isolated group in the midst of English society, now began to feel that they were, after all, of small moment in the counsels of Rome. They had laboured through the heat of the day, but now it seemed as if the harvest was to be gathered in by a crowd of converts, who were proclaiming on every side as something new and wonderful the truths which the Old Catholics, as they came to be called, had not only known, but for which they had suffered, for generations. Cardinal Wiseman, it is true, was no convert; he belonged to one of the oldest of the Catholic families; but he had spent most of his life in Rome, he was out of touch with English traditions, and his sympathy with Newman and his followers was only too apparent. One of his first acts as Archbishop was to appoint the convert W. G. Ward, who was not even in holy orders, to be Professor of Theology at St. Edmund's College—the chief seminary for young priests, in which the ancient traditions of Douay were still flourishing. Ward was an ardent Papalist, and his appointment indicated clearly enough that in Wiseman's opinion there was too little of the Italian spirit in the English community. The uneasiness of the Old Catholics was becoming intense, when they were reassured by Wiseman's appointing as his coadjutor and successor his intimate friend, Dr. Errington, who was created on the occasion Archbishop of Trebizond *in partibus infidelium*. Not only was Dr. Errington an Old Catholic of the most rigid type, he was a man of extreme energy, whose influence was certain to be great; and, in any case, Wiseman was growing old, so that before very long it seemed inevitable that the policy of the diocese would be in proper hands. Such was the position of affairs when, two years after Errington's appointment, Manning became head of the Oblates of St. Charles and Provost of the Chapter of Westminster.

The Archbishop of Trebizond had been for some time growing more and more suspicious of Manning's influence, and this sudden elevation appeared to justify his worst fears. But his alarm was turned to fury when he learnt that St. Edmund's College, from which he had just succeeded in removing the obnoxious W. G. Ward, was to be placed under the control of the Oblates of St. Charles. The Oblates did not attempt to conceal the fact that one of their principal aims was to introduce the customs of a Roman Seminary into England. A grim perspective of *espionage* and tale-bearing, foreign habits and Italian devotions, opened out before the dismayed eyes of the Old Catholics; they determined to resist to the utmost; and it was upon the question of the control of St. Edmund's that the first battle in the long campaign between Errington and Manning was fought.

Cardinal Wiseman was now obviously declining towards the grave. A man of vast physique—"your immense," an Irish servant used respectfully to call him—a sanguine temperament, of genial disposition, of versatile capacity, he seemed to have engrafted upon the robustness of his English nature the facile, child-like, and expansive qualities of the South. So far from being a Bishop Blougram (as the rumour went) he was, in fact, the very antithesis of that subtle and worldly-wise ecclesiastic. He had innocently looked forward all his life to the reunion of England to the See of Peter, and eventually had come to believe that, in God's hand, he was the instrument destined to bring about this miraculous consummation. Was not the Oxford Movement, with its flood of converts, a clear sign of the Divine will? Had he not himself been the author of that momentous article on St. Augustine and the Donatists, which had finally convinced Newman that the Church of England was in schism? And then had he not been able to set on foot a Crusade of Prayer throughout Catholic Europe for the conversion of England? He awaited the result with eager expectation, and in the meantime he set himself to smooth away the hostility of his countrymen by delivering courses of popular lectures on literature and archæology. He devoted much time and attention to the ceremonial details of his princely office. His knowledge of rubric and ritual and of the symbolical significations of vestments has rarely been equalled, and he took a profound delight in the ordering and the performance of elaborate processions. During one of these functions an unexpected difficulty arose: the Master of the Ceremonies suddenly gave the word for a halt, and, on being asked the reason, replied that he had been instructed that moment by special revelation to stop the procession. The Cardinal, however, was not at a loss. "You may let the procession go on," he smilingly replied. "I have just obtained permission, by special revelation, to proceed with it." His leisure hours he spent in the writing of edifying novels, the composition of acrostics in Latin Verse, and in playing battledore and shuttlecock with his little nieces. There was, indeed, only one point in which he resembled Bishop Blougram—his love of a good table. Some of Newman's disciples were astonished and grieved to find that he sat down to four courses of fish during Lent. "I am sorry to say," remarked one of them afterwards, "that there is a lobster salad side to the Cardinal."

It was a melancholy fate which ordained that the last years of this comfortable, easy-going, innocent old man should be distracted and embittered by the fury of opposing principles and the venom of personal animosities. But so it was. He had fallen into the hands of one who cared very little for the gentle pleasures of repose. Left to himself, Wiseman might have compromised with the Old Catholics and Dr. Errington; but when Manning had once appeared upon the scene all compromise became impossible. The late Archdeacon of Chichester, who had understood so well and practised with such careful skill the precept of the golden mean so dear to the heart of the Church of England, now, as Provost of Westminster, flung himself into the fray with that unyielding intensity of fervour, that passion for the extreme and the absolute, which is the very life-blood of the Church of Rome. Even the redoubtable Dr. Errington, short, thickset, determined, with his "hawk-like expression of face," as a contemporary described him, "as he looked at you through his blue spectacles," had been known to quail in the presence of his antagonist, with his tall and graceful figure, his pale ascetic features, his compressed and icy lips, his calm and penetrating gaze. As for the poor Cardinal, he was helpless indeed. Henceforward there was to be no paltering with that dangerous spirit of independence—was it not almost Gallicanism?—which possessed the Old Catholic families of England. The supremacy of the Vicar of Christ must be maintained at all hazards. Compared with such an object, what were the claims of personal affection and domestic peace? The Cardinal pleaded in vain; his life-long friendship with Dr. Errington was plucked up by the roots, and the harmony of his private life was utterly destroyed. His own household was turned against him. His favourite nephew, whom he had placed among the Oblates under Manning's special care, left the congregation and openly joined the party of Dr. Errington. His secretary followed suit; but saddest of all was the case of Monsignor Searle. Monsignor Searle, in the capacity of confidential man of affairs, had dominated over the Cardinal in private for years with the autocratic fidelity of a servant who has grown indispensable. His devotion, in fact, seemed to have taken the form of physical imitation, for he was hardly less gigantic than his master. The two were inseparable; their huge figures loomed together like neighbouring mountains; and on one occasion, meeting them in the street, a gentleman congratulated Wiseman on "your Eminence's fine son." Yet now even this companionship was broken up. The relentless Provost here too brought a sword. There were explosions and recriminations. Monsignor Searle, finding that his power was slipping from him, made scenes and protests, and at last was foolish enough to accuse Manning of peculation to his face; after that it was clear that his day was over; he was forced to slink snarling into the background, while the Cardinal shuddered through all his immensity and wished many times that he were already dead.

Yet he was not altogether without his consolations; Manning took care to see to that. His piercing eye had detected the secret way into the recesses of the Cardinal's heart—had discerned the core of simple faith which underlay that jovial manner and that facile talk. Others were content to laugh and chatter and transact their business; Manning was more artistic. He watched his opportunity, and then, when the moment came, touched with a deft finger the chord of the Conversion of England. There was an immediate response, and he struck the same chord again, and yet again. He became the repository of the Cardinal's most intimate aspirations. He alone sympathized and understood. "If God gives me strength to undertake a great wrestling-match with infidelity," Wiseman wrote, "I shall owe it to him."

But what he really found himself undertaking was a wrestling-match with Dr. Errington. The struggle over St. Edmund's College grew more and more acute. There were high words in the Chapter, where Monsignor Searle led the assault against the Provost, and carried a resolution declaring that the Oblates of St. Charles had intruded themselves illegally into the Seminary. The Cardinal quashed the proceedings of the Chapter; whereupon the Chapter appealed to Rome. Dr. Errington, carried away by the fury of the controversy, then appeared as the avowed opponent of the Provost and the Cardinal. With his own hand he drew up a document justifying the appeal of the Chapter to Rome by Canon Law and the decrees of the Council of Trent. Wiseman was deeply pained. "My own coadjutor," he exclaimed, "is acting as solicitor against me in a lawsuit." There was a rush to Rome, where, for several ensuing years, the hostile English parties were to wage a furious battle in the antechambers of the Vatican. But the dispute over the Oblates now sank into insignificance beside the rage of contention which centred round a new and far more deadly question; for the position of Dr. Errington himself was at stake. The Cardinal, in spite of illness, indolence, and the ties of friendship, had been brought at last to an extraordinary step: he was petitioning the Pope for nothing less than the deprivation and removal of the Archbishop of Trebizond.

The precise details of what followed are doubtful. It is only possible to discern with clearness, amid a vast cloud of official documents and unofficial correspondences in English, Italian, and Latin, of Papal decrees and voluminous *scritture,* of confidential reports of episcopal whispers and the secret agitations of Cardinals, the form of Manning, restless and indomitable, scouring like a stormy petrel the angry ocean of debate. Wiseman, dilatory, unbusinesslike, and infirm, was ready enough to leave the conduct of affairs in his hands. Nor was it long before Manning saw where the key of the whole position lay. As in the old days, at Chichester, he had secured the good will of Bishop Shuttleworth by cultivating the friendship of Archdeacon Hare, so now, on this vaster scale of operations, his sagacity led him swiftly and unerringly up the little winding staircase in the Vatican and through the humble door which opened into the cabinet of Monsignor Talbot, the private secretary of the Pope. Monsignor Talbot was a priest who embodied in a singular manner, if not the highest, at least the most persistent traditions of the Roman Curia. He was a master of various arts which the practice of ages has brought to perfection under the friendly shadow of the triple tiara. He could mingle together astuteness and holiness without any difficulty; he could make innuendoes as naturally as an ordinary man makes statements of fact; he could apply flattery with so unsparing a hand that even Princes of the Church found it sufficient; and, on occasion, he could ring the changes of torture on a human soul with a tact which called forth universal approbation. With such accomplishments, it could hardly be expected that Monsignor Talbot should be remarkable either for a delicate sense of conscientiousness or for an extreme refinement of feeling, but then it was not for those qualities that Manning was in search when he went up the winding stair. He was looking for the man who had the ear of Pio Nono; and, on the other side of the low-arched door, he found him. Then he put forth all his efforts; his success was complete; and an alliance began which was destined to have the profoundest effect upon Manning's career, and was only dissolved when, many years later, Monsignor Talbot was unfortunately obliged to exchange his apartment in the Vatican for a private lunatic asylum at Passy.

It was determined that the coalition should be ratified by the ruin of Dr. Errington. When the moment of crisis was seen to be approaching, Wiseman was summoned to Rome, where he began to draw up an immense *scrittura* containing his statement of the case. For months past the redoubtable energies of the Archbishop of Trebizond had been absorbed in a similar task. Folio was being piled upon folio, when a sudden blow threatened to put an end to the whole proceeding in a summary manner. The Cardinal was seized by violent illness, and appeared to be upon his deathbed. Manning thought for a moment that his labours had been in vain and that all was lost. But the Cardinal recovered; Monsignor Talbot used his influence as he alone knew how; and a papal decree was issued by which Dr. Errington was "liberated" from the Coadjutorship of Westminster, together with the right of succession to the See.

It was a supreme act of authority—a "colpo di stato di Dominiddio," as the Pope himself said—and the blow to the Old Catholics was correspondingly severe. They found themselves deprived at one fell swoop both of the influence of their most energetic supporter and of the certainty of coming into power at Wiseman's death. And in the meantime Manning was redoubling his energies at Bayswater. Though his Oblates had been checked over St. Edmund's, there was still no lack of work for them to do. There were missions to be carried on, schools to be managed, funds to be collected. Several new churches were built; a community of most edifying nuns of the Third Order of St. Francis was established; and £30,000, raised from Manning's private resources and from those of his friends, was spent in three years. "I hate that man," one of the Old Catholics exclaimed; "he is such a forward piece." The words were reported to Manning, who shrugged his shoulders.

"Poor man [he said] what is he made of? Does he suppose, in his foolishness, that after working day and night for twenty years in heresy and schism, on becoming a Catholic I should sit in an easy-chair and fold my hands all the rest of my life?"

But his secret thoughts were of a different caste.

"I am conscious of a desire [he wrote in his diary] to be in such a position (1) as I had in times past, (2) as my present circumstances imply, (3) as my friends think me fit for, (4) as I feel my own faculties tend to.

"But, God being my helper, I will not seek it by the lifting of a finger or the speaking of a word."

So Manning wrote, and thought, and prayed; but what are words, and thoughts, and even prayers, to the mysterious and relentless powers of circumstance and character? Cardinal Wiseman was slowly dying; the tiller of the Church was slipping from his feeble hand; and Manning was beside him, the one man with the energy, the ability, the courage, and the conviction to steer the ship upon her course. More than that; there was the sinister figure of a Dr. Errington crouching close at hand, ready to seize the helm and make straight— who could doubt it?—for the rocks. In such a situation the voice of self-abnegation must needs grow still and small indeed. Yet it spoke on, for it was one of the paradoxes in Manning's soul that that voice was never silent. Whatever else he was, he was not unscrupulous. Rather, his scruples deepened with his desires; and he could satisfy his most exorbitant ambitions in a profundity of self-abasement. And so now he vowed to Heaven that he would *seek* nothing—no, not by the lifting of a finger or the speaking of a word. But, if something came to him—? He had vowed not to seek; he had not vowed not to take. Might it not be his plain duty to take? Might it not be the will of God?

Something, of course, did come to him, though it seemed for a moment that it would elude his grasp. Wiseman died, and there ensued in Rome a crisis of extraordinary intensity. "Since the creation of the hierarchy," Monsignor Talbot wrote, "it is the greatest moment for the Church that I have yet seen." It was the duty of the Chapter of Westminster to nominate three candidates for succession to the Archbishopric; they made one last effort, and had the temerity to place upon the list, besides the names of two Old Catholic bishops, that of Dr. Errington. It was a fatal blunder. Pius IX. was furious;

the Chapter had committed an "insulta al Papa," he exclaimed, striking his breast three times in his rage. "It was the Chapter that did it," said Manning afterwards; but even after the Chapter's indiscretion, the fatal decision hung in the balance for weeks.

"The great point of anxiety with me [wrote Monsignor Talbot to Manning] is whether a Congregation will be held, or whether the Holy Father will perform a Pontifical act. He himself is doubting. I therefore say mass and pray every morning that he may have the courage to choose for himself, instead of submitting the matter to a Congregation. Although the Cardinals are determined to reject Dr. Errington, nevertheless I am afraid that they should select one of the others. You know very well that Congregations are guided by the documents that are placed before them; it is for this reason that I should prefer the Pope's acting himself."

But the Holy Father himself was doubting. In his indecision, he ordered a month of prayers and masses. The suspense grew and grew. Everything seemed against Manning. The whole English episcopate was opposed to him; he had quarrelled with the Chapter; he was a convert of but few years' standing; even the congregated Cardinals did not venture to suggest the appointment of such a man. But suddenly the Holy Father's doubts came to an end. He heard a voice— a mysterious inward voice—whispering something in his ear. "Met-tetelo lì! Mettetelo lì!" the voice repeated, over and over again. "Mettetelo lì!" It was an inspiration; and Pius IX., brushing aside the recommendations of the Chapter and the deliberations of the Cardinals, made Manning, by a Pontifical act, Archbishop of Westminster.

Monsignor Talbot's felicity was complete; and he took occasion, in conveying his congratulations to his friend, to make some illuminating reflections upon the great event.

"My policy throughout [he wrote] was never to propose you directly to the Pope, but to make others do so; so that both you and I can always say that it was not I who induced the Holy Father to name you, which would lessen the weight of your appointment. This I say, because many have said that your being named was all my doing. I do not say that the Pope did not know that I thought you the only man eligible; as I took care to tell him over and over again what was against all the other candidates; and in consequence he was almost driven into naming you. After he had named you, the Holy Father said to me, 'What a diplomatist you are, to make what you wished come to pass!'

"Nevertheless [concluded Monsignor Talbot] I believe your appointment was specially directed by the Holy Ghost."

Manning himself was apparently of the same opinion.

"My dear Child [he wrote to a lady penitent], I have in these last three weeks felt as if our Lord had called me by name. Everything else has passed out of my mind. The firm belief that I have long had that the Holy Father is the most supernatural person I have ever seen has given me this feeling more deeply still. I feel as if I had been brought, contrary to all human wills, by the Divine Will, into an immediate relation to our Divine Lord."

"If indeed [he wrote to Lady Herbert], it were the will of our Divine Lord to lay upon me this heavy burden, He could have done it in no way more strengthening and consoling to me. To receive it from the hands of His Vicar, and from Pius IX., and after long invocation of the Holy Ghost, and not only without human influences, but in spite of manifold and powerful human opposition, gives me the last strength for such a cross."

VI

MANNING's appointment filled his opponents with alarm. Wrath and vengeance seemed to be hanging over them; what might not be expected from the formidable enemy against whom they had struggled for so long, and who now stood among them armed with archiepiscopal powers and invested with the special confidence of Rome? Great was their amazement, great was their relief, when they found that their dreaded master breathed nothing but kindness, gentleness, and conciliation. The old scores, they found, were not to be paid off, but to be wiped out. The new archbishop poured forth upon every side all the tact, all the courtesy, all the dignified graces of a Christian magnanimity. It was impossible to withstand such treatment. Bishops who had spent years in thwarting him became his devoted adherents; even the Chapter of Westminster forgot its hatred. Monsignor Talbot was extremely surprised. "Your greatest enemies have entirely come round," he wrote. "I received the other day a panegyric of you from Searle. This change of feeling I cannot attribute to anything but the Holy Ghost." Monsignor Talbot was very fond of the Holy Ghost; but, so far at any rate as Searle was concerned, there was another explanation. Manning, instead of dismissing Searle from his position of "œconomus" in the episcopal household, had kept him on—at an increased salary; and the poor man, who had not scrupled in the days of his pride to call Manning a thief, was now duly grateful.

As to Dr. Errington, he gave an example of humility and submission by at once withdrawing into a complete obscurity. For years the Archbishop of Trebizond, the ejected heir to the See of Westminster, laboured as a parish priest in the Isle of Man. He nursed no resentment in his heart, and, after a long and edifying life of peace and silence, he died in 1886, a professor of theology at Clifton.

It might be supposed that Manning could now feel that his triumph was complete. His position was secure; his power was absolute; his prestige was daily growing. Yet there was something that irked him still. As he cast his eyes over the Roman Catholic community in England, he was aware of one figure which, by virtue of a peculiar eminence, seemed to challenge the supremacy of his own. That figure was Newman's.

Since his conversion, Newman's life had been a long series of misfortunes and disappointments. When he had left the Church of England, he was its most distinguished, its most revered member, whose words, however strange, were listened to with a profound attention, and whose opinions, however dubious, were followed in all their fluctuations with an eager and indeed a trembling respect. He entered the Church of Rome, and found himself forthwith an unimportant man. He was received at the Papal Court with a politeness which only faintly concealed a total lack of interest and understanding. His delicate mind, with its refinements, its hesitations, its complexities—his soft, spectacled, Oxford manner, with its half-effeminate diffidence—such things were ill calculated to impress a throng of busy Cardinals and Bishops, whose days were spent amid the practical details of ecclesiastical organization, the long-drawn involutions of papal diplomacy, and the delicious bickerings of personal intrigue. And when, at last, he did succeed in making some impression upon these surroundings, it was no better; it was worse. An uneasy suspicion gradually arose; it began to dawn upon the Roman authorities that Dr. Newman was a man of ideas. Was it possible that Dr. Newman did not understand that ideas in Rome were, to say the least of it, out of place? Apparently he did not; nor was that all; not content with having ideas, he positively seemed anxious to spread them. When that was known, the politeness in high places was seen to be wearing decidedly thin. His Holiness, who on Newman's arrival had graciously expressed the wish to see him "again and again," now, apparently, was constantly engaged. At first Newman supposed that the growing coolness was the result of misapprehension; his Italian was faulty, Latin was not spoken at Rome, his writings had only appeared in garbled translations. And even Englishmen had sometimes found his arguments difficult to follow. He therefore determined to take the utmost care to make his views quite clear; his opinions upon religious probability, his distinction between demonstrative and circumstantial evidence, his theory of the development of doctrine and the aspects of ideas—these and many other matters, upon which he had written so much, he would now explain in the simplest language. He would show that there was nothing dangerous in what he held, that there was a passage in De Lugo which supported him, that Perrone, by maintaining that the Immaculate Conception could be defined, had implicitly admitted one of his main positions, and that his language about Faith had been confused, quite erroneously, with the fideism of M. Bautain. Cardinal Barnabò, Cardinal Reisach, Cardinal Antonelli, looked at him with their shrewd eyes and hard faces, while he poured into their ears—which, as he had already noticed with distress, were large and not too clean—his careful disquisitions; but it was all in vain; they had clearly never read De Lugo or Perrone, and as for M. Bautain, they had never heard of him. Newman in despair fell back upon St. Thomas Aquinas; but, to his horror, he observed that St. Thomas himself did not mean very much to the Cardinals. With a sinking heart, he realized at last the painful truth: it was not the nature of his views, it was his having views at all, that was objectionable. He had hoped to devote the rest of his life to the teaching of Theology; but what sort of Theology could he teach which would be acceptable to such superiors? He left Rome, and settled down in Birmingham as the head of a small community of Oratorians. He did not complain; it was God's will; it was better so. He would watch and pray.

But God's will was not quite so simple as that. Was it right, after all, that a man with Newman's intellectual gifts, his devoted ardour, his personal celebrity, should sink away out of sight and use in the dim recesses of the Oratory at Birmingham? If the call were to come to him to take his talent out of the napkin, how could he refuse? And the call did come. A Catholic University was being started in Ireland, and Dr. Cullen, the Archbishop of Armagh, begged Newman to become the Rector. At first he hesitated, but when he learnt that it was the Holy Father's wish that he should take up the work, he could doubt no longer; the offer was sent from Heaven. The difficulties before him were very great; not only had a new University to be called up out of the void, but the position was complicated by the presence of a rival institution—the undenominational Queen's Colleges, founded by Peel a few years earlier with the object of giving Irish Catholics facilities for University education on the same terms as their fellow-countrymen. Yet Newman had the highest hopes. He dreamt of something greater than a merely Irish University—of a noble and flourishing centre of learning for the Catholics of Ireland and England alike. And why should not his dream come true? "In the midst of our difficulties," he said, "I have one ground of hope, just one stay, but, as I think, a sufficient one, which serves me in the stead of all other argument whatever. It is the decision of the Holy See; St. Peter has spoken."

The years that followed showed to what extent it was safe to depend upon St. Peter. Unforeseen obstacles cropped up on every side. Newman's energies were untiring, but so was the inertia of the Irish authorities. On his appointment, he wrote to Dr. Cullen asking that arrangements might be made for his reception in Dublin. Dr. Cullen did not reply. Newman wrote again, but still there was no answer. Weeks passed, months passed, years passed, and not a word, not a sign, came from Dr. Cullen. At last, after dangling for more than two years in the uncertainties and perplexities of so strange a situation, Newman was summoned to Dublin. There he found nothing but disorder and discouragement. The laity took no interest in the scheme, the clergy actively disliked it; Newman's authority was disregarded. He appealed to Cardinal Wiseman, and then at last a ray of hope dawned. The Cardinal suggested that a bishopric should be conferred upon him, to give him a status suitable to his position; Dr. Cullen acquiesced, and Pius IX. was all compliance. "Manderemo a Newman la crocetta," he said to Wiseman, smilingly drawing his hands down each side of his neck to his breast, "lo faremo vescovo di Porfirio, o qualche luogo." The news spread among Newman's friends, and congratulations began to come in. But the official intimation seemed to be unaccountably delayed; no *crocetta* came from Rome, and Cardinal Wiseman never again referred to the matter. Newman was left to gather that the secret representations of Dr. Cullen had brought about a change of counsel in high quarters. His pride did not allow him to enquire further; but one of his lady penitents, Miss Giberne, was less discreet. "Holy Father," she suddenly said to the Pope in an audience one day, "why don't you make Father Newman a bishop?" Upon which the Holy Father looked much confused and took a great deal of snuff.

For the next five years Newman, unaided and ignored, struggled desperately, like a man in a bog, with the overmastering difficulties of his task. His mind, whose native haunt was among the far aerial boundaries of fancy and philosophy, was now clamped down under the fetters of petty detail, and fed upon the mean diet of compromise and routine. He had to force himself to scrape together money, to write articles for the students' Gazette, to make plans for medical laboratories, to be ingratiating with the City Council; he was obliged to spend months travelling through the remote regions of Ireland in the company of extraordinary ecclesiastics and barbarous squireens. He was a thoroughbred harnessed to a four-wheeled cab; and he knew it. Eventually he realized something else: he saw that the whole project of a Catholic University had been evolved as a political and ecclesiastical weapon against the Queen's Colleges of Peel, and that was all. As an instrument of education, it was simply laughed at; and he himself had been called in because his name would be a valuable asset in a party game. When he understood that he resigned his rectorship and returned to the Oratory.

But his tribulations were not yet over. It seemed to be God's will that he should take part in a whole succession of schemes, which, no less than the project of the Irish University, were to end in disillusionment and failure. He was persuaded by Cardinal Wiseman to undertake the editorship of a new English version of the Scriptures, which was to be a monument of Catholic scholarship and an everlasting glory to Mother Church. He made elaborate preparations; he collected subscriptions, engaged contributors, and composed a long and learned *prolegomena* to the work. It was all useless; Cardinal Wiseman began to think of other things; and the scheme faded imperceptibly into thin air. Then a new task was suggested to him. The *Rambler,* a Catholic periodical, had fallen on evil days; would Dr. Newman come to the rescue, and accept the editorship? This time he hesitated rather longer than usual; he had burnt his fingers so often; he must be specially careful now. "I did all I could to ascertain God's Will," he said, and he came to the conclusion that it was his duty to undertake the work. He did so, and after two numbers had appeared Dr. Ullathorne, the Bishop of Birmingham, called upon him, and gently hinted that he had better leave the paper alone. Its tone was not liked at Rome; it had contained an article criticizing St. Pius V., and, most serious of all, the orthodoxy of one of Newman's own essays had appeared to be doubtful. He resigned, and in the anguish of his heart determined never to write again. One of his friends asked him why he was publishing nothing. "Hannibal's elephants," he replied, "never could learn the goose-step."

Newman was now an old man—he was sixty-three years of age. What had he to look forward to? A few last years of insignificance and silence. What had he to look back upon? A long chronicle of wasted efforts, disappointed hopes, neglected possibilities, unappreciated powers. And now all his labours had ended by his being accused at Rome of lack of orthodoxy. He could no longer restrain his indignation, and in a letter to one of his lady penitents he gave vent to the bitterness of his soul. When his *Rambler* article had been complained of, he said, there had been some talk of calling him to Rome.

"Call me to Rome [he burst out]—what does that mean? It means to sever an old man from his home, to subject him to intercourse with persons whose languages are strange to him—to food and to fashions which are almost starvation on the one hand, and involve restless days and nights on the other—it means to oblige him to dance attendance on Propaganda week after week and month after month—it means his death. (It was the punishment on Dr. Baines, 1840-41, to keep him at the door of Propaganda for a year.)

"This is the prospect which I cannot but feel probable, did I say anything which one Bishop in England chose to speak against and report. Others have been killed before me. Lucas went of his own accord indeed—but when he got there, oh! how much did he, as loyal a son of the Church and the Holy See as ever was, what did he suffer because Dr. Cullen was against him? He wandered (as Dr. Cullen *said* in a letter he published in a sort of triumph), he wandered from Church to Church without a friend, and hardly got an audience from the Pope. And I too should go from St. Philip to Our Lady, and to St. Peter and St. Paul, and to St. Laurence and to St. Cecilia, and, if it happened to me as to Lucas, should come back to die."

Yet, in spite of all, in spite of these exasperations of the flesh, these agitations of the spirit, what was there to regret? Had he not a mysterious consolation which outweighed every grief? Surely, surely, he had.

> Unveil, O Lord, and on us shine,
>   In glory and in grace,

he exclaims in a poem written at this time, called, "The Two Worlds"—

> This gaudy world grows pale before
>   The beauty of Thy face.
>
> Till Thou art seen it seems to be
>   A sort of fairy ground,
> Where suns unsetting light the sky,
>   And flowers and fruit abound.
>
> But when Thy keener, purer beam
>   Is poured upon our sight,
> It loses all its power to charm,
>   And what was day is night. . . .
>
> And thus, when we renounce for Thee
>   Its restless aims and fears,
> The tender memories of the past,
>   The hopes of coming years,
>
> Poor is our sacrifice, whose eyes
>   Are lighted from above;
> We offer what we cannot keep,
>   What we have ceased to love.

Such were Newman's thoughts when an unexpected event occurred which produced a profound effect upon his life. Charles Kingsley attacked his good faith and the good faith of Catholics in general in a magazine article; Newman protested, and Kingsley rejoined in an irate pamphlet. Newman's reply was the *Apologia pro Vita Sua,* which he wrote in seven weeks, sometimes working twenty-two hours at a stretch, "constantly in tears, and constantly crying out with distress." The success of the book, with its transparent candour, its controversial brilliance, the sweep and passion of its rhetoric, the depth of its personal feeling, was immediate and overwhelming; it was recognized at once as a classic, not only by Catholics, but by the whole English world. From every side expressions of admiration, gratitude, and devotion poured in. It was impossible for one so sensitive as Newman to the opinions of other people to resist the happy influence of such an unlooked-for, such an enormous triumph. The cloud of his dejection began to lift; *et l'espoir malgré lui s'est glissé dans son cœur.*

It was only natural that at such a moment his thoughts should return to Oxford. For some years past proposals had been on foot for establishing there a Hall, under Newman's leadership, for Catholic undergraduates. The scheme had been looked upon with disfavour in Rome, and it had been abandoned; but now a new opportunity presented itself; some land in a suitable position came into the market; Newman, with his reviving spirits, felt that he could not let this chance go by, and bought the land. It was his intention to build there not a Hall, but a Church, and to set on foot a "House of the Oratory." What possible objection could there be to such a scheme? He approached the Bishop of Birmingham, who gave his approval; in Rome itself there was no hostile sign. The laity were enthusiastic and subscriptions began to flow in. Was it possible that all was well at last? Was it conceivable that the strange and weary pilgrimage of so many years should end at length, in quietude if not in happiness, where it had begun?

It so happened that it was at this very time that Manning was appointed to the See of Westminster. The destinies of the two men, which had run parallel to one another in so strange a fashion and for so many years, were now for a moment suddenly to converge. Newly clothed with all the attributes of ecclesiastical supremacy, Manning found himself face to face with Newman, upon whose brows were glittering the fresh laurels of spiritual victory—the crown of an apostolical life. It was the meeting of the eagle and the dove. What followed showed, more clearly perhaps than any other incident in his career, the stuff that Manning was made of. Power had come to him at last; and he seized it with all the avidity of a born autocrat, whose appetite for supreme dominion had been whetted by long years of enforced abstinence and the hated simulations of submission. He was the ruler of Roman Catholic England, and he would rule. The nature of Newman's influence it was impossible for him to understand, but he saw that it existed; for twenty years he had been unable to escape the unwelcome iterations of that singular, that alien, that rival renown; and now it stood in his path, alone and inexplicable, like a defiant ghost. "It is remarkably interesting," he observed coldly, when somebody asked him what he thought of the *Apologia;* "it is like listening to the voice of one from the dead." And such voices, with their sepulchral echoes, are apt to be more dangerous than living ones; they attract too much attention; they must be silenced at all costs. It was the meeting of the eagle and the dove; there was a hovering, a swoop, and then the quick beak and the relentless talons did their work.

Even before his accession to the Archbishopric, Manning had scented a peculiar peril in Newman's Oxford scheme, and so soon as he came into power he privately determined that the author of the *Apologia* should never be allowed to return to his old University. Nor was there any lack of excellent reasons for such a decision. Oxford was by this time a nest of liberalism; it was no fit place for Catholic youths, and they would inevitably be attracted there by the presence of Father Newman. And then, had not Father Newman's orthodoxy been impugned? Had he not been heard to express opinions of most doubtful propriety upon the question of the Temporal Power? Was it not known that he might almost be said to have an independent mind? An influence? Yes, he had an influence, no doubt; but what a fatal kind of influence to which to subject the rising generation of Catholic Englishmen!

Such were the reflections which Manning was careful to pour into the receptive ear of Monsignor Talbot. That useful priest, at his post of vantage in the Vatican, was more than ever the devoted servant of the new Archbishop. A league, offensive and defensive, had been established between the two friends.

"I daresay I shall have many opportunities to serve you in Rome [wrote Monsignor Talbot modestly] and I do not think my support will be useless to you, especially on account of the peculiar character of the Pope, and the spirit which pervades Propaganda; therefore I wish you to understand that a compact exists between us; if you help me, I shall help you. [And a little later he added] I am glad you accept the league. As I have already done for years, I shall support you, and I have a hundred ways of doing so. A word dropped at the proper occasion works wonders."

Perhaps it was hardly necessary to remind his correspondent of that.

So far as Newman was concerned it so fell out that Monsignor Talbot needed no prompting. During the sensation caused by the appearance of the *Apologia,* it had occurred to him that it would be an excellent plan to secure Newman as a preacher during Lent for the fashionable congregation which attended his church in the Piazza del Popolo; and he had accordingly written to invite him to Rome. His letter was unfortunately not a tactful one. He assured Newman that he would find in the Piazza del Popolo "an audience of Protestants more educated than could ever be the case in England," and "I think myself," he had added by way of extra inducement, "that you will derive great benefit from visiting Rome, and showing yourself to the Ecclesiastical Authorities." Newman smiled grimly at this; he declared to a friend that the letter was "insolent"; and he could not resist the temptation of using his sharp pen.

"Dear Monsignor Talbot [he wrote in reply], I have received your letter, inviting me to preach in your Church at Rome to an audience of Protestants more educated than could ever be the case in England.

"However, Birmingham people have souls; and I have neither taste nor talent for the sort of work which you cut out for me. And I beg to decline your offer.

"I am, yours truly,

JOHN H. NEWMAN."

Such words were not the words of wisdom. It is easy to imagine the feelings of Monsignor Talbot. "Newman's work none here can understand," he burst out to his friend. "Poor man, by living almost ever since he has been a Catholic surrounded by a set of inferior men who idolize him, I do not think he has ever acquired the Catholic instincts." As for his views on the Temporal Power—well, people said that he had actually sent a subscription to Garibaldi. Yes, the man was incomprehensible, heretical, dangerous; he was "uncatholic and unchristian." Monsignor Talbot even trembled for the position of Manning in England.

"I am afraid that the old school of Catholics will rally round Newman in opposition to you and Rome. Stand firm, do not yield a bit in the line you have taken. As I have promised, I shall stand by you. You will have battles to fight, because every Englishman is naturally anti-Roman. To be Roman is to an Englishman an effort. Dr. Newman is more English than the English. His spirit must be crushed."

His spirit must be crushed! Certainly there could be no doubt of that.

"What you write about Dr. Newman [Manning replied] is true. Whether he knows it or not, he has become the centre of those who hold low views about the Holy See, are anti-Roman, cold and silent, to say no more, about the Temporal Power, national, English, critical of Catholic devotions, and always on the lower side. . . . You will take care [he concluded] that things are correctly known and understood where you are."

The confederates matured their plans. While Newman was making his arrangements for the Oxford Oratory, Cardinal Reisach visited London. "Cardinal Reisach has just left," wrote Manning to Monsignor Talbot: "he has seen and *understands* all that is going on in England." But Newman had no suspicions. It was true that persistent rumours of his unorthodoxy and his anti-Roman leanings had begun to float about, and these rumours had been traced to Rome. But what were rumours? Then, too, Newman found out that Cardinal Reisach had been to Oxford without his knowledge, and had inspected the land for the Oratory. That seemed odd; but all doubts were set at rest by the arrival from Propaganda of an official ratification of his scheme. There would be nothing but plain sailing now. Newman was almost happy; radiant visions came into his mind of a wonderful future in Oxford, the gradual growth of Catholic principles, the decay of liberalism, the inauguration of a second Oxford Movement, the conversion —who knows?—of Mark Pattison, the triumph of the Church. . . . "Earlier failures do not matter now," he exclaimed to a friend. "I see that I have been reserved by God for this."

Just then a long blue envelope was brought into the room. Newman opened it. "All is over," he said, "I am not allowed to go." The envelope contained a letter from the Bishop announcing that, together with the formal permission for an Oratory at Oxford, Propaganda had issued a secret instruction to the effect that Newman himself was by no means to reside there. If he showed signs of doing so, he was, blandly and suavely ("blande suaviterque" were the words of the Latin instrument) to be prevented. And now the secret instruction had come into operation: *blande suaviterque* Dr. Newman's spirit had been crushed.

His friends made some gallant efforts to retrieve the situation; but it was in vain. Father St. John hurried to Rome; and the indignant laity of England, headed by Lord Edward Howard, the guardian of the young Duke of Norfolk, seized the opportunity of a particularly virulent anonymous attack upon Newman to send him an address, in which they expressed their feeling that "every blow that touches you inflicts a wound upon the Catholic Church in this country." The only result was an outburst of redoubled fury upon the part of Monsignor Talbot. The address, he declared, was an insult to the Holy See. "What is the province of the laity?" he interjected. "To hunt, to shoot, to entertain. These matters they understand, but to meddle with ecclesiastical matters they have no right at all." Once more he warned Manning to be careful.

"Dr. Newman is the most dangerous man in England, and you will see that he will make use of the laity against your Grace. You must not be afraid of him. It will require much prudence, but you must be firm. The Holy Father still places his confidence in you; but if you yield and do not fight the battle of the Holy See against the detestable spirit growing up in England, he will begin to regret Cardinal Wiseman, who knew how to keep the laity in order."

Manning had no thought of "yielding"; but he pointed out to his agitated friend that an open conflict between himself and Newman would be "as great a scandal to the Church in England, and as great a victory to the Anglicans, as could be." He would act quietly, and there would be no more difficulty. The Bishops were united, and the Church was sound.

On this, Monsignor Talbot hurried round to Father St. John's lodgings in Rome to express his regret at the misunderstanding that had arisen, to wonder how it could possibly have occurred, and to hope that Dr. Newman might consent to be made a Protonotary Apostolic. That was all the satisfaction that Father St. John was to obtain from his visit to Rome. A few weeks later the scheme of the Oxford Oratory was finally quashed.

When all was over, Manning thought that the time had come for a reconciliation. He made advances through a common friend; what had he done, he asked, to offend Dr. Newman? Letters passed, and, naturally enough, they only widened the breach. Newman was not the man to be polite.

"I can only repeat [he wrote at last] what I said when you last heard from me. I do not know whether I am on my head or my heels when I have active relations with you. In spite of my friendly feelings, this is the judgment of my intellect. Meanwhile [he concluded], I propose to say seven masses for your intention amid the difficulties and anxieties of your ecclesiastical duties."

And Manning could only return the compliment.

At about this time the Curate of Littlemore had a singular experience. As he was passing by the Church he noticed an old man, very poorly dressed in an old grey coat with the collar turned up, leaning over the lych gate, in floods of tears. He was apparently in great trouble, and his hat was pulled down over his eyes, as if he wished to hide his features. For a moment, however, he turned towards the Curate, who was suddenly struck by something familiar in the face. Could it be—? A photograph hung over the Curate's mantelpiece of the man who had made Littlemore famous by his sojourn there more than twenty years ago; he had never seen the original; but now, was it possible—? He looked again, and he could doubt no longer. It was Dr. Newman. He sprang forward, with proffers of assistance. Could he be of any use? "Oh no, no!" was the reply. "Oh no, no!" But the Curate felt that he could not turn away, and leave so eminent a character in such distress. "Was it not Dr. Newman he had the honour of addressing?" he asked, with all the respect and sympathy at his command. "Was there nothing that could be done?" But the old man hardly seemed to understand what was being said to him. "Oh no, no!" he repeated, with the tears streaming down his face. "Oh no, no!"

VII

MEANWHILE a remarkable problem was absorbing the attention of the Catholic Church. Once more, for a moment, the eyes of all Christendom were fixed upon Rome. The temporal Power of the Pope had now almost vanished; but, as his worldly dominions steadily diminished, the spiritual pretensions of the Holy Father no less steadily increased. For seven centuries the immaculate conception of the Virgin had been highly problematical; Pio Nono spoke, and the doctrine became an article of faith. A few years later, the Court of Rome took another step: a *Syllabus Errorum* was issued, in which all the favourite beliefs of the modern world—the rights of democracies, the claims of science, the sanctity of free speech, the principles of toleration—were categorically denounced, and their supporters abandoned to the Divine wrath. Yet it was observed that the modern world proceeded as before. Something more drastic appeared to be necessary—some bold and striking measure which should concentrate the forces of the faithful, and confound their enemies. The tremendous doctrine of Papal Infallibility, beloved of all good Catholics, seemed to offer just the opening that was required. Let that doctrine be proclaimed, with the assent of the whole Church, an article of faith, and, in the face of such an affirmation, let the modern world do its worst! Accordingly a General Council—the first to be held since the Council of Trent more than 300 years before—was summoned to the Vatican, for the purpose, so it was announced, of providing "an adequate remedy to the disorders, intellectual and moral, of Christendom." The programme might seem a large one, even for a General Council; but everyone knew what it meant.

Everyone, however, was not quite of one mind. There were those to whom even the mysteries of Infallibility caused some searchings of heart. It was true, no doubt, that our Lord, by saying to Peter, "Thou art Cephas, which is by interpretation a stone," thereby endowed that Apostle with the supreme and full primacy and principality over the Universal Catholic Church; it was equally certain that Peter afterwards became the Bishop of Rome; nor could it be doubted that the Roman Pontiff was his successor. Thus it followed directly that the Roman Pontiff was the head, heart, mind, and tongue of the Catholic Church; and moreover it was plain that when Our Lord prayed for Peter that his faith should not fail, that prayer implied the doctrine of Papal Infallibility. All these things were obvious, and yet—and yet—. Might not the formal declaration of such truths in the year of grace 1870 be, to say the least of it, inopportune? Might it not come as an offence, as a scandal even, to those unacquainted with the niceties of Catholic dogma? Such were the uneasy reflections of grave and learned ecclesiastics and theologians in England, France, and Germany. Newman was more than usually upset; Monseigneur Dupanloup was disgusted; and Dr. Döllinger prepared himself for resistance. It was clear that there would be a disaffected minority at the Council.

Catholic apologists have often argued that the Pope's claim to infallibility implies no more than the necessary claim of every ruler, of every government, to the right of supreme command. In England, for instance, the Estates of the Realm exercise an absolute authority in secular matters; no one questions this authority, no one suggests that it is absurd or exorbitant; in other words, by general consent, the Estates of the Realm are, within their sphere, infallible. Why, therefore, should the Pope, within *his* sphere—the sphere of the Catholic Church—be denied a similar infallibility? If there is nothing monstrous in an Act of Parliament laying down what all men shall *do,* why should there be anything monstrous in a Papal Encyclical laying down what all men shall *believe?* The argument is simple; in fact, it is too simple; for it takes for granted the very question which is in dispute. Is there indeed no radical and essential distinction between supremacy and infallibility? between the right of a Borough Council to regulate the traffic and the right of the Vicar of Christ to decide upon the qualifications for Everlasting Bliss? There is one distinction, at any rate, which is palpable: the decisions of a supreme authority can be altered; those of an infallible authority cannot. A Borough Council may change its traffic regulations at the next meeting; but the Vicar of Christ, when, in certain circumstances and with certain precautions, he has once spoken, has expressed, for all the ages, a part of the immutable, absolute, and eternal Truth. It is this that makes the papal pretensions so extraordinary and so enormous. It is also this that gives them their charm. Catholic apologists, when they try to tone down those pretensions and to explain them away, forget that it is in their very exorbitance that their fascination lies. If the Pope were indeed nothing more than a magnified Borough Councillor, we should hardly have heard so much of him. It is not because he satisfies the reason, but because he astounds it, that men abase themselves before the Vicar of Christ.

And certainly the doctrine of Papal Infallibility presents to the reason a sufficiency of stumbling-blocks. In the fourteenth century, for instance, the following case arose. John XXII. asserted in his bull "Cum inter nonnullos" that the doctrine of the poverty of Christ was heretical. Now, according to the light of reason, one of two things must follow from this—either John XXII. was himself a heretic or he was no Pope. For his predecessor, Nicholas III., had asserted in his bull "Exiit qui seminat" that the doctrine of the poverty of Christ was the true doctrine, the denial of which was heresy. Thus if John XXII.

was right Nicholas III. was a heretic, and in that case Nicholas's nominations of Cardinals were void, and the conclave which elected John was illegal; so that John was no Pope, *his* nominations of Cardinals were void, and the whole Papal succession vitiated. On the other hand, if John was wrong—well, he was a heretic; and the same inconvenient results followed. And, in either case, what becomes of Papal Infallibility?

But such crude and fundamental questions as these were not likely to trouble the Council. The discordant minority took another line. Infallibility they admitted readily enough—the infallibility, that is to say, of the Church; what they shrank from was the pronouncement that this infallibility was concentrated in the Bishop of Rome. They would not actually deny that, as a matter of fact, it was so concentrated; but to *declare* that it was, to make the belief that it was an article of faith—what could be more—it was their favourite expression—more inopportune? In truth, the Gallican spirit still lingered among them. At heart, they hated the autocracy of Rome—the domination of the centralized Italian organization over the whole vast body of the Church. They secretly hankered, even at this late hour, after some form of constitutional government, and they knew that the last faint vestige of such a dream would vanish utterly with the declaration of the infallibility of the Pope. It did not occur to them, apparently, that a constitutional Catholicism might be a contradiction in terms, and that the Catholic Church without the absolute dominion of the Pope might resemble the play of *Hamlet* without the Prince of Denmark.

Pius IX. himself was troubled by no doubts. "Before I was Pope," he observed, "I *believed* in Papal Infallibility, now I *feel* it." As for Manning, his certainty was no less complete than his master's. Apart from the Holy Ghost, his appointment to the See of Westminster had been due to Pio Nono's shrewd appreciation of the fact that he was the one man in England upon whose fidelity the Roman Government could absolutely rely. The voice which kept repeating *"Mettetelo lì, mettetelo lì"* in his Holiness's ear whether or not it was inspired by God, was certainly inspired by political sagacity. For now Manning was to show that he was not unworthy of the trust which had been reposed in him. He flew to Rome in a whirlwind of Papal enthusiasm. On the way, in Paris, he stopped for a moment to interview those two great props of French respectability, M. Guizot and M. Thiers. Both were careful not to commit themselves, but both were exceedingly polite. "I am awaiting your Council," said M. Guizot, "with great anxiety. It is the last great moral power and may restore the peace of Europe." M. Thiers delivered a brief harangue in favour of the principles of the Revolution, which, he declared, were the very marrow of all Frenchmen; yet, he added, he had always supported the Temporal Power of the Pope. "Mais, M. Thiers," said Manning, "vous êtes effectivement croyant." "En Dieu," replied M. Thiers.

The Rome which Manning reached towards the close of 1869 was still the Rome which, for so many centuries, had been the proud and visible apex, the palpitating heart, the sacred sanctuary, of the most extraordinary mingling of spiritual and earthly powers that the world has ever known. The Pope now, it is true, ruled over little more than the City itself—the Patrimony of St. Peter—and he ruled there less by the grace of God than by the goodwill of Napoleon III.; yet he was still a sovereign Prince; and Rome was still the capital of the Papal State; she was not yet the capital of Italy. The last hour of this strange dominion had almost struck. As if she knew that her doom was upon her the Eternal City arrayed herself to meet it in all her glory. The whole world seemed to be gathered together within her walls. Her streets were filled with crowned heads and Princes of the Church, great ladies and great theologians, artists and friars, diplomats and newspaper reporters. Seven hundred bishops were there, from all the corners of Christendom, and in all the varieties of ecclesiastical magnificence—in falling lace and sweeping purple and flowing violet veils. Zouaves stood in the colonnade of St. Peter's, and Papal troops were on the Quirinal. Cardinals passed, hatted and robed, in their enormous carriages of state, like mysterious painted idols. Then there was a sudden hush: the crowd grew thicker and expectation filled the air. Yes! it was he! He was coming! The Holy Father! But first there appeared, mounted on a white mule and clothed in a magenta mantle, a grave dignitary bearing aloft a silver cross. The golden coach followed, drawn by six horses gorgeously caparisoned, and within the smiling white-haired Pio Nono, scattering his benedictions, while the multitude fell upon its knees as one man. Such were the daily spectacles of coloured pomp and of antique solemnity, which—so long as the sun was shining, at any rate—dazzled the onlooker into a happy forgetfulness of the reverse side of the Papal dispensation—the nauseating filth of the highways, the cattle stabled in the palaces of the great, and the fever flitting through the ghastly tenements of the poor.

In St. Peter's, the North Transept had been screened off; rows of wooden seats had been erected, covered with Brussels carpet; and upon these seats sat, each crowned with a white mitre, the seven hundred Bishops in Council. Here all day long rolled forth, in sonorous Latin, the interminable periods of episcopal oratory; but it was not here that the issue of the Council was determined. The assembled Fathers might talk till the marbles of St. Peter's themselves grew weary of the reverberations; the fate of the Church was decided in a very different manner—by little knots of influential persons meeting quietly of a morning in the back room of some inconspicuous lodging-house, by a sunset rendezvous in the Borghese Gardens between a Cardinal and a Diplomatist, by a whispered conference in an alcove at a Princess's evening party, with the gay world chattering all about. And, of course, on such momentous occasions as these, Manning was in his element. None knew those difficult ropes better than he; none used them with a more serviceable and yet discreet alacrity. In every juncture he had the right word, or the right silence; his influence ramified in all directions, from the Pope's audience chamber to the English Cabinet. "Il Diavolo del Concilio" his enemies called him; and he gloried in the name.

The real *crux* of the position was less ecclesiastical than diplomatic. The Papal Court, with its huge majority of Italian Bishops, could make sure enough, when it came to the point, of carrying its wishes through the Council; what was far more dubious was the attitude of the foreign Governments—especially those of France and England. The French Government dreaded a schism among its Catholic subjects; it disliked the prospect of an extension of the influence of the Pope over the mass of the population of France; and, since the very existence of the last remnant of the Pope's Temporal Power depended upon the French army, it was able to apply considerable pressure upon the Vatican. The interests of England were less directly involved, but it happened that at this moment Mr. Gladstone was Prime Minister, and Mr. Gladstone entertained strong views upon the Infallibility of the Pope. His opinions upon the subject were in part the outcome of his friendship with Lord Acton, a historian to whom learning and judgment had not been granted in equal proportions, and who, after years of incredible and indeed well-nigh mythical research, had come to the conclusion that the Pope could err. In this Mr. Gladstone entirely concurred, though he did not share the rest of his friend's theological opinions; for Lord Acton, while straining at the gnat of Infallibility, had swallowed the camel of the Roman Catholic Faith. "Que diable allait-il faire dans cette galère?" one cannot help asking, as one watches that laborious and scrupulous scholar, that life-long enthusiast for liberty, that almost hysterical reviler of priestcraft and persecution, trailing his learning so discrepantly along the dusty Roman way. But there are some who know how to wear their Rome with a difference; and Lord Acton was one of these.

He was now engaged in fluttering like a moth round the Council, and in writing long letters to Mr. Gladstone, impressing upon him the gravity of the situation, and urging him to bring his influence to bear. If the Dogma were carried, he declared, no man who accepted it could remain a loyal subject, and Catholics would everywhere become "irredeemable enemies of civil and religious liberty." In these circumstances, was it not plainly incumbent upon the English Government, involved as it was with the powerful Roman Catholic forces in Ireland, to intervene? Mr. Gladstone allowed himself to become convinced, and Lord Acton began to hope that his efforts would be successful. But he had forgotten one element in the situation; he had reckoned without the Archbishop of Westminster. The sharp nose of Manning sniffed out the whole intrigue. Though he despised Lord Acton almost as much as he disliked him—"such men," he said, "are all vanity: they have the inflation of German professors, and the ruthless talk of undergraduates"—yet he realized clearly enough the danger of his correspondence with the Prime Minister, and immediately took steps to counteract it. There was a semi-official agent of the English Government in Rome, Mr. Odo Russell, and round him Manning set to work to spin his spider's web of delicate and clinging diplomacy. Preliminary politenesses were followed by long walks upon the Pincio, and the gradual interchange of more and more important and confidential communications. Soon poor Mr. Russell was little better than a fly buzzing in gossamer. And Manning was careful to see that he buzzed on the right note. In his despatches to the Foreign Secretary, Lord Clarendon, Mr. Russell explained in detail the true nature of the Council, that it was merely a meeting of a few Roman Catholic prelates to discuss some internal matters of Church discipline, that it had no political significance whatever, that the question of Infallibility, about which there had been so much random talk, was a purely theological question, and that, whatever decision might be come to upon the subject, the position of Roman Catholics throughout the world would remain unchanged. Whether the effect of these affirmations upon Lord Clarendon was as great as Manning supposed, is somewhat doubtful; but it is at any rate certain that Mr. Gladstone failed to carry the Cabinet with him; and when at last a proposal was definitely made that the English Government should invite the Powers of Europe to intervene at the Vatican, it was rejected. Manning always believed that this was the direct result of Mr. Russell's despatches, which had acted as an antidote to the poison of Lord Acton's letters, and thus carried the day. If that was so—the discretion of biographers has not yet entirely lifted the veil from these proceedings— Manning had assuredly performed no small service for his cause. Yet his modesty would not allow him to assume for himself a credit which, after all, was due elsewhere; and, when he told the story of those days, he would add, with more than wonted seriousness, "It was by the Divine Will that the designs of His enemies were frustrated."

Meanwhile, in the North Transept of St. Peter's a certain amount of preliminary business had been carried through. Various miscellaneous points in Christian doctrine had been satisfactorily determined. Among others, the following Canons were laid down by the Fathers. "If anyone do not accept for sacred and canonical the whole and every part of the Books of Holy Scripture, or deny that they are divinely inspired, let him be anathema." "If anyone say that miracles cannot be, and therefore the accounts of them, even those in Holy Scriptures, must be assigned a place among fables and myths, or that the divine origin of the Christian religion cannot rightly be proved from them, let him be anathema." "If anyone say that the doctrines of the Church can ever receive a sense in accordance with the progress of science, other than that sense which the Church has understood and still understands, let him be anathema." "If anyone say that it is not possible, by the natural light of human reason, to acquire a certain knowledge of The One and True God, let him be anathema." In other words, it became an article of Faith that Faith was not necessary for a true knowledge of God. Having disposed of these minor matters, the Fathers found themselves at last approaching the great question of Infallibility. Two main issues, it soon appeared, were before them: the Pope's Infallibility was admitted, ostensibly at least, by all; what remained to be determined was, (1) whether the definition of the Pope's Infallibility was opportune, and (2) what the definition of the Pope's Infallibility was. (1) It soon became clear that the sense of the Council was overwhelming in favour of a definition. The Inopportunists were a small minority; they were outvoted, and they were obliged to give way. It only remained, therefore, to come to a decision upon the second question—what the definition should actually be. (2) It now became the object of the Inopportunists to limit the scope of the definition as much as possible, while the Infallibilists were no less eager to extend it. Now everyone—or nearly everyone—was ready to limit the Papal Infallibility to pronouncements *ex cathedrâ*—that is to say, to those made by the Pope in his capacity of Universal Doctor; but this only served to raise the ulterior, the portentous, and indeed the really crucial question—to *which* of the Papal pronouncements *ex cathedrâ* did Infallibility adhere? The discussions which followed were, naturally enough, numerous, complicated, and embittered, and in all of them Manning played a conspicuous part. For two months the Fathers deliberated; through fifty sessions they sought the guidance of the Holy Ghost. The wooden seats, covered though they were with Brussels carpet, grew harder and harder; and still the mitred Councillors sat on. The Pope himself began to grow impatient; for one thing, he declared, he was being ruined by the mere expense of lodging and keeping the multitude of his adherents. "Questi infallibilisti mi faranno fallire," said his Holiness. At length it appeared that the Inopportunists were dragging out the proceedings in the hope of obtaining an indefinite postponement. Then the authorities began to act; a bishop was shouted down, and the closure was brought into operation. At this point the French Government, after long hesitation, finally decided to intervene, and Cardinal Antonelli was informed that if the Definition was proceeded with the French troops would be withdrawn from Rome. But the astute Cardinal judged that he could safely ignore the threat. He saw that Napoleon III. was tottering to his fall and would never risk an open rupture with the Vatican. Accordingly it was determined to bring the proceedings to a close by a final vote. Already the Inopportunists, seeing that the game was up, had shaken the dust of Rome from their feet. On July 18, 1870, the Council met for the last time. As the first of the Fathers stepped forward to declare his vote, a storm of thunder and lightning suddenly burst over St. Peter's. All through the morning the voting continued, and every vote was accompanied by a flash and a roar from heaven. Both sides, with equal justice, claimed the portent as a manifestation of the Divine Opinion. When the votes were examined, it was found that 533 were in favour of the proposed definition and two against it. Next day war was declared between France and Germany, and a few weeks later the French troops were withdrawn from Rome. Almost in the same moment the successor of St. Peter had lost his Temporal Power and gained Infallibility.

What the Council had done was merely to assent to a definition of the dogma of the Infallibility of the Roman Pontiff which Pius IX. had issued, *proprio motu,* a few days before. The definition itself was perhaps somewhat less extreme than might have been expected. The Pope, it declared, is possessed, when he speaks *ex cathedrâ,* of "that infallibility with which the Redeemer willed that his Church should be endowed for defining doctrine regarding faith or morals." Thus it became a dogma of faith that a Papal definition regarding faith or morals is infallible; but beyond that both the Holy Father and the Council maintained a judicious reserve. Over what *other* matters besides faith and morals the Papal infallibility might or might not extend still remained in doubt. And there were further questions, no less serious, to which no decisive answer was then, or ever has been since provided. How was it to be determined, for instance, which particular Papal decisions did in fact come within the scope of the definition? Who was to decide what was or what was not a matter of faith or morals? Or precisely *when* the Roman Pontiff was speaking *ex cathedrâ?* Was the famous Syllabus Errorum, for example, issued *ex cathedrâ* or not? Grave theologians have never been able to make up their minds. Yet to admit doubts in such matters as these is surely dangerous. "In duty to our supreme pastoral office," proclaimed the Sovereign Pontiff, "by the bowels of Christ we earnestly entreat all Christ's faithful people, and we also command them by the authority of God and our Saviour, that they study and labour to expel and eliminate errors and display the light of the purest faith." Well might the faithful study and labour to such ends! For, while the offence remained ambiguous, there was no ambiguity about the penalty. One hair's breadth from the unknown path of truth, one shadow of impurity in the mysterious light of faith—and there shall be anathema! anathema! anathema! When the framers of such edicts called upon the bowels of Christ to justify them, might they not have done well to have paused a little, and to have called to mind the counsel of another sovereign ruler, though a heretic—Oliver Cromwell? "Bethink ye, bethink ye, in the bowels of Christ, that ye may be mistaken!"

One of the secondary results of the Council was the excommunication of Dr. Döllinger and a few more of the most uncompromising of the Inopportunists. Among these, however, Lord Acton was not included. Nobody ever discovered why. Was it because he was too important for the Holy See to care to interfere with him? Or was it because he was not important enough?

Another ulterior consequence was the appearance of a pamphlet by Mr. Gladstone, entitled "Vaticanism," in which the awful implications involved in the declaration of Infallibility were laid before the British public. How was it possible, Mr. Gladstone asked, with all the fulminating accompaniments of his most agitated rhetoric, to depend henceforward upon the civil allegiance of Roman Catholics? To this question the words of Cardinal Antonelli to the Austrian Ambassador might have seemed a sufficient reply. "There is a great difference," said his Eminence, "between theory and practice. No one will ever prevent the Church from proclaiming the great principles upon which its Divine fabric is based; but, as regards the *application* of those sacred laws, the Church, imitating the example of its Divine Founder, is inclined to take into consideration the natural weaknesses of mankind." And, in any case, it was hard to see how the system of Faith, which had enabled Pope Gregory XIII. to effect, by the hands of English Catholics, a whole series of attempts to murder Queen Elizabeth, can have been rendered a much more dangerous engine of disloyalty by the Definition of 1870. But such considerations failed to reassure Mr. Gladstone; the British public was of a like mind; and 145,000 copies of the pamphlet were sold within two months. Various replies appeared, and Manning was not behindhand. His share in the controversy led to a curious personal encounter.

His conversion had come as a great shock to Mr. Gladstone. Manning had breathed no word of its approach to his old and intimate friend, and when the news reached him, it seemed almost an act of personal injury. "I felt," Mr. Gladstone said, "as if Manning had murdered my mother by mistake." For twelve years the two men did not meet, after which they occasionally saw each other and renewed their correspondence. This was the condition of affairs when Mr. Gladstone published his pamphlet. As soon as it appeared Manning wrote a letter to the *New York Herald,* contradicting its conclusions, and declaring that its publication was "the first event that has overcast a friendship of forty-five years." Mr. Gladstone replied to this letter in a second pamphlet. At the close of his theological arguments, he added the following passage:—

"I feel it necessary, in concluding this answer, to state that Archbishop Manning has fallen into most serious inaccuracy in his letter of November 10th, where he describes my Expostulation as the first event which has overcast a friendship of forty-five years. I allude to the subject with regret; and without entering into details."

Manning replied in a private letter.

"My dear Gladstone [he wrote], you say that I am in error in stating that your former pamphlet is the first act which has overcast our friendship.

"If you refer to my act in 1851 in submitting to the Catholic Church, by which we were separated for some twelve years, I can understand it.

"If you refer to any other act either on your part or mine I am not conscious of it, and would desire to know what it may be.

"My act in 1851 may have overcast your friendship for me. It did not overcast my friendship for you, as I think the last years have shown.

"You will not, I hope, think me over-sensitive in asking for this explanation. Believe me, yours affectionately,

"† H. E. M."

"My dear Archbishop Manning [Mr. Gladstone answered], it did, I confess, seem to me an astonishing error to state in public that a friendship had not been overcast for forty-five years until now, which your letter declares has been suspended as to all action for twelve. . . . ,

"I wonder, too, at your forgetting that during the forty-five years I had been charged by you with doing the work of Antichrist in regard to the Temporal Power of the Pope. . . .

"Our differences, my dear Archbishop, are indeed profound. We refer them, I suppose, in humble silence to a Higher Power. . . . You assured me once of your prayers at all and at the most solemn time. I received that assurance with gratitude and still cherish it. As and when they move upwards, there is a meeting-point for those whom a chasm separates below. I remain always, affectionately yours,

"W. E. GLADSTONE."

Speaking of this correspondence in after years, Cardinal Manning said—"From the way in which Mr. Gladstone alluded to the overcasting of our friendship, people might have thought that I had picked his pocket."

VIII

In 1875 Manning's labours received their final reward: he was made a Cardinal. His long and strange career, with its high hopes, its bitter disappointments, its struggles, its renunciations, had come at last to fruition in a Princedom of the Church.

"Ask in faith and in perfect confidence [he himself once wrote], and God will give us what we ask. You may say, 'But do you mean that He will give us the very thing?' That, God has not said. God has said that He will give you whatsoever you ask; but the form in which it will come, and the time in which He will give it, He keeps in His own power. Sometimes our prayers are answered in the very things which we put from us; sometimes it may be a chastisement, or a loss, or a visitation against which our hearts rise, and we seem to see that God has not only forgotten us, but has begun to deal with us in severity. Those very things are the answers to our prayers. He knows what we desire, and He gives us the things which we ask; but in the form which His own Divine Wisdom sees to be best."

There was one to whom Manning's elevation would no doubt have given a peculiar satisfaction—his old friend Monsignor Talbot. But this was not to be. That industrious worker in the cause of Rome had been removed some years previously to a sequestered Home at Passy, whose padded walls were impervious to the rumours of the outer world. Pius IX. had been much afflicted by this unfortunate event; he had not been able to resign himself to the loss of his secretary, and he had given orders that Monsignor Talbot's apartment in the Vatican should be preserved precisely as he had left it, in case of his return. But Monsignor Talbot never returned. Manning's feelings upon the subject appear to have been less tender than the Pope's. In all his letters, in all his papers, in all his biographical memoranda, not a word of allusion is to be found to the misfortune, nor to the death, of the most loyal of his adherents. Monsignor Talbot's name disappears suddenly and for ever—like a stone cast into the waters.

Manning was now an old man, and his outward form had assumed that appearance of austere asceticism which is, perhaps, the one thing immediately suggested by his name to the ordinary Englishman. The spare and stately form, the head, massive, emaciated, terrible, with the great nose, the glittering eyes, and the mouth drawn back and compressed into the grim rigidities of age, self-mortification, and authority —such is the vision that still lingers in the public mind—the vision which, actual and palpable like some embodied memory of the Middle Ages, used to pass and repass, less than a generation since, through the streets of London. For the activities of this extraordinary figure were great and varied. He ruled his diocese with the despotic zeal of a born administrator. He threw himself into social work of every kind; he organized charities, he lectured on temperance. He delivered innumerable sermons; he produced an unending series of devotional books. And he brooked no brother near the throne: Newman languished in Birmingham; and even the Jesuits trembled and obeyed.

Nor was it only among his own community that his energy and his experience found scope. He gradually came to play an important part in public affairs, upon questions of labour, poverty, and education. He sat on Royal Commissions, and corresponded with Cabinet Ministers. At last no philanthropic meeting at the Guildhall was considered complete without the presence of Cardinal Manning. A special degree of precedence was accorded to him. Though the rank of a Cardinal-Archbishop is officially unknown in England, his name appeared in public documents—as a token, it must be supposed, of personal consideration—above the names of peers and bishops, and immediately below that of the Prince of Wales.

In his private life he was secluded. The ambiguities of his social position and his desire to maintain intact the peculiar eminence of his office combined to hold him aloof from the ordinary gatherings of society, though on the rare occasions of his appearance among fashionable and exalted persons he carried all before him. His favourite haunt was the Athenæum Club, where he sat scanning the newspapers, or conversing with the old friends of former days. He was a member, too, of that distinguished body, the Metaphysical Society, which met once a month during the palmy years of the Seventies to discuss, in strict privacy, the fundamental problems of the destiny of man. After a comfortable dinner at the Grosvenor Hotel, the Society, which included Professor Huxley and Professor Tyndall, Mr. John Morley and Sir James Stephen, the Duke of Argyll, Lord Tennyson, and Dean Church, would gather round to hear and discuss a paper read by one of the members upon such questions as "What is death?" "Is God unknowable?" or "The Nature of the Moral Principle." Sometimes, however, the speculations of the society ranged in other directions.

"I think the paper that interested me most of all that were ever read at our meetings [says Sir Mountstuart Elphinstone Grant-Duff], was one on 'Wherein consists the special beauty of imperfection and decay?' in which were propounded the questions 'Are not ruins recognized and felt to be more beautiful than perfect structures? Why are they so? Ought they to be so?' "

Unfortunately, however, the answers given to these questions by the Metaphysical Society have not been recorded for the instruction of mankind.

Manning read several papers, and Professor Huxley and Mr. John Morley listened with attention while he expressed his views upon "The Soul before and after Death," or explained why it is "That legitimate Authority is an Evidence of Truth." Yet, somehow or other, his Eminence never felt quite at ease in these assemblies; he was more at home with audiences of a different kind; and we must look in other directions for the free and full manifestation of his speculative gifts. In a series of lectures, for instance, delivered in 1861—it was the first year of the unification of Italy—upon "The Present Crisis of the Holy See, tested by Prophecy," we catch some glimpses of the kind of problems which were truly congenial to his mind.

"In the following pages [he said] I have endeavoured, but for so great a subject most insufficiently, to show that what is passing in our times is the prelude of the anti-christian period of the final dethronement of Christendom, and of the restoration of society without God in the world. My intention is [he continued] to examine the present relation of the Church to the civil powers of the world, by the light of a prophecy recorded by St. Paul."

This prophecy (2 Thess. ii. 3 to 11) is concerned with the coming of Antichrist, and the greater part of the lectures is devoted to a minute examination of this subject. There is no passage in Scripture, Manning pointed out, relating to the coming of Christ more explicit and express than those foretelling Antichrist; it therefore behoved the faithful to consider the matter more fully than they are wont to do. In the first place, Antichrist is a person. "To deny the personality of Antichrist is to deny the plain testimony of Holy Scripture." And we must remember that "it is a law of Holy Scripture that when persons are prophesied of, persons appear." Again, there was every reason to believe that Antichrist, when he did appear, would turn out to be a Jew.

"Such was the opinion of St. Irenæus, St. Jerome, and of the author of the work *De Consummatione Mundi,* ascribed to St. Hippolytus, and of a writer of a Commentary on the Epistle to the Thessalonians, ascribed to St. Ambrose, of many others, who add, that he will be of the tribe of Dan: as, for instance, St. Gregory the Great, Theodoret, Aretas of Cæsarea, and many more. Such also is the opinion of Bellarmine, who calls it certain. Lessius affirms that the Fathers, with unanimous consent, teach as undoubted that Antichrist will be a Jew. Ribera repeats the same opinion, and adds that Aretas, St. Bede, Haymo, St. Anselm, and Rupert affirm that for this reason the tribe of Dan is not numbered among those who are sealed in the Apocalypse. . . . Now I think no one can consider the dispersion and providential preservation of the Jews among all the nations of the world and the indestructible vitality of their race, without believing that they are reserved for some future action of His Judgment and Grace. And this is foretold again and again in the New Testament.

"Our Lord [continued Manning, widening the sweep of his speculations] has said of these latter times: 'There shall arise false Christs and false prophets, insomuch as to deceive even the elect'; that is, they shall not be deceived; but those who have lost faith in the Incarnation, such as humanitarians, rationalists, and pantheists, may well be deceived by any person of great political power and success, who should restore the Jews to their own land, and people Jerusalem once more with the sons of the Patriarchs. And there is nothing in the political aspect of the world which renders such a combination impossible; indeed, the state of Syria, and the tide of European diplomacy, which is continually moving eastward, render such an event within a reasonable probability."

Then Manning threw out a bold suggestion. "A successful medium," he said, "might well pass himself off by his preternatural endowments as the promised Messias."

Manning went on to discuss the course of events which would lead to the final catastrophe. But this subject, he confessed,

"deals with agencies so transcendent and mysterious, that all I shall venture to do will be to sketch in outline what the broad and luminous prophecies, especially of the Book of Daniel and the Apocalypse, set forth; without attempting to enter into minute details, which can only be interpreted by the event."

While applauding his modesty, we need follow Manning no further in his commentary upon those broad and luminous works; except to observe that "the apostacy of the City of Rome from the Vicar of Christ and its destruction by Antichrist" was, in his opinion, certain. Nor was he without authority for this belief. For it was held by "Malvenda, who writes expressly on the subject," and who, besides, "states as the opinion of Ribera, Gaspar Melus, Viegas, Suarez, Bellarmine, and Bosius that Rome shall apostatize from the faith."

I X

THE death of Pius IX. brought to Manning a last flattering testimony of the confidence with which he was regarded at the court of Rome. In one of the private consultations preceding the Conclave, a Cardinal suggested that Manning should succeed to the Papacy. He replied that he was unfitted for the position, because it was essential for the interests of the Holy See that the next Pope should be an Italian. The suggestion was pressed, but Manning held firm. Thus it happened that the Triple Tiara seemed to come, for a moment, within the grasp of the late Archdeacon of Chichester; and the cautious hand refrained.

Leo XIII. was elected, and there was a great change in the policy of the Vatican. Liberalism became the order of the day. And now at last the opportunity seemed ripe for an act which, in the opinion of the majority of English Catholics, had long been due—the bestowal of some mark of recognition from the Holy See upon the labours and the sanctity of Father Newman. It was felt that a Cardinal's hat was the one fitting reward for such a life, and accordingly the Duke of Norfolk, representing the Catholic laity of England, visited Manning, and suggested that he should forward the proposal to the Vatican. Manning agreed, and then there followed a curious series of incidents —the last encounter in the jarring lives of those two men. A letter was drawn up by Manning for the eye of the Pope, embodying the Duke of Norfolk's proposal; but there was an unaccountable delay in the transmission of this letter; months passed, and it had not reached the Holy Father. The whole matter would, perhaps, have dropped out of sight and been forgotten, in a way which had become customary when honours for Newman were concerned, had not the Duke of Norfolk himself, when he was next in Rome, ventured to recommend to Leo XIII. that Dr. Newman should be made a Cardinal. His Holiness welcomed the proposal; but, he said, he could do nothing until he knew the views of Cardinal Manning. Thereupon the Duke of Norfolk wrote to Manning, explaining what had occurred; shortly afterwards Manning's letter of recommendation, after a delay of six months, reached the Pope, and the offer of a Cardinalate was immediately dispatched to Newman.

But the affair was not yet over. The offer had been made; would it be accepted? There was one difficulty in the way. Newman was now an infirm old man of seventy-eight; and it is a rule that all Cardinals who are not also diocesan Bishops or Archbishops reside, as a matter of course, at Rome. The change would have been impossible for one of his years—for one, too, whose whole life was now bound up with the Oratory at Birmingham. But, of course, there was nothing to prevent His Holiness from making an exception in Newman's case, and allowing him to end his days in England. Yet how was Newman himself to suggest this? The offer of the Hat had come to him as an almost miraculous token of renewed confidence, of ultimate reconciliation. The old, long, bitter estrangement was ended at last. "The cloud is lifted from me for ever!" he exclaimed when the news reached him. It would be melancholy indeed if the cup were now to be once more dashed from his lips and he were obliged to refuse the signal honour. In his perplexity he went to the Bishop of Birmingham, and explained the whole situation. The Bishop assured him that all would be well; that he himself would communicate with the authorities, and put the facts of the case before them. Accordingly, while Newman wrote formally refusing the Hat, on the ground of his unwillingness to leave the Oratory, the Bishop wrote two letters to Manning, one official and one private, in which the following passages occurred:—

"Dr. Newman has far too humble and delicate a mind to dream of thinking or saying anything which would look like hinting at any kind of terms with the Sovereign Pontiff. . . . I think, however, that I ought to express my own sense of what Dr. Newman's dispositions are, and that it will be expected of me. . . . I am thoroughly confident that nothing stands in the way of his most grateful acceptance, except what he tells me greatly distresses him, namely, the having to leave the Oratory at a critical period of its existence and the impossibility of his beginning a new life at his advanced age."

And in his private letter the Bishop said:

"Dr. Newman is very much aged, and softened with age and the trials he has had, especially the loss of his two brethren St. John and Caswell; he can never refer to these losses without weeping and becoming speechless for the time. He is very much affected by the Pope's kindness, would, I know, like to receive the great honour offered him, but feels the whole difficulty at his age of changing his life, or having to leave the Oratory, which I am sure he could not do. If the Holy Father thinks well to confer on him the dignity, leaving him where he is, I know how immensely he would be gratified, and you will know how generally the conferring on him the Cardinalate will be applauded."

These two letters, together with Newman's refusal, reached Manning as he was on the point of starting for Rome. After he had left England, the following statement appeared in the *Times:*—

"Pope Leo XIII. has intimated his desire to raise Dr. Newman to the rank of Cardinal, but with expressions of deep respect for the Holy See, Dr. Newman has excused himself from accepting the Purple."

When Newman's eyes fell upon this announcement, he realized at once that a secret and powerful force was working against him. He trembled, as he had so often trembled before; and certainly the danger was not imaginary. In the ordinary course of things, how could such a paragraph have been inserted without his authority? And consequently, did it not convey to the world, not only an absolute refusal which he had never intended, but a wish on his part to emphasize publicly his rejection of the proffered honour? Did it not imply that he had lightly declined a proposal for which in reality he was deeply thankful? And when the fatal paragraph was read in Rome, might it not actually lead to the offer of the Cardinalate being finally withheld?

In great agitation, Newman appealed to the Duke of Norfolk.

"As to the statement [he wrote] of my refusing a Cardinal's Hat, which is in the papers, you must not believe it, for this reason:—

"Of course it implies that an offer has been made me, and I have sent an answer to it. Now I have ever understood that it is a point of propriety and honour to consider such communications sacred. This statement therefore cannot come from me. Nor could it come from Rome, for it was made public before my answer got to Rome.

"It could only come, then, from someone who not only read my letter, but, instead of leaving to the Pope to interpret it, took upon himself to put an interpretation upon it, and published that interpretation to the world.

"A private letter, addressed to Roman Authorities, is interpreted on its way and published in the English papers. How is it possible that anyone can have done this?"

The crushing indictment pointed straight at Manning. And it was true. Manning had done the impossible deed. Knowing what he did, with the Bishop of Birmingham's two letters in his pocket, he had put it about that Newman had refused the Hat. But a change had come over the spirit of the Holy See. Things were not as they had once been: Monsignor Talbot was at Passy, and Pio Nono was—where? The Duke of Norfolk intervened once again; Manning was profuse in his apologies for having misunderstood Newman's intentions, and hurried to the Pope to rectify the error. Without hesitation, the Sovereign Pontiff relaxed the rule of Roman residence, and Newman became a Cardinal.

He lived to enjoy his glory for more than ten years. Since he rarely left the Oratory, and since Manning never visited Birmingham, the two Cardinals met only once or twice. After one of these occasions, on returning to the Oratory, Cardinal Newman said, "What do you think Cardinal Manning did to me? He kissed me!"

On Newman's death, Manning delivered a funeral oration, which opened thus:—

"We have lost our greatest witness for the Faith, and we are all poorer and lower by the loss.

"When these tidings came to me, my first thought was this, in what way can I, once more, show my love and veneration for my brother and friend of more than sixty years?"

In private, however, the surviving Cardinal's tone was apt to be more . . . direct. "Poor Newman!" he once exclaimed in a moment of genial expansion. "Poor Newman! He was a great hater!"

x

In that gaunt and gloomy building—more like a barracks than an Episcopal palace—Archbishop's House, Westminster, Manning's existence stretched itself out into an extreme old age. As his years increased, his activities, if that were possible, increased too. Meetings, missions, lectures, sermons, articles, interviews, letters—such things came upon him in redoubled multitudes, and were dispatched with an unrelenting zeal. But this was not all; with age, he seemed to acquire what was almost a new fervour, an unaccustomed, unexpected, freeing of the spirit, filling him with preoccupations which he had hardly felt before. "They say I am ambitious," he noted in his diary, "but do I rest in my ambition?" No, assuredly he did not rest; but he worked now with no *arrière pensée* for the greater glory of God. A kind of frenzy fell upon him. Poverty, drunkenness, vice, all the horrors and terrors of our civilization, seized upon his mind, and urged him forward to new fields of action and new fields of thought. The temper of his soul assumed almost a revolutionary cast. "I am a Mosaic Radical," he exclaimed; and, indeed, in the exaltation of his energies, the incoherence of his conceptions, the democratic urgency of his desires, combined with his awe-inspiring aspect and his venerable age, it was easy enough to trace the mingled qualities of the patriarch, the prophet, and the demagogue. As, in his soiled and shabby garments, the old man harangued in the crowds of Bermondsey or Peckham upon the virtues of Temperance, assuring them, with all the passion of conviction, as a final argument, that the majority of the Apostles were total abstainers, this Prince of the Church might have passed as a leader of the Salvation Army. His popularity was immense, reaching its height during the great Dock Strikes of 1889, when after the victory of the men was assured, Manning was able, by his persuasive eloquence and the weight of his character, to prevent its being carried to excess. After other conciliators—among whom was the Bishop of London—had given up the task in disgust, the octogenarian Cardinal worked on with indefatigable resolution. At last, late at night, in the schools in Kirby Street, Bermondsey, he rose to address the strikers. An enthusiastic eye-witness had described the scene.

"Unaccustomed tears glistened in the eyes of his rough and work-stained hearers as the Cardinal raised his hand, and solemnly urged them not to prolong one moment more than they could help the perilous uncertainty and the sufferings of their wives and children. Just above his uplifted hand was a figure of the Madonna and Child; and some among the men tell how a sudden light seemed to swim round it as the speaker pleaded for the women and children. When he sat down all in the room knew that he had won the day, and that, so far as the Strike Committee was concerned, the matter was at an end."

In those days, there were strange visitors at Archbishop's House. Careful priests and conscientious secretaries wondered what the world was coming to when they saw labour leaders like Mr. John Burns and Mr. Ben Tillett, and land-reformers like Mr. Henry George, being ushered into the presence of his Eminence. Even the notorious Mr. Stead appeared, and his scandalous paper with its unspeakable revelations lay upon the Cardinal's table. This proved too much for one of the faithful tonsured dependents of the place, and he ventured to expostulate with his master. But he never did so again.

When the guests were gone, and the great room was empty, the old man would draw himself nearer to the enormous fire, and review once more, for the thousandth time, the long adventure of his life. He would bring out his diaries and his memoranda, he would rearrange his notes, he would turn over again the yellow leaves of faded correspondences; seizing his pen, he would pour out his comments and reflections, and fill, with an extraordinary solicitude, page after page with elucidations, explanations, justifications, of the vanished incidents of a remote past. He would snip with scissors the pages of ancient journals, and with delicate ecclesiastical fingers drop unknown mysteries into the flames.

Sometimes he would turn to the four red folio scrapbooks with their collection of newspaper cuttings concerning himself over a period of thirty years. Then the pale cheeks would flush and the close-drawn lips grow more menacing even than before. "Stupid, mulish malice," he would note. "Pure lying—conscious, deliberate, and designed." "Suggestive lying. Personal animosity is at the bottom of this."

And then he would suddenly begin to doubt. After all, where was he? What had he accomplished? Had any of it been worth while? Had he not been out of the world all his life? Out of the world!

"Croker's 'Life and Letters,' and Hayward's 'Letters' [he notes] are so full of politics, literature, action, events, collision of mind with mind, and that with such a multitude of men in every state of life, that when I look back, it seems as if I had been simply useless."

And again, "the complete isolation and exclusion from the official life of England in which I have lived, makes me feel as if I had done nothing." He struggled to console himself with the reflection that all this was only "the natural order." "If the natural order is moved by the supernatural order, then I may not have done nothing. Fifty years of witness for God and His Truth, I hope, has not been in vain." But the same thoughts recurred. "In reading Macaulay's life I had a haunting feeling that his had been a life of public utility and mine a *vita umbratilis,* a life in the shade." Ah! it was God's will. "Mine has been a life of fifty years out of the world as Gladstone's has been in it. The work of his life in this world is manifest. I hope mine may be in the next. I suppose our Lord called me out of the world because he saw that I should lose my soul in it." Clearly, that was the explanation.

And yet he remained sufficiently in the world to discharge with absolute efficiency the complex government of his diocese almost up to the last moment of his existence. Though his bodily strength gradually ebbed, the vigour of his mind was undismayed. At last, supported by cushions, he continued by means of a dictated correspondence to exert his accustomed rule. Only occasionally would he lay aside his work, to plunge into the yet more necessary duties of devotion. Never again would he preach; never again would he put into practice those three salutary rules of his in choosing a subject for a sermon: "(1) asking God to guide the choice; (2) applying the matter to myself; (3) making the sign of the cross on my head and heart and lips in honour of the Sacred Mouth;" but he could still pray; he could turn especially to the Holy Ghost.

"A very simple but devout person [he wrote in one of his latest memoranda] asked me why in my first volume of sermons I said so little about the Holy Ghost. I was not aware of it; but I found it to be true. I at once resolved that I would make a reparation every day of my life to the Holy Ghost. This I have never failed to do to this day. To this I owe the light and faith which brought me into the true fold. I bought all the books I could about the Holy Ghost. I worked out the truths about His personality, His presence, and His office. This made me understand the last paragraph in the Apostles' Creed and made me a Catholic Christian."

So, though Death came slowly, struggling step by step with that bold and tenacious spirit, when he did come at last the Cardinal was ready. Robed, in his archiepiscopal vestments, his rochet, his girdle, and his mozeta, with the scarlet biretta on his head, and the pectoral cross upon his breast, he made his solemn Profession of Faith in the Holy Roman Church. A crowd of lesser dignitaries, each in the garments of his office, attended the ceremonial. The Bishop of Salford held up the Pontificale and the Bishop of Amycla bore the wax taper. The provost of Westminster, on his knees, read aloud the Profession of Faith, surrounded by the Canons of the Diocese. Towards those who gathered about him the dying man was still able to show some signs of recognition, and even, perhaps, of affection; yet it seemed that his chief preoccupation, up to the very end, was with his obedience to the rules prescribed by the Divine Authority. "I am glad to have been able to do everything in due order," were among his last words. "Si fort qu'on soit," says one of the profoundest of the observers of the human heart, "on peut éprouver le besoin de s'incliner devant quelqu'un ou quelque chose. S'incliner devant Dieu, c'est toujours le moins humiliant."

Manning died on January 14, 1892, in the eighty-fifth year of his age. A few days later Mr. Gladstone took occasion, in a letter to a friend, to refer to his relations with the late Cardinal. Manning's conversion was, he said,

"altogether the severest blow that ever befell me. In a late letter the Cardinal termed it a quarrel, but in my reply I told him it was not a quarrel, but a death; and that was the truth. Since then there have been vicissitudes. But I am quite certain that to the last his personal feelings never changed; and I believe also that he kept a promise made in 1851, to remember me before God at the most solemn moments; a promise which I greatly valued. The whole subject is to me at once of extreme interest and of considerable restraint."

"His reluctance to die," concluded Mr. Gladstone, "may be explained by an intense anxiety to complete unfulfilled service."

The funeral was the occasion of a popular demonstration such as has rarely been witnessed in the streets of London. The route of the procession was lined by vast crowds of working people, whose imaginations, in some instinctive manner, had been touched. Many who had hardly seen him declared that in Cardinal Manning they had lost their best friend. Was it the magnetic vigour of the dead man's spirit that moved them? Or was it his valiant disregard of common custom and those conventional reserves and poor punctilios which are wont to hem about the great? Or was it something untamable in his glances and in his gestures? Or was it, perhaps, the mysterious glamour lingering about him of the antique organization of Rome? For whatever cause, the mind of the people had been impressed; and yet, after all, the impression was more acute than lasting. The Cardinal's memory is a dim thing today. And he who descends into the crypt of that

Cathedral which Manning never lived to see, will observe, in the quiet niche with the sepulchral monument, that the dust lies thick on the strange, the incongruous, the almost impossible object which, with its elaborations of dependent tassels, hangs down from the dim vault like some forlorn and forgotten trophy—the Hat.

AN AFTERWORD ON
"CARDINAL MANNING"

THE obituary of Lytton Strachey, which was written for the *New York Herald Tribune Books* by his compatriot, Rebecca West, is included in this volume not only as an illuminating preface to the famous and probably enduring essay on Cardinal Manning, but also, and even primarily, on its own account. It has a penetration and a pungency, a swift, sure, sinewy thrust and a vitality which filled with despairing envy those of her fellow-journalists who read it when it was first published. At that time the editor clapped it into print under the caption "Lytton Strachey: Father of Modern Biography," an ascription of paternity which would be assented to, I suppose, even by those disaffected readers who had found the strongest family resemblance in some of his least seemly spawn. Somewhat as was the case with *The Way of All Flesh* among the novels, Strachey's work in critical biography was most potent as an antidote. All of it was an enjoyable exercise in ironical deflation. But nearly always such indulgences in the luxury of dissent do not merely leave the truth incomplete. They miss its very core. Granted that the state of mind we call hero-worship is not the most desirable mood for a biographer. But ah, my foes, and oh, my friends, neither is its antithesis. Thus two scribes who severally undertook in this spirit to dispose, once and for all, of the late Mrs. Eddy did provide much entertainment for the unregenerate by underscoring that amazing old woman's infinite skullduggery. But when they were finished, they had left unexplained, and, indeed, scarcely mentioned, the personal magic by which, to the end, she held a very multitude in thrall.

So, too, in his calm, cold dissection of American behavior as it manifested itself between the years August 1914 and April 1917 young Walter Millis (in his *Road to War*) succeeds in making not a little ridiculous all who were active or even vocal during those bewildering years. Still damp from exposure to his fine drizzle of disparagement, I talked about this dispiriting work to a man more familiar with the subject matter than even Mr. Millis himself. I hereby quote, without permission but also without signature, the comment my wise man made. "Walter Millis," he said, "has dangerous brilliance. The fact is that nobody can get anywhere by being completely detached. Human beings ought to act with detachment, but they do not. As a consequence, when a great historical event comes to be judged by a completely detached person, most of its episodes seem irrational and most of its motives questionable. Either you or I could treat the American Revolution or the Protestant Reformation with complete detachment and make them both absurd, when, as a matter of fact, neither of them was absurd and the consequences of both of them are immeasurably important to the progress of the human race."

The word dissection has hereinbefore been used advisedly. Many a biographer who has taken his cue and his encouragement from Lytton Strachey is a little too much like the anatomist who cuts up a cadaver and thereafter thinks he knows the inner workings of *Homo sapiens*. He has indeed been able to inspect some of the mechanism. He has been denied only a view of that which had made the creature man. Although, for the sheer refreshment offered by its incomparable prose and for other reasons which Miss West has set down better than I (or anyone else) could do, I should battle fiercely against any proposal to exclude the Manning essay from this collection, I do think that even the best of Strachey's work—including, besides this essay, the two which followed it in *Eminent Victorians* and the delightful but unfortunately truncated biography of Queen Victoria—must be thought of chiefly as tonic and cleansing correctives, which taken alone, however, do, in each case, leave out the essence. Yes, as Miss West has said, Strachey did prod with a deflating finger the rounded waistcoat of Dr. Arnold and named him "a pompous and superstitious ignoramus whose inability to conceive one single valid idea regarding education led him to support customs which did much to make the young gentlemen of England brainless oafs and bullies." But surely Tom Brown knelt in the chapel at Rugby in memory of one who was more than that.

The Lamb portrait in the Tate Gallery is a luminous likeness of Strachey. Not merely his astounding whiskers but his hands were an extension of his personality. To say nothing of his feet which, when he sat him down, he usually left carelessly abandoned in some far corner of the room. Hands, feet, whiskers, they hung from him like fronds in some tropical verdure and at times seemed to sway ever so slightly as if stirred by all the winds of doctrine. Since I share Miss West's mistrust of *Elizabeth and Essex,* I may be justified in furnishing at least one of the reasons. In the passage devoted to his brilliant guesswork as to what went on in the Virgin Queen's mind while she was having her disturbing Earl decapitated, you will find this paragraph:

After all the long years of her life-time, and in this appalling consummation, was it her murdered mother who had finally emerged? The wheel had come full circle. Manhood—the fascinating, detestable entity, which had first come upon her concealed in yellow magnificence in her father's lap—manhood was overthrown at last, and in the person of that traitor it should be rooted out. Literally, perhaps . . . she knew well enough the punishment for high treason. But no! She smiled sardonically. She would not deprive him of the privilege of his rank. It would be enough if he suffered as so many others—the Lord Admiral Seymour among the rest—had suffered before him; it would be enough if she cut off his head.

At the time I wondered in what manner of document or memoir bearing on Elizabeth's childhood Mr. Strachey could possibly have found this nugget of intimate information, and at my first opportunity I asked him. "Oh, that," he made answer in a voice which only a piccolo could imitate, "I invented it."

A. W.

IN THE
GREEN MOUNTAIN
COUNTRY

by

CLARENCE DAY

IN THE GREEN MOUNTAIN COUNTRY
PUBLISHED IN BOOK FORM, 1934, BY YALE UNIVERSITY PRESS, WITH AC-
KNOWLEDGMENT TO THE NEW YORK AMERICAN. REPRINTED BY ARRANGE-
MENT WITH THE AUTHOR AND YALE UNIVERSITY PRESS, FROM WHOM
PERMISSION FOR REPRODUCTION MUST BE SECURED

IN THE GREEN MOUNTAIN COUNTRY

H~E~ got up at seven as usual, and he and his wife had breakfast together. At half past eight he went to his office in the town. His old friend and partner was already there when he entered. They were both early risers. They spoke with each other for a moment and then he went to his desk.

He was not feeling quite well. He said nothing about it. He had no idea that this was his last day of life.

There were a number of letters and other matters for him to go over and settle. He went to work methodically at them. He disliked to leave things undone. All his life he had attended to his duties, large or small, systematically. He was a sound, seasoned New Englander of sixty, and he had accomplished a lot.

By ten o'clock he had finished. He still wasn't feeling any better. He said to his secretary, "Mr. Ross, I guess we'll go to the house."

They motored back together through the streets and under the bare, spreading trees, till they came to the beeches and elms that surrounded his home. He had lived in half of a two-family house most of his life, but it had no grounds around it, and when he was fifty-eight he had moved; "so the doggies can have a place to play," he had said.

His wife was out—she had gone down town on foot to do some shopping. He and his secretary went to the library. He toyed with a jigsaw puzzle a moment. They spoke of the partridge hunting they had had in October, and of the hay fever that had bothered him in July—a "pollen attack" he called it. He made little of it. He had been lucky—he had had very few illnesses.

As they sat there talking he said he was thirsty. The cook and maid were at hand, and so was Mr. Ross, but he didn't like to be waited on —he went to the kitchen and got a glass of water himself. He heard the gardener in the cellar and he went down there to say something to him. The gardener was the last man he spoke to. When people asked him later what his employer had said he couldn't remember. He told them that it was something about the house or the grounds, and that it had not seemed important—to him.

Leaving the gardener this man went upstairs to his bedroom. He took off his coat and waistcoat to shave, but sank to the floor. He was dead.

The news spread through the town. Children on their way home from school stopped to look through the gates. A few policemen arrived. When reporters and camera men came the Chief of Police took them aside and asked them not to bother the family. He left one policeman on guard and everyone else went away.

The flag on the schoolhouse had been lowered. Now, on all public buildings, other flags went to half-mast. In town after town, and city after city, the flags fluttered down.

The next day the guns began booming. For thousands of miles throughout the nation, and at its army posts over-seas, at half hour intervals all day long, cannon by cannon they spoke. And when evening came and the bugles had sounded retreat, there were last, long, slow salutes everywhere of forty-eight guns, one for each of the forty-eight States of his country.

The hotel in Northampton was crowded that night. Friends of his had arrived for the funeral, and there were many reporters. The reporters swapped stories of the days before he had retired. One time when he had been suddenly needed, they said, for some national conference, and when nobody knew where he was, he had been found down in the storeroom, fishing a pickle out of a jar with two fingers. He had liked homemade pickles and people had sent him quantities of them, but he never got any at table, they were all kept on shelves in the storeroom, because of the chance that cranks might send jars that were poisoned.

Early in the morning the long special trains came rolling in. The President and his wife, the Vice-President, the Chief Justice, several Cabinet members, and committees of Senators and Congressmen got out of the sleeping cars from Washington and walked through the crowd at the station. Governors of near-by States and other officials arrived in their motors. They went to the Congregational Church and sat in its plain oak pews.

The service was brief. There was no eulogy, no address of any kind. Two hymns were sung, parts of the Bible were read, and the young minister prayed. He rose, and gave the great of the land who stood before him his blessing. They filed slowly out.

The streets emptied as the visitors left. The motors and trains rolled away.

When the town was alone with its own again, six sober-faced policemen lifted the coffin and carried it out to the street. Light rain was falling. Drops glistened on the coffin as it was placed in the hearse. A few motors fell in behind it, and the little procession moved off along the old country roads.

In every village they went through, there were small troops of boy scouts and veterans of the great war, standing at attention in silence as the motors sped by. In the yards of factories and mills, workmen stood in groups, waiting. Men held their hats or caps to their hearts, women folded their hands. Farms and fields on the road had been tidied up, as a mark of respect, and at a place where carpenters were building a house they had cleared away the lumber and chips.

The rain stopped for a while. The mists that had drifted low over the mountains gave place to blue sky. White, straight birch trunks glistened, and ice began to melt in the sunshine. But as they drove on, deeper into the Green Mountain country, black clouds spread and rain fell again, harder. The red tail lights of the cars gleamed on the road in the wintry and dark afternoon.

When the cars reached the end of the journey, the skies lightened palely a moment. The burying ground was outside the village where the dead man was born. Generations of his ancestors had been laid to rest there, in graves on the hillside. The cars climbed the steep road and stopped. The family and a handful of friends got out and stood waiting.

Across the road, in a rocky field, the men and women of the village had gathered. They were not the kind of people to intrude or crowd nearer, and they kept complete silence. The young minister said a few words as the coffin was lowered. A sudden storm of hail pelted down.

The widow, who had tried to smile that morning coming out of the church, could no longer hold back her tears.

The cars left. The bent shouldered sexton signaled to his helpers. They filled in the grave. Four country militiamen took up their positions on guard. Snow fell that night on the hillside and the slopes of Salt Ash Mountain.

The headstone that now marks the quiet spot bears no inscription but the name, Calvin Coolidge, the dates, and the President's seal.

AN AFTERWORD ON "IN THE GREEN MOUNTAIN COUNTRY"

THIS grave is in an unkempt little cemetery on a bit of gnarled hillside—just such stony, stubborn land as had been tilled and clung to for generations by the dead and gone Coolidges who lie all about him. Many of their headstones were chiseled in a century when such names as Abigail and Ebenezer and Ichabod were given oftener at baptisms than they are in the New England of today. Some of these stones have come loose with time and stand rakishly askew so that in the autumn moonlight they seem to be whispering to one another about the newcomer.

The most celebrated of the tribe lies beside the younger Calvin he lost when he was in the White House—two graves resting precariously on the side of a hill so steep that the neighbors have brought many bits of slate from a near-by quarry and therewith fashioned a retaining wall to keep the spring rains from stripping the bones of their shelter. The father's stone is distinguished from the other only by the eagle and the "E pluribus unum" cut into it by the local stone-mason, who used as his model the reverse side of a twenty-five cent piece.

This elegiac piece by Clarence Day is a bit of atypical writing with which he once filled a newspaper column, but the perspicacious Yale University Press fished it out from the oblivious ash-barrel and issued it as a book. Those who would know Mr. Day's more characteristic vein should read God and My Father and its companion, *Life with Father,* an incomparable family portrait which is unique in American letters. I suppose it can be savored best by those whose own memories reach back into the era so engagingly evoked by this fondly derisive work.

A. W.

A HANDFUL
OF DUST

by

EVELYN WAUGH

" . . . I WILL SHOW YOU SOMETHING DIFFERENT FROM EITHER
YOUR SHADOW AT MORNING STRIDING BEHIND YOU
OR YOUR SHADOW AT EVENING RISING TO MEET YOU;
I WILL SHOW YOU FEAR IN A HANDFUL OF DUST."

The Waste Land.

A HANDFUL OF DUST

À CÔTÉ DE CHEZ BEAVER

"Was anyone hurt?"

"No one I am thankful to say," said Mrs. Beaver, "except two house-maids who lost their heads and jumped through a glass roof into the paved court. They were in no danger. The fire never properly reached the bedrooms I am afraid. Still they are bound to need doing up, every-thing black with smoke and drenched in water and luckily they had that old-fashioned sort of extinguisher that ruins *everything*. One really cannot complain. The chief rooms were *completely* gutted and everything was insured. Sylvia Newport knows the people. I must get on to them this morning before that ghoul Mrs. Shutter snaps them up."

Mrs. Beaver stood with her back to the fire, eating her morning yoghort. She held the carton close under her chin and gobbled with a spoon.

"Heavens, how nasty this stuff is. I wish you'd take to it, John. You're looking so tired lately. I don't know how I should get through my day without it."

"But, mumsey, I haven't as much to do as you have."

"That's true, my son."

John Beaver lived with his mother at the house in Sussex Gardens where they had moved after his father's death. There was little in it to suggest the austerely elegant interiors which Mrs. Beaver planned for her customers. It was crowded with the unsaleable furniture of two larger houses, without pretension to any period, least of all to the present. The best pieces and those which had sentimental interest for Mrs. Beaver were in the L-shaped drawing room upstairs.

Beaver had a dark little sitting room on the ground floor behind the dining room, and his own telephone. The elderly parlourmaid looked after his clothes. She also dusted, polished and maintained in symmetrical order on his dressing table and on the top of his chest of drawers, the collection of sombre and bulky objects that had stood in his father's dressing room; indestructible presents for his wedding and twenty-first birthday, ivory, brass bound, covered in pigskin, crested and gold mounted, suggestive of expensive Edwardian masculinity— racing flasks and hunting flasks, cigar cases, tobacco jars, jockeys, elaborate meerschaum pipes, button hooks and hat brushes.

There were four servants, all female and all, save one, elderly.

When anyone asked Beaver why he stayed there instead of setting up on his own, he sometimes said that he thought his mother liked having him there (in spite of her business she was lonely); sometimes that it saved him at least five pounds a week.

His total income varied around six pounds a week, so this was an important saving.

He was twenty-five years old. From leaving Oxford until the beginning of the slump he had worked in an advertising agency. Since then no one had been able to find anything for him to do. So he got up late and sat near his telephone most of the day, hoping to be called up.

Whenever it was possible, Mrs. Beaver took an hour off in the middle of the morning. She was always at her shop punctually at nine, and by half past eleven she needed a break. Then, if no important customer was imminent, she would get into her two-seater and drive home to Sussex Gardens. Beaver was usually dressed by then and she had grown to value their morning interchange of gossip.

"What was your evening?"

"Audrey rang me up at eight and asked me to dinner. Ten of us at the Embassy, rather dreary. Afterwards we all went on to a party by a woman called de Trommet."

"I know who you mean. American. She hasn't paid for the toile-de-

jouy chaircovers we made her last April. I had a dull time too; didn't
hold a card all the evening and came away four pounds ten to the
bad."

"Poor mumsey."

"I'm lunching at Viola Chasm's. What are you doing? I didn't order
anything here I'm afraid."

"Nothing so far. But I can always go round to Brat's."

"But that's so expensive. I'm sure if we ask Chambers she'll be able
to get you something in. I thought you were certain to be out."

"Well I still may be. It isn't twelve yet."

Most of Beaver's invitations came to him at the last moment; occasionally even later, when he had already begun to eat a solitary meal
from a tray (. . . "John, darling, there's been a muddle and Sonia has
arrived without Reggie. Could you be an angel and help me out. Only
be quick, because we're going in now"). Then he would go precipi-
tately for a taxi and arrive, with apologies, after the first course. . . .
One of his few recent quarrels with his mother had occurred when he
left a luncheon party of hers in this way.

"Where are you going for the week-end?"

"Hetton."

"Who's that? I forget?"

"Tony Last."

"Yes, of course. She's lovely, he's rather a stick. I didn't know you
knew them."

"Well I don't really. Tony asked me in Brat's the other night. He
may have forgotten."

"Send a telegram and remind them. It is far better than ringing up.
It gives them less chance to make excuses. Send it tomorrow just before you start. They owe me for a table."

"What's their dossier?"

"I used to see her quite a lot before she married. She was Brenda
Rex, Lord St. Cloud's daughter, very fair, under-water look. People
used to be mad about her when she was a girl. Everyone thought she
would marry Jock Grant-Menzies at one time. Wasted on Tony Last,
he's a prig. I should say it was time she began to be bored. They've

been married five or six years. Quite well off but everything goes in keeping up the house. I've never seen it but I've an idea it's huge and quite hideous. They've got one child at least, perhaps more."

"Mumsey, you are wonderful. I believe you know about everyone."

"It's a great help. All a matter of paying attention while people are talking."

Mrs. Beaver smoked a cigarette and then drove back to her shop. An American woman bought two patch-work quilts at thirty guineas each, Lady Metroland telephoned about a bathroom ceiling, an unknown young man paid cash for a cushion; in the intervals between these events, Mrs. Beaver was able to descend to the basement where two dispirited girls were packing lampshades. It was cold down there in spite of a little oil stove and the walls were always damp. The girls were becoming quite deft, she noticed with pleasure, particularly the shorter one who was handling the crates like a man.

"That's the way," she said, "you are doing very nicely, Joyce. I'll soon get you on to something more interesting."

"Thank you, Mrs. Beaver."

They had better stay in the packing department for a bit, Mrs. Beaver decided; as long as they would stand it. They had neither of them enough chic to work upstairs. Both had paid good premiums to learn Mrs. Beaver's art.

Beaver sat on beside his telephone. Once it rang and a voice said, "Mr. Beaver? Will you please hold the line, sir, Lady Tipping would like to speak to you."

The intervening silence was full of pleasant expectation. Lady Tipping had a luncheon party that day, he knew; they had spent some time together the evening before and he had been particularly successful with her. Someone had chucked . . .

"Oh, Mr. Beaver, I *am* so sorry to trouble you. I was wondering, could you *possibly* tell me the name of the young man you introduced to me last night at Madame de Trommet's? The one with the reddish moustache. I think he was in Parliament."

"I expect you mean Jock Grant-Menzies."

"Yes, that's the name. You don't by any chance know where I can find him, do you?"

"He's in the book but I don't suppose he'll be at home now. You might be able to get him at Brat's at about one. He's almost always there."

"Jock Grant-Menzies, Brat's Club. Thank you so *very* much. It *is* kind of you. I hope you will come and see me some time. *Good*-bye."

After that the telephone was silent. At one o'clock Beaver despaired. He put on his overcoat, his gloves, his bowler hat and with neatly rolled umbrella set off to his club, taking a penny bus as far as the corner of Bond Street.

The air of antiquity pervading Brat's, derived from its elegant Georgian façade and finely panelled rooms, was entirely spurious, for it was a club of recent origin, founded in the burst of *bonhomie* immediately after the war. It was intended for young men, to be a place where they could straddle across the fire and be jolly in the card room without incurring scowls from older members. But now these founders were themselves passing into middle age; they were heavier, balder and redder in the face than when they had been demobilized, but their joviality persisted and it was their turn now to embarrass their successors, deploring their lack of manly and gentlemanly qualities.

Six broad backs shut Beaver from the bar. He settled in one of the armchairs in the outer room and turned over the pages of the *New Yorker,* waiting until someone he knew should turn up.

Jock Grant-Menzies came upstairs. The men at the bar greeted him saying, "Hullo, Jock old boy, what are you drinking?" or simply "Well, old boy?" He was too young to have fought in the war but these men thought he was all right; they liked him far more than they did Beaver, who, they thought, ought never to have got into the club at all. But Jock stopped to talk to Beaver. "Well, old boy," he said. "What are you drinking?"

"Nothing so far." Beaver looked at his watch. "But I think it's time I had one. Brandy and ginger ale."

Jock called to the barman and then said:

"Who was the old girl you wished on me at that party last night?"

"She's called Lady Tipping."

"I thought she might be. That explains it. They gave me a message downstairs that someone with a name like that wanted me to lunch with her."

"Are you going?"

"No, I'm no good at lunch parties. Besides I decided when I got up that I'd have oysters here."

The barman came with the drinks.

"Mr. Beaver, sir, there's ten shillings against you in my books for last month."

"Ah, thank you, Macdougal, remind me some time, will you?"

"Very good, sir."

Beaver said, "I'm going to Hetton tomorrow."

"Are you now? Give Tony and Brenda my love."

"What's the form?"

"Very quiet and enjoyable."

"No paper games?"

"Oh, no, nothing like that. A certain amount of bridge and backgammon and low poker with the neighbours."

"Comfortable?"

"Not bad. Plenty to drink. Rather a shortage of bathrooms. You can stay in bed all the morning."

"I've never met Brenda."

"You'll like her, she's a grand girl. I often think Tony Last's one of the happiest men I know. He's got just enough money, loves the place, one son he's crazy about, devoted wife, not a worry in the world."

"Most enviable. You don't know anyone else who's going, do you? I was wondering if I could get a lift down there."

"I don't I'm afraid. It's quite easy by train."

"Yes, but it's more pleasant by road."

"And cheaper."

"Yes, and cheaper I suppose . . . well, I'm going down to lunch. You won't have another?"

Beaver rose to go.

"Yes, I think I will."

"Oh, all right. Macdougal. Two more please."

Macdougal said, "Shall I book them to you, sir?"

"Yes, if you will."

Later, at the bar, Jock said, "I made Beaver pay for a drink."

"He can't have liked that."

"He nearly died of it. Know anything about pigs?"

"No. Why?"

"Only that they keep writing to me about them from my constituency."

Beaver went downstairs but before going into the dining room he told the porter to ring up his home and see if there was any message for him.

"Lady Tipping rang up a few minutes ago and asked whether you could come to luncheon with her today."

"Will you ring her up and say that I shall be delighted to but that I may be a few minutes late."

It was just after half past one when he left Brat's and walked at a good pace towards Hill Street.

I I

ENGLISH GOTHIC

BETWEEN *the villages of Hetton and Compton Last lies the extensive park of Hetton Abbey. This, formerly one of the notable houses of the county, was entirely rebuilt in 1864 in the Gothic style and is now devoid of interest. The grounds are open to the public daily until sunset and the house may be viewed on application by writing. It contains some good portraits and furniture. The terrace commands a fine view.*

This passage from the county Guide Book did not cause Tony Last any serious annoyance. Unkinder things had been said. His aunt Frances, embittered by an upbringing of unremitting severity, remarked that the plans of the house must have been adapted by Mr.

Pecksniff from one of his pupils' designs for an orphanage. But there was not a glazed brick or encaustic tile that was not dear to Tony's heart. In some ways, he knew, it was not convenient to run; but what big house was? It was not altogether amenable to modern ideas of comfort; he had many small improvements in mind, which would be put into effect as soon as the death duties were paid off. But the general aspect and atmosphere of the place; the line of its battlements against the sky; the central clock tower where quarterly chimes disturbed all but the heaviest sleepers; the ecclesiastical gloom of the great hall, its ceiling groined and painted in diapers of red and gold, supported on shafts of polished granite with carved capitals, half-lit by day through lancet windows of armorial stained glass, at night by a vast gasolier of brass and wrought iron, wired now and fitted with twenty electric bulbs; the blasts of hot air that rose suddenly at one's feet, through grills of cast-iron trefoils from the antiquated heating apparatus below, the cavernous chill of the more remote corridors where, economizing in coke, he had had the pipes shut off; the dining hall with its hammer-beam roof and pitch-pine minstrels' gallery; the bedrooms with their brass bedsteads, each with a frieze of Gothic text, each named from Malory, Yseult, Elaine, Mordred and Merlin, Gawaine and Bedivere, Lancelot, Perceval, Tristram, Galahad, his own dressing room, Morgan le Fay, and Brenda's Guinevere, where the bed stood on a dais, its walls hung with tapestry, its fireplace like a tomb of the thirteenth century, from whose bay window one could count the spires of six churches—all these things with which he had grown up were a source of constant delight and exultation to Tony; things of tender memory and proud possession.

They were not in the fashion, he fully realized. Twenty years ago people had liked half timber and old pewter; now it was urns and colonnades; but the time would come, perhaps in John Andrew's day, when opinion would reinstate Hetton in its proper place. Already it was referred to as "amusing" and a very civil young man had asked permission to photograph it for an architectural review.

The ceiling of Morgan le Fay was not in perfect repair. In order to make an appearance of coffered wood, moulded slats had been nailed in a chequer across the plaster. They were painted in chevrons of blue and gold. The squares between were decorated alternately with Tudor roses and fleur-de-lis. But damp had penetrated into one corner, leaving a large patch where the gilt had tarnished and the colour flaked away; in another place the wooden laths had become warped and separated from the plaster. Lying in bed, in the grave ten minutes between waking and ringing, Tony studied these defects and resolved anew to have them put right. He wondered whether it would be easy, nowadays, to find craftsmen capable of such delicate work.

Morgan le Fay had always been his room since he left the night nursery. He had been put there so that he would be within calling distance of his parents, inseparable in Guinevere; for until quite late in his life he was subject to nightmare. He had taken nothing from the room since he had slept there, but every year added to its contents, so that it now formed a gallery representative of every phase of his adolescence—the framed picture of a dreadnought (a coloured supplement from *Chums*), all its guns spouting flame and smoke; a photographic group of his private school; a cabinet called "the Museum," filled with a dozen desultory collections, eggs, butterflies, fossils, coins; his parents, in the leather diptych which had stood by his bed at school; Brenda, eight years ago when he had been trying to get engaged to her; Brenda with John, taken just after the christening; an aquatint of Hetton, as it had stood until his great-grandfather demolished it; some shelves of books, *Bevis, Woodwork at Home, Conjuring for All, The Young Visiters, The Law of Landlord and Tenant, Farewell to Arms.*

All over England people were waking up, queasy and despondent. Tony lay for ten minutes very happily planning the renovation of his ceiling. Then he rang the bell.

"Has her ladyship been called yet?"

"About quarter of an hour ago, sir."

"Then I'll have breakfast in her room."

He put on his dressing gown and slippers and went through into Guinevere.

Brenda lay on the dais. She had insisted on a modern bed. Her tray was beside her and the quilt was littered with envelopes, letters and the daily papers. Her head was propped against a very small blue pillow; clean of make-up, her face was almost colourless, rose-pearl, scarcely deeper in tone than her arms and neck.

"Well?" said Tony.

"Kiss."

He sat by the tray at the head of the bed; she leant forward to him (a nereid emerging from fathomless depths of clear water). She turned her lips away and rubbed against his cheek like a cat. It was a way she had.

"Anything interesting?"

He picked up some of the letters.

"No. Mamma wants nanny to send John's measurements. She's knitting him something for Christmas. And the mayor wants me to open something next month. Please, needn't I?"

"I think you'd better, we haven't done anything for him for a long time."

"Well you must write the speech. I'm getting too old for the girlish one I used to give them all. And Angela says will we stay for the New Year?"

"That's easy. Not on her life, we won't."

"I guessed not . . . though it sounds an amusing party."

"You go if you like. I can't possibly get away."

"That's all right. I knew it would be 'no' before I opened the letter."

"Well what sort of pleasure can there be in going all the way to Yorkshire in the middle of winter . . ."

"Darling, don't be cross. I know we aren't going. I'm not making a thing about it. I just thought it might be fun to eat someone else's food for a bit."

Then Brenda's maid brought in the other tray. He had it put by the window seat, and began opening his letters. He looked out of the window. Only four of the six church towers were visible that morning. Presently he said, "As a matter of fact I probably *can* manage to get away that week-end."

"Darling, are you sure you wouldn't hate it?"

"I daresay not."

While he ate his breakfast Brenda read to him from the papers. "Reggie's been making another speech . . . There's such an extraordinary picture of Babe and Jock . . . a woman in America has had twins by two different husbands. Would you have thought that possible? . . . Two more chaps in gas ovens . . . a little girl has been strangled in a cemetery with a bootlace . . . that play we went to about a farm is coming off." Then she read him the serial. He lit his pipe. "I don't believe you're listening. Why doesn't Sylvia want Rupert to get the letter?"

"Eh? Oh well, you see, she doesn't really trust Rupert."

"I *knew* it. There's no such character as Rupert in the story. I shall never read to you again."

"Well to tell you the truth I was just thinking."

"Oh."

"I was thinking how delightful it is, that it's Saturday morning and we haven't got anyone coming for the week-end."

"Oh you thought that?"

"Don't you?"

"Well it sometimes seems to me rather pointless keeping up a house this size if we don't now and then ask some other people to stay in it."

"*Pointless?* I can't think what you mean. I don't keep up this house to be a hostel for a lot of bores to come and gossip in. We've always lived here and I hope John will be able to keep it on after me. One has a duty towards one's employees, and towards the place too. It's a definite part of English life which would be a serious loss if . . ." Then Tony stopped short in his speech and looked at the bed. Brenda had turned on her face and only the top of her head appeared above the sheets.

"Oh God," she said into the pillow. "What have I done?"

"I say, am I being pompous again?"

She turned sideways so that her nose and one eye emerged. "Oh no, darling, not *pompous*. You wouldn't know how."

"Sorry."

Brenda sat up. "And, please, I didn't mean it. I'm jolly glad too, that no one's coming."

These scenes of domestic playfulness had been more or less continuous in Tony and Brenda's life for seven years.

Outside, it was soft English weather; mist in the hollows and pale sunshine on the hills; the coverts had ceased dripping, for there were no leaves to hold the recent rain, but the undergrowth was wet, dark in the shadows, iridescent where the sun caught it; the lanes were soggy and there was water running in the ditches.

John Andrews sat his pony, solemn and stiff as a Life-Guard, while Ben fixed the jump. Thunderclap had been a present on his sixth birthday from Uncle Reggie. It was John who had named her, after lengthy consultation. Originally she had been called Christabelle which, as Ben said, was more the name for a hound than a horse. Ben had known a strawberry roan called Thunderclap who killed two riders and won the local point-to-point four years running. He had been a lovely little horse, said Ben, till he staked himself in the guts, hunting, and had to be shot. Ben knew stories about a great many different horses. There was one called Zero on whom he had won five Jimmy-o-goblins at ten to three at Chester one year. And there was a mule he had known during the war, called Peppermint, who had died of drinking the company's rum rations. But John was not going to name his pony after a drunken mule. So in the end they had decided on Thunderclap, in spite of her imperturbable disposition.

She was a dark bay, with long tail and mane. Ben had left her legs shaggy. She cropped the grass, resisting John's attempts to keep her head up.

Before her arrival riding had been a very different thing. He had jogged around the paddock on a little Shetland pony called Bunny, with his nurse panting at the bridle. Now it was a man's business. Nanny sat at a distance, crocheting, on her camp stool; out of ear shot. There had been a corresponding promotion in Ben's position. From being the hand who looked after the farm horses, he was now, perceptibly, assuming the air of a stud groom. The handkerchief round his neck gave place to a stock with a fox-head pin. He was a man of varied experience in other parts of the country.

Neither Tony nor Brenda hunted but they were anxious that John should like it. Ben foresaw the time when the stables would be full and himself in authority; it would not be like Mr. Last to get anyone in from outside.

Ben had got two posts bored for iron pegs, and a whitewashed rail. With these he erected a two foot jump in the middle of the field.

"Now take it quite easy. Canter up slow and when she takes off lean forward in the saddle and you'll be over like a bird. Keep her head straight at it."

Thunderclap trotted forwards, cantered two paces, thought better of it and, just before the jump, fell into a trot again and swerved round the obstacle. John recovered his balance by dropping the reins and gripping the mane with both hands; he looked guiltily at Ben, who said, "What d'you suppose your bloody legs are for? Here take this and just give her a tap when you get up to it." He handed John a switch.

Nanny sat by the gate re-reading a letter from her sister.

John took Thunderclap back and tried the jump again. This time they made straight for the rail.

Ben shouted "Legs!" and John kicked sturdily, losing his stirrups. Ben raised his arms as if scaring crows. Thunderclap jumped; John rose from the saddle and landed on his back in the grass.

Nanny rose in alarm. "Oh what's happened, Mr. Hacket, is he hurt?"

"He's all right," said Ben.

"I'm all right," said John, "I think she put in a short step."

"Short step my grandmother. You just opened your bloody legs and took an arser. Keep hold on to the reins next time. You can lose a hunt that way."

At the third attempt John got over and found himself, breathless and insecure, one stirrup swinging loose and one hand grabbing its old support in the mane, but still in the saddle.

"There, how did that feel? You just skimmed over like a swallow. Try it again?"

Twice more John and Thunderclap went over the little rail, then nanny called that it was time to go indoors for his milk. They walked the pony back to the stable. Nanny said, "Oh dear, look at all the mud on your coat."

Ben said, "We'll have you riding the winner at Aintree soon."

"Good morning, Mr. Hacket."

"Good morning, miss."

"Good-bye, Ben, may I come and see you doing the farm horses this evening?"

"That's not for me to say. You must ask nanny. Tell you what though, the grey carthorse has got worms. Would you like to see me give him a pill?"

"Oh yes, please, nanny, may I?"

"You must ask mother. Come along now, you've had quite enough of horses for one day."

"Can't have enough of horses," said John, "ever." On the way back to the house, he said, "Can I have my milk in mummy's room?"

"That depends."

Nanny's replies were always evasive, like that—"We'll see" or "That's asking" or "Those that ask no questions, hear no lies"—so unlike Ben's decisive and pungent judgments.

"What does it depend on?"

"Lots of things."

"Tell me one of them."

"On your not asking a lot of silly questions."

"Silly old tart."

"*John.* How dare you? What do you mean?"

Delighted by the effect of this sally John broke away from her hand and danced in front of her saying, "Silly old tart, silly old tart" all the way to the side entrance. When they entered the porch his nurse silently took off his leggings; he was sobered a little by her grimness.

"Go straight up to the nursery," she said. "I am going to speak to your mother about you."

"Please, nanny. I don't know what it means, but I didn't mean it."
"Go straight to the nursery."

Brenda was doing her face.

"It's been the same ever since Ben Hacket started teaching him to ride, my lady, there's been no doing anything with him."

Brenda spat in the eye black. "But, nanny, what exactly did he say?"

"Oh I couldn't repeat it, my lady."

"Nonsense, you must tell me. Otherwise I shall be thinking it something far worse than it was."

"It couldn't have been worse . . . he called me a silly old tart, my lady."

Brenda choked slightly into her face towel. "He said *that?*"

"Repeatedly. He danced in front of me all the way up the drive, *singing it.*"

"I see . . . well you were quite right to tell me."

"Thank you, my lady, and since we are talking about it I think I ought to say that it seems to me that Ben Hacket is making the child go ahead far too quickly with his riding. It's very dangerous. He had what might have been a serious fall this morning."

"All right, nanny, I'll speak to Mr. Last about it."

She spoke to Tony. They both laughed about it a great deal. "Darling," she said. *"You* must speak to him. You're so much better at being serious than I am."

"I should have thought it was very nice to be called a tart," John argued, "and anyway it's a word Ben often uses about people."

"Well, he's got no business to."

"I like Ben more than anyone in the world. And I should think he's cleverer too."

"Now you know you don't like him more than your mother."

"Yes I do. *Far* more."

Tony felt that the time had come to cut out the cross talk and deliver the homily he had been preparing. "Now, listen, John. It was very wrong of you to call nanny a silly old tart. First, because it was unkind to her. Think of all the things she does for you every day."

"She's paid to."

"Be quiet. And secondly because you were using a word which people of your age and class do not use. Poor people use certain expressions which gentlemen do not. You are a gentleman. When you grow up all this house and lots of other things besides will belong to you. You must learn to speak like someone who is going to have these things and to be considerate to people less fortunate than you, particularly women. Do you understand?"

"Is Ben less fortunate than me?"

"That has nothing to do with it. Now you are to go upstairs and say you are sorry to nanny and promise never to use that word about anyone again."

"All right."

"And because you have been so naughty today you are not to ride tomorrow."

"Tomorrow's Sunday."

"Well next day, then."

"But you said 'tomorrow.' It isn't fair to change now."

"John, don't argue. If you are not careful I shall send Thunderclap back to Uncle Reggie and say that I find you are not a good enough boy to keep him. You wouldn't like that would you?"

"What would Uncle Reggie do with her? She couldn't carry him. Besides he's usually abroad."

"He'd give him to some other little boy. Anyway that's got nothing to do with it. Now run off and say you're sorry to nanny."

At the door John said, "It's all right about riding on Monday, isn't it? You did *say* 'tomorrow.'"

"Yes, I suppose so."

"Hooray. Thunderclap went very well today. We jumped a big post and rails. She refused to first time but went like a bird after that."

"Didn't you come off?"

"Yes, once. It wasn't Thunderclap's fault. I just opened my bloody legs and cut an arser."

"How did the lecture go?" Brenda asked.

"Bad. Rotten bad."

"The trouble is that nanny's jealous of Ben."

"I'm not sure we shan't both be soon."

They lunched at a small, round table in the centre of the dining hall. There seemed no way of securing an even temperature in that room; even when one side was painfully roasting in the direct blaze of the open hearth, the other was numbed by a dozen converging drafts. Brenda had tried numerous experiments with screens and a portable, electric radiator, but with little success. Even today, mild elsewhere, it was bitterly cold in the dining hall.

Although they were both in good health and of unexceptionable figure, Tony and Brenda were on a diet. It gave an interest to their meals and saved them from the two uncivilized extremes of which solitary diners are in danger—absorbing gluttony or an irregular regimen of scrambled eggs and raw beef sandwiches. Under their present system they denied themselves the combination of protein and starch at the same meal. They had a printed catalogue telling them which foods contained protein and which starch. Most normal dishes seemed to be compact of both so that it was fun for Tony and Brenda to choose the menu. Usually it ended by their declaring some food "joker."

"I'm sure it does me a great deal of good."

"Yes, darling, and when we get tired of it we might try an alphabetical diet, having things beginning with a different letter every day. J would be hungry, nothing but jam and jellied eels . . . What are your plans for the afternoon?"

"Nothing much. Carter's coming up at five to go over a few things. I may go over to Pigstanton after luncheon. I think we've got a tenant for Lowater Farm but it's been empty some time and I ought to see how much needs doing to it."

"I wouldn't say 'no' to going in to the 'movies.' "

"All right. I can easily leave Lowater till Monday."

"And we might go to Woolworth's afterwards, eh?"

What with Brenda's pretty ways and Tony's good sense, it was not

surprising that their friends pointed to them as a pair who were pre-
eminently successful in solving the problem of getting along well
together.

The pudding, without protein, was unattractive.

Five minutes afterwards a telegram was brought in. Tony opened
it and said "Hell."

"Badders?"

"Something too horrible has happened. Look at this."

Brenda read. *Arriving 3.18 so looking forward visit. Beaver.* And
asked, "What's Beaver?"

"It's a young man."

"That sounds all right."

"Oh no it's not, wait till you see him."

"What's he coming here for? Did you ask him to stay?"

"I suppose I did in a vague kind of way. I went to Brat's one evening and he was the only chap there so we had some drinks and he
said something about wanting to see the house . . ."

"I suppose you were tight."

"Not really, but I never thought he'd hold it against me."

"Well it jolly well serves you right. That's what comes of going up
to London on business and leaving me alone here . . . Who is he
anyway?"

"Just a young man. His mother keeps that shop."

"I used to know her. She's hell. Come to think of it we owe her
some money."

"Look here we must put a call through and say we're ill."

"Too late, he's in the train now, recklessly mixing starch and protein in the Great Western three and sixpenny lunch . . . Anyway he
can go into Sir Galahad. No one who sleeps there ever comes again—
the bed's agony I believe."

"What on earth are we going to do with him? It's too late to get
anyone else."

"You go over to Pigstanton. I'll look after him. It's easier alone.
We can take him to the movies tonight and tomorrow he can see over

the house. If we're lucky he may go up by the evening train. Does he have to work on Monday morning?"

"I shouldn't know."

Three-eighteen was far from being the most convenient time for arrival. One reached the house at about a quarter to four and if, like Beaver, one was a stranger there was an awkward time until tea; but without Tony being there to make her self-conscious, Brenda could carry these things off quite gracefully and Beaver was so seldom wholly welcome anywhere that he was not sensitive to the slight constraint of his reception.

She met him in what was still called the smoking room; it was in some ways the least gloomy place in the house. She said, "It is nice that you were able to come. I must break it to you at once that we haven't got a party. I'm afraid you'll be terribly bored . . . Tony had to go out but he'll be in soon . . . was the train crowded? It often is on Saturdays . . . would you like to come outside? It'll be dark soon and we might get some of the sun while we can . . ." and so on. If Tony had been there it would have been difficult for she would have caught his eye and her manner as châtelaine would have collapsed. And Beaver was well used to making conversation, so they went out together through the French windows on to the terrace, down the steps, into the Dutch garden, and back round the orangery without suffering a moment's real embarrassment. She even heard herself telling Beaver that his mother was one of her oldest friends.

Tony returned in time for tea. He apologized for not being at home to greet his guest and almost immediately went out again to interview the agent in his study.

Brenda asked about London and what parties there were. Beaver was particularly knowledgeable.

"Polly Cockpurse is having one soon."

"Yes, I know."

"Are you coming up for it?"

"I don't expect so. We never go anywhere nowadays."

The jokes that had been going round for six weeks were all new to Brenda; they had become polished and perfected with repetition and Beaver was able to bring them out with good effect. He told her of numerous changes of alliance among her friends.

"What's happening to Mary and Simon?"

"Oh, didn't you know? That's broken up."

"When?"

"It began in Austria this summer . . ."

"And Billy Angmering?"

"He's having a terrific walk out with a girl called Sheila Shrub."

"And the Helm-Hubbards?"

"That marriage isn't going too well either . . . Daisy has started a new restaurant. It's going very well . . . and there's a new night club called the Warren . . ."

"Dear me," Brenda said at last. "What fun everyone seems to be having."

After tea John Andrew was brought in and quickly usurped the conversation. "How do you do?" he said. "I didn't know you were coming. Daddy said he had a week-end to himself for once. Do you hunt?"

"Not for a long time."

"Ben says it stands to reason everyone ought to hunt who can afford to, for the good of the country."

"Perhaps I can't afford to."

"Are you poor?"

"Please, Mr. Beaver, you mustn't let him bore you."

"Yes, very poor."

"Poor enough to call people tarts?"

"Yes, quite poor enough."

"How did you get poor?"

"I always have been."

"Oh." John lost interest in this topic. "The grey horse at the farm has got worms."

"How do you know?"

"Ben says so. Besides you've only got to look at his dung."

"Oh dear," said Brenda, "what would nanny say if she heard you talking like that?"

"How old are you?"

"Twenty-five. How old are you?"

"What do you do?"

"Nothing much."

"Well if I was you I'd do something and earn some money. Then you'd be able to hunt."

"But I shouldn't be able to call people tarts."

"I don't see any point in that anyway."

Later in the nursery, while he was having supper, John said: "I think Mr. Beaver's a very silly man, don't you?"

"I'm sure I don't know," said nanny.

"I think he's the silliest man who's ever been here."

"Comparisons are odious."

"There just isn't anything nice about him. He's got a silly voice and a silly face, silly eyes and silly nose," John's voice fell into a liturgical sing-song, "silly feet and silly toes, silly head and silly clothes . . ."

"Now you eat your supper," said nanny.

That evening before dinner Tony came up behind Brenda as she sat at her dressing table and made a face over her shoulder in the glass.

"I feel rather guilty about Beaver—going off and leaving you like that. You were heavenly to him."

She said, "Oh it wasn't bad really. He's rather pathetic."

Further down the passage Beaver examined his room with the care of an experienced guest. There was no reading lamp. The ink pot was dry. The fire had been lit but had gone out. The bathroom, he had already discovered, was a great distance away, up a flight of turret steps. He did not at all like the look or feel of the bed; the springs were broken in the centre and it creaked ominously when he lay down to try it. The return ticket, third class, had been eighteen shillings. Then there would be tips.

Owing to Tony's feeling of guilt they had champagne for dinner, which neither he nor Brenda particularly liked. Nor, as it happened, did Beaver, but he was glad that it was there. It was decanted into a tall jug and was carried round the little table, between the three of them as a pledge of hospitality. Afterwards they drove into Pigstanton to the Picturedrome where there was a film Beaver had seen some months before. When they got back there was a grog tray and some sandwiches in the smoking room. They talked about the film but Beaver did not let on that he had seen it. Tony took him to the door of Sir Galahad.

"I hope you sleep well."

"I'm sure I shall."

"D'you like to be called in the morning?"

"May I ring?"

"Certainly. Got everything you want?"

"Yes thanks. Goodnight."

"Goodnight."

But when he got back he said, "You know, I feel awful about Beaver."

"Oh Beaver's all right," said Brenda.

But he was far from being comfortable and as he rolled patiently about the bed in quest of a position in which it was possible to go to sleep, he reflected that, since he had no intention of coming to the house again, he would give the butler nothing and only five shillings to the footman who was looking after him. Presently he adapted himself to the rugged topography of the mattress and dozed, fitfully, until morning. But the new day began dismally with the information that all the Sunday papers had already gone to her ladyship's room.

Tony invariably wore a dark suit on Sundays and a stiff white collar. He went to church, where he sat in a large pitch-pine pew, put in by his great-grandfather at the time of rebuilding the house, furnished with very high crimson hassocks and a fireplace, complete with iron grate and a little poker which his father used to rattle when any point in the sermon attracted his disapproval. Since his father's day a fire had not been laid there; Tony had it in mind to revive the practice next winter. On Christmas Day and Harvest Thanksgiving Tony read the lessons from the back of the brass eagle.

When service was over he stood for a few minutes at the porch chatting affably with the vicar's sister and the people from the village. Then he returned home by a path across the fields which led to a side door in the walls garden; he visited the hot houses and picked himself a button-hole, stopped by the gardeners' cottages for a few words (the smell of Sunday dinners rising warm and overpowering from the little doorways) and then, rather solemnly, drank a glass of sherry in the library. That was the simple, mildly ceremonious order of his Sunday morning, which had evolved, more or less spontaneously, from the more severe practices of his parents; he adhered to it with great satisfaction. Brenda teased him whenever she caught him posing as an upright, God-fearing gentleman of the old school and Tony saw the joke, but this did not at all diminish the pleasure he derived from his weekly routine, or his annoyance when the presence of guests suspended it.

For this reason his heart sank when, emerging from his study into the great hall at quarter to eleven, he met Beaver already dressed and prepared to be entertained; it was only a momentary vexation, however, for while he wished him good morning he noticed that his guest had an *A.B.C.* in his hands and was clearly looking out a train.

"I hope you slept all right?"

"Beautifully," said Beaver, though his wan expression did not confirm the word.

"I'm so glad. I always sleep well here myself. I say I don't like the look of that train guide. I hope you weren't thinking of leaving us yet?"

"Alas, I've got to get up tonight I'm afraid."

"Too bad. I've hardly seen you. The trains aren't very good on Sundays. The best leaves at five-forty-five and gets up about nine. It stops a lot and there's no restaurant car."

"That'll do fine."

"Sure you can't stay until tomorrow?"

"Quite sure."

The church bells were ringing across the park.

"Well I'm just off to church. I don't suppose you'd care to come."

Beaver always did what was expected of him when he was staying away, even on a visit as unsatisfactory as the present one. "Oh yes. I should like to very much."

"No, really I shouldn't, if I were you. You wouldn't enjoy it. I only go because I more or less have to. You stay here. Brenda will be down directly. Ring for a drink when you feel like it."

"Oh, all right."

"See you later then." Tony took his hat and stick from the lobby and let himself out. "Now I've behaved inhospitably to that young man again," he reflected.

The bells were clear and clamorous in the drive and Tony walked briskly towards them. Presently they ceased and gave place to a single note, warning the village that there was only five minutes to go before the organist started the first hymn.

He caught up nanny and John also on their way to church. John was in one of his rare confidential moods; he put his small gloved hand into Tony's and, without introduction, embarked upon a story which lasted them all the way to the church door; it dealt with the mule Peppermint who had drunk the company's rum ration, near Wipers in 1917; it was told breathlessly, as John trotted to keep pace with his father. At the end, Tony said, "How very sad."

"Well *I* thought it was sad too, but it isn't. Ben said it made him laugh fit to bust his pants."

The bell had stopped and the organist was watching from behind his curtain for Tony's arrival. He walked ahead up the aisle, nanny and John following. In the pew he occupied one of the armchairs; they sat on the bench at his back. He leant forward for half a minute with his forehead on his hand, and as he sat back, the organist played the first bars of the hymn.

"Enter not into judgment with thy servant, O Lord. . . ." The service followed its course. As Tony inhaled the agreeable, slightly musty atmosphere and performed the familiar motions of sitting, standing, and leaning forward, his thoughts drifted from subject to subject, among the events of the past week and his plans for the future. Occasionally some arresting phrase in the liturgy would recall him to his surroundings, but for the most part that morning he occupied himself with the question of bathrooms and lavatories, and of how more of them could best be introduced without disturbing the character of his house.

The village postmaster took round the collection bag. Tony put in his half-crown; John and nanny their pennies.

The vicar climbed, with some effort, into the pulpit. He was an elderly man who had served in India most of his life. Tony's father had given him the living at the instance of his dentist. He had a noble and sonorous voice and was reckoned the best preacher for many miles around.

His sermons had been composed in his more active days for delivery at the garrison chapel; he had done nothing to adapt them to the changed conditions of his ministry and they mostly concluded with some reference to homes and dear ones far away. The villagers did not find this in any way surprising. Few of the things said in church seemed to have any particular reference to themselves. They enjoyed their vicar's sermons very much and they knew that when he began about their distant homes, it was time to be dusting their knees and feeling for their umbrellas.

". . . And so as we stand here bareheaded at this solemn hour of the week," he read, his powerful old voice swelling up for the peroration, "let us remember our Gracious Queen Empress in whose services we are here and pray that she may long be spared to send us at her bidding to do our duty in the uttermost parts of the earth; and let us think of our dear ones far away and the homes we have left in her name, and remember that though miles of barren continent and leagues of ocean divide us, we are never so near to them as on these Sunday mornings, united with them across dune and mountain in our loyalty to our sovereign and thanksgiving for her welfare; one with them as proud subjects of her sceptre and crown."

("The Reverend Tendril 'e do speak uncommon high of the Queen," a gardener's wife had once remarked to Tony.)

After the choir had filed out, during the last hymn, the congregation crouched silently for a few seconds and then made for the door. There was no sign of recognition until they were outside among the graves; then there was an exchange of greetings, solicitous, cordial, garrulous.

Tony spoke to the vet's wife and Mr. Partridge from the shop; then he was joined by the vicar.

"Lady Brenda is not ill I hope?"

"No, nothing serious." This was the invariable formula when he appeared at church without her. "A most interesting sermon, vicar."

"My dear boy, I'm delighted to hear you say so. It is one of my favourites. But have you never heard it before?"

"No, I assure you."

"I haven't used it here lately. When I am asked to supply elsewhere it is the one I invariably choose. Let me see now, I always make a note of the times I use it." The old clergyman opened the manuscript book he was carrying. It had a limp black cover and the pages were yellow with age. "Ah yes, here we are. I preached it first in Jelalabad when the Coldstream Guards were there; then I used it in the Red Sea coming home from my fourth leave; then at Sidmouth . . . Mentone . . . Winchester . . . to the Girl Guides at their summer rally in 1921 . . . the Church Stage Guild at Leicester . . . twice at Bournemouth during the winter of 1926 when poor Ada was so ill . . . No, I don't seem to have used it here since 1911 when you would have been too young to enjoy it. . . ."

The vicar's sister had engaged John in conversation. He was telling her the story of Peppermint ". . . he'd have been all right, Ben says, if he had been able to cat the rum up, but mules can't cat, neither can horses . . ."

Nanny grasped him firmly and hurried him towards home. "How many times have I told you not to go repeating whatever Ben Hacket tells you? Miss Tendril didn't want to hear about Peppermint. And don't ever use that rude word 'cat' again."

"It only means to be sick."

"Well Miss Tendril isn't interested in being sick . . ."

As the gathering between porch and lych gate began to disperse, Tony set off towards the gardens. There was a good choice of buttonhole in the hot houses; he picked lemon carnations with crinkled, crimson edges for himself and Beaver and a camellia for his wife.

Shafts of November sunshine streamed down from lancet and oriel, tinctured in green and gold, gules and azure by the emblazoned coats, broken by the leaded devices into countless points and patches of coloured light. Brenda descended the great staircase step by step through alternations of dusk and rainbow. Both hands were occupied, holding to her breast a bag, a small hat, a half finished panel of petit-point embroidery and a vast disordered sheaf of Sunday newspapers, above which only her eyes and forehead appeared as though over a yashmak. Beaver emerged from the shadows below and stood at the foot of the stairs looking up at her.

"I say can't I carry something?"

"No, thanks, I've got everything safe. How did you sleep?"

"Beautifully."

"I bet you didn't."

"Well I'm not a very good sleeper."

"Next time you come you shall have a different room. But I daresay you won't ever come again. People so seldom do. It is very sad because it's such fun for us having them and we never make any new friends living down here."

"Tony's gone to church."

"Yes, he likes that. He'll be back soon. Let's go out for a minute or two, it looks lovely."

When Tony came back they were sitting in the library. Beaver was telling Brenda's fortune with cards. ". . . Now cut to me again," he was saying, "and I'll see if it's any clearer. . . . Oh yes . . . there is going to be a sudden death which will cause you great pleasure and profit. In fact you are going to kill someone. I can't tell if it's a man or a woman . . . yes, a woman . . . then you are going to go on a long journey across the sea, marry six dark men and have eleven children, grow a beard and die."

"Beast. And all this time I've been thinking it was serious. Hullo, Tony, jolly church?"

"Most enjoyable; how about some sherry?"

When they were alone together, just before luncheon, he said, "Darling, you're being heroic with Beaver."

"Oh, I quite enjoy coping—in fact I'm bitching him rather."

"So I saw. Well I'll look after him this afternoon and he's going this evening."

"Is he, I'll be quite sorry. You know that's a difference between us, that when someone's awful you just run away and hide, while I actually enjoy it—making up to them and showing off to myself how well I can do it. Besides Beaver isn't so bad. He's quite like us in some ways."

"He's not like me," said Tony.

After luncheon Tony said, "Well if it would really amuse you, we might go over the house. I know it isn't fashionable to like this sort of architecture now—my Aunt Frances says it is an authentic Pecksniff—but I think it's good of its kind."

It took them two hours. Beaver was well practised in the art of being shown over houses; he had been brought up to it in fact, ever since he had begun to accompany his mother, whose hobby it had always been, and later, with changing circumstances, the profession. He made apt and appreciative comments and greatly enhanced the pleasure Tony always took in exposing his treasures.

It was a huge building conceived in the late generation of the Gothic revival, when the movement had lost its fantasy and become structurally logical and stodgy. They saw it all: the shuttered drawing room, like a school speech-hall, the cloistral passages, the dark inner courtyard, the chapel where, until Tony's succession, family prayers had been daily read to the assembled household, the plate room and estate office, the bedrooms and attics, the watertank concealed among the battlements; they climbed the spiral staircase into the works of the

clock and waited to see it strike half past three. Thence they descended with ringing ears to the collections—enamel, ivories, seals,
snuff boxes, china, ormolu, cloisonné; they paused before each picture
in the oak gallery and discussed its associations; they took out the
more remarkable folios in the library and examined prints of the
original buildings, manuscript account books of the old abbey, travel
journals of Tony's ancestors. At intervals Beaver would say, "The
So-and-sos have got one rather like that at Such-and-such a place," and
Tony would say, "Yes, I've seen it but I think mine is the earlier."
Eventually they came back to the smoking room and Tony left Beaver
to Brenda.

She was stitching away at the petit point, hunched in an armchair.
"Well," she asked, without looking up from her needlework, "what
did you think of it?"

"Magnificent."

"You don't have to say that to me, you know."

"Well, a lot of the things are very fine."

"Yes, the *things* are all right I suppose."

"But don't you like the house?"

"Me? I *detest* it . . . at least I don't mean that really, but I do wish
sometimes that it wasn't *all,* every bit of it, so appallingly ugly. Only
I'd die rather than say that to Tony. We could never live anywhere
else, of course. He's crazy about the place . . . It's funny. None of us
minded very much when my brother Reggie sold *our* house—and that
was built by Vanburgh, you know . . . I suppose we're lucky to be
able to afford to keep it up at all. Do you know how much it costs
just to live here? We should be quite rich if it wasn't for that. As it is
we support fifteen servants indoors, besides gardeners and carpenters
and a night watchman and all the people at the farm and odd little
men constantly popping in to wind the clocks and cook the accounts
and clean the moat, while Tony and I have to fuss about whether it's
cheaper to take a car up to London for the night or buy an excursion
ticket . . . I shouldn't feel so badly about it if it were a really lively
house—like my home for instance . . . but of course Tony's been
brought up here and sees it all differently . . ."

Tony joined them for tea. "I don't want to seem inhospitable, but if you're going to catch that train, you ought really to be getting ready."

"That's all right. I've persuaded him to stay on till tomorrow."

"If you're sure you don't . . ."

"Splendid. I *am* glad. It's beastly going up at this time, particularly by that train."

When John came in he said, "I thought Mr. Beaver was going."

"Not till tomorrow."

"Oh."

After dinner Tony sat and read the papers. Brenda and Beaver were on the sofa playing games together. They did a cross word. Beaver said, "I've thought of something," and Brenda asked him questions to find what it was. He was thinking of the rum Peppermint drank. John had told him the story at tea. Brenda guessed it quite soon. Then they played "Analogies" about their friends and finally about each other.

They said good-bye that night because Beaver was catching the 9.10.

"Do let me know when you come to London."

"I may be up this week."

Next morning Beaver tipped both butler and footman ten shillings each. Tony, still feeling rather guilty in spite of Brenda's heroic coping, came down to breakfast to see his guest off. Afterwards he went back to Guinevere.

"Well, that's the last of *him*. You were superb, darling. I'm sure he's gone back thinking that you're mad about him."

"Oh, he wasn't too awful."

"No. I must say he took a very intelligent interest when we went round the house."

Mrs. Beaver was eating her yoghort when Beaver reached home. "Who was there?"

"No one."

"No one? My poor boy."

"They weren't expecting me. It was awful at first but got better. They were just as you said. She's very charming. He scarcely spoke."

"I wish I saw her sometimes."

"She talked of taking a flat in London."

"Did she?" The conversation of stables and garages was an important part of Mrs. Beaver's business. "What does she want?"

"Something quite simple. Two rooms and a bath. But it's all quite vague. She hasn't said anything to Tony yet."

"I am sure I shall be able to find her something."

2

If Brenda had to go to London for a day's shopping, hair-cutting, or bone-setting (a recreation she particularly enjoyed), she went on Wednesday, because the tickets on that day were half the usual price. She left at eight in the morning and got home soon after ten at night. She travelled third class and the carriages were often full, because other wives on the line took advantage of the cheap fare. She usually spent the day with her younger sister Marjorie who was married to the prospective conservative candidate for a South London constituency of strong Labour sympathies. She was more solid than Brenda. The newspapers used always to refer to them as "the lovely Rex sisters." Marjorie and Allan were hard up and smart; they could not afford a baby; they lived in a little house in the neighbourhood of Portman Square, very convenient for Paddington Station. They had a Pekingese dog named Djinn.

Brenda had come on impulse, leaving the butler to ring up and tell Marjorie of her arrival. She emerged from the train, after two hours and a quarter in a carriage crowded five a side, looking as fresh and fragile as if she had that moment left a circle of masseuses, chiropodists, manicurists and coiffeuses in an hotel suite. It was an aptitude she had, never to look half finished; when she was really exhausted, as she often was on her return to Hetton after these days in London, she went completely to pieces quite suddenly and became a waif; then she would sit over the fire with a cup of bread and milk, hardly alive, until Tony took her up to bed.

Marjorie had her hat on and was sitting at her writing table puzzling over her cheque book and a sheaf of bills.

"Darling, what *does* the country do to you? You look like a thousand pounds. Where *did* you get that suit?"

"I don't know. Some shop."

"What's the news at Hetton?"

"All the same. Tony madly feudal. John Andrew cursing like a stable boy."

"And you?"

"Me? Oh, I'm all right."

"Who's been to stay?"

"No one. We had a friend of Tony's called Mr. Beaver last weekend."

"John Beaver? . . . How very odd. I shouldn't have thought he was at all Tony's tea."

"He wasn't . . . What's he like?"

"I hardly know him. I see him at Margot's sometimes. He's a great one for going everywhere."

"I thought he was rather pathetic."

"Oh, he's *pathetic* all right. D'you fancy him?"

"Heavens, no."

They took Djinn for a walk in the Park. He was a very unrepaying dog who never looked about him and had to be dragged along by his harness; they took him to Watt's *Physical Energy;* when loosed he stood perfectly still, gazing moodily at the asphalt until they turned towards home; only once did he show any sign of emotion, when he snapped at a small child who attempted to stroke him; later he got lost and was found a few yards away, sitting under a chair and staring at a shred of waste paper. He was quite colourless with pink nose and lips and pink circles of bald flesh round his eyes. "I don't believe he has a spark of human feeling," said Marjorie.

They talked about Mr. Cruttwell, their bonesetter, and Marjorie's new treatment. "He's never done that to me," said Brenda enviously; presently, "What do you suppose is Mr. Beaver's sex-life?"

"I shouldn't know. Pretty dim I imagine . . . You *do* fancy him?"

"Oh well," said Brenda, "I don't see such a lot of young men . . ."

They left the dog at home and did some shopping—towels for the nursery, pickled peaches, a clock for one of the lodge-keepers who was celebrating his sixtieth year of service at Hetton, a pot of More-cambe Bay shrimps as a surprise for Tony; they made an appointment with Mr. Cruttwell for that afternoon. They talked about Polly Cockpurse's party. "Do come up for it. It's certain to be amusing."

"I might . . . if I can find someone to take me. Tony doesn't like her . . . I can't go to parties alone at my age."

They went out to luncheon, to a new restaurant in Albemarle Street which a friend of theirs named Daisy had recently opened. "You're in luck," said Marjorie, as soon as they got inside the door, "there's your Mr. Beaver's mother."

She was entertaining a party of eight at a large round table in the centre of the room; she was being paid to do so by Daisy, whose restaurant was not doing all she expected of it—that is to say the luncheon was free and Mrs. Beaver was getting the order, should the restaurant still be open, for its spring redecorations. It was, transparently, a made-up party, the guests being chosen for no mutual bond—least of all affection for Mrs. Beaver or for each other—except that their names were in current use—an accessible but not wholly renegade Duke, an unmarried girl of experience, a dancer and a novelist and a scene designer, a shamefaced junior minister who had not realized what he was in for until too late, and Lady Cockpurse; "God, what a party," said Marjorie, waving brightly to them all.

"You're both coming to my party, darlings?" Polly Cockpurse's strident tones rang across the restaurant. "Only don't tell anyone about it. It's just a very small, secret party. The house will only hold a few people—just old friends."

"It would be wonderful to see what Polly's *real* old friends were like," said Marjorie. "She hasn't known anyone more than five years."

"I wish Tony could see her point."

(Although Polly's fortune was derived from men, her popularity was chiefly among women, who admired her clothes and bought them from her second hand at bargain prices; her first steps to eminence had been in circles so obscure that they had made her no enemies in the world to which she aspired; some time ago she had married a good-natured Earl, whom nobody else happened to want at the time, since then she had scaled all but the highest peaks of every social mountain.)

After luncheon Mrs. Beaver came across to their table. "I *must* just come and speak to you though I'm in a great hurry. It's *so* long since we met and John has been telling me about a *delightful* week-end he had with you."

"It was very quiet."

"That's just what he *loves*. Poor boy he gets rushed off his feet in London. Tell me, Lady Brenda, is it true you are looking for a flat, because I think I've got just the place for you? It's being done up now and will be ready well before Christmas." She looked at her watch. "Oh dear, I must fly. You couldn't possibly come in for a cocktail, this evening? Then you could hear all about it."

"I *could* . . ." said Brenda doubtfully.

"Then *do*. I'll expect you about six. I daresay you don't know where I live." She told her and left the table.

"What's all this about a flat?" Marjorie asked.

"Oh just something I thought of . . ."

That afternoon, as she lay luxuriously on the osteopath's table, and her vertebræ, under his strong fingers, snapped like patent fasteners, Brenda wondered whether Beaver would be at home that evening. "Probably not, if he's so keen on going about," she thought, "and, anyhow, what's the sense? . . ."

But he was there, in spite of two other invitations.

She heard all about the maisonette. Mrs. Beaver knew her job. What people wanted, she said, was somewhere to dress and telephone. She was subdividing a small house in Belgravia into six flats at three pounds a week, of one room each and a bath; the bathrooms were going to be slap-up, with limitless hot water and every transatlantic refinement; the other room would have a large built-in wardrobe with electric light inside, and space for a bed. It would fill a long felt need, Mrs. Beaver said.

"I'll ask my husband and let you know."

"You *will* let me know soon, won't you, because *everyone* will be wanting one."

"I'll let you know very soon."

When she had to go, Beaver came with her to the station. She usually ate some chocolate and buns in her carriage; they bought them together at the buffet. There was plenty of time before the train left and the carriage was not yet full. Beaver came in and sat with her.

"I'm sure you want to go away."

"No, really."

"I've got lots to read."

"I *want* to stay."

"It's very sweet of you." Presently she said, rather timidly, for she was not used to asking for that sort of thing, "I suppose you wouldn't like to take me to Polly's party, would you?"

Beaver hesitated. There would be several dinner parties that evening and he was almost certain to be invited to one or other of them . . . if he took Brenda out it would mean the Embassy or some smart restaurant . . . three pounds at least . . . and he would be responsible for her and have to see her home . . . and if, as she said, she really did not know many people nowadays (why indeed should she have asked him if that were not true?) it might mean tying himself up for the whole evening . . . "I wish I could," he said, "but I've promised to dine out for it."

Brenda had observed his hesitation. "I was afraid you would have."

"But we'll meet there."

"Yes, if I go."

"I wish I could have taken you."

"It's quite all right . . . I just wondered."

The gaiety with which they had bought the buns was all gone now.

They were silent for a minute. Then Beaver said. "Well, I think perhaps I'll leave you now."

"Yes, run along. Thank you for coming."

He went off down the platform. There were still eight minutes to go. The carriage suddenly filled up and Brenda felt tired out. "Why *should* he want to take me, poor boy?" she thought, "only he might have done it better."

"Barnardo case?"

Brenda nodded. "Down and out," she said, "sunk, right under." She sat nursing her bread and milk, stirring it listlessly. Every bit of her felt good for nothing.

"Good day?"

She nodded. "Saw Marjorie and her filthy dog. Bought some things. Lunched at Daisy's new joint. Bone setter. That's all."

"You know I wish you'd give up these day trips to London. They're far too much for you."

"Me? Oh, I'm all right. Wish I was dead, that's all . . . and please, please, darling Tony, don't say anything about bed, because I can't move."

Next day a telegram came from Beaver. *Have got out of dinner 16th. Are you still free.*

She replied: *Delighted. Second thoughts always best. Brenda.*

Up till then they had avoided Christian names.

"You seem in wonderful spirits today," Tony remarked.

"I feel big. I think it's Mr. Cruttwell. He puts all one's nerves right and one's circulation and everything."

3

"Where's mummy gone?"

"London."

"Why?"

"Someone called Lady Cockpurse is giving a party."

"Is she nice?"

"Mummy thinks so. I don't."

"Why?"

"Because she looks like a monkey."

"I should love to see her. Does she live in a cage? Has she got a tail? Ben saw a woman who looked like a fish, with scales all over instead of skin. It was in a circus in Cairo. Smelt like a fish too, Ben says."

They were having tea together on the afternoon of Brenda's departure. "Daddy, what does Lady Cockpurse eat?"

"Oh, nuts and things."

"Nuts and what things?"

"Different kinds of nuts."

For days to come the image of this hairy, mischievous Countess occupied John Andrew's mind. She became one of the inhabitants of his world, like Peppermint, the mule who died of rum. When kindly people spoke to him in the village he would tell them about her and how she swung head down from a tree throwing nutshells at passers-by.

"You mustn't say things like that about real people," said nanny. "Whatever would Lady Cockpurse do if she heard about it."

"She'd gibber and chatter and lash round with her tail, and then I expect she'd catch some nice, big, juicy fleas and forget all about it."

Brenda was staying at Marjorie's for the night. She was dressed first and came into her sister's room. "Lovely, darling, new?"

"Fairly."

Marjorie was rung up by the woman at whose house she was dining. ("Look here are you absolutely sure you can't make Allan come tonight?" "Absolutely. He's got a meeting in Camberwell. He may not even come to Polly's." "Is there *any* man you can bring?" "Can't think of anybody." "Well we shall have to be one short, that's all. I can't think what's happened tonight. I rang up John Beaver but even *he* won't come.")

"You know," said Marjorie, putting down the telephone, "you're causing a great deal of trouble. You've taken London's only spare man."

"Oh dear, I didn't realize . . ."

Beaver arrived at quarter to nine in a state of high self-approval; he had refused two invitations to dinner while dressing that evening; he had cashed a cheque for ten pounds at his club; he had booked a divan table at Espinosa's. It was almost the first time in his life that he had taken anyone out to dinner, but he knew perfectly how it was done.

"I must see your Mr. Beaver properly," said Marjorie. "Let's make him take off his coat and drink something."

The two sisters were a little shy as they came downstairs, but Beaver was perfectly at his ease. He looked very elegant and rather more than his age.

"Oh, he's not so bad, your Mr. Beaver," Marjorie's look seemed to say, "not by any means," and he, seeing the two women together, who were both beautiful, though in a manner so different that, although it was apparent that they were sisters, they might have belonged each to a separate race, began to understand what had perplexed him all the week; why, contrary to all habit and principle, he had telegraphed to Brenda asking her to dine.

"Mrs. Jimmy Deane's very upset that she couldn't get you for to-night. I didn't give away what you were doing."

"Give her my love," said Beaver. "Anyway we'll all meet at Polly's."

"I must go, we're dining at nine."

"Stay a bit," said Brenda. "She's sure to be late."

Now that it was inevitable, she did not want to be left alone with Beaver.

"No, I must go. Enjoy yourselves, bless you both."

She felt as though she were the elder sister, seeing Brenda timid and expectant at the beginning of an adventure.

They were awkward when Marjorie left, for in the week that they had been apart, each had, in thought, grown more intimate with the other than any actual occurrence warranted. Had Beaver been more experienced, he might have crossed to where Brenda was sitting on the arm of a chair, and made love to her at once; and probably he would have got away with it. Instead he remarked in an easy manner, "I suppose we ought to be going too."

"Yes, where?"

"I thought Espinosa's."

"Yes, lovely. Only listen: I want you to understand right away that it's *my* dinner."

"Of course not . . . nothing of the sort."

"Yes, it is. I'm a year older than you and an old married woman and quite rich, so, please, I'm going to pay."

Beaver continued protesting to the taxi door.

But there was still a constraint between them and Beaver began to wonder, "Does she expect me to pounce?" So as they waited in a traffic block by the Marble Arch, he leaned forward to kiss her; when he was quite near, she drew back. He said, *"Please,* Brenda," but she turned away and looked out of the window shaking her head several times quickly. Then still fixed on the window she put out her hand to his and they sat in silence till they reached the restaurant. Beaver was thoroughly puzzled.

Once they were in public again, his confidence returned. Espinosa led them to their table; it was the one by itself on the right of the door, the only table in the restaurant at which one's conversation was not overheard. Brenda handed him the card. "You choose. Very little for me, but it must only have starch, no protein."

The bill at Espinosa's was, as a rule, roughly the same whatever one ate, but Brenda would not know this so, since it was now understood that she was paying, Beaver felt constrained from ordering anything that looked obviously expensive. However she insisted on champagne, and later a ballon of liqueur brandy for him. "You can't think how exciting it is for me to take a young man out. I've never done it before."

They stayed at Espinosa's until it was time to go to the party, dancing once or twice, but most of the time sitting at the table talking. Their interest in each other had so far outdistanced their knowledge that there was a great deal to say.

Presently Beaver said, "I'm sorry I was an ass in the taxi just now."

"Eh?"

He changed it and said, "Did you mind when I tried to kiss you just now?"

"Me? No, not particularly."

"Then why wouldn't you let me?"

"Oh dear, you've got a lot to learn."

"How d'you mean?"

"You mustn't ever ask questions like that. Will you try and remember?"

Then he was sulky. "You talk to me as if I was an undergraduate having his first walk out."

"Oh, is this a walk out?"

"Not as far as I am concerned."

There was a pause in which Brenda said, "I am not sure it hasn't been a mistake, taking you out to dinner. Let's ask for the bill and go to Polly's."

But they took ten minutes to bring the bill, and in that time Beaver and Brenda had to say something, so he said he was sorry.

"You've got to learn to be nicer," she said soberly. "I don't believe you'd find it impossible." When the bill eventually came, she said, "How much do I tip him?" and Beaver showed her. "Are you sure that's enough? I should have given twice as much."

"It's exactly right," said Beaver, feeling older again, exactly as Brenda had meant him to.

When they sat in the taxi Beaver knew at once that Brenda wished him to make love to her. But he decided it was time he took the lead. So he sat at a distance from her and commented on an old house that was being demolished to make way for a block of flats.

"Shut up," said Brenda. "Come here."

When he had kissed her, she rubbed against his cheek in the way she had.

Polly's party was exactly what she wished it to be, an accurate replica of all the best parties she had been to in the last year; the same band, the same supper, and, above all, the same guests. Hers was not the ambition to create a sensation, to have the party talked about in months to come for any unusual feature, to hunt out shy celebrities or introduce exotic strangers. She wanted a perfectly straight, smart party and she had got it. Practically everyone she asked had come. If there were other, more remote worlds upon which she did not impinge, Polly did not know about them. These were the people she was after, and here they were. And looking round on her guests, with Lord Cockpurse who was for the evening loyally putting in one of his rare appearances at her side, she was able to congratulate herself that there were very few people present whom she did not want. In other years people had taken her hospitality more casually and brought on with them anyone with whom they happened to have been dining. This year, without any conscious effort on her part, there had been more formality. Those who wanted to bring friends had rung up in the morning and asked whether they might do so, and on the whole they had been cautious of even so much presumption. People, who only eighteen months before would have pretended to be ignorant of her existence, were now crowding up her stairs. She had got herself in line with the other married women of her world.

As they started to go up, Brenda said, "You're not to leave me, please. I'm not going to know anybody," and Beaver again saw himself as the dominant male.

They went straight through to the band and began dancing, not talking much except to greet other couples whom they knew. They danced for half an hour and then she said, "All right, I'll give you a rest. Only don't let me get left."

She danced with Jock Grant-Menzies and two or three old friends and did not see Beaver again until she came on him alone in the bar. He had been there a long time, talking sometimes to the couples who came in and out, but always ending up alone. He was not enjoying the evening and he told himself rather resentfully that it was because of Brenda; if he had come there in a large party it would have been different.

Brenda saw he was out of temper and said, "Time for supper."

It was early, and the tables were mostly empty except for earnest couples sitting alone. There was a large round table between the windows, with no one at it; they sat there.

"I don't propose to move for a long time, d'you mind?" She wanted to make him feel important again so she asked him about the other people in the room.

Presently their table filled up. These were Brenda's old friends, among whom she used to live when she came out and in the first two years of her marriage, before Tony's father died; men in the early thirties, married women of her own age, none of whom knew Beaver or liked him. It was by far the gayest table in the room. Brenda thought "How my poor young man must be hating this"; it did not occur to her that, from Beaver's point of view, these old friends of hers were quite the most desirable people at the party, and that he was delighted to be seen at their table. "Are you dying of it?" she whispered.

"No, indeed, never happier."

"Well I am. Let's go and dance."

But the band was taking a rest and there was no one in the ballroom except the earnest couples who had migrated there away from the crowd and were sitting huddled in solitude round the walls, lost in conversation. "Oh dear," said Brenda, "now we're done. We can't go back to the table . . . it almost looks as though we should have to go home."

"It's not two."

"That's late for me. Look here, don't you come. Stay and enjoy yourself."

"Of course I'll come," said Beaver.

It was a cold, clear night. Brenda shivered and he put his arm around her in the taxi. They did not say much.

"There already?"

They sat for a few seconds without moving. Then Brenda slipped free and Beaver got out.

"I'm afraid I can't ask you in for a drink. You see it isn't my house and I shouldn't know where to find anything."

"No, of course not."

"Well, goodnight, my dear. Thank you a thousand times for looking after me. I'm afraid I rather bitched your evening."

"No, of course not," said Beaver.

"Will you ring me in the morning . . . promise?" She touched her hand to her lips and then turned to the keyhole.

Beaver hesitated a minute whether he should go back to the party, but decided not to. He was near home, and everyone at Polly's would have settled down by now; so he gave his address in Sussex Gardens, and went up to bed.

Just as he was undressed he heard the telephone ringing downstairs. It was his telephone. He went down, two flights in the cold. It was Brenda's voice.

"Darling, I was just going to ring off. I thought you must have gone back to Polly's. Is the telephone not by your bed?"

"No, it's on the ground floor."

"Oh dear, then it wasn't a very good idea to ring up, was it?"

"Oh, I don't know. What is it?"

"Just to say 'goodnight.'"

"Oh, I see, well—goodnight."

"And you'll ring me in the morning?"

"Yes."

"Early, before you've made any plans."

"Yes."

"Then goodnight, bless you."

Beaver went up the two flights of stairs again, and got into bed.

". . . going away in the middle of the party."

"I can't tell you how innocent it was. He didn't even come in."

"No one is going to know that."

"And he was furious when I rang him up."

"What does he think of you?"

"Simply can't make me out at all . . . terribly puzzled, and rather bored in bits."

"Are you going to go on with it?"

"I shouldn't know." The telephone rang. "Perhaps that's him."
But it was not.

Brenda had come into Marjorie's room and they were having breakfast in bed. Marjorie was more than ever like an elder sister that
morning. "But really, Brenda, he's such a *dreary* young man."

"I know it all. He's second rate and a snob and, I should think, as
cold as a fish, but I happen to have a fancy for him, that's all . . .
besides I'm not sure he's *altogether* awful . . . he's got that odious
mother whom he adores . . . and he's always been very poor. I don't
think he's had a fair deal. I heard all about it last night. He got engaged once but they couldn't get married because of money and since
then he's never had a proper affaire with anyone decent . . . he's got
to be taught a whole lot of things. That's part of his attraction."

"Oh dear, I see you're very serious."

The telephone rang.

"Perhaps *that's* him."

But a familiar voice rang out from the instrument so that Brenda
too could hear it, "Good morning, darling, what's the diet today?"

"Oh, Polly, what a good party last night."

"Not so bad for the old girl was it? I say what about your sister
and Mr. Beaver."

"What about them?"

"How long has *that* been on?"

"There's nothing doing there, Polly."

"Don't you tell me. They were well away last night. How's the boy
managed it? That's what I want to know. He must have something
we didn't know about . . ."

"So Polly's on to your story. She'll be telling everyone in London
at this moment."

"How I wish there was anything to tell. The cub hasn't even rung
me up . . . Well, I'll leave him in peace. If he doesn't do anything
about me, I'll go down to Hetton this afternoon. Perhaps that's him."
But it was only Allan from the Conservative Central Office, to say
how sorry he had been not to get to the party the night before. "I
hear Brenda disgraced herself," he said.

"Goodness," said Brenda. "People do think that young men are easily come by."

"I scarcely saw you at Polly's last night," said Mrs. Beaver. "What became of you?"

"We went early. Brenda Last was tired."

"She was looking lovely. I am so glad you've made friends with her. When are you going to see her again?"

"I said I'd ring up."

"Well, why don't you?"

"Oh, mumsey, what's the use! I can't afford to start taking about women like Brenda Last. If I ring up she'll say, what are you doing, and I shall have to ask her to something, and it will be the same thing every day. I simply haven't the money."

"I know, my son. It's very difficult for you . . . and you're wonderful about money. I ought to be grateful that I haven't a son always coming to me with debts. Still, it doesn't do to deny yourself *everything* you know. You're getting to be an old bachelor already at twenty-five. I could see Brenda liked you, that evening she came here."

"Oh she likes me all right."

"I hope she makes up her mind about that flat. They're going like hot cakes. I shall have to look about for another suitable house to split up. You'd be surprised who've been taking them—quite a number of people with houses in London already . . . Well, I must be getting back to work. I'm away for two nights by the way. See that Chambers looks after you properly. There are some Australians Sylvia Newport discovered who want to take a house in the country, so I'm driving them around to one or two that might do for them. Where are you lunching?"

"Margot's."

By one o'clock when they came back from taking Djinn to the Park, Beaver had not rung up. "So that's that," said Brenda, "I expect I'm glad really." She sent a telegram to Tony to expect her by the afternoon train and, in a small voice, ordered her things to be packed. "I don't seem to have anywhere to lunch," she said.

"Why don't you come to Margot's. I know she'd love it."

"Well ring up and ask her."

So she met Beaver again.

He was sitting some way from her and they did not speak to each other until everyone was going. "I kept trying to get through to you this morning," he said, "but the line was always engaged."

"Oh come on," said Brenda, "I'll sock you a movie."

Later she wired to Tony: *Staying with Marjorie another day or two all love to you both.*

4

"Is mummy coming back today?"

"I hope so."

"That monkey-woman's party has lasted a long time. Can I come in to the station and meet her?"

"Yes, we'll both go."

"She hasn't seen Thunderclap for four days. She hasn't seen me jump the new post and rail, has she daddy?"

She was coming by the 3.18. Tony and John Andrew were there early. They wandered about the station looking at things, and bought some chocolate from a slot machine. The stationmaster came out to talk to them. "Her ladyship coming back today?" He was an old friend of Tony's.

"I've been expecting her every day. You know what it is when ladies get to London."

"Sam Brice's wife went to London and he couldn't get her back. Had to go up and fetch her himself. And then she gave him a hiding."

Presently the train came in and Brenda emerged exquisitely from her third class carriage. "You've *both* come. What angels you are. I don't at all deserve it."

"Oh, mummy, have you brought the monkey-lady?"

"What *does* the child mean?"

"He's got it into his head that your chum Polly has a tail."

"Come to think of it, I shouldn't be surprised if she had."

Two little cases held all her luggage. The chauffeur strapped them on behind the car, and they drove to Hetton.

"What's all the news?"

"Ben's put the rail up ever so high and Thunderclap and I jumped it six times yesterday and six times again today and two more of the fish in the little pond are dead, floating upside down all swollen and nanny burnt her finger on the kettle yesterday and daddy and I saw a fox just as near as anything and he sat quite still and then went away into the wood and I began drawing a picture of a battle only I couldn't finish it because the paints weren't right and the grey carthorse the one that had worms is quite well again."

"Nothing much has happened," said Tony. "We've missed you. What did you find to do in London all this time?"

"Me? Oh I've been behaving rather badly to tell you the truth."

"Buying things?"

"Worse. I've been carrying on madly with young men and I've spent heaps of money and I've enjoyed it very much indeed. But there's one awful thing."

"What's that?"

"No, I think it had better keep. It's something you won't like at all."

"You've bought a Pekingese."

"Worse, far worse. Only I haven't done it yet. But I *want* to dreadfully."

"Go on."

"Tony, I've found a flat."

"Well you'd better lose it again quick."

"All right. I'll attack you about it again later. Meanwhile try not to brood about it."

"I shan't give it another thought."

"What's a flat, daddy?"

Brenda wore pyjamas at dinner, and afterwards sat close to Tony on the sofa and ate some sugar out of his coffee cup.

"I suppose all this means that you're going to start again about your flat?"

"Mmmm."

"You haven't signed any papers yet, have you?"

"Oh no." Brenda shook her head emphatically.

"Then no great harm's done." Tony began to fill his pipe.

Brenda knelt on the sofa, sitting back on her heels. "Listen, you haven't been brooding?"

"No."

"Because, you see, when you say 'flat' you're thinking of something quite different to me. *You* mean by a flat, a lift and a man in uniform, and a big front door with knobs, and an entrance hall and doors opening in all directions, with kitchens and sculleries and dining rooms and drawing rooms and servants' bathrooms . . . don't you, Tony?"

"More or less."

"Exactly. Now *I* mean just a bedroom and a bath and a telephone. You see the difference? Now a woman I know——"

"Who?"

"Just a woman—has fixed up a whole house like that off Belgrave Square and they are three pounds a week, no rates and taxes, constant hot water and central heating, woman comes in to make bed when required, what d'you think of that?"

"I see."

"Now this is how I look at it. What's three pounds a week? Less than nine bob a night. Where could one stay for less than nine bob a night with all those advantages. You're always going to the club and that costs more and I can't stay often with Marjorie because it's hell for her having me and anyway she's got that dog, and you're always saying when I come back in the evenings after shopping, 'Why didn't you stay the night,' you say, 'instead of killing yourself?' Time and again you say it. I'm sure we spend much more than three pounds a week through not having a flat. Tell you what, I'll give up Mr. Cruttwell. How's that?"

"D'you really want this thing?"

"Mmm."

"Well, I'll have to see. We *might* manage it, but it'll mean putting off the improvements down here."

"I don't really deserve it," she said, clinching the matter. "I've been carrying on *anyhow* this week."

Brenda's stay at Hetton lasted only for three nights. Then she returned to London saying that she had to see about the flat. It did not, however, require very great attention. There was only the colour of the paint to choose and some few articles of furniture. Mrs. Beaver had them ready for her inspection, a bed, a carpet, a dressing table and chair—there was not room for more. Mrs. Beaver tried to sell her a set of needlework pictures for the walls, but these she refused, also an electric bed warmer, a miniature weighing machine for the bathroom, a frigidaire, an antique grandfather clock, a backgammon set of looking-glass and synthetic ivory, a set of prettily bound French eighteenth century poets, a massage apparatus, and a wireless set fitted in a case of Regency lacquer, all of which had been grouped in the shop for her as a "suggestion." Mrs. Beaver bore Brenda no ill will for the modesty of her requirements; she was doing very well on the floor above with a Canadian lady who was having her walls covered with chromium plating at immense expense.

Meanwhile Brenda stayed with Marjorie, on terms which gradually became acrimonious. "I'm sorry to be pompous," she said one morning, "but I just don't want your Mr. Beaver hanging about the house all day and calling me Marjorie."

"Oh well, the flat won't be long now."

"And I shall go on saying that I think you're making a ridiculous mistake."

"It's just that you don't like Mr. Beaver."

"It isn't only that. I think it's hard cheese on Tony."

"Oh, Tony's all right."

"And if there's a row——"

"There won't be a row."

"You never know. If there is, I don't want Allan to think I've been helping to arrange things."

"I wasn't so disagreeable to you about Robin Beaseley."

"There was never much in that," said Marjorie.

But with the exception of her sister's, opinion was greatly in favour of Brenda's adventure. The morning telephone buzzed with news of her; even people with whom she had the barest acquaintance were delighted to relate that they had seen her and Beaver the evening before at restaurant or cinema. It had been an autumn of very sparse and meagre romance; only the most obvious people had parted or come together, and Brenda was filling a want long felt by those whose simple, vicarious pleasure it was to discuss the subject in bed over the telephone. For them her circumstances shed peculiar glamour; for five years she had been a legendary, almost ghostly name, the imprisoned princess of fairy story, and now that she had emerged there was more enchantment in the occurrence, than in the mere change of habit of any other circumspect wife. Her very choice of partner gave the affair an appropriate touch of fantasy; Beaver, the joke figure they had all known and despised, suddenly caught up to her among the luminous clouds of deity. If, after seven years looking neither to right nor left, she had at last broken away with Jock Grant-Menzies or Robin Beaseley or any other young buck with whom nearly everyone had had a crack one time or another, it would have been thrilling no doubt, but straightforward, drawing-room comedy. The choice of Beaver raised the whole escapade into a realm of poetry for Polly and Daisy and Angela and all the gang of gossips.

Mrs. Beaver made no bones about her delight. "Of course the subject has not been mentioned between John and myself, but if what I hear is true, I think it will do the boy a world of good. Of course he's always been very much in demand and had a great number of friends, but *that isn't the same thing*. I've felt for a long time a lack of something in him, and I think that a charming and experienced woman like Brenda Last is just the person to help him. He's got a *very* affectionate nature, but he's so sensitive that he hardly ever lets it appear . . . to tell you the truth I felt something of the kind was in the air last week, so I made an excuse to go away for a few days. If I had been there things might never have come to anything. He's very shy and reserved even to me. I'll have the chess-men done up and sent round to you this afternoon. Thank you so much."

And Beaver, for the first time in his life, found himself a person of interest and, almost of consequence. Women studied him with a new scrutiny, wondering what they had missed in him; men treated him as an equal, even as a successful fellow competitor. "How on earth has *he* got away with it?" they may have asked themselves, but now, when he came into Brat's, they made room for him at the bar and said, "Well, old boy, how about one?"

Brenda rang Tony up every morning and evening. Sometimes John Andrew spoke to her, too, as shrill as Polly Cockpurse; quite unable to hear her replies. She went to Hetton for the week-end, and then back to London, this time to the flat where the paint was already dry, though the hot water was not yet in perfect working order; every-thing smelt very new—walls, sheets, curtains—and the new radiators gave off a less agreeable reek of hot iron.

That evening she telephoned to Hetton. "I'm talking from the flat."

"Oh, ah."

"*Darling,* do try to sound interested. It's very exciting for me."

"What's it like?"

"Well there are a good many smells at present and the bath makes odd sounds and when you turn on the hot tap there's just a rush of air and that's all, and the cold tap keeps dripping and the water is rather brown and the cupboard doors are jammed and the curtains won't pull right across so that the street lamp shines in all night . . . but it's *lovely.*"

"You don't say so."

"Tony, you must be nice about it. It's all so exciting—front door and a latch key and all . . . And someone sent me a lot of flowers today—so many that there's hardly room for them and I've had to put them in the basin on account of having no pots. It wasn't you, was it?"

"Yes . . . as a matter of fact."

"Darling, I did so hope it was . . . how like you."

"Three minutes please."

"Must stop now."

"When are you coming back?"

"Almost at once. Goodnight, my sweet."

"What a lot of talk," said Beaver.

All the time that she was speaking, she had been kept busy with one hand warding him off the telephone, which he threatened playfully to disconnect.

"Wasn't it sweet of Tony to send those flowers?"

"I'm awfully fond of Tony."

"Don't let that worry you, my beauty, he doesn't like you *at all*."

"*Doesn't* he? Why not?"

"No one does except me. You must get that clear . . . it's very odd that *I* should."

Beaver and his mother were going to Ireland for Christmas, to stay with cousins. Tony and Brenda had a family party at Hetton; Marjorie and Allan, Brenda's mother, Tony's Aunt Frances and two families of impoverished Lasts, humble and uncomplaining victims of primogeniture, to whom Hetton meant as much as it did to Tony. There was a little Christmas tree in the nursery for John Andrew and a big one downstairs in the central hall which was decorated by the impoverished Lasts and lit up for half an hour after tea (two footmen standing by with wet sponges on the end of poles, to extinguish the candles which turned turtle and threatened to start a fire). There were presents for all the servants, of value strictly graded according to their rank, and for all the guests (cheques for the impoverished Lasts). Allan always brought a large croûte of foie gras, a delicacy of which he was particularly fond. Everyone ate a great deal and became slightly torpid towards Boxingday evening; silver ladles of burning brandy went around the table, crackers were pulled and opened; paper hats, indoor fireworks, mottoes. This year, everything happened in its accustomed way; nothing seemed to menace the peace and stability of the house. The choir came up and sang carols in the pitch-pine gallery, and later devoured hot punch and sweet biscuits.

The vicar preached his usual Christmas sermon. It was one to which his parishioners were particularly attached. "How difficult it is for us," he began, blandly surveying his congregation, who coughed into their mufflers and chafed their chilblains under their woollen gloves, "to realize that this is indeed Christmas. Instead of the glowing log fire and windows tight shuttered against the drifting snow, we have only the harsh glare of the alien sun; instead of the happy circle of loved faces, of home and family, we have the uncomprehending stares of the subjugated, though no doubt grateful, heathen. Instead of the placid ox and ass of Bethlehem," said the vicar, slightly losing the thread of his comparisons, "we have for companions the ravening tiger and the exotic camel, the furtive jackal and the ponderous elephant . . ." And so on, through the pages of faded manuscript. The words had temporarily touched the heart of many an obdurate trooper, and hearing them again, as he had heard them year after year since Mr. Tendril had come to the parish, Tony and most of Tony's guests felt that it was an integral part of their Christmas festivities; one with which they would find it very hard to dispense. "The ravening tiger and the exotic camel" had long been bywords in the family, of frequent recurrence in all their games.

These games were the hardest part for Brenda. They did not amuse her and she still could not see Tony dressed up for charades without a feeling of shyness. Moreover she was tortured by the fear that any lack of gusto on her part might be construed by the poor Lasts as superiority. These scruples, had she known it, were quite superfluous for it never occurred to her husband's relatives to look on her with anything but cousinly cordiality and a certain tolerance, for, as Lasts, they considered they had far more right in Hetton than herself. Aunt Frances, with acid mind, quickly discerned the trouble and attempted to reassure her, saying, "Dear child, all these feelings of delicacy are valueless; only the rich realize the gulf that separates them from the poor," but the uneasiness persisted and night after night she found herself being sent out of the room, asking or answering questions, performing actions in uncouth manners, paying forfeits, drawing pictures, writing verses, dressing herself up and even being chased about the house, and secluded in cupboards, at the will of her relatives. Christmas was on a Friday that year, so the party was a long one from Thursday until Monday.

She had forbidden Beaver to send her a present or to write to her; in self-protection, for she knew that whatever he said would hurt her by its poverty, but in spite of this she awaited the posts nervously, hoping that he might have disobeyed her. She had sent him to Ireland a ring of three interlocked hoops of gold and platinum. An hour after ordering it she regretted her choice. On Tuesday a letter came from him thanking her. *Darling Brenda,* he wrote. *Thank you so very much for the charming Christmas present. You can imagine my delight when I saw the pink leather case and my surprise at opening it. It really was sweet of you to send me such a charming present. Thank you again very much for it. I hope your party is being a success. It is rather dull here. The others went hunting yesterday. I went to the meet. They did not have a good day. Mother is here too and sends you her love. We shall be leaving tomorrow or the day after. Mother has got rather a cold.*

It ended there at the bottom of a page. Beaver had been writing it before dinner and later had put it in the envelope without remembering to finish it.

He wrote a large, schoolgirlish hand with wide spaces between the lines.

Brenda showed it to Marjorie who was still at Hetton. "I can't complain," she said. "He's never pretended to like me much. And anyway it was a damned silly present."

Tony had become fretful about his visit to Angela's. He always hated staying away.

"Don't come, darling. I'll make it all right with them."

"No, I'll come. I haven't seen so much of you in the last three weeks."

They had the whole of Wednesday alone together. Brenda exerted herself and Tony's fretfulness subsided. She was particularly tender to him at this time and scarcely teased him at all.

On Thursday they went North to Yorkshire. Beaver was there.

Tony discovered him in the first half hour and brought the news to Brenda upstairs.

"I'll tell you something very odd," he said. "Who do you think is here?"

"Who?"

"Our old friend Beaver."

"Why's that odd particularly?"

"Oh I don't know. I'd forgotten all about him, hadn't you? D'you think he sent Angela a telegram as he did to us?"

"I daresay."

Tony supposed Beaver must be fairly lonely and took pains to be agreeable to him. He said, "All kinds of changes since we saw you last. Brenda's taken a flat in London."

"Yes, I know."

"How?"

"Well, my mother let it to her, you know."

Tony was greatly surprised and taxed Brenda with this. "You never told me who was behind your flat. I might not have been so amiable if I'd known."

"No, darling, that's why."

Half the house party wondered why Beaver was there; the other half knew. As a result of this he and Brenda saw each other very little, less than if they had been casual acquaintances, so that Angela remarked to her husband, "I daresay it was a mistake to ask him. It's so hard to know."

Brenda never started the subject of the half finished letter, but she noticed that Beaver was wearing his ring, and had already acquired a trick of twisting it as he talked.

On New Year's Eve there was a party at a neighbouring house. Tony went home early and Beaver and Brenda returned together in the back of a car. Next morning, while they were having breakfast, she said to Tony, "I've made a New Year resolution."

"Anything to do with spending more time at home?"

"Oh no, *quite* the reverse. Listen, Tony, it's serious. I think I'll take a course of something."

"Not bone setters again. I thought that was over."

"No, something like economics. You see I've been thinking. I don't really *do* anything at all at present. It's absurd to pretend I'm any use to John, the house runs itself. It seemed to me time I *took* to something. Now you're always talking about going into Parliament. Well if I had done a course of economics I could be some use canvassing and writing speeches and things—you know, the way Marjorie did when Allan was standing on the Clydeside. There are all sorts of lectures in London, to do with the University, where girls go. Don't you think it's rather a good idea?"

"It's one better than the bone setters," Tony admitted.

That was how the New Year began.

I I I

HARD CHEESE ON TONY

It is not uncommon at Brat's Club, between nine and ten in the evening, to find men in white ties and tail coats sitting by themselves and eating, in evident low spirits, large and extravagant dinners. They are those who have been abandoned at the last minute by their women. For twenty minutes or so they have sat in the foyer of some restaurant, gazing expectantly towards the revolving doors and alternately taking out their watches and ordering cocktails, until at length a telephone message has been brought them that their guests are unable to come. Then they go to Brat's half hoping to find friends but, more often than not, taking a melancholy satisfaction in finding the club deserted or peopled by strangers. So they sit there, round the walls, morosely regarding the mahogany tables before them, and eating and drinking heavily.

It was in this mood and for this reason that, one evening towards the middle of February, Jock Grant-Menzies arrived at the club.

"Anyone here?"

"Very quiet tonight, sir. Mr. Last is in the dining room."

Jock found him seated in a corner; he was in day clothes; the table and the chair at his side were littered with papers and magazines; one was propped up in front of him. He was half way through dinner and three quarters of the way through a bottle of burgundy. "Hullo," he said. "Chucked? Come and join me."

It was some time since Jock had seen Tony; the meeting embarrassed him slightly, for like all his friends, he was wondering how Tony felt and how much he knew about Brenda and John Beaver. However, he sat down at Tony's table.

"Been chucked?" asked Tony again.

"Yes, it's the last time I ask that bitch out."

"Better have a drink. I've been drinking a whole lot. Much the best thing."

They took what was left of the burgundy and ordered another bottle.

"Just come up for the night," said Tony. "Staying here."

"You've got a flat now haven't you?"

"Well Brenda has. There isn't really room for two . . . we tried it once and it wasn't a success."

"What's she doing tonight?"

"Out somewhere. I didn't let her know I was coming . . . silly not to, but you see I got fed up with being alone at Hetton and thought I'd like to see Brenda so I came up suddenly on the spur of the moment, just like that. Damned silly thing to do. Might have known she'd be going out somewhere . . . she's very high principled about chucking . . . so there it is. She's going to ring me up here later, if she can get away."

They drank a lot. Tony did most of the talking. "Extraordinary idea of hers, taking up economics," he said. "I never thought it would last but she seems really keen on it . . . I suppose it's a good plan. You know there wasn't really much for her to do all the time at Hetton. Of course she'd rather die than admit it, but I believe she got a bit bored there sometimes. I've been thinking it over and that's the conclusion I came to. Brenda must have been bored . . . Daresay she'll get bored with economics some time . . . Anyway she seems

cheerful enough now. We've had parties every week-end lately . . .
I wish you'd come down sometimes, Jock. I don't seem to get on with
Brenda's new friends."

"People from the school of economics?"

"No, but ones I don't know. I believe I bore them. Thinking it over
that's the conclusion I've come to. I bore them. They talk about me
as 'the old boy.' John heard them."

"Well, that's friendly enough."

"Yes, that's friendly."

They finished the burgundy and drank some port. Presently Tony
said, "I say, come next week-end, will you?"

"I think I'd love to."

"Wish you would. I don't see many old friends . . . Sure to be lots
of people in the house, but you won't mind that will you? . . . sociable chap, Jock . . . doesn't mind people about. *I* mind it like hell."
They drank some more port. Tony said, "Not enough bathrooms, you
know . . . but of course you know. You've been there before, often.
Not like the new friends who think me a bore. You don't think I'm a
bore, do you?"

"No, old boy."

"Not even when I'm tight, like this? . . . There would have been
bathrooms. I had the plans out. Four new ones. A chap down there
made the plans . . . but then Brenda wanted the flat so I had to postpone them as an economy . . . I say, that's funny. We had to econ-
omize because of Brenda's economics."

"Yes, that's funny. Let's have some port."

Tony said, "You seem pretty low tonight."

"I am rather. Worried about the Pig Scheme. Constituents keep
writing."

"*I* felt low, *bloody* low, but I'm all right again now. The best thing
is to get tight. That's what I did and I don't feel low any more . . .
discouraging to come to London and find you're not wanted. Funny
thing, *you* feel low because your girl's chucked, and *I* feel low because
mine won't chuck."

"Yes, that's funny."

"But you know I've felt low for weeks now . . . bloody low . . . how about some brandy?"

"Yes, why not? After all there are other things in life besides women and pigs."

They had some brandy and after a time Jock began to cheer up.

Presently a page came to their table to say, "A message from Lady Brenda, sir."

"Good, I'll go and speak to her."

"It's not her ladyship speaking. Someone was sending a message."

"I'll come and speak to her."

He went to the telephone in the lobby outside. "Darling," he said.

"Is that Mr. Last. I've got a message here, from Lady Brenda."

"Right, put me through to her."

"She can't speak herself, but she asked me to give you this message, that she's very sorry but she cannot join you tonight. She's very tired and has gone home to bed."

"Tell her I want to speak to her."

"I can't I'm afraid, she's gone to bed. She's very tired."

"She's very tired and she's gone to bed?"

"That's right."

"Well, I want to speak to her."

"Goodnight," said the voice.

"The old boy's plastered," said Beaver as he rang off.

"Oh dear. I feel rather awful about him. But what *can* he expect, coming up suddenly like this. He's got to be taught not to make surprise visits."

"Is he often like that?"

"No, it's quite new."

The telephone bell rang. "D'you suppose that's him again? I'd better answer it."

"I want to speak to Lady Brenda Last."

"Tony, darling, this *is* me, Brenda."

"Some damn fool said I couldn't speak to you."

"I left a message from where I was dining. Are you having a lovely evening?"

"Hellish. I'm with Jock. He's worried about the Pig Scheme. Shall we come around and see you?"

"No, not now, darling, I'm terribly tired and just going to bed."

"We'll come and see you."

"Tony, are you a tiny bit tight?"

"Stinking. Jock and I'll come and see you."

"Tony, you're *not* to. D'you hear? I can't have you making a brawl. The flats are getting a bad name anyhow."

"Their name'll be mud when Jock and I come."

"Tony, listen, will you please not come, not tonight. Be a good boy and stay at the club. Will you *please* not?"

"Shan't be long." He rang off.

"Oh God," said Brenda. "This isn't the least like Tony. Ring up Brat's and get on to Jock. He'll have more sense."

"That was Brenda."

"So I gathered."

"She's at the flat. I said that we'll go around."

"Splendid. Haven't seen her for weeks. Very fond of Brenda."

"So am I. Grand girl."

"Grand girl."

"A lady on the telephone for you, Mr. Grant-Menzies."

"Who?"

"She didn't give a name."

"All right. I'll come."

Brenda said to him, "Jock, what *have* you been doing to my husband?"

"He's a bit tight, that's all."

"He's roaring. Look here he threatens to come round. I simply can't face him tonight in that mood, I'm tired out. You understand, don't you?"

"Yes, I understand."

"So, will you, *please,* keep him away. Are you tight too?"

"A little bit."

"Oh dear, can I trust you?"

"I'll try."

"Well, it doesn't sound too good. Good-bye" . . . "John, you've got to go. Those hooligans may turn up at any moment. Have you got your taxi fare? You'll find some change in my bag."

"Was that your girl?"

"Yes."

"Made it up?"

"Not exactly."

"Far better to make it up. Shall we have some more brandy and go round to Brenda straight away?"

"Let's have some more brandy."

"Jock, you aren't still feeling low are you? Doesn't do to feel low. *I'm* not feeling low. I *was,* but I'm not any more."

"No, I'm not feeling low."

"Then we'll have some brandy and then go to Brenda's."

"All right."

Half an hour later they got into Jock's car.

"Tell you what, I shouldn't drive if I were you."

"Not drive?"

"No, I shouldn't drive. They'd say you were drunk."

"Who would?"

"Anyone you ran over. They'd say you were drunk."

"Well, so I am."

"Then I shouldn't drive."

"Too far to walk."

"We'll take a taxi."

"Oh hell, I can drive."

"Or let's not go to Brenda's at all."

"We'd better go to Brenda's," said Jock. "She's expecting us."

"Well I can't walk all that way. Besides I don't think she really wanted us to come."

"She'll be pleased when she sees us."

"Yes, but it's a long way. Let's go some other place."

"I'd like to see Brenda," said Jock. "I'm very fond of Brenda."

"She's a grand girl."

"She's a grand girl."

"Well let's take a taxi to Brenda's."

But half way Jock said, "Don't let's go there. Let's go some other place. Let's go to some low joint."

"All the same to me. Tell him to go to some low joint."

"Go to some low joint," said Jock, putting his head through the window.

The cab wheeled round and made towards Shaftesbury Avenue.

"We can always ring Brenda from the low joint."

"Yes, I think we ought to do that. She's a grand girl."

"Grand girl."

The cab turned down Wardour Street and then into Sink Street, a dingy little place inhabited for the most part by Asiatics.

"D'you know, I believe he's taking us to the old Sixty-four."

"Can't still be open? Thought they closed it down years ago."

But the door was brightly illumined and a seedy figure in peaked cap and braided overcoat stepped out to open the taxi for them.

The Sixty-four has never been shut. For a generation, while other night clubs have sprung into being, with various names and managers, and various pretensions to respectability, have enjoyed a precarious and brief existence, and come to grief at the hands either of police or creditors, the Sixty-four has maintained a solid front against all adversity. It has not been immune from persecution; far from it. Times out of number, magistrates have struck it off, cancelled its license, condemned its premises; the staff and until her death, the proprietress, have been constantly in and out of prison; there have been questions in the House and committees of inquiry, but whatever Home Secretaries and Commissioners of Police have risen into eminence and retired discredited, the doors of the Sixty-four have always been open from nine in the evening until four at night, and inside there has been an unimpeded flow of dubious, alcoholic preparations.

A kindly young lady admitted Tony and Jock to the ramshackle building.

"D'you mind signing in?" Tony and Jock inscribed fictitious names at the foot of a form which stated, *I have been invited to a Bottle Party at 64 Sink Street given by Mr. Charles Weybridge.* "That's five bob each please."

It is not an expensive club to run, because none of the staff, except the band, receive any wages; they make what they can by going through the overcoat pockets and giving the wrong change to drunks. The young ladies get in free but they have to see to it that their patrons spend money.

"Last time I was here, Tony, was the bachelor party before your wedding."

"Tight that night."

"Stinking."

"I'll tell you who else was tight that night—Reggie. Broke a fruit gum machine."

"Reggie was stinking."

"I say, you don't still feel low about that girl?"

"I don't feel low."

"Come on, we'll go downstairs."

The dance room was fairly full. An elderly man had joined the band and was trying to conduct it. "I like this joint," said Jock. "What'll we drink?"

"Brandy." They had to buy a whole bottle. They filled in an order form to the Montmorency Wine Company and paid two pounds. When it came it had a label saying *Very Old Liquor Fine Champagne. Imported by the Montmorency Wine Co.* The waiter brought ginger ale and four glasses. Two young ladies came and sat with them. They were called Milly and Babs. Milly said, "Are you in town for long?" Babs said, "Have you got such a thing as a cigarette?"

Tony danced with Babs. She said, "Are you fond of dancing?"

"No, are you?"

"So-so."

"Well, let's sit down."

The waiter said, "Will you buy a ticket in a raffle for a box of chocolates?"

"No."

"Buy one for me," said Babs.

Jock began to describe the specifications of the Basic Pig.

. . . Milly said, "You're married, aren't you?"

"No," said Jock.

"Oh I can always tell," said Milly. "Your friend is too."

"Yes, *he* is."

"You'd be surprised how many gentlemen come here just to talk about their wives."

"He hasn't."

Tony was leaning across the table and saying to Babs, "You see the trouble is my wife is studious. She's taking a course in economics."

Babs said, "I think it's nice for a girl to be interested in things."

The waiter said, "What will you be taking for supper?"

"Why we've only just had dinner."

"How about a nice haddock?"

"I tell you what I must do, is to telephone. Where is it?"

"D'you mean really the telephone or the gentlemen's?"

"No, the telephone."

"U'stairs in the office."

Tony rang up Brenda. It was some time before she answered, then, "Yes, who is it?"

"I have a message here from Mr. Anthony Last and Mr. Jocelyn Grant-Menzies."

"Oh, it's you Tony. Well, what do you want?"

"You recognized my voice?"

"I did."

"Well, I only wanted to give a message but as I am speaking to you I can give it myself, can't I?"

"Yes."

"Well Jock and I are terribly sorry but we can't come round this evening after all."

"Oh."

"You don't think it very rude I hope, but we have a lot to attend to."

"That's all right, Tony."

"Did I wake you up by any chance?"

"That's all right, Tony."

"Well, goodnight."

"Goodnight."

Tony went down to the table. "I've been talking to Brenda. She sounded rather annoyed. D'you think we *ought* to go round there."

"We promised we would," said Jock.

"You should never disappoint a lady," said Milly.

"Oh it's too late now."

Babs said, "You two are officers, aren't you?"

"No, why?"

"I thought you were."

Milly said, "I like business gentlemen best, myself. They've more to say."

"What d'you do?"

"I design postman's hats," said Jock.

"Oh, go on."

"And my friend here trains sea lions."

"Tell us another."

Babs said, "I got a gentleman friend who works on a newspaper."

After a time Jock said, "I say, ought we to do something about Brenda?"

"You told her we weren't coming, didn't you?"

"Yes . . . but she might still be *hoping*."

"I tell you what, you go and ring her up and find out if she really wants us."

"All right." He came back ten minutes later. "*I* thought she sounded rather annoyed," he reported. "But I said in the end we wouldn't come."

"She may be tired," said Tony. "Has to get up early to do economics. Now I come to think of it someone *did* say she was tired, earlier on in the evening."

"I say what's this frightful piece of fish?"

"The waiter said you ordered it."

"Perhaps I did."

"I'll give it to the club cat," said Babs, "she's a dear called Blackberry."

They danced once or twice. Then Jock said, "D'you think we ought to ring up Brenda again?"

"Perhaps we ought. She sounded annoyed with us."

"Let's go now and ring her up on the way out."

"Aren't you coming home with us?" said Babs.

"Not tonight, I'm afraid."

"Be a sport," said Milly.

"No, we can't really."

"All right. Well how about a little present? We're professional dancing partners, you know," said Babs.

"Oh yes, sorry, how much?"

"Oh, we leave that to the gentlemen."

Tony gave them a pound. "You might make it a bit more," said Babs. "We've sat with you two hours."

Jock gave another pound. "Come and see us again one evening when you've more time," said Milly.

"I'm feeling rather ill," said Tony on the way upstairs. "Don't think I shall bother to ring up Brenda."

"Send a message."

"That's a good idea . . . Look here," he said to the seedy commissionaire. "Will you ring up this Sloane number and speak to her ladyship and say Mr. Grant-Menzies and Mr. Last are very sorry but they cannot call this evening. Got that?" He gave the man half a crown and they sauntered out into Sink Street. "Brenda can't expect us to do more than that," he said.

"I tell you what I'll do. I go almost past her door so I'll ring the bell a bit just in case she's awake and still waiting up for us."

"Yes, you do that. What a good friend you are, Jock."

"Oh I'm fond of Brenda . . . a grand girl."

"Grand girl . . . I wish I didn't feel ill."

Tony was awake at eight next morning, miserably articulating in his mind the fragmentary memories of the preceding night. The more he remembered, the baser his conduct appeared to him. At nine he had his bath and some tea. At ten he was wondering whether he should ring Brenda up when the difficulty was solved by her ringing him.

"Well, Tony, how do you feel?"

"Awful. I *was* tight."

"You were."

"I'm feeling pretty guilty too."

"I'm not surprised."

"I don't remember everything very clearly but I have the impression that Jock and I were rather bores."

"You were."

"Are you in a rage?"

"Well, I was last night. What made you do it, Tony, grown up men like you two?"

"We felt low."

"I bet you feel lower this morning . . . A box of white roses has just arrived from Jock."

"I wish I'd thought of that."

"You're such infants both of you."

"You aren't really in a rage?"

"Of course I'm not, darling. Now just you go straight back to the country. You'll feel all right again tomorrow."

"Am I not going to see you?"

"Not today I'm afraid. I've got lectures all the morning and I'm lunching out. But I'll be coming down on Friday evening or anyway Saturday morning."

"I see. You couldn't possibly chuck lunch or one of the lectures?"

"Not possibly, darling."

"I see. You are an angel to be so sweet about last night."

"Nothing could have been more fortunate," Brenda said. "If I know Tony he'll be tortured with guilt for weeks to come. It was maddening last night but it was worth it. He's put himself so much in the wrong now that he won't dare to *feel* resentful, let alone say anything, whatever I do. And he hasn't really enjoyed himself at all, the poor sweet, so *that's* a good thing too. He had to learn not to make surprise visits."

"You are one for making people learn things," said Beaver.

Tony emerged from the 3.18 feeling cold, tired, and heavy with guilt. John Andrew had come in with the car to meet him. "Hullo, daddy, had a good time in London? You didn't mind me coming to the station did you? I *made* nanny let me."

"Very pleased to see you, John."

"How was mummy?"

"She sounded very well. I didn't see her."

"But you *said* you were going to see her."

"Yes, I thought I was, but I turned out to be wrong. I talked to her several times on the telephone."

"But you can telephone her from here, can't you, daddy? Why did you go all the way to London to telephone her? . . . *Why,* daddy?"

"It would take too long to explain."

"Well, tell me some of it . . . *Why,* daddy?"

"Look here I'm tired. If you don't stop asking questions I shan't let you ever come and meet the trains again."

John Andrew's face began to pucker. "I thought you'd *like* me to come and meet you."

"If you cry I shall put you in front with Dawson. It's absurd to cry at your age."

"I'd *sooner* go in front with Dawson," said John Andrew between his tears.

Tony picked up the speaking tube to tell the chauffeur to stop, but he could not make him hear. So he hitched the mouthpiece back on its hook and they drove on in silence, John Andrew leaning against the window and snivelling slightly. When they got to the house, he said, "Nanny, I don't want John to come to the station in future unless her ladyship or I specially say he can."

"No, sir, I wouldn't have him come today only he went on so. Come along now, John, and take off your coat. Goodness, child, where's your handkerchief."

Tony went and sat alone in front of the library fire. "Two men of thirty," he said to himself, "behaving as if they were up for the night from Sandhurst—getting drunk and ringing people up and dancing with tarts at the Sixty-four . . . And it makes it all the worse that Brenda was so nice about it." He dozed a little; then he went up to change. At dinner he said, "Ambrose, when I'm alone I think in future I'll have dinner at a table in the library." Afterwards he sat with a book in front of the fire, but he was unable to read. At ten o'clock he scattered the logs in the fireplace before going upstairs. He fastened the library windows and turned out the lights. That night he went into Brenda's empty room to sleep.

2

That was Wednesday; on Thursday Tony felt well again. He had a meeting of the County Council in the morning. In the afternoon he went down to the home farm and discussed a new kind of tractor with his agent. From then onwards he was able to say to himself, "Tomorrow this time Brenda and Jock will be here." He dined in front of the fire in the library. He had given up the diet some weeks ago. "Ambrose, when I am alone I don't really need a long dinner. In future I'll just have two courses." He looked over some accounts his agent had left for him and then went to bed, saying to himself, "When I wake up it will be the week-end."

But there was a telegram for him next morning from Jock saying, *Week end impossible have to go to constituency how about one after next.* He wired back, *Delighted any time always here.* "I suppose he's made it up with that girl," Tony reflected.

There was also a note from Brenda, written in pencil:

Coming Sat. with Polly and a friend of Polly's called Veronica in P.'s car. Maids and luggage on 3.18. Will you tell Ambrose and Mrs.

Massop. We had better open Lyonesse for Polly you know what she is about comfort. Veronica can go anywhere—not Galahad. Polly says she's v. amusing. Also Mrs. Beaver coming, please don't mind it is only on business, she thinks she can do something to morning room. Only Polly bringing maid. Also chauffeur. By the way I'm leaving Grimshawe at Hetton next week tell Mrs. Mossop. It's a bore and expense boarding her out in London. In fact I think I might do without her altogether what do you think? except she's useful for sewing. Longing to see John again. All going back Sunday evening. Keep sober, darling. Try.

x x x x x x

B.

Tony found very little to occupy his time on Friday. His letters were all finished by ten o'clock. He went down to the farm but they had no business for him there. The duties which before had seemed so multifarious, now took up a very small part of his day; he had not realized how many hours he used to waste with Brenda. He watched John riding in the paddock. The boy clearly bore him ill will for their quarrel on Wednesday; when he applauded a jump, John said, "She usually does better than this." Later, "When's mummy coming down?"

"Not till tomorrow."

"Oh."

"I've got to go over to Little Bayton this afternoon. Would you like to come too and perhaps we could see the kennels?"

John had for weeks past been praying for this expedition. "No, thank you," he said. "I want to finish a picture I am painting."

"You can do that any time."

"I want to do it this afternoon."

When Tony had left them Ben said, "Whatever made you speak to your dad like that for? You've been going on about seeing the kennels since Christmas."

"Not with *him*," said John.

"You ungrateful little bastard, that's a lousy way to speak of your dad."

"And you ought not to say bastard or lousy in front of me, nanny says not."

So Tony went over alone to Little Bayton where he had some business to discuss with Colonel Brink. He hoped they would ask him to stay on, but the Colonel and his wife were themselves going out to tea, so he drove back in the dusk to Hetton.

A thin mist lay breast high over the park; the turrets and battlements of the abbey stood grey and flat; the boiler man was hauling down the flag on the main tower.

"My poor Brenda, it's an appalling room," said Mrs. Beaver.

"It's not one we use a great deal," said Tony very coldly.

"I should think not," said the one they called Veronica.

"I can't see much wrong with it," said Polly, "except it's a bit mouldy."

"You see," Brenda explained, not looking at Tony. "What I thought was that I must have *one* habitable room downstairs. At present there's only the smoking room and the library. The drawing room is vast and quite out of the question. I thought what I needed was a small sitting room more or less to myself. Don't you think it has possibilities?"

"But, my angel, the *shape's* all wrong," said Daisy, "and that chimney piece—what is it made of, pink granite, and all the plaster work and the dado. *Everything's* horrible. It's so *dark.*"

"I know exactly what Brenda wants," said Mrs. Beaver more moderately. "I don't think it will be impossible. I must think about it. As Veronica says, the structure does rather limit one . . . you know I think the only thing to do would be to disregard it altogether and find some treatment so definite that it *carried* the room if you see what I mean . . . supposing we covered the walls with white chromium plating and had natural sheepskin carpet . . . I wonder if that would be running you in for more than you meant to spend."

"I'd blow the whole thing sky-high," said Veronica.

Tony left them to their discussion.

"D'you really want Mrs. Beaver to do up the morning room?"

"Not if you don't, sweet."

"But can you imagine it—white chromium plating?"

"Oh, that was just an idea."

Tony walked in and out between Mordred and Guinevere as he always did while they were dressing. "I say," he said, returning with his waistcoat. "You aren't going away tomorrow too, are you?"

"Must."

He went back to Mordred for his tie and bringing it to Brenda's room again, sat by her side at the dressing table to fasten it.

"By the way," said Brenda, "what did you think about keeping on Grimshawe?—it seems rather a waste."

"You used always to say you couldn't get on without her."

"Yes, but now I'm living at the flat everything's so simple."

"*Living?* Darling, you talk as though you had settled there for good."

"D'you mind moving a second, sweet? I can't see properly."

"Brenda, how long are you going on with this course of economics?"

"Me? I don't know."

"But you must have some idea?"

"Oh it's surprising what a lot there is to learn . . . I was so backward when I started . . ."

"Brenda . . ."

"Now run and put on your coat. They'll all be downstairs waiting for us."

That evening Polly and Mrs. Beaver played backgammon. Brenda and Veronica sat together on the sofa sewing and talking about their needlework; occasionally there were bursts of general conversation between the four women; they had the habit of lapsing into a jargon of their own which Tony did not understand; it was a thieves' slang, by which the syllables of each word were transposed. Tony sat just outside the circle, reading under another lamp.

That night when they went upstairs, the three guests came to sit in Brenda's room and talk to her while she went to bed. Tony could hear their low laughter through the dressing-room door. They had boiled water in an electric kettle and were drinking Sedobrol together.

Presently, still laughing, they left and Tony went into Brenda's room. It was in darkness, but hearing him come and seeing the square of light in the doorway, she turned on the little lamp by the bedside.

"Why, Tony," she said.

She was lying on the dais with her head deep back in the pillows; her face was shining with the grease she used for cleaning it; one bare arm on the quilted eiderdown, left there from turning the switch. "Why, Tony," she said, "I was almost asleep."

"Very tired?"

"Mm."

"Want to be left alone?"

"So tired . . . and I've just drunk a lot of that stuff of Polly's."

"I see . . . well goodnight."

"Goodnight . . . don't mind do you? . . . so tired."

He crossed to the bed and kissed her; she lay quite still, with closed eyes. Then he turned out the light and went back to the dressing room.

"Lady Brenda not ill, I hope?"

"No, nothing serious, thank you very much. She gets rather done up in London, you know, during the week, and likes to take Sunday quietly."

"And how are the great studies progressing?"

"Very well, I gather. She seems keen on it still."

"Splendid. We shall all be coming to her soon to solve our economic problems. But I daresay you and John miss her?"

"Yes, we do rather."

"Well please give her my kindest regards."

"I will indeed. Thank you so much."

Tony left the church porch and made his accustomed way to the hot houses; a gardenia for himself; four almost black carnations for the ladies. When he reached the room where they were sitting there was a burst of laughter. He paused on the threshold rather bewildered.

"Come in, darling, it isn't anything. It's only we had a bet on what coloured button-hole you'd be wearing and none of us won."

They still giggled a little as they pinned on the flowers he had brought them; all except Mrs. Beaver who said, "Any time you are buying cuttings or seeds do get them through me. I've made quite a little business of it, perhaps you didn't know . . . all kinds of rather unusual flowers. I do everything like that for Sylvia Newport and all sort of people."

"You must talk to my head man about it."

"Well to tell you the truth I *have*—this morning while you were in church. He seems quite to understand."

They left early, so as to reach London in time for dinner. In the car Daisy said, "Golly what a house."

"Now you can see what I've been through all these years."

"My poor Brenda," said Veronica, unpinning her carnation and throwing it from the window into the side of the road.

"You know," Brenda confided next day, "I'm not *absolutely* happy about Tony."

"What's the old boy been up to?" asked Polly.

"Nothing much yet, but I do see it's pretty boring for him at Hetton all this time."

"I shouldn't worry."

"Oh, I'm not *worrying*. It's only, supposing he took to drink or something. It would make everything very difficult."

"I shouldn't have said that was his thing . . . We must get him interested in a girl."

"If only we could . . . Who is there?"

"There's always old Sybil."

"Darling, he's known her all his life."

"Or Souki de Foucauld-Esterhazy."

"He isn't his best with Americans."

"Well we'll find him someone."

"The trouble is that I've become such a habit with him—he won't take easily to a new one . . . ought she to be like me, or quite different?"

"I'd say, different, but it's hard to tell."

They discussed this problem in all its aspects.

3

Brenda wrote:

Darling Tony,

Sorry not to have written or rung up but I've had such a busy time with bimetallism v. complicated.

Coming down Saturday with Polly again. Good her coming twice— Lyonesse can't be as beastily as most of the rooms can it.

Also charming girl I have taken up with who I want us to be kind to. She'd had a terrible life and she lives in one of these flats called Jenny Abdul Akbar. Not black but married one. Get her to tell you. She'll come by train 3.18 I expect. Must stop now and go to lecture.

Keep away from the Demon Rum.

x x x x x
Brenda.

Saw Jock last night at Café de Paris with shameless blonde. Who? Cin no Djinñ how? has rheumatism and Marjorie is v. put out about it. She thinks his pelvis is out of place and Cruttwell won't do him which is pretty mean considering all the people she has brought there.

"Are you *certain* Jenny will be Tony's tea?"

"You can't ever be certain," said Polly. "She bores my pants off, but she's a good trier."

"Is mummy coming down today, daddy?"

"Yes."

"Who else?"

"Someone called Abdul Akbar."

"What a silly name. Is she foreign?"

"I don't know."

"Sounds foreign, doesn't she, daddy? D'you think she won't be able to talk any English? Is she black?"

"Mummy says not."

"Oh . . . who else?"

"Lady Cockpurse."

"The monkey woman. You know she wasn't a bit like a monkey except perhaps her face and I don't think she had a tail because I looked as close as anything . . . unless perhaps she has it rolled up between her legs. D'you think she has, daddy?"

"I shouldn't be surprised."

"*Very* uncomfortable."

Tony and John were friends again; but it had been a leaden week.

It was part of Polly Cockpurse's plan to arrive late at Hetton. "Give the girl a chance to get down to it," she said. So she and Brenda did not leave London until Jenny was already on her way from the station. It was a day of bitter cold and occasional rain. The resolute little figure huddled herself in the rugs until they reached the gates. Then she opened her bag, tucked up her veil, shook out her powder puff and put her face to rights. She licked the rouge from her finger with a sharp red tongue.

Tony was in the smoking room when she was announced; the library was now too noisy during the daytime for there were men at work on the walls of the morning room next door, tearing down the plaster tracery.

"Princess Abdul Akbar."

He rose to greet her. She was preceded by a heavy odour of musk.

"Oh, Mr. Last," she said, "what a sweet old place this is."

"I'm afraid it's been restored a great deal," said Tony.

"Ah, but its *atmosphere*. I always think that's what counts in a house. Such dignity, and repose, but of course you're used to it. When you've been very unhappy as I have, you appreciate these things."

Tony said, "I'm afraid Brenda hasn't arrived yet. She's coming by car with Lady Cockpurse."

"Brenda's been *such* a friend to me." The Princess took off her furs and sat down on the stool before the fire, looking up at Tony. "D'you mind if I take off my hat?"

"No, no . . . of course."

She threw it on to the sofa and shook out her hair, which was dead black and curled. "D'you know, Mr. Last, I'm going to call you Teddy right away. You don't think that very fresh of me? And you must call me Jenny. Princess is so formal, isn't it, and suggests tight trousers and gold braid . . . Of course," she went on, stretching out her hands to the fire and letting her hair fall forwards a little across her face, "my husband was not called 'Prince' in Morocco; his title was Moulay —but there's no proper equivalent for a woman so I've always called myself Princess in Europe . . . Moulay is *far* higher really . . . my husband was a descendant of the Prophet. Are you interested in the East?"

"No . . . yes. I mean I know very little about it."

"It has an uncanny fascination for me. You must go there, Teddy. I know you'd like it. I've been saying the same to Brenda."

"I expect you'd like to see your room," said Tony. "They'll bring tea soon."

"No, I'll stay here. I like just to curl up like a cat in front of the fire, and if you're nice to me I'll purr, and if you're cruel I shall pretend not to notice—just like a cat . . . Shall I purr, Teddy?"

"Er . . . yes . . . do, please, if that's what you like doing."

"Englishmen are so gentle and considerate. It's wonderful to be back among them . . . mine own people. Sometimes when I look back at my life, especially at times like this among lovely old English things and kind people, I think the whole thing must be a frightful nightmare . . . then I remember my *scars* . . ."

"Brenda tells me you've taken one of the flats in the same house as hers. They must be very convenient."

"How English you are, Teddy—so shy of talking about personal things, intimate things . . . I like you for that, you know. I love everything that's solid and homely and *good* after . . . after all I've been through."

"You're not studying economics too, are you, like Brenda?"

"No; is Brenda? She never told me. What a wonderful person she is. When *does* she find the time?"

"Ah, here comes tea at last," said Tony. "I hope you allow yourself to eat muffins. So many of our guests nowadays are on a diet. I think muffins one of the few things that make the English winter endurable."

"Muffins stand for so much," said Jenny.

She ate heartily; often she ran her tongue over her lips, collecting crumbs that had become embedded there and melted butter from the muffin. One drop of butter fell on her chin and glittered there unobserved except by Tony. It was a relief to him when John Andrew was brought in. "Come and be introduced to Princess Abdul Akbar."

John Andrew had never before seen a Princess; he gazed at her fascinated. "Aren't you going to give me a kiss?"

He walked over to her and she kissed him on the mouth.

"Oh," he said, recoiling and rubbing away the taste of the lipstick; and then "What a beautiful smell."

"It's my last link with the East," she said.

"You've got butter on your chin."

She reached for her bag, laughing. "Why so I have. Teddy, you *might* have told me."

"Why do you call daddy, Teddy?"

"Because I hope we are going to be great friends."

"What a funny reason."

John stayed with them for an hour and all the time watched her fascinated. "Have you got a crown?" he asked. "How did you learn to speak English? What is that big ring made of? Did it cost much? Why are your nails that colour? Can you ride?"

She answered all his questions, sometimes enigmatically with an eye on Tony. She took out a little heavily scented handkerchief and showed John the monogram. "That is my only crown . . . now," she said. She told him about the horses she used to have—glossy black, with arched necks; foam round their silver bits; plumes tossing on their foreheads; silver studs on the harness, crimson saddle-cloths. "On the Moulay's birthday——"

"What's the Moulay?"

"A beautiful and a very bad man," she said gravely, "and on his birthday all his horsemen used to assemble round a great square, with all their finest clothes and trappings and jewels, with long swords in their hands. The Moulay used to sit on a throne under a great crimson canopy."

"What's a canopy?"

"Like a tent," she said more sharply, and then resuming her soft voice, "and all the horsemen used to gallop across the plain, in a great cloud of dust, waving their swords, straight towards the Moulay. And everyone used to hold their breath, thinking the horsemen were bound to ride right on top of the Moulay, but when they were a few feet away, as near as I am to you, galloping at full speed, they used to rein their horses back, up on to their hind legs and salute——"

"Oh but they *shouldn't*," said John. "It's *very* bad horsemanship indeed. Ben says so."

"They're the most wonderful horsemen in the world. Everyone knows that."

"Oh no, they can't be, if they do *that*. It's one of the *worst* things. Were they natives?"

"Yes, of course."

"Ben says natives aren't humans at all really."

"Ah but he's thinking of Negroes I expect. These are pure Semitic type."

"What's that?"

"The same as Jews."

"Ben says Jews are worse than natives."

"Oh dear, what a very severe boy you are. I was like that once. Life teaches one to be tolerant."

"It hasn't taught Ben," said John. "When's mummy coming? I thought she'd be here, otherwise I wouldn't have stopped painting my picture."

But when nanny came to fetch him, John, without invitation, went over and kissed Jenny goodnight. "Goodnight Johnny-boy," she said.

"What did you call me?"

"Johnny-boy."

"You are funny with names."

Upstairs, meditatively splashing his spoon in the bread and milk, he said, "Nanny, I do think that Princess is beautiful, don't you?"

Nanny sniffed. "It would be a dull world if we all thought alike," she said.

"She's more beautiful than Miss Tendril, even. I think she's the most beautiful lady I've ever seen . . . D'you think she'd like to watch me have my bath?"

Downstairs, Jenny said, "What a heavenly child . . . I love children. That has been my great tragedy. It was when he found I couldn't have children that the Moulay first showed the Other Side of his Nature. It wasn't my fault . . . you see my womb is out of place . . . I don't know why I'm telling you all this, but I feel you'll understand. It's such a *waste of time,* isn't it, when one knows one is going to like someone and one goes on *pretending* . . . I know at once if someone is going to be a real friend . . ."

Polly and Brenda arrived just before seven. Brenda went straight up to the nursery. "Oh, mummy," said John. "There's such a beautiful lady downstairs. Do ask her to come and say goodnight. Nanny doesn't think she'd want to."

"Did daddy seem to like her?"

"He didn't talk much . . . She doesn't know anything about horses or natives but she *is* beautiful. Please tell her to come up."

Brenda went downstairs and found Jenny with Polly and Tony in the smoking room. "You've made a wild success with John Andrew. He won't go to sleep until he's seen you again."

They went up together, and Jenny said, "They're both such dears."

"Did you and Tony get on? I was so sorry not to be here when you arrived."

"He was *so* sympathetic and gentle . . . and so wistful."

They sat on John's small bed in the night-nursery. He threw the clothes back and crawled out, nestling against Jenny. "Back to bed," she said, "or I shall spank you."

"Would you do it hard? I shouldn't mind."

"Oh dear," said Brenda, "what a terrible effect you seem to have. He's never like this as a rule."

When they had gone nanny threw open another window. "Poof!" she said, "making the whole place stink."

"Don't you like it? *I* think it's lovely."

Brenda took Polly up to Lyonesse. It was a large suite, fitted up with satinwood for King Edward when, as Prince of Wales, he was once expected at a shooting party; he never came.

"How's it going?" she asked anxiously.

"Too soon to tell. I'm sure it will be all right."

"She's got the wrong chap. John Andrew's mad about her . . . quite embarrassing."

"I should say Tony was a slow starter. It's a pity she's got his name wrong. Ought we to tell her?"

"No, let's leave it."

When she was dressing Tony said, "Brenda, who *is* this joke-woman?"

"Darling, don't you like her?"

The disappointment and distress in her tone were so clear that Tony was touched. "I don't know about not liking her exactly. She's just a joke, isn't she?"

"Is she . . . oh dear . . . She's had a terrible life you know."

"So I gathered."

"Be nice to her, Tony, please."

"Oh, I'll be nice to her. Is she Jewish?"

"I don't know. I never thought. Perhaps she is."

Soon after dinner Polly said she was tired and asked Brenda to come with her while she undressed. "Leave the young couple to it," she whispered outside the door.

"My dear, I don't believe it's going to be any good . . . the poor boy's got *some* taste you know, and a sense of humour."

"She didn't show up too well at dinner, did she?"

"She will *go on* so . . . and after all Tony's been used to me for seven years. It's rather a sudden change."

"Tired?"

"Mmm. Little bit."

"You gave me a pretty long bout of Abdul Akbar."

"I know. I'm sorry, darling, but Polly takes so long to get to bed . . . Was it awful? I wish you liked her more."

"She's awful."

"One has to make allowances . . . she's got the most terrible scars."

"So she told me."

"I've seen them."

"Besides I hoped to see something of you."

"Oh."

"Brenda, you aren't angry still about my getting tight that night and waking you up?"

"No, sweet, do I seem angry?"

". . . I don't know. You do rather . . . Has it been an amusing week?"

"Not amusing, very hard work. Bimetallism you know."

"Oh yes . . . well, I suppose you want to go to sleep."

"Mm . . . so tired. Goodnight, darling."

"Goodnight."

"Can I go and say good morning to the Princess, mummy?"

"I don't expect she's awake yet."

"Please, mummy, may I go and see? I'll just peep and if she's asleep, go away."

"I don't know what room she's in."

"Galahad, my lady," said Grimshawe who was putting out her clothes.

"Oh dear, why was she put there."

"It was Mr. Last's orders, my lady."

"Well, she's probably awake then."

John slipped out of the room and trotted down the passage to Galahad. "May I come in?"

"Hullo, Johnny-boy. Come in."

He swung on the handles of the door, half in, half out of the
room. "Have you had breakfast? Mummy said you wouldn't be
awake."

"I've been awake a long time. You see I was once very badly hurt,
and now I don't always sleep well. Even the softest beds are too hard
for me now."

"Ooh. What did you do? Was it a motor car accident?"

"Not an accident, Johnny-boy, not an accident . . . but come. It's
cold with the door open. Look there are some grapes here. Would
you like to eat them?"

John climbed on to the bed. "What are you going to do today?"

"I don't know yet. I haven't been told."

"Well I'll tell you. We'll go to church in the morning because I have
to and then we'll go and look at Thunderclap and I'll show you the
place we jump and then you can come with me while I have dinner
because I have it early and afterwards we can go down to Bruton
wood and we needn't take nanny because it makes her so muddy and
you can see where they dug out a fox in the drain just outside the
wood, he nearly got away and then you can come and have tea in the
nursery and I've got a little gramophone Uncle Reggie gave me for
Christmas and it plays 'When Father Papered the Parlour,' do you
know that song? Ben can sing it, and I've got some books to show you
and a picture I did of the battle of Marston Moor."

"I think that sounds a lovely day. But don't you think I ought to
spend some with with daddy and mummy and Lady Cockpurse?"

"Oh, *them* . . . besides it's all my foot about Lady Cockpurse having a tail. Please you *will* spend the day with me?"

"Well, we'll see."

"She's gone to church with him. That's a good sign, isn't it?"

"Well, not really, Polly. He likes going alone, or with me. It's the
time he gossips to the village."

"She won't stop him."

"I'm afraid you don't understand the old boy altogether. He's much odder than you'd think."

"I could see from your sermon that you knew the East, rector."

"Yes, yes, most of my life."

"It has an uncanny fascination, hasn't it?"

"Oh come on," said John, pulling at her coat. "We must go and see Thunderclap."

So Tony returned alone with the button-holes.

After luncheon Brenda said, "Why don't you show Jenny the house?"

"Oh yes, *do.*"

When they reached the morning room he said, "Brenda's having it done up."

There were planks and ladders and heaps of plaster about.

"Oh, Teddy, what a shame. I do hate seeing things modernized."

"It isn't a room we used very much."

"No, but still . . ." She stirred the mouldings of fleur-de-lis that littered the floor, fragments of tarnished gilding and dusty stencil-work. "You know, Brenda's been a wonderful friend to me. I wouldn't say anything against her . . . but ever since I came here I've been wondering whether she really understands this beautiful place and all it means to you."

"Tell me more about your terrible life," said Tony, leading her back to the central hall.

"You are shy of talking about yourself, aren't you, Teddy? It's a mistake, you know, to keep things bottled up. I've been very unhappy too."

Tony looked about him desperately in search of help; and help came. "Oh there you are," said a firm, child's voice. "Come on. We're going down to the woods now. We must hurry, otherwise it will be dark."

"Oh, Johnny-boy, must I really? I was just talking to daddy."

"*Come on*. It's all arranged. And afterwards you're to be allowed to have tea with me upstairs."

Tony crept into the library, habitable today, since the workmen were at rest. Brenda found him there two hours later. "*Tony, here all alone?* We thought you were with Jenny. What have you done with her?"

"John took her off . . . just in time before I said something rude."

"Oh dear . . . well there's only me and Polly in the smoking room. Come and have some tea. You look all funny—have you been asleep?"

"We must write it down a failure, definitely."

"What *does* the old boy expect? It isn't as though he was every-body's money."

"I daresay it would all have been all right, if she hadn't got his name wrong."

"Anyway, this lets you out. You've done far more than most wives would to cheer the old boy up."

"Yes, that's certainly true," said Brenda.

4

Another five days; then Brenda came to Hetton again. "I shan't be here next week-end," she said, "I'm going to stay with Veronica."

"Am I asked?"

"Well you *were,* of course, but I refused for you. You know you always hate staying away."

"I wouldn't mind coming."

"Oh, darling, I wish I'd known. Veronica would have loved it so . . . but I'm afraid it will be too late now. She's only got a tiny house . . . to tell you the truth I didn't think you liked her much."

"I hated her like hell."

"Well then . . . ?"

"Oh, it doesn't matter. I suppose you must go back on Monday? The hounds are meeting here on Wednesday, you know."

"Are we giving them a lawner?"

"Yes, darling, you know we do every year."

"So we do."

"You couldn't stay down till then?"

"Not possibly, darling. You see if I miss one lecture I get right behind and can't follow the next. Besides I am not mad keen to see the hounds."

"Ben was asking if we'd let John go out."

"Oh, he's far too young."

"Not to hunt. But I thought he might bring his pony to the meet and ride with them to the first covert. He'd love it so."

"Is it quite safe?"

"Oh, yes, surely?"

"Bless his heart, I wish I could be here to see him."

"Do change your mind."

"Oh no, that's quite out of question. Don't make a thing about it, Tony."

That was when she first arrived; later everything got better. Jock was there that week-end, also Allan and Marjorie and another married couple whom Tony had known all his life. Brenda had arranged the party for him and he enjoyed it. He and Allan went out with rook rifles and shot rabbits in the twilight; after dinner the four men played billiard fives while one wife watched. "The old boy's happy as a lark," said Brenda to Marjorie. "He's settling down wonderfully to the new regime."

They came in breathless and rather hurried for whisky and soda.

"Tony nearly had one through the window," said Jock.

That night Tony slept in Guinevere.

"Everything *is* all right, isn't it?" he said once.

"Yes of course, darling."

"I get depressed down here all alone and imagine things."

"You aren't to *brood*, Tony. You know that's one of the things that aren't allowed."

"I won't brood any more," said Tony.

Next day Brenda came to church with him. She had decided to devote the week-end wholly to him; it would be the last for some time.

"And how are the abstruse sciences, Lady Brenda?"

"Absorbing."

"We shall all be coming to you for advice about our overdrafts."

"Ha, ha."

"And how's Thunderclap?" asked Miss Tendril.

"I'm taking her out hunting on Wednesday," said John. He had forgotten Princess Abdul Akbar in the excitement of the coming meet. "Please God make there be a good scent. Please God make me see the kill. Please God don't let me do anything wrong. God bless Ben and Thunderclap. Please God make me jump an enormous great oxer," he had kept repeating throughout the service.

Brenda did the round with Tony of cottages and hot houses; she helped him choose his button-hole.

Tony was in high spirits at luncheon. Brenda had begun to forget how amusing he could be. Afterwards he changed into other clothes and went with Jock to play golf. They stayed some time at the club house. Tony said, "We've got the hounds meeting at Hetton on Wednesday. Couldn't you stay down till then?"

"Must be back. There's going to be a debate on the Pig Scheme."

"I wish you'd stay. Look here why don't you ask that girl down? Everyone goes tomorrow. You could ring her up, couldn't you?"

"I *could.*"

"Would she hate it? She could have Lyonesse—Polly slept there two week-ends running so it can't be too uncomfortable."

"She'd probably love it. I'll ring up and ask her."

"Why don't you hunt too? There's a chap called Brinkwell who's got some quite decent hirelings I believe."

"Yes, I might."

"Jock's staying on. He's having the shameless blonde down. You don't mind?"

"Me? Of course not."

"This has been a jolly week-end."

"I thought you were enjoying it."

"Just like old times—before the economics began."

Marjorie said to Jock, "D'you think Tony knows about Mr. Beaver?"

"Not a thing."

"I haven't mentioned it to Allan. D'you suppose he knows?"

"I doubt it."

"Oh, Jock, how d'you think it'll end?"

"She'll get bored with Beaver soon enough."

"The trouble is that he doesn't care for her in the least. If he did, it would soon be over . . . What an ass she is being."

"I should say she was managing it unusually well, if you asked me."

The other married couples said to each other, "D'you think Marjorie and Allan know about Brenda?"

"I'm sure they don't."

Brenda said to Allan, "Tony's as happy as a sandboy, isn't he?"

"Full of beans."

"I was getting worried about him . . . You don't think he's got any idea about my goings on?"

"Lord no. It's the last thing that would come into his head."

Brenda said, "I don't want him to be unhappy you know . . . Marjorie's been frightfully governessy about the whole thing."

"Has she? I haven't discussed it with her."

"How did *you* hear?"

"My dear girl, until this minute I didn't know you had any goings on. And I'm not asking any questions about them now."

"Oh . . . I thought everyone knew."

"That's always the trouble with people when they have affaires. They either think no one knows, or everybody. The truth is that a few people like Polly and Sybil make a point of finding out about everyone's private life; the rest of us just aren't interested."

"Oh."

Later he said to Marjorie, "Brenda tried to be confidential about Beaver this evening."

"I didn't know you knew."

"Oh I knew all right. But I wasn't going to let her feel important by talking about it."

"I couldn't disapprove more of the whole thing. Do you know Beaver?"

"I've seen him about. Anyway, it's her business and Tony's, not ours."

5

Jock's blonde was called Mrs. Rattery. Tony had conceived an idea of her from what he overheard of Polly's gossip and from various fragments of information let fall by Jock. She was a little over thirty. Somewhere in the Cottesmore country there lived a long-legged, slightly discredited Major Rattery, to whom she had once been married. She was American by origin, now totally denationalized, rich, without property or possessions, except those that would pack in five vast trunks. Jock had had his eye on her last summer at Biarritz and had fallen in with her again in London where she played big bridge, very ably, for six or seven hours a day and changed her hotel, on an average, once every three weeks. Periodically she was liable to bouts of morphine; then she gave up her bridge and remained for several days at a time alone in her hotel suite, refreshed at intervals with glasses of cold milk.

She arrived by air on Monday afternoon. It was the first time that a guest had come in this fashion and the household was appreciably excited. Under Jock's direction the boiler man and one of the gardeners pegged out a dust sheet in the park to mark a landing for her and lit a bonfire of damp leaves to show the direction of the wind. The five trunks arrived in the ordinary way by train, with an elderly, irreproachable maid. She brought her own sheets with her in one of the trunks; they were neither silk nor coloured, without lace or ornament of any kind, except small, plain monograms.

Tony, Jock and John went out to watch her land. She climbed out of the cockpit, stretched, unbuttoned the flaps of her leather helmet, and came to meet them. "Forty-two minutes," she said, "not at all bad with the wind against me."

She was tall and erect, almost austere in helmet and overalls; not at all as Tony had imagined her. Vaguely, at the back of his mind he had secreted the slightly absurd expectation of a chorus girl, in silk shorts and brassière, popping out of an immense beribboned Easter Egg with a cry of "Whooppee, boys." Mrs. Rattery's greetings were deft and impersonal.

"Are you going to hunt on Wednesday?" asked John. "They're meeting here you know."

"I might go out for half the day, if I can find a horse. It'll be the first time this year."

"It's my first time too."

"We shall both be terribly stiff." She spoke to him exactly as though he were a man of her own age. "You'll have to show me the country."

"I expect they'll draw Bruton wood first. There's a big fox there, daddy and I saw him."

When they were alone together, Jock said, "It's delightful your coming down. What d'you think of Tony?"

"Is he married to that rather lovely woman we saw at the Café de Paris?"

"Yes."

"The one you said was in love with that young man?"

"Yes."

"Funny of her . . . What's this one's name again?"

"Tony Last. It's a pretty ghastly house, isn't it?"

"Is it? I never notice houses much."

She was an easy guest to entertain. After dinner on Monday she produced four packs of cards and laid out for herself on the smoking room table a very elaborate patience, which kept her engrossed all the evening. "Don't wait up for me," she said. "I shall stay here until it comes out. It often takes several hours."

They showed her where to put the lights out and left her to it.

Next day Jock said, "Have you got any pigs at the farm?"

"Yes."

"Would you mind if I went to see them?"

"Not the least—but why?"

"And is there a man who looks after them, who will be able to explain about them?"

"Yes."

"Well, I think I'll spend the morning with him. I've got to make a speech about pigs, fairly soon."

They did not see Mrs. Rattery until luncheon. Tony assumed she was asleep until she appeared in overalls from the morning room. "I was down early," she explained, "and found the men at work stripping the ceiling. I couldn't resist joining in. I hope you don't mind."

In the afternoon they went to a neighbouring livery stable to look for hirelings. After tea Tony wrote to Brenda; he had taken to writing letters in the past few weeks.

How enjoyable the week-end was, he wrote. *Thank you a thousand times for all your sweetness. I wish you were coming down next week-end, or that you had been able to stay on a little, but I quite understand.*

The Shameless Blonde is not the least what we expected—very serene and distant. Not at all like Jock's usual taste. I am sure she hasn't any idea where she is or what my name is.

The work in the morning room is going on well. The foreman told me today he thought he would begin on the chromium plating by the end of the week. You know what I think about that.

John can talk of nothing except his hunting tomorrow. I hope he doesn't break his neck. Jock and his S.B. are going out too.

Hetton lay near the boundary of three packs; the Pigstanton, who hunted it, had in the division of territory come off with the worst country and they cherished a permanent resentment about some woods near Bayton. They were a somewhat ill-tempered lot, contemptuous of each other's performance, hostile to strangers, torn by internal rancour; united only in their dislike of the Master. In the case of Colonel Inch this unpopularity, traditional to the hunt, was quite undeserved; he was a timid, inconspicuous man who provided the neighbourhood with sport of a kind at great personal expense. He himself was seldom in sight of hounds and could often be found in another part of the county morosely nibbling ginger nut biscuits in a lane or towards the end of the day cantering heavily across country, quite lost, a lonely scarlet figure against the ploughed land, staring about him in the deepening twilight and shouting at yokels for information. The only pleasure he gained from his position, but that a substantial one, was in referring to it casually at Board Meetings of the various companies he directed.

The Pigstanton met twice a week. There was seldom a large field on Wednesdays, but the Hetton meet was popular; it lay in their best country and the prospect of stirrup cups had drawn many leathery old ladies from the neighbouring packs. There were also followers on foot and in every kind of vehicle, some hanging back diffidently, others, more or less known to Tony, crowding round the refreshment table. Mr. Tendril had a niece staying with him, who appeared on a motor bicycle.

John stood beside Thunderclap, solemn with excitement. Ben had secured a powerful, square-headed mare from a neighbouring farmer; he hoped to have a hunt after John had been taken home; at John's earnest entreaty nanny was confined indoors, among the housemaids whose heads obtruded at the upper windows; it was not her day. She had been out of temper while dressing him. "If I'm in at the death I expect Colonel Inch will blood me."

"You won't see any death," said nanny.

Now she stood with her eyes at a narrow slit gazing rather resentfully at the animated scene below. "It's all a lot of nonsense of Ben Hacket's," she thought. She deplored it all, hounds, Master, field, huntsman and whippers-in, Miss Tendril's niece in her mackintosh, Jock in rat-catcher, Mrs. Rattery in tall hat and cutaway coat oblivious of the suspicious glances of the subscribers, Tony smiling and chatting to his guests, the crazy old man with the terriers, the Press photographer, pretty Miss Ripon in difficulties with a young horse, titapping sideways over the lawn, the grooms and second horses, the humble, unknown followers in the background—it was all a lot of nonsense of Ben Hacket's. "It was after eleven before the child got to sleep last night," she reflected, "he was that over-excited."

Presently they moved off towards Bruton wood. The way lay down the South drive through Compton Last, along the main road for half a mile, and then through fields. "He can ride with them as far as the covert," Tony had said.

"Yes, sir, and there'd be no harm in his staying a bit to see hounds working, would there?"

"No, I suppose not."

"And if he breaks away towards home, there'd be no harm in our following a bit, if we keeps to the lanes and gates, would there, sir?"

"No, but he's not to stay out more than an hour."

"You wouldn't have me take him home with hounds running, would you, sir?"

"Well he's got to be in before one."

"I'll see to that, sir. Don't you worry, my beauty," he said to John, "you'll get a hunt right enough."

They waited until the end of the line of horses and then trotted soberly behind them. Close at their heels followed the motor-cars, at low gear, in a fog of exhaust gas. John was breathless and slightly dizzy. Thunderclap was tossing her head and worrying at her snaffle. Twice while the field was moving off, she had tried to get away and had taken John round in a little circle, so that Ben had said, "Hold on to her, son" and had come up close beside him so as to be able to catch the reins if she looked like bolting. Once boring forwards with her head she took John by surprise and pulled him forwards out of his balance; he caught hold of the front of the saddle to steady himself and looked guiltily at Ben. "I'm afraid I'm riding very badly today. D'you think anyone has noticed?"

"That's all right, son. You can't keep riding-school manners when you're hunting."

Jock and Mrs. Rattery trotted side by side. "I rather like this absurd horse," she said; she rode astride and it was evident from the moment she mounted that she rode extremely well.

The members of the Pigstanton noted this with ill-concealed resentment for it disturbed their fixed opinion according to which, though all fellow members of the hunt were clowns and poltroons, strangers were without exception mannerless lunatics, and a serious menace to anyone within quarter of a mile of them.

Half way through the village Miss Ripon had difficulties in getting past a stationary baker's van. Her horse plunged and reared, trembling all over, turning about, and slipping frantically over the tarmac. They rode round her giving his heels the widest berth, scowling ominously and grumbling about her. They all knew that horse. Miss Ripon's father had been trying to sell him all the season, and had lately come down to eighty pounds. He was a good jumper on occasions but a beast of a horse to ride. Did Miss Ripon's father really imagine he was improving his chances of a sale by letting Miss Ripon make an exhibition of herself? It was like that skinflint Miss Ripon's father, to risk Miss Ripon's neck for eighty pounds. And anyway Miss Ripon had no business out on *any* horse . . .

Presently she shot past them at a canter; she was flushed in the face and her bun was askew; she leant back, pulling with all her weight. "That girl will come to no good," said Jock.

They encountered her later at the covert. Her horse was sweating and lathered at the bridle but temporarily at rest cropping the tufts of sedge that lay round the woods. Miss Ripon was much out of breath, and her hands shook as she fiddled with veil, bun and bowler. John rode up to Jock's side.

"What's happening, Mr. Grant-Menzies?"

"Hounds are drawing the covert."

"Oh."

"Are you enjoying yourself?"

"Oh yes. Thunderclap's terribly fresh. I've never known her like this."

There was a long wait as the horn sounded in the heart of the wood. Everyone stood at the corner of the big field, near a gate. Every-one, that is to say, except Miss Ripon who some minutes ago had dis-appeared suddenly, indeed in the middle of a sentence, at full gallop towards Hetton hills. After half an hour Jock said, "They're calling hounds off."

"Does that mean it's a blank?"

"I'm afraid so."

"I hate this happening in *our* woods," said Ben. "Looks bad."

Indeed the Pigstantons were already beginning to forget their recent hospitality and to ask each other what did one expect when Last did not hunt himself, and to circulate dark reports of how one of the keepers had been observed last week burying Something late in the evening.

They moved off again, away from Hetton. Ben began to feel his responsibility. "D'you think I ought to take the young gentleman home, sir?"

"What did Mr. Last say?"

"He said he could go as far as the covert. He didn't say which, sir."

"I'm afraid it sounds as if he ought to go."

"Oh, Mr. Grant-Menzies."

"Yes, come along, Master John. You've had enough for today."

"But I haven't had *any.*"

"If you come back in good time today your dad will be all the more willing to let you come out another day."

"But there mayn't *be* another day. The world may come to an end. *Please,* Ben. *Please,* Mr. Grant-Menzies."

"It is a shame they shouldn't have found," said Ben. "He's been looking forward to it."

"Still I think Mr. Last would want him to go back," said Jock.

So John's fate was decided; hounds went in one direction, he and Ben in another. John was very near tears as they reached the main road.

"Look," said Ben, to encourage him. "Here comes Miss Ripon on that nappy bay. Seems as if she's going in, too. Had a fall by the looks of her."

Miss Ripon's hat and back were covered with mud and moss. She had had a bad twenty minutes since her disappearance. "I'm taking him away," she said. "I can't do anything with him this morning." She jogged along beside them towards the village. "I thought perhaps Mr. Last would let me come up to the house and telephone for the car. I don't feel like hacking him home in his present state. I can't think what's come over him," she added loyally. "He was out on Saturday. I've never known him like this before."

"He wants a man up," said Ben.

"Oh, he's no better with the groom and daddy won't go near him," said Miss Ripon, stung to indiscretion. "At least . . . I mean . . . I don't think that they'd be any better with him in this state."

He was quiet enough at that moment, keeping pace with the other horses. They rode abreast, she on the outside with John's pony between her and Ben.

Then this happened: they reached a turn in the road and came face to face with one of the single decker, country buses that covered that neighbourhood. It was not going fast and, seeing the horses, the driver slowed down still further and drew into the side. Miss Tendril's niece who had also despaired of the day's sport was following behind them at a short distance on her motor bicycle; she too slowed down and, observing that Miss Ripon's horse was likely to be difficult, stopped.

Ben said, "Let me go first, miss. He'll follow. Don't hold too hard on his mouth and just give him a tap."

Miss Ripon did as she was told; everyone in fact behaved with complete good-sense.

They drew abreast of the omnibus. Miss Ripon's horse did not like it, but it seemed as though he would get by. The passengers watched with amusement. At that moment the motor bicycle, running gently in neutral gear, fired back into the cylinder with a sharp detonation. For a second the horse stood rigid with alarm; then, menaced in front and behind, he did what was natural to him and shied sideways, cannoning violently into the pony at his side. John was knocked from the saddle and fell on the road while Miss Ripon's bay, rearing and skidding, continued to plunge away from the bus.

"Take a hold of him, miss. Use your whip," shouted Ben. "The boy's down."

She hit him and the horse collected himself and bolted up the road into the village, but before he went one of his heels struck out and sent John into the ditch, where he lay bent double, perfectly still.

Everyone agreed that it was nobody's fault.

It was nearly an hour before the news reached Jock and Mrs. Rattery, where they were waiting beside another blank covert. Colonel Inch stopped hunting for the day and sent the hounds back to the kennels. The voices were hushed which, five minutes before, had been proclaiming that they knew it for a fact, Last had given orders to shoot every fox on the place. Later, after their baths, they made up for it in criticism of Miss Ripon's father, but at the moment everyone was shocked and silent. Someone lent Jock and Mrs. Rattery a car to get home in, and a groom to see to the hirelings.

"It's the most appalling thing," said Jock in the borrowed car. "What on earth are we going to say to Tony?"

"I'm the last person to have about on an occasion like this," said Mrs. Rattery.

They passed the scene of the accident; there were still people hanging about, talking. There were people hanging about, talking, in the hall at the house. The doctor was buttoning up his coat, just going.

"Killed instantly," he said. "Took it full on the base of the skull. Very sad, awfully fond of the kid. No one to blame though."

Nanny was there in tears; also Mr. Tendril and his niece; a policeman and Ben and two men who had helped bring up the body were in the servants' hall. "It wasn't the kid's fault," said Ben.

"It wasn't anyone's fault," they said.

"He'd had a lousy day too poor little bastard," said Ben. "If it was anyone's fault it was Mr. Grant-Menzies making him go in."

"It wasn't anyone's fault," they said.

Tony was alone in the library. The first thing he said, when Jock came in was, "We've got to tell Brenda."

"D'you know where to get her?"

"She's probably at that school . . . But we can't tell her over the telephone . . . Anyway Ambrose has tried there and the flat but he can't get through . . . What on earth are we going to say to her?"

Jock was silent. He stood in the fireplace with his hands in the pockets of his breeches, with his back to Tony. Presently Tony said, "You weren't anywhere near were you?"

"No, we'd gone on to another covert."

"That niece of Mr. Tendril's told me first . . . then we met them coming up, and Ben told me all that happened . . . It's awful for the girl."

"Miss Ripon?"

"Yes, she's just left . . . she had a nasty fall too, just after. Her horse slipped up in the village . . . she was in a terrible state, poor child, what with that and . . . John. She didn't know she'd hurt him until quite a time afterwards . . . she was in the chemist's shop having a bandage put on her forehead, when they told her. She cut it falling. She was in a terrible state. I sent her back in the car . . . it wasn't her fault."

"No, it wasn't anybody's fault. It just happened."

"That's it," said Tony. "It just happened . . . how are we going to tell Brenda?"

"One of us will have to go up."

"Yes . . . I think I shall have to stay here. I don't know why really, but there will be things to see to. It's an awful thing to ask anyone to do . . ."

"I'll go," said Jock.

"There'll be things to see to here . . . there's got to be an inquest the doctor says. It's purely formal of course, but it will be ghastly for that Ripon girl. She'll have to give evidence . . . she was in a terrible state. I hope I was all right to her. They'd just brought John in and I was rather muddled. She looked awful. I believe her father's bloody to her . . . I wish Brenda had been here. She's so good with everyone. I get in a muddle."

The two men stood in silence.

Tony said, "Can you really face going up and seeing Brenda?"

"Yes, I'll go," said Jock.

Presently Mrs. Rattery came in. "Colonel Inch has been here," she said. "I talked to him. He wanted to give you his sympathy."

"Is he still here?"

"No, I told him you'd probably prefer to be left alone. He thought you'd be glad to hear he stopped the hunt."

"Nice of him to come . . . Were you having a good day?"

"No."

"I'm sorry. We saw a fox in Bruton wood last week, John and I . . . Jock's going up to London to fetch Brenda."

"I'll take him in the aeroplane. It'll be quicker."

"Yes that will be quicker."

"My maid can follow with the luggage by train . . . I'll go and change now. I won't be ten minutes."

"I'll change too," said Jock.

When he was alone Tony rang the bell. A young footman answered; he was quite young and had not been long at Hetton.

"Will you tell Mr. Ambrose that Mrs. Rattery is leaving today. She is flying up with Mr. Grant-Menzies. Her ladyship will probably be coming by the evening train."

"Very good, sir."

"They had better have some luncheon before they go. Something cold in the dining room. I will have it with them . . . And will you put a call through to Colonel Inch and thank him for coming. Say I will write. And to Mr. Ripon's to inquire how Miss Ripon is. And to the vicarage and ask Mr. Tendril if I can see him this evening. He's not here still?"

"No, sir, he left a few minutes ago."

"Tell him I shall have to discuss arrangements with him."

"Very good, sir."

Mr. Last was very matter of fact about everything, the footman reported later.

It was perfectly quiet in the library for the workmen in the morning room had laid aside their tools for the day.

Mrs. Rattery was ready first.

"They're just getting luncheon."

"We shan't want any," she said. "You forget we were going hunting."

"Better have something," said Tony, and then, "It's awful for Jock, having to tell Brenda. I wonder how long it will be before she arrives."

There was something in Tony's voice as he said this which made Mrs. Rattery ask, "What are you going to do while you're waiting?"

"I don't know. I suppose there will be things to see to."

"Look here," said Mrs. Rattery, "Jock had better go up by car. I'll stay here until Lady Brenda comes."

"It would be awful for you."

"No, I'll stay."

Tony said, "I suppose it's ridiculous of me, but I wish you would . . . I mean won't it be awful for you? I am all in a muddle. It's so hard to believe yet, that it really happened."

"It happened all right."

The footman came to say that Mr. Tendril would call after tea that day; that Miss Ripon had gone straight to bed and was asleep.

"Mr. Grant-Menzies is going up in his car. He may be back tonight," said Tony. "Mrs. Rattery is waiting until her ladyship arrives."

"Very good, sir. And Colonel Inch wanted to know whether you would care to have the huntsman blow 'Gone Away' at the funeral."

"Say that I'll write to him," and when the footman had left the room Tony said, "An atrocious suggestion."

"Oh, I don't know. He's very anxious to be helpful."

"They don't like him much as Master."

Jock left soon after half past two. Tony and Mrs. Rattery had coffee in the library.

"I'm afraid this is a very difficult situation," said Tony. "After all we scarcely know each other."

"You don't have to think about me."

"But it must be awful for you."

"And you must stop thinking that."

"I'll try . . . the absurd thing is that I'm not thinking it, just saying it . . . I keep thinking of other things all the time."

"I know. You don't have to say anything."

Presently Tony said, "It's going to be so much worse for Brenda. You see she's got nothing else, much, except John. I've got her, and I love the house . . . but with Brenda John always came first . . . naturally . . . And then you know she's seen so little of John lately. She's been in London such a lot. I'm afraid that's going to hurt her."

"You can't ever tell what's going to hurt people."

"But, you see, I know Brenda so well."

6

The library windows were open and the clock, striking the hour, high overhead among its crockets and finials, was clearly audible in the quiet room. It was some time since they had spoken. Mrs. Rattery sat with her back to Tony; she had spread out her intricate four pack patience on a card table; he was in front of the fire, in the chair he had taken after lunch.

"Only four o'clock?" he said.

"I thought you were asleep."

"No, just thinking . . . Jock will be more than half way there by now, about Aylesbury or Tring."

"It's a slow way to travel."

"It's less than four hours ago that it happened . . . it's odd to think that this is the same day; that it's only five hours ago they were all here at the meet having drinks." There was a pause in which Mrs. Rattery swept up the cards and began to deal them again. "It was twenty-eight minutes past twelve when I heard. I looked at my watch . . . It was ten to one when they brought John in . . . just over three hours ago . . . It's almost incredible, isn't it, everything becoming absolutely different, suddenly like that?"

"It's always that way," said Mrs. Rattery.

"Brenda will hear in an hour now . . . if Jock finds her in. Of course she may very likely be out. He won't know where to find her because there's no one else in the flat. She leaves it locked up, empty, when she goes out . . . and she's out half the day. I know because I sometimes ring up and can't get an answer. He may not find her for hours . . . It may be as long again as the time since it happened. That would only make it eight o'clock. It's quite likely she won't come in until eight . . . Think of it, all the time between now and when it happened, before Brenda hears. It's scarcely credible, is it? And then she's got to get down here. There's a train that leaves at nine something. She might get that. I wonder if I ought to have gone up too . . . I didn't like to leave John."

(Mrs. Rattery sat intent over her game, moving little groups of cards adroitly backward and forwards about the table like shuttles across a loom; under her fingers order grew out of chaos; she established sequence and precedence; the symbols before her became coherent, interrelated.)

". . . Of course she may be at home when he arrives. In that case she can get the evening train, she used always to come by, when she went to London for the day, before she got the flat . . . I'm trying to see it all, as it's going to happen, Jock coming and her surprise at seeing him, and then his telling her . . . It's awful for Jock . . . She may know at half past five or a bit earlier."

"It's a pity you don't play patience," said Mrs. Rattery.

"In a way I shall feel happier when she knows . . . it feels all wrong as it is at present, having it as a secret that Brenda doesn't know . . . I'm not sure how she fits in her day. I suppose her last lecture is over at about five . . . I wonder if she goes home first to change if she's going out to tea or cocktails. She can't sit about much in the flat, it's so small."

Mrs. Rattery brooded over her chequer of cards and then drew them towards her into a heap, haphazard once more and without meaning; it had nearly come to a solution that time, but for a six of diamonds out of place, and a stubbornly congested patch at one corner, where nothing could be made to move. "It's a heartbreaking game," she said.

The clock struck again.

"Is that only quarter past? . . . You know I think I should have gone off my head if I were alone. It's nice of you to stay with me."

"Do you play bezique?"

"I'm afraid not."

"Or piquet?"

"No. I've never been able to learn any card game except animal snap."

"Pity."

"There's Marjorie and several people I ought to wire to, but I'd better wait until I know that Jock has seen Brenda. Suppose she was with Marjorie when the telegram arrived."

"You've got to try and stop thinking about things. Can you throw craps?"

"No."

"That's easy; I'll show you. There'll be some dice in the backgammon board."

"I'm all right, really. I'd sooner not play."

"You get the dice and sit up here at the table. We've got six hours to get through."

She showed him how to throw craps. He said, "I've seen it on the cinema—pullman porters and taxi men."

"Of course you have, it's easy . . . there you see you've won, you take all."

Presently Tony said, "I've just thought of something."

"Don't you ever take a rest from thinking?"

"Suppose the evening papers have got hold of it already. Brenda may see it on a placard, or just pick up a paper casually and there it will be . . . perhaps with a photograph."

"Yes, I thought of that just now, when you were talking about telegraphing."

"But it's quite likely, isn't it? They get hold of everything so quickly. What can we do about it?"

"There isn't anything we can do. We've just got to wait . . . Come on, boy, throw up."

"I don't want to play any more. I'm worried."

"I know you're worried. You don't have to tell me . . . you aren't going to give up playing just when the luck's running your way?"

"I'm sorry . . . it isn't any good."

He walked about the room, first to the window, then to the fireplace. He began to fill his pipe. "At least we can find out whether the evening papers have got it in. We can ring up and ask the hall porter at my club."

"That's not going to prevent your wife reading it. We've just got to wait. What was the game you said you knew? Animal something?"

"Snap."

"Well you come show me that."

"It's just a child's game. It would be ridiculous with two."

"I'll learn it."

"Well each of us chooses an animal."

"All right, I'm a hen and you're a dog. Now what?"

Tony explained.

"I'd say it was one of those games that you have to feel pretty good first, before you can enjoy them," said Mrs. Rattery. "But I'll try anything."

They each took a pack and began dealing. Soon a pair of eights appeared. "Bow-wow," said Mrs. Rattery, scooping in the cards.

Another pair. "Bow-wow," said Mrs. Rattery. "You know you aren't putting your heart into this."

"Oh," said Tony. "Coop-coop-coop."

Presently he said again, "Coop-coop-coop."

"Don't be dumb," said Mrs. Rattery, "that isn't a pair . . ."

They were still playing when Albert came in to draw the curtains. Tony had only two cards left which he turned over regularly; Mrs. Rattery was obliged to divide hers, they were too many to hold. They stopped playing when they found that Albert was in the room.

"What must that man have thought?" said Tony, when he had gone out.

("Sitting there clucking like a 'en," Albert reported, "and the little fellow lying dead upstairs.")

"We'd better stop."

"It wasn't a very good game. And to think it's the only one you know."

She collected the cards and began to deal them into their proper packs. Ambrose and Albert brought in tea. Tony looked at his watch. "Five o'clock. Now that the shutters are up we shan't hear the chimes. Jock must be in London by now."

Mrs. Rattery said, "I'd rather like some whisky."

Jock had not seen Brenda's flat. It was in a large, featureless house, typical of the district. Mrs. Beaver deplored the space wasted by the well staircase and empty, paved hall. There was no porter; a woman came three mornings a week with bucket and mop. A board painted with the names of the tenants informed Jock that Brenda was IN. But he put little reliance on this information, knowing that Brenda was not one to remember as she came in and out, to change the indicator. He found her front door on the second floor. After the first flight the staircase changed from marble to a faded carpet that had been there before Mrs. Beaver undertook the reconstruction. Jock pressed the bell and heard it ringing just inside the door. Nobody came to open it. It was ten past five, and he had not expected to find Brenda at home. He had decided on the road up that after trying the flat, he would go to his club and ring up various friends of Brenda's who might know where she was. He rang again, from habit, and waited a little; then turned to go. But at that moment the door next to Brenda's opened and a dark lady in a dress of crimson velvet looked out at him; she wore very large earrings of oriental filigree, set with bosses of opaque, valueless stone.

"Are you looking for Lady Brenda Last?"

"I am. Is she a friend of yours?"

"Oh *such* a friend," said Princess Abdul Akbar.

"Then perhaps you can tell me where I can find her?"

"I think she's bound to be at Lady Cockpurse's. I'm just going there myself. Can I give her any message?"

"I had better come and see her."

"Well wait five minutes and you can go with me. Come inside."

The Princess's single room was furnished promiscuously and with truly Eastern disregard of the right properties of things; swords meant to adorn the state robes of a Moorish caid were swung from the picture rail; mats made for prayer were strewn on the divan; the carpet on the floor had been made in Bokhara as a wall covering; while over the dressing table was draped a shawl made in Yokohama for sale to cruise-passengers; an octagonal table from Port Said held a Tibetan Buddha of pale soapstone; six ivory elephants from Bombay stood along the top of the radiator. Other cultures, too, were represented by a set of Lalique bottles and powder boxes, a phallic fetish from Senegal, a Dutch copper bowl, a wastepaper basket made of varnished aquatints, a golliwog presented at the gala dinner of a seaside hotel, a dozen or so framed photographs of the Princess, a garden scene ingeniously constructed in pieces of coloured wood, and a radio set in fumed oak, Tudor style. In so small a room the effect was distracting. The Princess sat at the looking glass, Jock behind her on the divan.

"What's your name?" she asked over her shoulder. He told her. "Oh, yes, I've heard them mention you. I was at Hetton the week-end before last . . . such a quaint old place."

"I'd better tell you. There's been a frightful accident there this morning."

Jenny Abdul Akbar spun round on the leather stool; her eyes were wide with alarm, her hand pressed to her heart. "Quick," she whispered, *"tell me. I can't bear it. Is it death?"*

Jock nodded. "Their little boy . . . kicked by a horse."

"Little Jimmy."

"John."

"John . . . *dead*. It's *too* horrible."

"It wasn't anybody's fault."

"Oh yes," said Jenny. "It was. It was *my* fault. I ought never to have gone there . . . a terrible curse hangs over me. Wherever I go I bring nothing but sorrow . . . if only it was *I* that was dead . . . I shall never be able to face them again. I feel like a murderess . . . that brave little life snuffed out."

"I say you know, really, I shouldn't take that line about it."

"It isn't the first time it's happened . . . always, anywhere, I am hunted down . . . without remorse. O God," said Jenny Abdul Akbar. "What have I done to deserve it?"

She rose to leave him; there was nowhere she could go except the bathroom. Jock said, through the door, "Well I must go along to Polly's and see Brenda."

"Wait a minute and I'll come too." She had brightened a little when she emerged. "Have you got a car here," she asked, "or shall I ring up a taxi?"

After tea Mr. Tendril called. Tony saw him in his study and was away half an hour. When he returned he went to the tray, which, on Mrs. Rattery's instructions, had been left in the library, and poured himself out whiskey and ginger ale. Mrs. Rattery had resumed her patience. "Bad interview?" she asked without looking up.

"Awful." He drank the whiskey quickly and poured out some more.

"Bring me one too, will you?"

Tony said, "I only wanted to see him about arrangements. He tried to be comforting. It was very painful . . . after all the last thing one wants to talk about at a time like this is religion."

"Some like it," said Mrs. Rattery.

"Of course," Tony began, after a pause, "when you haven't got children yourself——"

"I've got two sons," said Mrs. Rattery.

"Have you? I'm so sorry. I didn't realize . . . we know each other so little. How very impertinent of me."

"That's all right. People are always surprised. I don't see them often. They're at school somewhere. I took them to the cinema last summer. They're getting quite big. One's going to be good looking I think. His father is."

"Quarter past six," said Tony. "He's bound to have told her by now."

There was a little party at Lady Cockpurse's, Veronica and Daisy and Sybil, Souki de Foucauld-Esterhazy, and four or five others, all women. They were there to consult a new fortune-teller called Mrs.

Northcote. Mrs. Beaver had discovered her and for every five guineas that she earned at her introduction Mrs. Beaver took a commission of two pounds twelve and sixpence. She told fortunes in a new way, by reading the soles of the feet. They waited their turn impatiently. "What a time she is taking over Daisy."

"She is very thorough," said Polly, "and it tickles rather."

Presently Daisy emerged. "What was she like?" they asked.

"I mustn't tell or it spoils it all," said Daisy.

They had dealt cards for precedence. It was Brenda's turn now. She went next door to Mrs. Northcote, who was sitting at a stool beside an armchair. She was a dowdy, middle-aged woman with a slightly genteel accent. Brenda sat down and took off her shoe and stocking. Mrs. Northcote laid the foot on her knee and gazed at it with great solemnity; then she picked it up and began tracing the small creases of the sole with the point of a silver pencil case. Brenda wriggled her toes luxuriously and settled down to listen.

Next door they said, "Where's her Mr. Beaver today?"

"He's flown over to France with his mother to see some new wall papers. She's been worrying all day thinking he's had an accident."

"It's all very touching, isn't it? Though I can't see his point my-self . . ."

"You must never do anything on Thursdays," said Mrs. Northcote.

"Nothing?"

"Nothing important. You are intellectual, imaginative, sympathetic, easily led by others, impulsive, affectionate. You are highly artistic and are not giving full scope to your capabilities."

"Isn't there anything about love?"

"I am coming to love. All these lines from the great toe to the in-step represent lovers."

"Yes, go on some more about that . . ."

Princess Abdul Akbar was announced.

"Where's Brenda?" she said. "I thought she'd be here."

"Mrs. Northcote's doing her now."

"Jock Grant-Menzies wants to see her. He's downstairs."

"Darling Jock . . . Why on earth didn't you bring him up."

"No, it's something terribly important. He's got to see Brenda alone."

"My dear, how mysterious. Well she won't be long now. We can't disturb them. It would upset Mrs. Northcote."

Jenny told them her news.

On the other side of the door, Brenda's leg was beginning to feel slightly chilly. "Four men dominate your fate," Mrs. Northcote was saying, "one is loyal and tender but he has not yet disclosed his love, one is passionate and overpowering, you are a little afraid of him."

"Dear me," said Brenda. "How very exciting. Who *can* they be?"

"One you must avoid; he bodes no good for you, he is steely hearted and rapacious."

"I bet that's my Mr. Beaver, bless him."

Downstairs Jock sat waiting in the small front room where Polly's guests usually assembled before luncheon. It was five past six.

Soon Brenda pulled on her stocking, stepped into her shoe, and joined the ladies. "*Most* enjoyable," she pronounced. "Why how odd you all look."

"Jock Grant-Menzies wants to see you downstairs."

"Jock? How very extraordinary. It isn't anything awful is it?"

"You better go and see him."

Suddenly Brenda became frightened by the strange air of the room and the unfamiliar expression in her friends' faces. She ran downstairs to the room where Jock was waiting.

"What is it, Jock? Tell me quickly, I'm scared. It's nothing awful is it?"

"I'm afraid it is. There's been a very serious accident."

"John?"

"Yes."

"Dead?"

He nodded.

She sat down on a hard little Empire chair against the wall, perfectly still with her hands folded in her lap, like a small well-brought-up child introduced into a room full of grown-ups. She said, "Tell me what happened? Why do you know about it first?"

"I've been down at Hetton since the week-end."

"Hetton?"

"Don't you remember? John was going hunting today."

She frowned, not at once taking in what he was saying. "John . . . John Andrew . . . I . . . Oh thank God . . ." Then she burst into tears.

She wept helplessly, turning round in the chair and pressing her forehead against its gilt back.

Upstairs Mrs. Northcote had Souki de Foucauld-Esterhazy by the foot and was saying, "There are four men dominating your fate. One is loyal and tender but has not yet disclosed his love . . ."

In the silence of Hetton, the telephone rang near the housekeeper's room and was switched through to the library. Tony answered it.

"This is Jock speaking. I've just seen Brenda. She's coming down by the seven o'clock train."

"Is she terribly upset?"

"Yes, naturally."

"Where is she now?"

"She's with me. I'm speaking from Polly's."

"Shall I talk to her?"

"Better not."

"All right . . . I'll meet that train. Are you coming too?"

"No."

"Well you've been wonderful. I don't know what I should have done without you and Mrs. Rattery."

"Oh, that's all right. I'll see Brenda off."

She had stopped crying and sat crouched in the chair. She did not look up while Jock telephoned. Then she said, "Yes, I'll go by that train."

"We ought to start. I suppose you will have to get some things from the flat."

"My bag . . . upstairs. You get it. I can't go in there again."

She did not speak on the way to her flat. She sat beside Jock as he drove, looking straight ahead. When they arrived she unlocked her door and led him in. The room was extremely empty of furniture. She sat down in the only chair. "There's plenty of time really. Tell me exactly what happened."

Jock told her.

"Poor little boy," she said. "Poor little boy."

Then she opened her cupboard and began to put a few things into a suitcase; she went in and out from the bathroom once or twice. "That's everything," she said. "There's still too much time."

"Would you like anything to eat?"

"Oh no, nothing to eat." She sat down again and looked at herself in the glass. She did not attempt to do anything to her face. "When you first told me," she said, "I didn't understand. I didn't know what I was saying."

"I know."

"I didn't say anything, did I?"

"You know what you said."

"Yes, I know . . . I didn't mean . . . I don't think it's any good trying to explain."

Jock said, "Are you sure you've got everything?"

"Yes, that's everything," she nodded towards the little case on the bed. She looked quite hopeless.

"Well, we'd better go to the station."

"All right. It's early. But it doesn't matter."

Jock took her to the train. As it was Wednesday the carriages were full of women returning after their day's shopping.

"Why not go first class?"

"No, no. I always go third."

She sat in the middle of a row. The women on either side looked at her curiously wondering if she were ill.

"Don't you want anything to read?"

"Nothing to read."

"Or eat?"

"Or eat."

"Then I'll say good-bye."

"Good-bye."

Another woman pushed past Jock into the carriage, laden with light parcels.

When the news became known Marjorie said to Allan, "Well, anyway, this will mean the end of Mr. Beaver."

But Polly Cockpurse said to Veronica, "That's the end of Tony so far as Brenda is concerned."

The impoverished Lasts were stunned by the telegram. They lived on an extensive but unprofitable chicken farm near Great Missenden. It did not enter the heads of any of them that now, if anything happened, they were the heirs to Hetton. Had it done so, their grief would have been just as keen.

Jock drove from Paddington to Brat's. One of the men by the bar said, "Ghastly thing about Tony Last's boy."

"Yes, I was there."

"No, were you? What a ghastly thing."

Later a telephone message came: "Princess Abdul Akbar wishes to know whether you are in the club."

"No, no, tell her I'm not here," said Jock.

7

The inquest was held at eleven o'clock next morning; it was soon over. The doctor, the bus-driver, Ben and Miss Ripon gave evidence. Miss Ripon was allowed to remain seated. She was very white and spoke in a trembling voice; her father glared at her from a near-by seat; under her hat was a small bare patch, where they had shaved off the hair to clean her cut. In his summary the coroner remarked that it was clear from the evidence that nobody was in any way to blame for the misadventure; it only remained to express the deep sympathy of the court to Mr. Last and Lady Brenda in their terrible loss. The people fell back to allow Tony and Brenda to reach their car. Colonel Inch and the hunt secretary were both present. Everything was done with delicacy and to show respect for their sorrow.

Brenda said, "Wait a minute. I must just speak to that poor Ripon girl."

She did it charmingly. When they were in the car, Tony said, "I wish you had been here yesterday. There were so many people about and I didn't know what to say to them."

"What did you do all day?"

"There was the shameless blonde . . . we played animal snap some of the time."

"Animal snap? Was that any good?"

"Not much . . . It's odd to think that yesterday this time it hadn't happened."

"Poor little boy," said Brenda.

They had scarcely spoken to each other since Brenda's arrival. Tony had driven to the station to meet her; by the time they reached the house Mrs. Rattery had gone to bed; that morning she left in her aeroplane without seeing either of them. They heard the machine pass over the house, Brenda in her bath, Tony downstairs in his study attending to the correspondence that had become necessary.

A day of fitful sunshine and blustering wind; white and grey clouds were scarcely moving, high overhead, but the bare trees round the house swayed and shook and there were swift whirlpools of straw in the stable yard. Ben changed from the Sunday suit he had worn at the inquest and went about his duties. Thunderclap, too, had been kicked yesterday and was very slightly lame in the off fore.

Brenda took off her hat and threw it down on a chair in the hall. "Nothing to say, is there?"

"There's no need to talk."

"No. I suppose there'll have to be a funeral."

"Well, of course."

"Yes; tomorrow?"

She looked into the morning room. "They've done quite a lot, haven't they?"

All Brenda's movements were slower than usual and her voice was flat and expressionless. She sank down into one of the armchairs in the centre of the hall, which nobody ever used. She sat there doing nothing. Tony put his hand on her shoulder but she said "Don't," not impatiently or nervously but without any expression. Tony said, "I'll go and finish those letters."

"Yes."

"See you at luncheon."

"Yes."

She rose, looked round listlessly for her hat, found it and went very slowly upstairs, the sunlight through the stained glass windows glowing and sparkling all about her.

In her room she sat on the window seat, looking out across the meadows and dun ploughland, the naked tossing trees, the church towers, the maelstroms of dust and leaf which eddied about the terrace below; she still held her hat and fidgeted with her fingers on the brooch which was slipped to one side of it.

Nanny knocked at the door and came in, red eyed. "If you please, my lady, I've been going through John's things. There's this handkerchief doesn't belong to him."

The heavy scent and crowned cypher at its corner proclaimed its origin.

"I know whose it is. I'll send it back to her."

"Can't think how it came to be there," said nanny.

"Poor little boy. Poor little boy," said Brenda to herself, when nanny had left her, and gazed out across the troubled landscape.

"I was thinking about the pony, sir."

"Oh yes, Ben."

"Will you want to be keeping her now?"

"I hadn't thought . . . no, I suppose not."

"Mr. Westmacott over at Restall was asking about her. He thought she might do for his little girl."

"Yes."

"How much shall we be asking?"

"Oh, I don't know . . . whatever you think is right."

"She's a good little pony and she's always been treated well. I don't think she ought to go under twenty-five quid, sir."

"All right, Ben, you see about it."

"I'll ask thirty, shall I, sir, and come down a bit."

"Do just what you think best."

"Very good, sir."

At luncheon Tony said, "Jock rang up. He wanted to know if there was anything he could do."

"How sweet of him. Why don't you have him down for the week-end?"

"Would you like that?"

"I shan't be here. I'm going to Veronica's."

"You're going to Veronica's?"

"Yes, don't you remember?"

There were servants in the room so that they said nothing more until later, when they were alone in the library. Then, "Are you really going away?"

"Yes. I can't stay here. You understand that, don't you?"

"Yes, of course. I was thinking we might both go away, abroad somewhere."

Brenda did not answer him but continued in her own line. "I couldn't stay here. It's all over, don't you see, our life down here."

"Darling, what *do* you mean?"

"Don't ask me to explain . . . not just now."

"But, Brenda, sweet, I don't understand. We're both young. Of course we can never forget John. He'll always be our eldest son but . . ."

"Don't go on, Tony, please don't go on."

So Tony stopped and after a time said, "So you're going to Veronica's tomorrow?"

"Mmmm."

"I think I will ask Jock to come."

"Yes, I should."

"And we can think about plans later when we've got more used to things."

"Yes, later."

Next morning. "A sweet letter from mother," said Brenda, handing it across. Lady St. Cloud had written:

> . . . *I shall not come down to Hetton for the funeral, but I shall be thinking of you both all the time and my dear grandson. I shall think of you as I saw you all three, together, at Christmas. Dear children, at a time like this only yourselves can be any help to each other. Love is the only thing that is stronger than sorrow* . . .

"I got a telegram from Jock," said Tony, "he *can* come."

"It's really rather embarrassing for us all, Brenda coming," said Veronica. "I do think she might have chucked. I shan't in the least know what to say to her."

Tony said to Jock, as they sat alone after dinner, "I've been trying to understand, and I think I do now. It's not how I feel myself but Brenda and I are quite different in lots of ways. It's *because* they were strangers and didn't know John, and were never in our life here, that she wants to be with them. That's it, don't you think? She wants to be absolutely alone and away from everything that reminds her of what has happened . . . all the same I feel awful about letting her go. I can't tell you what she was like here . . . quite mechanical. It's so much worse for her than it is for me, I see that. It's so terrible not being able to do anything to help."

Jock did not answer.

Beaver was staying at Veronica's. Brenda said to him, "Until Wednesday, when I thought something had happened to you, I had no idea that I loved you."

"Well you've said it often enough."

"I'm going to make you understand," said Brenda. "You clod."

On Monday morning Tony found this letter on his breakfast tray.

Darling Tony,

I am not coming back to Hetton. Grimshawe can pack everything and bring it to the flat. Then I shan't want her any more.

You must have realized for some time that things were going wrong. I am in love with John Beaver and I want to have a divorce and marry him. If John Andrew had not died things might not have happened like this. I can't tell. As it is, I simply can't begin over again. Please do not mind too much. I suppose we shan't be allowed to meet while the case is on but I hope afterwards we shall be great friends. Anyway I shall always look on you as one whatever you think of me.

Best love from

Brenda.

When Tony read this his first thought was that Brenda had lost her reason. "She's only seen Beaver twice to my knowledge," he said.

But later he showed the letter to Jock who said, "I'm sorry it should have happened like this."

"But it's not true, is it?"

'Yes, I'm afraid it is. Everyone has known for some time."

But it was several days before Tony fully realized what it meant. He had got into a habit of loving and trusting Brenda.

I V

ENGLISH GOTHIC—II

"How's the old boy taking it?"

"Not so well. It makes me feel rather a beast," said Brenda. "I'm afraid he minds a lot."

"Well you wouldn't like it if he didn't," said Polly to console her.

"No, I suppose not."

"I shall stick by you whatever happens," said Jenny Abdul Akbar.

"Oh everything is going quite smoothly now," said Brenda. "There was a certain amount of *gêne* with relatives."

Tony had been living with Jock for the last three weeks. Mrs. Rattery had gone to California and he was grateful for company. They dined together most evenings. They had given up going to Brat's; so had Beaver; they were afraid of meeting each other. Instead they went to Brown's where Beaver was not a member. Beaver was continually with Brenda nowadays, at one of half a dozen houses.

Mrs. Beaver did not like the turn things had taken; her workmen had been sent back from Hetton with their job unfinished.

In the first week Tony had had several distasteful interviews. Allan had attempted to act as peacemaker.

"You just wait a few weeks," he had said. "Brenda will come back. She'll soon get sick of Beaver."

"But I don't want her back."

"I know just how you feel, but it doesn't do to be mediæval about it. If Brenda hadn't been upset at John's death this need never have come to a crisis. Why last year Marjorie was going everywhere with that ass Robin Beaseley. She was mad about him at the time but I pretended not to notice and it all blew over. If I were you I should refuse to recognize that anything has happened."

Marjorie had said, "Of *course* Brenda doesn't love Beaver. How could she? . . . And if she thinks she does at the moment, I think it's your duty to prevent her making a fool of herself. You must refuse to be divorced—anyway until she has found someone more reasonable."

Lady St. Cloud had said, "Brenda has been very, very foolish. She always was an excitable girl, but I am sure there was never anything *wrong,* quite sure. *That* wouldn't be like Brenda at all. I haven't met Mr. Beaver and I do not wish to. I understand he is unsuitable in every way. Brenda would never want to marry anyone like that. I will tell you exactly how it happened, Tony. Brenda must have felt a tiny bit neglected—people often do at that stage of marriage. I have known countless cases—and it was naturally flattering to her to find a young man to beg and carry for her. That's all it was, nothing *wrong.* And then the terrible shock of little John's accident unsettled her and she didn't know what she was saying or writing. You'll both laugh over this little fracas in years to come."

Tony had not set eyes on Brenda since the afternoon of the funeral. Once he spoke to her over the telephone.

It was during the second week when he was feeling most lonely and bewildered by various counsels. Allan had been with him urging a reconciliation. "I've been talking to Brenda," he had said. "She's sick of Beaver already. The one thing she wants is to go back to Hetton and settle down with you again."

While Allan was there, Tony resolutely refused to listen but later the words, and the picture they evoked, would not leave his mind. So he rang her up and she answered him calmly and gravely.

"Brenda, this is Tony."

"Hullo, Tony, what is it?"

"I've been talking to Allan. He's just told me about your change of mind."

"I'm not sure I know what you mean."

"That you want to leave Beaver and come back to Hetton."

"Did Allan say that?"

"Yes, isn't it true?"

"I'm afraid it's not. Allan is an interfering ass. I had him here this afternoon. He told me that you didn't want a divorce but that you were willing to let me stay on alone in London and do as I liked provided there was no public scandal. It seemed a good idea and I was going to ring you up about it. But I suppose that's just his diplomacy too. Anyway I'm afraid there's no prospect of my coming back to Hetton just at present."

"Oh I see. I didn't think it was likely . . . I just rang you up."

"That's all right. How are you, Tony?"

"All right, thanks."

"Good, so am I. Good-bye."

That was all he had heard of her. Both avoided places where there was a likelihood of their meeting.

It was thought convenient that Brenda should appear as the plaintiff. Tony did not employ the family solicitors in the matter but another, less reputable firm who specialized in divorce. He had steeled himself to expect a certain professional gusto, even levity, but found them instead disposed to melancholy and suspicion.

"I gather Lady Brenda is being far from discreet. It is quite likely that the King's Proctor may intervene . . . Moreover there is the question of money. You understand that by the present arrangement since she is the innocent and injured party she will be entitled to claim substantial alimony from the courts."

"Oh that's all right," said Tony. "I've been into all that with her brother-in-law and have decided to make a settlement of five hundred a year. She has four hundred of her own and I understand Mr. Beaver has something."

"It's a pity we can't put it in writing," said the solicitor, "but that might constitute Conspiracy."

"Lady Brenda's word is quite good enough," said Tony.

"We like to protect our clients against even the most remote contingencies," said the lawyer with an air of piety, for he had not had Tony's opportunities to contract the habit of loving and trusting Brenda.

The fourth week-end after Brenda's departure from Hetton was fixed for Tony's infidelity. A suite was engaged at a seaside hotel ("We always send our clients there. The servants are well accustomed to giving evidence") and private detectives were notified. "It only remains to select a partner," said the solicitor; no hint of naughtiness lightened his gloom. "We have on occasions been instrumental in accommodating our clients but there have been frequent complaints, so we find it best to leave the choice to them. Lately we had a particularly delicate case involving a man of very rigid morality and a certain diffidence. In the end his own wife consented to go with him and supply the evidence. She wore a red wig. It was quite successful."

"I don't think that would do in this case."

"No. Exactly. I was merely quoting it as a matter of interest."

"I expect I shall be able to find someone," said Tony.

"I have no doubt of it," said the solicitor, bowing politely.

But when he came to discuss the question later with Jock, it did not seem so easy. "It's not a thing one can ask every girl to do," he said, "whichever way you put it. If you say it is merely a legal form it is rather insulting, and if you suggest going the whole hog it's rather fresh—suddenly, I mean, if you've never paid any particular attention to her before and don't propose to carry on with it afterwards . . . Of course there's always old Sybil."

But even Sybil refused. "I'd do it like a shot any other time," she said, "but just at the moment it wouldn't suit my book. There's a certain person who might hear about it and take it wrong . . . There's an awfully pretty girl called Jenny Abdul Akbar. I wonder if you've met her."

"Yes, I've met her."

"Well won't she do?"

"No."

"Oh dear, I don't know who to suggest."

"We'd better go and study the market at the Sixty-four," said Jock.

They dined at Jock's house. Lately they had found it a little gloomy at Brown's for people tended to avoid anyone they knew to be unhappy. Though they drank a magnum of champagne they could not recapture the light-hearted mood in which they had last visited Sink Street. And then Tony said, "Is it any good going there yet?"

"We may as well try. After all we aren't going there for enjoyment."

"No, indeed."

The doors were open at 64 Sink Street and the band was playing to an empty ballroom. The waiters were eating at a little table in the corner. Two or three girls were clustered round the Jack-Pot machine, losing shillings hard and complaining about the cold. They ordered a bottle of the Montmorency Wine Company's brandy and sat down to wait.

"Any of those do?" asked Jock.

"I don't much care."

"Better get someone you like. You've got to put in a lot of time with her."

Presently Milly and Babs came downstairs.

"How are the postman's hats?" said Milly.

They could not recognize the allusion.

"You are the two boys who were here last month, aren't you?"

"Yes. I'm afraid we were rather tight."

"You don't say?" It was very seldom that Milly and Babs met anyone who was quite sober during their business hours.

"Well come and sit down. How are you both?"

"I think I'm starting a cold," said Babs. "I feel awful. Why can't
they heat this hole, the mean hounds?"

Milly was more cheerful and swayed in her chair to the music.
"Care to dance?" she said, and she and Tony began to shuffle across
the empty floor.

"My friend is looking for a lady to take to the seaside," said Jock.

"What, this weather? That'll be a nice treat for a lonely girl." Babs
sniffed into a little ball of handkerchief.

"It's for a divorce."

"Oh, I see. Well, why doesn't he take Milly? She doesn't catch cold
easy. Besides she knows how to behave at a hotel. Lots of the girls
here are all right to have a lark with in town but you have to have a
lady for a divorce."

"D'you often get asked to do that?"

"Now and then. It's a nice rest—but it means so much *talking* and
the gentlemen will always go on so about their wives."

While they were dancing Tony came straight to business. "I suppose you wouldn't care to come away for the week-end?" he asked.

"Shouldn't mind," said Milly. "Where?"

"I thought of Brighton."

"Oh . . . Is it for a divorce?"

"Yes."

"You wouldn't mind if I brought my little girl with us? She
wouldn't be any trouble."

"Yes."

"You mean you wouldn't mind?"

"I mean I should mind."

"Oh . . . You wouldn't think I had a little girl of eight, would
you?"

"No."

"She's called Winnie. I was only sixteen when I had her. I was the youngest of the family and our stepfather wouldn't leave any of us girls alone. That's why I have to work for a living. She lives with a lady at Finchley. Twenty-eight bob a week it costs me, not counting her clothes. She does like the seaside."

"No," said Tony. "I'm sorry but it would be quite impossible. We'll get a lovely present for you to take back to her."

"All right . . . One gentleman gave her a fairy bicycle for Christmas. She fell off and cut her knee . . . When do we start?"

"Would you like to go by train or car?"

"Oh train. Winnie's sick if she goes in a car."

"Winnie's not coming."

"No, but let's go by train anyway."

So it was decided that they should meet at Victoria on Saturday afternoon.

Jock gave Babs ten shillings and he and Tony went home. Tony had not slept much lately. He could not prevent himself, when alone, from rehearsing over and over in his mind all that had happened since Beaver's visit to Hetton; searching for clues he had missed at the time; wondering where something he had said or done might have changed the course of events; going back further to his earliest acquaintance with Brenda to find indications that should have made him more ready to understand the change that had come over her; reliving scene after scene in the last eight years of his life. All this kept him awake.

2

There was a general rendezvous at the first class booking office. The detectives were the first, ten minutes before their time. They had been pointed out to Tony at the solicitor's office so that he should not lose them. They were cheerful middle-aged men in soft hats and heavy overcoats. They were looking forward to their week-end, for most of their daily work consisted in standing about at street corners watching front doors and a job of this kind was eagerly competed for in the office. In more modest divorces the solicitors were content to rely on the evidence of the hotel servants. The detectives were a luxury and proposed to treat themselves as such.

There was a slight fog in London that day. The station lamps were alight prematurely.

Tony came next, with Jock at his side, loyally there to see him off. They bought the tickets and waited. The detectives, sticklers for professional etiquette, made an attempt at self-effacement, studying the posters on the walls and peering from behind a pillar.

"This is going to be hell," said Tony.

It was ten minutes before Milly came. She emerged from the gloom with a porter in front carrying her suitcase and a child dragging back on her arm behind her. Milly's wardrobe consisted mainly of evening dresses, for during the day she usually spent her time sitting before a gas-fire in her dressing gown. She made an insignificant and rather respectable appearance. "Sorry if I'm late," she said. "Winnie here couldn't find her shoes. I brought her along too. I knew you wouldn't really mind. She travels on a half ticket."

Winnie was a plain child with large gold-rimmed spectacles. When she spoke she revealed that two of her front teeth were missing.

"I hope you don't imagine she's coming with us."

"Yes, that's the idea," said Milly. "She won't be any trouble—she's got her puzzle."

Tony bent down to speak to the little girl. "Listen," he said. "You don't want to come to a nasty big hotel. You go with this kind gentleman here. He'll take you to a shop and let you choose the biggest doll you can find and then he'll drive you back in his motor to your home. You'll like that, won't you?"

"No," said Winnie. "I want to go to the seaside. I won't go with that man. I don't want a doll. I want to go to the seaside with my mummy."

Several people besides the detectives were beginning to take notice of the oddly assorted group.

"Oh God!" said Tony, "I suppose she's got to come."

The detectives followed at a distance down the platform. Tony settled his companions in a pullman car. "Look," said Milly, "we're travelling first class. Isn't that fun? We can have tea."

"Can I have an ice?"

"I don't expect they've got an ice. But you can have some nice tea."

"But I want an ice."

"You shall have an ice when you get to Brighton. Now be a good girl and play with your puzzle or mother won't take you to the seaside again."

"The Awful Child of popular fiction," said Jock as he left Tony.

Winnie sustained the part throughout the journey to Brighton. She was not inventive but she knew the classic routine thoroughly, even to such commonplace but alarming devices as breathing heavily, grunting and complaining of nausea.

Room at the hotel had been engaged for Tony by the solicitors. It was therefore a surprise to the reception clerk when Winnie arrived. "We have reserved in your name double and single communicating rooms, bathroom and sitting room," he said. "We did not understand you were bringing your daughter. Will you require a further room?"

"Oh Winnie can come in with me," said Milly.

The two detectives who were standing nearby at the counter, exchanged glances of disapproval.

Tony wrote *Mr. and Mrs. Last* in the Visitors' Book.

"And daughter," said the clerk with his finger on the place.

Tony hesitated. "She is my niece," he said, and inscribed her name on another line, as *Miss Smith*.

The detective, registering below, remarked to his colleague, "He got out of that all right. Quite smart. But I don't like the look of this case. Most irregular. Sets a nasty, respectable note bringing a kid into it. We've got the firm to consider. It doesn't do them any good to get mixed up with the King's Proctor."

"How about a quick one?" said his colleague indifferently.

Upstairs, Winnie said, "Where's the sea?"

"Just there across the street."

"I want to go and see it."

"But it's dark now, pet. You shall see it tomorrow."

"I want to see it tonight."

"You take her to see it now," said Tony.

"Sure you won't be lonely?"

"Quite sure."

"We won't be long."

"That's all right. You let her see it properly."

Tony went down to the bar where he was pleased to find the two detectives. He felt the need of male company. "Good evening," he said.

They looked at him askance. Everything in this case seemed to be happening as though with deliberate design to shock their professional feelings. "Good evening," said the senior detective. "Nasty, raw evening."

"Have a drink."

Since Tony was paying their expenses in any case, the offer seemed superfluous but the junior detective brightened instinctively and said, "Don't mind if I do."

"Come and sit down. I feel rather lonely."

They took their drinks to a table out of hearing of the bar man. "Mr. Last, sir, this is all *wrong,*" said the senior detective. "You haven't no business to recognize us at all. I don't know what they'd say at the office."

"Best respects," said the junior detective.

"This is Mr. James, my colleague," said the senior detective. "My name is Blenkinsop. James is new to this kind of work."

"So am I," said Tony.

"A pity we've such a nasty week-end for the job," said Blenkinsop, "very damp and blowy. Gets me in the joints."

"Tell me," said Tony. "Is it usual to bring children on an expedition of this kind?"

"It is *not.*"

"I thought it couldn't be."

"Since you ask me, Mr. Last, I regard it as most irregular and injudicious. It looks wrong, and cases of this kind depend very much on making the right impression. Of course as far as James and I are concerned, the matter is O.K. There won't be a word about it in our evidence. But you can't trust the servants. You might very likely happen to strike one who was new to the courts, who'd blurt it out, and then where would we be? I don't like it, Mr. Last, and that's the truth."

"You can't feel more strongly about it than I do."

"Fond of kids myself," said James, who was new to this kind of work. "How about one with us."

"Tell me," said Tony, when they had been at their table some little time. "You must have observed numerous couples in your time, qualifying for a divorce; tell me, how do they get through their day?"

"It's easier in the summer," said Blenkinsop, "the young ladies usually bathe and the gentlemen read the papers on the esplanade; some goes for motor drives and some just hangs around the bar. They're mostly glad when Monday comes."

Milly and her child were in the sitting room when Tony came up.

"I've ordered an ice," said Milly.

"Quite right."

"I want late dinner. I want late dinner."

"No, dear, not late dinner. You have an ice up here."

Tony returned to the bar. "Mr. James," he said. "Did I understand you to say you were fond of children."

"Yes, in their right place."

"You wouldn't I suppose consider dining tonight with the little girl who has accompanied me? I should take it as a great kindness."

"Oh no, sir, hardly that."

"You would not find me ungrateful."

"Well, sir, I don't like to appear unobliging, but it's not part of my duties."

He seemed to be wavering but Blenkinsop interposed. "Quite out of the question, sir."

When Tony left them Blenkinsop spoke from the depth of his experience; it was the first job that he and James had been on together, and he felt under some obligation to put his junior wise. "Our trouble is always the same—to make the clients realize that divorce is a serious matter."

Eventually extravagant promises for the morrow, two or three ices and the slight depression induced by them, persuaded Winnie to go to bed.

"How are we going to sleep?" asked Milly.

"Oh, just as you like."

"Just as *you* like."

"Well perhaps Winnie would be happier with you . . . she'll have to go into the other room tomorrow morning when they bring in breakfast, of course."

So she was tucked up in a corner of the double bed and to Tony's surprise was asleep before they went down to dinner.

A change of clothes brought to both Tony and Milly a change of temper. She, in her best evening frock, backless and vermilion, her face newly done and her bleached curls brushed out, her feet in high red shoes, some bracelets on her wrists, a dab of scent behind the large sham pearls in her ears, shook off the cares of domesticity and was once more in uniform, reporting for duty, a legionary ordered for active service after the enervating restraints of a winter in barracks; and Tony, filling his cigar case before the mirror, and slipping it into the pocket of his dinner jacket, reminded himself that phantasmagoric, and even gruesome as the situation might seem to him, he was nevertheless a host, so that he knocked at the communicating door and passed with a calm manner into his guest's room; for a month now he had lived in a world suddenly bereft of order; it was as though the whole reasonable and decent constitution of things, the sum of all he had experienced or learned to expect, were an inconspicuous, inconsiderable object mislaid somewhere on the dressing table; no outrageous circumstance in which he found himself, no new mad thing brought to his notice could add a jot to the all-encompassing chaos that shrieked about his ears. He smiled at Milly from the doorway. "Charming," he said, "perfectly charming. Shall we go down to dinner?"

Their rooms were on the first floor. Step by step, with her hand on his arm, they descended the staircase into the bright hall below.

"Cheer up," said Milly. "You have a tongue sandwich. That'll make you talk."

"Sorry, am I being a bore?"

"I was only joking. You are a serious boy, aren't you?"

In spite of the savage weather the hotel seemed full of week-end visitors. More were arriving through the swing doors, their eyes moist and their cheeks rigid from the icy cold outside.

"Yids," explained Milly superfluously. "Still it's nice to get a change from the club once in a while."

One of the new arrivals was a friend of Milly's. He was supervising the collection of his luggage. Anywhere else he would have been a noticeable figure, for he wore a large fur coat and a beret; under the coat appeared tartan stockings and black and white shoes. "Take 'em up and get 'em unpacked and quick about it," he said. He was a stout little young man. His companion, also in furs, was staring resentfully at one of the showcases that embellished the hall.

"Oh for Christ's sake," she said.

Milly and the young man greeted each other. "This is Dan," she said.

"Well, well, well," said Dan, "what next."

"Do I get a drink?" said Dan's girl.

"Baby, you do, if I have to get it myself. Won't you two join us, or are we de trop?"

They went together into the glittering lounge. "I'm cold like hell," said Baby.

Dan had taken off his greatcoat and revealed a suit of smooth, purplish plus fours, and a silk shirt of a pattern Tony might have chosen for pyjamas. "We'll soon warm you up," he said.

"This place stinks of yids," said Baby.

"I always think that's the sign of a good hotel, don't you?" said Tony.

"Like hell," said Baby.

"You mustn't mind Baby, she's cold," Dan explained.

"Who wouldn't be in your lousy car?"

They had some cocktails. Then Dan and Baby went to their room; they must doll up, they explained, as they were going to a party given by a friend of Dan's, at a place of his near there. Tony and Milly went in to dinner. "He's a very nice boy," she said, "and comes to the club a lot. We get all sorts there, but Dan's one of the decent ones. I was going to have gone abroad with him once but in the end he couldn't get away."

"His girl didn't seem to like us much."

"Oh, she was cold."

Tony did not find conversation easy at dinner. At first he commented on their neighbours as he would have done if he had been dining with Brenda at Espinosa's. "That's a pretty girl in the corner."

"I wonder you don't go and join her, dear," said Milly testily.

"Look at that woman's diamonds. Do you think they can be real?"

"Why don't you ask her, if you're so interested?"

"That's an interesting type—the dark woman dancing."

"I'm sure she'd be delighted to hear it."

Presently Tony realized that it was not etiquette in Milly's world, to express interest in women, other than the one you were with.

They drank champagne. So, Tony noticed with displeasure, did the two detectives. He would have something to say about that when their bill for expenses came in. It was not as though they had been accommodating in the matter of Winnie. All the time, at the back of his mind, he was worrying with the problem of what they could possibly do after dinner, but it was solved for him, just as he was lighting his cigar, by the appearance of Dan from the other side of the dining room. "Look here," he said, "if you two aren't doing anything special why don't you join up with us and come to the party at my friend's place. You'll like it. He always gives one the best of everything."

"Oh do let's," said Milly.

Dan's evening clothes were made of blue cloth that was supposed to appear black in artificial light; for some reason, however, they remained very blue.

So Milly and Tony went to Dan's friend's place and had the best of everything. There was a party of twenty or thirty people, all more or less like Dan. Dan's friend was most hospitable. When he was not fiddling with the wireless, which gave trouble off and on throughout the evening, he was sauntering among his guests refilling their glasses. "This stuff's all right," he said, showing the label, "it won't hurt you. It's the right stuff."

They had a lot of the right stuff.

Quite often Dan's friend noticed that Tony seemed to be out of the party. Then he would come across and put his hand on Tony's shoulder. "I'm so glad Dan brought you," he would say. "Hope you're getting all you want. Delighted to see you. Come again when there isn't a crowd and see over the place. Interested in roses?"

"Yes, I like them very much."

"Come when the roses are out. You'd like that if you're interested in roses. Damn that radio, it's going wonky again."

Tony wondered whether he was as amiable when people he did not know were brought over unexpectedly to Hetton.

At one stage in the evening he found himself sitting on a sofa with Dan. "Nice kid Milly," he said.

"Yes."

"I'll tell you a thing I've noticed about her. She attracts quite a different type from the other girls. People like you and me."

"Yes."

"You wouldn't think she had a daughter of eight, would you?"

"No, it's very surprising."

"I didn't know for ages. Then I was taking her to Dieppe for the week-end and she wanted to bring the child along too. Of course that put the kibosh on it, but I've always liked Milly just the same. You can trust her to behave anywhere." He said this with a sour glance towards Baby who was full of the right stuff and showing it.

It was after three before the party broke up. Dan's friend renewed his invitation to come again when the roses were out. "I doubt if you'll find a better show of roses anywhere in the south of England," he said.

Dan drove them back to the hotel. Baby sat beside him in front, disposed to be quarrelsome. "Where were you?" she kept asking. "Never saw you all the evening. Where did you get to? Where were you hiding? I call it a lousy way to take a girl out."

Tony and Milly sat at the back. From habit and exhaustion she put her head on his shoulder and her hand in his. When they reached their rooms, however, she said, "Go quietly. We don't want to wake Winnie."

For an hour or so Tony lay in the warm little bedroom, reviewing over and over again the incidents of the last three months; then he too fell asleep.

He was awakened by Winnie. "Mother's still asleep," she said.

Tony looked at his watch. "So I should think," he said. It was quarter past seven. "Go back to bed."

"No, I'm dressed. Let's go out."

She went to the window and pulled back the curtains, filling the room with glacial morning light. "It's hardly raining at all," she said.

"What do you want to do?"

"I want to go on the pier."

"It won't be open yet."

"Well I want to go down to the sea. Come on."

Tony knew that he would not get to sleep again that morning. "All right. You go and wait while I dress."

"I'll wait here. Mother snores so."

Twenty minutes later they went downstairs into the hall where aproned waiters were piling up the furniture and brushing the carpets. A keen wind met them as they emerged from the swing door. The asphalt promenade was wet with spray and rain. Two or three female figures were scudding along, bowed to the wind, prayer books clutched in their gloved hands. Four or five rugged old men were hobbling down to bathe, hissing like ostlers. "Oh come on," said Winnie.

They went down to the beach and stumbled painfully across the shingle to the margin of the sea. Winnie threw some stones. The bathers were in the water now; some of them had dogs who swam snorting beside them. "Why don't you bathe?" asked Winnie.

"Far too cold."

"But *they're* bathing. I want to."

"You must ask your mother."

"I believe you're afraid. Can you swim?"

"Yes."

"Well why don't you? Bet you can't."

"All right. I can't."

"Then why did you say you could? Fibber."

They walked along the shingle. Winnie slithered about astride a backwater. "Now I'm all wet," she said.

"Better come back and change."

"It feels horrible. Let's go and have breakfast."

The hotel did not, as a rule, cater for guests who breakfasted downstairs at eight o'clock on Sunday morning. It took a long time before anything could be got ready. There were no ices, much to Winnie's annoyance. She ate grapefruit and kippers and scrambled eggs on toast, complaining fitfully about her wet clothing. After breakfast Tony sent her upstairs to change and, himself, smoked a pipe in the lounge and glanced over the Sunday papers. Here at nine o'clock he was interrupted by the arrival of Blenkinsop. "We missed you last night," he said.

"We went to a party."

"You shouldn't have done that—not strictly, but I daresay no harm will come of it. Have you had your breakfast?"

"Yes, in the dining room with Winnie."

"But, Mr. Last, what are you thinking of? You've got to get evidence from the hotel servants."

"Well, I didn't like to wake Milly."

"She's paid for it, isn't she? Come, come, Mr. Last, this won't do at all. You'll never get your divorce if you don't give your mind to it more."

"All right," said Tony. "I'll have breakfast again."

"In bed mind."

"In bed." And he went wearily upstairs to his rooms.

Winnie had drawn the curtains but her mother was still asleep.

"She woke up once and then turned over. Do get her to come out. I want to go on the pier."

"Milly," said Tony firmly. "Milly."

"Oh," she said. "What time is it?"

"We've got to have breakfast."

"Don't want any breakfast. I think I'll sleep a little."

"You have had breakfast," said Winnie.

"Come on," said Tony. "Plenty of time to sleep afterwards. This is what we came for."

Milly sat up in bed. "O.K.," she said. "Winnie darling, give mother her jacket off the chair." She was a conscientious girl, ready to go through with her job however unattractive it might seem. "But it's early."

Tony went into his room and took off his shoes, collar and tie, coat and waistcoat, and put on a dressing gown.

"You are greedy," said Winnie, "eating two breakfasts."

"When you're a little older you'll understand these things. It's the Law. Now I want you to stay in the sitting room for quarter of an hour very quietly. Promise? And afterwards you can do exactly what you like."

"Can I bathe?"

"Yes certainly, if you're quiet now."

Tony got into bed beside Milly and pulled the dressing gown tight round his throat. "Does that look all right?"

"Love's young dream," said Milly.

"All right then. I'll ring the bell."

When the tray had been brought Tony got out of bed and put on his things. "So much for my infidelity," he said. "It is curious to reflect that this will be described in the papers as 'intimacy.'"

"Can I bathe now?"

"Certainly."

Milly turned over to sleep again. Tony took Winnie to the beach. The wind had got up and a heavy sea was pounding on the shingle.

"This little girl would like to bathe," said Tony.

"No bathing for children today," said the beach attendant.

"The very idea," said various onlookers. "Does he want to drown the child?" "He's no business to be trusted with children." *"Unnatural beast."*

"But I *want* to bathe," said Winnie. "You said I could bathe if you had two breakfasts."

The people who had clustered round to witness Tony's discomfort, looked at one another askance. "Two breakfasts? Wanting to let the child bathe? The man's balmy."

"Never mind," said Tony. "We'll go on the pier."

Several of the crowd followed them round the slots, curious to see what new enormity this mad father might attempt. "There's a man who's eaten two breakfasts and tries to drown his little girl," they informed other spectators, sceptically observing his attempts to amuse Winnie with skee-ball. Tony's conduct confirmed the view of human nature derived from the weekly newspapers which they had all been reading that morning.

"Well," said Brenda's solicitor. "We have our case now, all quite regular and complete. I don't think it can come on until next term—there's a great rush at the moment, but there's no harm in you having your own evidence ready. I've got it typed out for you. You'd better keep it by you and get it clear in your mind."

". . . My marriage was an ideally happy one," she read, *"until shortly before Christmas last year when I began to suspect that my husband's attitude had changed towards me. He always remained in the country when my studies took me to London. I realized that he no longer cared for me as he used to. He began to drink heavily and on one occasion made a disturbance at our flat in London, constantly ringing up when drunk and sending a drunken friend round to knock on the door.* Is that necessary?"

"Not strictly, but it is advisable to put it in. A great deal depends on psychological impression. Judges in their more lucid moments sometimes wonder why perfectly respectable, happily married men go off for week-ends to the seaside with women they do not know. It is always helpful to offer evidence of general degeneracy."

"I see," said Brenda. *"From then onwards I had him watched by private agents and as a result of what they told me, I left my husband's house on April 5th.* Yes, that all seems quite clear."

3

Lady St. Cloud preserved an atavistic faith in the authority and preternatural good judgment of the Head of the Family; accordingly her first act, on learning from Marjorie of Brenda's wayward behaviour, was to cable for Reggie's return from Tunisia where he was occupied in desecrating some tombs. His departure, like all his movements, was leisurely. He did not take the first available boat or the second, but eventually he arrived in London on the Monday after Tony's visit to Brighton. He held a family conclave in his library consisting of his mother, Brenda, Marjorie, Allan and the solicitor; later he discussed the question fully with each of them severally; he took Beaver out to luncheon; he dined with Jock; he even called on Tony's Aunt Frances. Finally on Thursday evening he arranged to meet Tony for dinner at Brown's.

He was eight years older than Brenda; very occasionally a fugitive, indefinable likeness was detectable between him and Marjorie, but both in character and appearance he was as different from Brenda as it was possible to imagine. He was prematurely, unnaturally stout, and he carried his burden of flesh as though he were not yet used to it; as though it had been buckled on to him that morning for the first time and he were still experimenting for its better adjustment; there was an instability in his gait and in his eyes a furtive look as though he were at any moment liable to ambush and realized that he was unfairly handicapped for flight. This impression, however, was made solely by his physical appearance; it was the deep bed of fat in which his eyes lay, which gave them this look of suspicion; the caution of his movements resulted from the exertion of keeping his balance and not from any embarrassment at his own clumsiness, for it had never occurred to him that he looked at all unusual.

Rather more than half Reggie St. Cloud's time and income was spent abroad in modest archæological expeditions. His house in London was full of their fruit—fragmentary amphoras, corroded bronze axe-heads, little splinters of bone and charred stick, a Græco-Roman head in marble, its features obliterated and ground smooth with time. He had written two little monographs about his work, privately printed and both dedicated to members of the royal family. When he came to London he was regular in attendance at the House of Lords; all his friends were well over forty and for some years now he had established himself as a member of their generation; few mothers still regarded him as a possible son-in-law.

"This whole business of Brenda is *very* unfortunate," said Reggie St. Cloud.

Tony agreed.

"My mother is extremely upset about it, naturally. I'm upset myself. I don't mind admitting, perfectly frankly, that I think she has behaved very foolishly, foolishly and wrongly. I can quite understand your being upset about it too."

"Yes," said Tony.

"But all the same, making every allowance for your feelings, I do think that you are behaving rather vindictively in the matter."

"I'm doing exactly what Brenda wanted."

"My dear fellow, she doesn't know what she wants. I saw this chap Beaver yesterday. I didn't like him *at all*. Do you?"

"I hardly know him."

"Well I can assure you I didn't like him. Now you're just throwing Brenda into his arms. That's what it amounts to, as I see it, and I call it vindictive. Of course at the moment Brenda's got the idea that she's in love with him. But it won't last. It couldn't with a chap like Beaver. She'll want to come back in a year, just you see. Allan says the same."

"I've told Allan. I don't want her back."

"Well, that's vindictive."

"No, I just couldn't feel the same about her again."

"Well, why feel *the same?* One has to change as one gets older. Why, ten years ago I couldn't be interested in anything later than the Sumerian age and I assure you that now I find even the Christian era full of significance."

For some time he spoke about some *tabulæ execrationum* that he had lately unearthed. "Almost every grave had them," he said, "mostly referring to the circus factions, scratched on lead. They used to be dropped in through a funnel. We had found forty-three up to date, before this wretched business happened, and I had to come back. Naturally I'm upset."

He sat for a little eating silently. This last observation had brought the conversation back to its point of departure. He clearly had more to say on the subject and was meditating the most convenient approach. He ate in a ruthless manner, champing his food (it was his habit, often, without noticing it, to consume things that others usually left on their plates, the heads and tails of whiting, whole mouthfuls of chicken bone, peach stones and apple cores, cheese rinds and the fibrous parts of the artichoke). "Besides, you know," he said, "it isn't as though it was all Brenda's fault."

"I haven't been thinking particularly whose fault it is."

"Well that's all very well but you seem rather to be taking the line of the injured husband—saying you can't feel the same again, and all that. I mean to say, it takes two to make a quarrel and I gather things had been going wrong for some time. For instance you'd been drinking a lot—have some more burgundy by the way."

"Did Brenda say that?"

"Yes. And then you'd been going round a bit with other girls yourself. There was some woman with a Moorish name you had to stay at Hetton while Brenda was there. Well that's a bit thick you know. I'm all for people going their own way but if they do, they can't blame others, if you see what I mean."

"Did Brenda say that?"

"Yes. Don't think I'm trying to lecture you or anything, but all I feel is that you haven't any right to be vindictive to Brenda, as things are."

"She said I drank and was having an affair with the woman with a Moorish name?"

"Well I don't know she actually said that, but she said you'd been getting tight lately and that you were certainly interested in that girl."

The fat young man opposite Tony ordered prunes and cream. Tony said he had finished dinner.

He had imagined during the preceding week-end that nothing could now surprise him.

"So that really explains what I want to say," continued Reggie blandly. "It's about money. I understand that when Brenda was in a very agitated state just after the death of her child, she consented to some verbal arrangement with you about settlements."

"Yes, I'm allowing her five hundred a year."

"Well you know I don't think that you have any right to take advantage of her generosity in that way. It was most imprudent of her to consider your proposal—she admits now that she was not really herself when she did so."

"What did she suggest instead?"

"Let's go outside and have coffee."

When they were settled in front of the fire in the empty smoking room, he answered, "Well I've discussed it with the lawyers and with the family and we decided that the sum should be increased to two thousand."

"That's quite out of the question. I couldn't begin to afford it."

"Well, you know, I have to consider Brenda's interests. She has very little of her own and there will be no more coming to her. My mother's income is an allowance which I pay under my father's will. I shan't be able to give her anything. I am trying to raise everything I can for an expedition to one of the oases in the Libyan desert. This chap Beaver has got practically nothing and doesn't look like earning any. So you see——"

"But, my dear Reggie, you know as well as I do that it's out of the question."

"It's rather less than a third of your income."

"Yes but almost every penny goes on the estate. Do you realize that

Brenda and I together haven't spent half the amount a year on our personal expenses. It's all I can do to keep things going as it is."

"I didn't expect you to take this line, Tony. I think it's extremely unreasonable of you. After all it's absurd to pretend in these days that a single man can't be perfectly comfortable on four thousand a year. It's more than I've ever had."

"It would mean giving up Hetton."

"Well I gave up Brakeleigh, and I assure you, my dear fellow, I never regret it. It was a nasty wrench at the time of course, old association and everything like that, but I can tell you this, that when the sale was finally through I felt a different man, free to go where I liked . . ."

"But I don't happen to want to go anywhere else except Hetton."

"There's a lot in what these labour fellows say, you know. Big houses are a thing of the past in England I'm afraid."

"Tell me, did Brenda realize when she agreed to this proposal that it meant my leaving Hetton."

"Yes, it was mentioned I think. I daresay you'll find it quite easy to sell to a school or something like that. I remember the agent said when I was trying to get rid of Brakeleigh that it was a pity it wasn't Gothic because schools and convents always go for Gothic. I daresay you'll get a very comfortable price and find yourself better off in the end than you are now."

"No. It's impossible," said Tony.

"You're making things extremely awkward for everyone," said Reggie. "I can't understand why you are taking up this attitude."

"What is more I don't believe that Brenda ever expected or wanted me to agree."

"Oh yes, she did, my dear fellow. I assure you of that."

"It's inconceivable."

"Well," said Reggie, puffing at his cigar. "There's more to it than just money. Perhaps I'd better tell you everything. I hadn't meant to. The truth is that Beaver is cutting up nasty. He says he can't marry Brenda unless she's properly provided for. Not fair on her, he says. I quite see his point on a way."

"Yes, I see his point," said Tony. "So what your proposal really amounts to is that I should give up Hetton in order to buy Beaver for Brenda."

"It's not how I should have put it," said Reggie.

"Well I'm not going to and that's the end of it. If that's all you wanted to say, I may as well leave you."

"No, it isn't quite all I wanted to say. In fact I think I must have put things rather badly. It comes from trying to respect people's feelings too much. You see I wasn't so much asking you to agree to anything as explaining what our side propose to do. I've tried to keep everything on a friendly basis but I see it's not possible. Brenda will ask for alimony of two thousand a year from the Court and on our evidence we shall get it. I'm sorry you oblige me to put it so bluntly."

"I hadn't thought of that."

"No, nor had we to be quite frank. It was Beaver's idea."

"You seem to have got me in a fairly hopeless position."

"It's not how I should have put it."

"I should like to make absolutely sure that Brenda is in on this. D'you mind if I ring her up."

"Not at all, my dear fellow. I happen to know she's at Marjorie's tonight."

"Brenda, this is Tony . . . I've just been dining with Reggie."

"Yes, he said something about it."

"He tells me that you are going to sue for alimony. Is that so?"

"Tony, don't be so bullying. The lawyers are doing everything. It's no use coming to me."

"But did you know that they proposed to ask for two thousand?"

"Yes. They did say that. I know it sounds a lot but . . ."

"And you know exactly how my money stands, don't you? You know it means selling Hetton, don't you? . . . hullo, are you still there?"

"Yes, I'm here."

"You know it means that?"

"Tony, don't make me feel a beast. Everything has been so difficult."

"You do know just what you are asking?"

"Yes . . . I suppose so."

"All right, that's all I wanted to know."

"Tony, how odd you sound . . . don't ring off."

He hung up the receiver and went back to the smoking room. His mind had suddenly become clearer on many points that had puzzled him. A whole Gothic world had come to grief . . . there was now no armour, glittering in the forest glades, no embroidered feet on the greensward; the cream and dappled unicorns had fled . . .

Reggie sat expanded in his chair. "Well?"

"I got on to her. You were quite right. I'm sorry I didn't believe you. It seemed so unlikely at first."

"That's all right, my dear fellow."

"I've decided exactly what's going to happen."

"Good."

"Brenda is not going to get her divorce. The evidence I provided at Brighton isn't worth anything. There happens to have been a child there all the time. She slept both nights in the room I am supposed to have occupied. If you care to bring the case I shall defend it and win, but I think when you have seen my evidence you will drop it. I am going away for six months or so. When I come back, if she wishes it, I shall divorce Brenda without settlements of any kind. Is that clear?"

"But look here, my dear fellow."

"Goodnight. Thank you for the dinner. Good luck to the excavations."

On his way out of the club he noticed that John Beaver of Brat's Club was up for election.

"Who on earth would have expected the old boy to turn up like that?" asked Polly Cockpurse.

"Now I understand why they keep going on in the papers about divorce law reform," said Veronica. "It's *too* monstrous that he should be allowed to get away with it."

"The mistake they made was in telling him first," said Souki.

"It's so like Brenda to trust everyone," said Jenny.

"I do think Tony comes out of this pretty poorly," said Marjorie. "Oh I don't know," said Allan. "I expect your ass of a brother put the thing wrong."

v

IN SEARCH OF A CITY

"Any idea how many times round the deck make a mile?"

"None, I'm afraid," said Tony. "But I should think you must have walked a great distance."

"Twenty-two times. One soon gets out of sorts at sea if you're used to an active life. She's not much of a boat. Travel with this line often?"

"Never before."

"Ah. Thought you might have been in business in the islands. Not many tourists going out this time of year. Just the other way about. All coming home, if you see what I mean. Going far?"

"Demerara."

"Ah. Looking for minerals perhaps?"

"No, to tell you the truth I am looking for a city."

The genial passenger was surprised and then laughed. "Sounded just like you said you were looking for a city."

"Yes."

"That *was* what you said?"

"Yes."

"I thought it sounded like that . . . well, so long. I must do another few rounds before dinner."

He paced off up the deck, straddling slightly in order to keep his balance and occasionally putting out a hand to the rail for support.

Regularly every three minutes for the last hour or so, this man had come by. At first Tony had looked up at his approach and then turned away again out to sea. Presently the man had taken to nodding, then to saying "Hullo" or "Bit choppy" or "Here we are again"; finally he had stopped and begun a conversation.

Tony went aft to break this rather embarrassing recurrence. He descended the companion-way which led to the lower deck. Here, in crates lashed to the side, was a variety of livestock—some stud bulls, a heavily blanketed race-horse, a couple of beagles, being exported to various West Indian islands. Tony threaded a way between them and the hatches to the stern, where he sat against a winch watching the horizon mount above the funnels, then fall until they stood out black against the darkening sky. The pitch was more sensible here than it had been amidships; the animals shifted restlessly in their cramped quarters; the beagles whined intermittently. A lascar took down from a line some washing which had been flapping there all day.

The wash of the ship was quickly lost in the high waves. They were steaming westward down the Channel. As it grew to be night, lighthouses appeared flashing from the French coast. Presently a steward walked round the bright, upper deck striking chimes on a gong of brass cylinders and the genial passenger went below to prepare himself for dinner in hot sea water which splashed from side to side of the bath and dissolved the soap in a thin, sticky scum. He was the only man to dress that evening. Tony sat in the mustering darkness until the second bell. Then he left his greatcoat in the cabin and went down to dinner.

It was the first evening at sea.

Tony sat at the captain's table, but the captain was on the bridge that evening. There were empty chairs on either side of him. It was not rough enough for the fiddles to be out, but the stewards had removed the flower vases and damped the table-cloth to make it adhesive. A coloured archdeacon sat facing him. He ate with great refinement but his black hands looked immense on the wet, whitish cloth. "I'm afraid our table is not showing up very well tonight," he said. "I see you are not a sufferer. My wife is in her cabin. *She* is a sufferer."

He was returning from a Congress, he told Tony.

At the top of the stairs was a lounge named the Music and Writing Room. The light here was always subdued, in the day by the stained glass of the windows, at night by pink silk shades which hid the electric candles. Here the passengers assembled for their coffee, sitting on bulky, tapestry covered chesterfields or on swivel chairs irremovably fastened before the writing tables. Here too the steward for an hour every day presided over the cupboardful of novels which constituted the ship's library.

"It's not much of a boat," said the genial passenger, sitting himself beside Tony. "But I expect things will look brighter when we get into the sun."

Tony lit a cigar and was told by a steward that he must not smoke in this room. "That's all right," said the genial passenger, "we're just going down to the bar." "You know," he said a few minutes later, "I feel I owe you an apology. I thought you were potty just now before dinner. Honestly I did, when you said you were going to Demerara to look for a city. Well it sounded pretty potty. Then the purser—I'm at his table. Always get the cheeriest crowd at the purser's table *and* the best attention—the purser told me about you. You're the explorer aren't you?"

"Yes, come to think of it, I suppose I am," said Tony.

It did not come easily to him to realize that he was an explorer. It was barely a fortnight ago that he had become one. Even the presence in the hold of two vast crates, bearing his name and labelled *NOT WANTED ON THE VOYAGE*—crates containing such new and unfamiliar possessions as a medicine chest, an automatic shot gun, camping equipment, pack saddles, a cinema camera, dynamite, disinfectants, a collapsible canoe, filters, tinned butter and, strangest of all, an assortment of what Dr. Messinger called "trade goods"—failed to convince him fully of the serious nature of his expedition. Dr. Messinger had arranged everything. It was he who chose the musical boxes and mechanical mice, the mirrors, combs, perfumery, pills, fish-hooks, axe-heads, coloured rockets, and rolls of artificial silk, which were packed in the box of "trade goods." And Dr. Messinger himself was a new acquaintance who, prostrate now in his bunk with what the Negro clergyman would have called "suffering," that day, for the first time since Tony had met him, seemed entirely human.

Tony had spent very little of his life abroad. At the age of eighteen,

before going to the University, he had been boarded for the summer
with an elderly gentleman near Tours, with the intention that he
should learn the language. (. . . a grey stone house surrounded by
vines. There was a stuffed spaniel in the bathroom. The old man had
called it "Stop" because it was chic at that time to give dogs an English name. Tony had bicycled along straight, white roads to visit the
châteaux; he carried rolls of bread and cold veal tied to the back of
the machine, and the soft dust seeped into them through the paper
and gritted against his teeth. There were two other English boys there,
so he had learned little French. One of them fell in love and the other
got drunk for the first time on sparkling vouvray at a fair that had
been held in the town. That evening Tony won a live pigeon at a
tombola; he set it free and later saw it being recaptured by the proprietor of the stall with a butterfly net . . .) Later he had gone to central Europe for a few weeks with a friend from Balliol. (They had
found themselves suddenly rich with the falling mark and had lived
in unaccustomed grandeur in the largest hotel suites. Tony had bought
a fur for a few shillings and given it to a girl in Munich who spoke
no English.) Later still his honeymoon with Brenda in a villa, lent
to them, on the Italian Riviera. (. . . cypress and olive trees, a domed
church half way down the hill, between the villa and the harbour, a
café where they sat out in the evening, watching the fishing boats and
the lights reflected in the quiet water, waiting for the sudden agitation
of sound and motion as the speed boat came in. It had been owned by
a dashing young official, who called it *JAZZ GIRL*. He seemed to
spend twenty hours a day running in and out of the little harbour . . .) Once Brenda and he had gone to Le Touquet with Brat's
golf team. That was all. After his father died he had not left England.
They could not easily afford it; it was one of the things they postponed
until death duties were paid off; besides that, he was never happy
away from Hetton and Brenda did not like leaving John Andrew.

Thus Tony had no very ambitious ideas about travel, and when he
decided to go abroad his first act was to call at a tourist agency and
come away laden with a sheaf of brightly coloured prospectuses, which
advertised commodious cruises among palm trees, Negresses and ruined

arches. He was going away because it seemed to be the conduct expected of a husband in his circumstances, because the associations of Hetton were for the time poisoned for him, because he wanted to live for a few months away from people who would know him or Brenda, in places where there was no expectation of meeting her or Beaver or Reggie St. Cloud at every corner he frequented, and with this feeling of evasion dominant in his mind, he took the prospectuses to read at the Greville Club. He had been a member there for some years, but rarely used it; his resignation was only postponed by his recurrent omission to cancel the banker's order for his subscription. Now that Brat's and Brown's were distasteful to him he felt thankful that he had kept on with the Greville. It was a club of intellectual flavour, composed of dons, a few writers and the officials of museums and learned societies. It had a tradition of garrulity so that he was not surprised when, seated in an armchair and surrounded with his illustrated folders, he was addressed by a member unknown to him who asked if he were thinking of going away. He was more surprised when he looked up and studied the questioner.

Dr. Messinger, though quite young, was bearded, and Tony knew few young men with beards. He was also very small, very sunburned and prematurely bald; the ruddy brown of his face and hands ended abruptly along the line of his forehead, which rose in a pale dome; he wore steel-rimmed spectacles and there was something about his blue serge suit which suggested that the wearer found it uncomfortable.

Tony admitted that he was considering taking a cruise.

"I am going away shortly," said Dr. Messinger, "to Brazil. At least it may be Brazil or Dutch Guiana. One cannot tell. The frontier has never been demarcated. I ought to have started last week only my plans were upset. Do you by any chance know a Nicaraguan calling himself alternately Ponsonby and Fitz Clarence?"

"No, I don't think I do."

"You are fortunate. That man has just robbed me of two hundred pounds and some machine guns."

"Machine guns?"

"Yes, I travel with one or two, mostly for show you know, or for trade, and they are not easy to buy nowadays. Have you ever tried?"

"No."

"Well you can take it from me that it's not easy. You can't just walk into a shop and order machine guns."

"No, I suppose not."

"Still at a pinch I can do without them. But I can't do without the two hundred pounds."

Tony had open on his knee a photograph of the harbour at Agadir. Dr. Messinger looked over his shoulder at it. "Ah yes," he said, "interesting little place. I expect you know Zingerman there?"

"No, I've not been there yet."

"You'd like him—a very straight fellow. He used to do quite a lot, selling ammunition to the Atlas caids before the pacification. Of course it was easy money with the capitulations, but he did it better than most of them. I believe he's running a restaurant now in Mogador." Then he continued dreamily, "The pity is I can't let the R.G.S. in on this expedition. I've got to find the money privately."

It was one o'clock and the room was beginning to fill up; an Egyptologist was exhibiting a handkerchief-ful of scarabs to the editor of a church weekly.

"We'd better go up and lunch," said Dr. Messinger.

Tony had not intended to lunch at the Greville but there was something compelling about the invitation; moreover, he had no other engagement.

Dr. Messinger lunched off apples and a rice pudding. ("I have to be careful what I eat," he said.) Tony ate cold steak and kidney pie. They sat at a window in the big dining room upstairs. The places round them were soon filled with members, who even carried the tradition of general conversation so far as to lean back in their chairs and chat over their shoulders from table to table—a practice which greatly hindered the already imperfect service. But Tony remained oblivious to all that was said, absorbed in what Dr. Messinger was telling him.

". . . You see there has been a continuous tradition about the City since the first explorers of the sixteenth century. It has been variously allocated, sometimes down in Matto Grosso, sometimes on the upper Orinoco in what is now Venezuela. I myself used to think it lay somewhere on the Uraricuera. I was out there last year and it was then that I established contact with the Pie-wie Indians; no white man had ever visited them and got out alive. And it was from the Pie-wies that I learned where to look. None of them had ever visited the City, of course, but they *knew about it*. Every Indian between Ciudad Bolívar and Para knows about it. But they won't talk. Queer people. But I became blood-brother with a Pie-wie—interesting ceremony. They buried me up to the neck in mud and all the women of the tribe spat on my head. Then we ate a toad and a snake and a beetle and after that I was a blood-brother—well, he told me that the City lies between the head waters of the Courantyne and the Takutu. There's a vast track of unexplored country there. I've often thought of visiting it.

"I've been looking up the historical side too, and I more or less know how the City got there. It was the result of a migration from Peru at the beginning of the fifteenth century when the Incas were at the height of their power. It is mentioned in all the early Spanish documents as a popular legend. One of the younger princes rebelled and led his people off into the forest. Most of the tribes have a tradition in one form or another of a strange race passing through their territory."

"But what do you suppose this city will be like?"

"Impossible to say. Every tribe has a different word for it. The Pie-wies call it the 'Shining' or 'Glittering,' the Arekuna the 'Many Watered,' the Patamonas the 'Bright Feathered,' the Warau oddly enough, use the same word for it that they use for a kind of aromatic jam they make. Of course one can't tell how a civilization may have developed or degenerated in five hundred years of isolation . . ."

Before Tony left the Greville that day, he tore up his sheaf of cruise prospectuses, for he had arranged to join Dr. Messinger in his expedition.

"Done much of that kind of thing?"

"No, to tell you the truth it is the first time."

"Ah. Well I daresay it's more interesting than it sounds," conceded the genial passenger, "else people wouldn't do it so much."

The ship, so far as any consideration of comfort had contributed to her design, was planned for the tropics. It was slightly colder in the smoking room than on deck. Tony went to his cabin and retrieved his cap and greatcoat; then he went aft again, to the place where he had sat before dinner. It was a starless night and nothing was visible beyond the small luminous area round the ship, save for a single lighthouse that flashed short-long, short-long, far away on the port bow. The crests of the waves caught the reflection from the promenade deck and shone for a moment before plunging away into the black depths behind. The beagles were awake, whining.

For some days now Tony had been thoughtless about the events of the immediate past. His thoughts were occupied with the City, the Shining, the Many Watered, the Bright Feathered, the Aromatic Jam. He had a clear picture of it in his mind. It was Gothic in character, all vanes and pinnacles, gargoyles, battlements, groining and tracery, pavilions and terraces, a transfigured Hetton, pennons and banners floating on the sweet breeze, everything luminous and translucent; a coral citadel crowning a green hill top sown with daisies, among groves and streams; a tapestry landscape filled with heraldic and fabulous animals and symmetrical, disproportionate blossom.

The ship tossed and tunnelled through the dark waters towards this radiant sanctuary.

"I wonder if anyone is doing anything about those dogs," said the genial passenger, arriving at his elbow. "I'll ask the purser tomorrow. We might exercise them a bit. Kind of mournful the way they go on."

Next day they were in the Atlantic. Ponderous waves rising over murky, opaque depths. Dappled with foam at the crests, like downland where on the high, exposed places, snow has survived the thaw. Lead-grey and slate in the sun, olive, field-blue and khaki like the uniforms of a battlefield; the sky overhead was neutral and steely with swollen clouds scudding across it, affording rare half hours of sunlight. The masts swung slowly across this sky and the bows heaved and wallowed below the horizon. The man who had made friends with Tony paraded the deck with the two beagles. They strained at the end of their chains, sniffing the scuppers; the man lurched behind them unsteadily. He wore a pair of race glasses with which he occasionally surveyed the seas; he offered them to Tony whenever they passed each other.

"Been talking to the wireless operator," he said. "We ought to pass quite near the *Yarmouth Castle* at about eleven."

Few of the passengers were on their feet. Those who had come on deck lay in long chairs on the sheltered side, pensive, wrapped in tartan rugs. Dr. Messinger kept to his cabin. Tony went to see him and found him torpid, for he was taking large doses of chloral. Towards evening the wind freshened and by dinner time was blowing hard; portholes were screwed up and all destructible objects disposed on the cabin floors; a sudden roll broke a dozen coffee cups in the music and reading room. That night there was little sleep for anyone on board; the plating creaked, luggage shifted from wall to wall. Tony wedged himself firm in his bunk with the life-belt and thought of the City.

. . . Carpet and canopy, tapestry and velvet, portcullis and bastion, water fowl on the moat and kingcups along its margin, peacocks trailing their finery across the lawns; high overhead in a sky of sapphire and swansdown silver bells chiming in a turret of alabaster.

Days of shadow and exhaustion, salt wind and wet mist, foghorn and the constant groan and creak of straining metal. Then they were clear of it, after the Azores. Awnings were out and passengers moved their chairs to windward. High noon and an even keel; the blue water lapping against the sides of the ship, rippling away behind her to the horizon; gramophones and deck tennis; bright arcs of flying fish ("Look, Ernie, come quick, there's a shark." "That's not a shark, it's a dolphin." "Mr. Brink said it was a porpoise." "There he is again. Oh if I had my camera."), clear, tranquil water and the regular turn and tread of the screw; there were many hands to caress the beagles as they went loping by. Mr. Brink amid laughter suggested that he should exercise the race-horse, or, with a further burst of invention, the bull. Mr. Brink sat at the purser's table with the cheery crowd.

Dr. Messinger left his cabin and appeared on deck and in the dining saloon. So did the wife of the archdeacon; she was very much whiter than her husband. On Tony's other side at table sat a girl named Thérèse de Vitré. He had noticed her once or twice during the grey days, a forlorn figure almost lost among furs and cushions and rugs; a colourless little face with wide dark eyes. She said, "The last days have been terrible. I saw you walking about. How I envied you."

"It ought to be calm all the way now," and inevitably, "are you going far?"

"Trinidad. That is my home . . . I tried to decide who you were from the passenger list."

"Who was I?"

"Well . . . someone called Colonel Strapper."

"Do I look so old?"

"Are colonels old? I didn't know. It's not a thing we have much in Trinidad. Now I know who you are because I asked the head steward. Do tell me about your exploring."

"You'd better ask Doctor Messinger. He knows more about it than I do."

"No, *you* tell me."

She was eighteen years old; small and dark, with a face that disappeared in a soft pointed chin so that attention was drawn to the large, grave eyes and the high forehead; she had not long outgrown her school-girl plumpness and she moved with an air of exultance, as though she had lately shed an encumbrance and was not yet fatigued by the other burdens that would succeed it. For two years she had been at school in Paris.

". . . Some of us used to keep lipstick and rouge secretly in our bedrooms and try it on at night. One girl called Antoinette came to Mass on Sunday wearing it. There was a terrible row with Madame de Supplice and she left after that term. It was awfully brave. We all envied her . . . But she was an ugly girl, always eating chocolates . . .

". . . Now I am coming home to be married . . . No, I am not yet affiancée but you see there are so few young men I can marry. They must be Catholic and of an island family. It would not do to marry an official and go back to live in England. But it will be easy because I have no brothers or sisters and my father has one of the best houses in Trinidad. You must come and see it. It is a stone house, outside the town. My family came to Trinidad in the French Revolution. There are two or three other rich families and I shall marry one of them. Our son will have the house. It will be easy . . ."

She wore a little coat, of the kind that were then fashionable, and no ornament except a string of pearls. ". . . There was an American girl at Madame de Supplice's who was engaged. She had a ring with a big diamond but she could never wear it except in bed. Then one day she had a letter from her young man saying he was going to marry another girl. How she cried. We all read the letter and most of us cried too . . . But in Trinidad it will be quite easy."

Tony told her about the expedition; of the Peruvian emigrants in the middle age and their long caravan working through the mountains and forests, llamas packed with works of intricate craftsmanship; of the continual rumours percolating to the coast and luring adventurers up into the forests; of the route they would take up the rivers, then cutting through the bush along Indian trails and across untravelled country; of the stream they might strike higher up and how, Dr. Messinger said, they would make woodskin canoes and take to the water again; how finally they would arrive under the walls of the city like the Vikings at Byzantium. "But of course," he added, "there may be nothing in it. It ought to be an interesting journey in any case."

"How I wish I was a man," said Thérèse de Vitré.

After dinner they danced to the music of an amplified gramophone and the girl drank lemon squash on the bench outside the deck bar, sucking it through two straws.

A week of blue water that grew clearer and more tranquil daily, of sun that grew warmer, radiating the ship and her passengers, filling them with good humour and ease; blue water that caught the sun in a thousand brilliant points, dazzling the eyes as they searched for porpoises and flying fish; clear blue water in the shallows revealing its bed of silver sand and smooth pebble, fathoms down; soft warm shade on deck under the awnings; the ship moved amid unbroken horizons on a vast blue disc of blue, sparkling with sunlight.

Tony and Miss de Vitré played quoits and shuffleboard; they threw rope rings into a bucket from a short distance. ("We'll go in a small boat," Dr. Messinger had said, "so as to escape all that hideous nonsense of deck games.") Twice consecutively Tony won the sweepstake on the ship's run; the prize was eighteen shillings. He bought Miss de Vitré a woollen rabbit at the barber's shop.

It was unusual for Tony to use "Miss" in talking to anyone. Except Miss Tendril he could think of no one he addressed in that way. But it was Thérèse who first called him "Tony," seeing it engraved in Brenda's handwriting in his cigarette case. "How funny," she said, "that was the name of the man who didn't marry the American girl at Madame de Supplice's"; and after that they used each other's Christian names to the great satisfaction of the other passengers who had little to interest them on board except the flowering of this romance.

"I can't believe this is the same ship as in those cold, rough days," said Thérèse.

They reached the first of the islands; a green belt of palm trees with wooded hills rising beyond them and a small town heaped up along the shores of a bay. Thérèse and Tony went ashore and bathed. Thérèse swam badly with her head ridiculously erect out of the water. There was practically no bathing in Trinidad, she explained. They lay for some time on the firm, silver beach; then drove back into the town in the shaky, two-horse carriage he had hired, past ramshackle cabins from which little black boys ran out to beg or swing behind on the axle, in the white dust. There was nowhere in the town to dine so they returned to the ship at sundown. She lay out at some distance but from where they stood after dinner, leaning over the rail, they could just hear in the intervals when the winch was not working, the chatter and singing in the streets. Thérèse put her arm through Tony's, but the decks were full of passengers and agents and swarthy little men with lists of cargo. There was no dancing that night. They went above on to the boat deck and Tony kissed her.

Dr. Messinger came on board by the last launch. He had met an acquaintance in the town. He had observed the growing friendship between Tony and Thérèse with the strongest disapproval and told him of a friend of his who had been knifed in a back street of Smyrna, as a warning of what happened if one got mixed up with women.

In the islands the life of the ship disintegrated. There were changes of passengers; the black archdeacon left after shaking hands with everyone on board; on their last morning his wife took round a collecting box in aid of an organ that needed repairs. The captain never appeared at meals in the dining saloon. Even Tony's first friend no longer changed for dinner; the cabins were stuffy from being kept locked all day.

Tony and Thérèse bathed again at Barbados and drove round the island visiting castellated churches. They dined at an hotel high up out of town and ate flying fish.

"You must come to my home and see what real creole cooking is like," said Thérèse. "We have a lot of old recipes that the planters used to use. You must meet my father and mother."

They could see the lights of the ship from the terrace where they were dining; the bright decks with figures moving about and the double line of portholes.

"Trinidad the day after tomorrow," said Tony.

They talked of the expedition and she said it was sure to be dangerous. "I don't like Doctor Messinger at all," she said. "Not anything about him."

"And you will have to choose your husband."

"Yes. There are seven of them. There was one called Honoré I liked but of course I haven't seen him for two years. He was studying to be an engineer. There's one called Mendoza who's very rich but he isn't really a Trinidadian. His grandfather came from Dominica and they say he has coloured blood. I expect it will be Honoré. Mother always brought in his name when she wrote to me and he sent me things at

Christmas and on my fête. Rather silly things because the shops aren't good in Port of Spain."

Later she said, "You'll be coming back by Trinidad, won't you? So I shall see you then. Will you be a long time in the bush?"

"I expect you'll be married by then."

"Tony, why haven't you ever got married?"

"But I am."

"Married?"

"Yes."

"You're teasing me."

"No, honestly I am. At least I was."

"Oh."

"Are you surprised?"

"I don't know. Somehow I didn't think you were. Where is she?"

"In England. We had a row."

"Oh . . . What's the time?"

"Quite early."

"Let's go back."

"D'you want to?"

"Yes, please. It's been a delightful day."

"You said that as if you were saying good-bye."

"Did I? I don't know."

The Negro chauffeur drove them at great speed into the town. Then they sat in a rowing boat and bobbed slowly out to the ship. Earlier in the day in good spirits they had bought a stuffed fish. Thérèse found she had left it behind at the hotel. "It doesn't matter," she said.

Blue water came to an end after Barbados. Round Trinidad the sea was opaque and colourless, full of the mud which the Orinoco brought down from the mainland. Thérèse spent all that day in her cabin, doing her packing.

Next day she said good-bye to Tony in a hurry. Her father had come out to meet her in the tender. He was a wiry bronzed man with a long grey moustache. He wore a panama hat and smart silk clothes, and smoked a cheroot; the complete slave-owner of the last century.

Thérèse did not introduce him to Tony. "He was someone on the ship," she explained, obviously.

Tony saw her once next day in the town, driving with a lady who was obviously her mother. She waved but did not stop. "Reserved lot, these real old creoles," remarked the passenger who had first made friends with Tony and had now attached himself again. "Poor as church mice most of them but stinking proud. Time and again I've palled up with them on board and when we got to port it's been good-bye. Do they ever so much as ask you to their houses? Not they."

Tony spent the two days with this first friend who had business connexions in the place. On the second day it rained heavily and they could not leave the terrace of the hotel. Dr. Messinger was engaged on some technical inquiries at the Agricultural Institute.

Muddy sea between Trinidad and Georgetown; and the ship lightened of cargo rolled heavily in the swell. Dr. Messinger took to his cabin once more. Rain fell continuously and a slight mist enclosed them so that they seemed to move in a small puddle of brown water; the foghorn sounded regularly through the rain. Scarcely a dozen passengers remained on board and Tony prowled disconsolately about the deserted decks or sat alone in the music room, his mind straying back along the path he had forbidden it, to the tall elm avenue at Hetton and the budding copses.

Next day they arrived at the mouth of the Demarara. The customs sheds were heavy with the reek of sugar and loud with the buzzing of bees. There were lengthy formalities in getting their stores ashore. Dr. Messinger saw to it while Tony lit a cigar and strayed out on to the quay. Small shipping of all kinds lay round them; on the further bank a low, green fringe of mangrove; behind, the tin roofs of the town were visible among feathery palm trees; everything steamed from the recent rain. Black stevedores grunted rhythmically at their work; East Indians trotted to and fro busily with invoices and bills of lading. Presently Dr. Messinger pronounced that everything was in order and that they could go into the town to their hotel.

2

The storm lantern stood on the ground between the two hammocks, which in their white sheaths of mosquito net, looked like the cocoons of gigantic silkworms. It was eight o'clock, two hours after sundown; river and forest were already deep in night. The howler monkeys were silent but tree frogs near at hand set up a continuous, hoarse chorus; birds were awake, calling and whistling, and far in the depths about them came the occasional rending and reverberation of dead wood falling among the trees.

The six black boys who manned the boat squatted at a distance round their fire. They had collected some cobs of maize, three days back in a part of the bush, deserted now, choked and overrun with wild growth, that had once been a farm. (The gross second growth at that place had been full of alien plants, fruit and cereals, all rank now, and reverting to earlier type.) The boys were roasting their cobs in the embers.

Fire and storm lantern together shed little light; enough only to suggest the dilapidated roof about their heads, the heap of stores, disembarked and overrun by ants and, beyond, the undergrowth that had invaded the clearing and the vast columns of tree-trunk that rose beyond it, disappearing out of sight in the darkness.

Bats like blighted fruit hung in clusters from the thatch and great spiders rode across it astride their shadows. This place had once been a ballata station. It was the furthest point of commercial penetration from the coast. Dr. Messinger marked it on his map with a triangle and named it in red "First Base Camp."

The first stage of the journey was over. For ten days they had been chugging up-stream in a broad, shallow boat. Once or twice they had passed rapids (there the outboard engine had been reinforced by paddles; the men strained in time to the captain's count; the bosun stood in the bows with a long pole warding them off the rocks). They had camped at sundown on patches of sand bank or in clearings cut from the surrounding bush. Once or twice they came to a "house" left behind by ballata bleeders or gold washers.

All day Tony and Dr. Messinger sprawled amidships among their stores, under an improvised canopy of palm thatch; sometimes in the hot hours of the early afternoon they fell asleep. They ate in the boat, out of tins, and drank rum mixed with the water of the river which was mahogany brown but quite clear. The nights seemed interminable to Tony; twelve hours of darkness, noisier than a city square with the squealing and croaking and trumpeting of the bush denizens. Dr. Messinger could tell the hours by the succession of sounds. It was not possible to read by the light of the storm lantern. Sleep was irregular and brief after the days of lassitude and torpor. There was little to talk about; everything had been said during the day, in the warm shade among the stores. Tony lay awake, scratching.

Since they had left Georgetown there had not been any part of his body that was ever wholly at ease. His face and neck were burned by the sun reflected from the water; the skin was flaking off them so that he was unable to shave. The stiff growth of beard pricked him between chin and throat. Every exposed part of his skin was also bitten by cabouri fly. They had found a way into the button-holes of his shirt and the laces of his breeches; mosquitoes had got him at the ankles when he changed into slacks for the evening. He had picked up *bêtes rouges* in the bush and they were crawling and burrowing under his skin; the bitter oil which Dr. Messinger had given him as protection, had set up a rash of its own wherever he had applied it. Every evening after washing he had burned off a few ticks with a cigarette end but they had left irritable little scars behind them; so had the chigoes which one of the black boys had dug out from under his toe nails and the horny skin on his heels and the balls of his feet. A marabunta had left a painful swelling on his left hand.

As Tony scratched he shook the framework from which the hammocks hung. Dr. Messinger turned over and said, "Oh, for God's sake." He tried not to scratch; then he tried to scratch quietly; then in a frenzy he scratched as hard as he could, breaking the skin in a dozen places. "Oh, for God's sake," said Dr. Messinger.

"Half past eight," thought Tony. "In London they are just beginning to collect for dinner." It was the time of year in London when there were parties every night. (Once, when he was trying to get engaged to Brenda, he had gone to them all. If they had dined in different houses, he would search the crowd for Brenda and hang about by the stairs waiting for her to arrive. Later he would hang about to take her home. Lady St. Cloud had done everything to make it easy for him. Later, after they were married, in the two years they had spent in London before Tony's father died, they had been to fewer parties, one or two a week at the most, except for a very gay month just when Brenda was well again, after John Andrew's birth.) Tony began to imagine a dinner party assembling at that moment in London, with Brenda there and the surprised look with which she greeted each new arrival. If there was a fire she would be as near it as she could get. Would there be a fire at the end of May? He could not remember. There were nearly always fires at Hetton in the evening, whatever the season.

Then after another bout of scratching it occurred to Tony that it was not half past eight in England. There was five hours difference in time. They had altered their watches daily on the voyage out. Which way? It ought to be easy to work out. The sun rose in the east. England was east of America so they got the sun later. It came to them at second hand and slightly soiled after Polly Cockpurse and Mrs. Beaver and Princess Abdul Akbar had finished with it . . . Like Polly's dresses which Brenda used to buy for ten or fifteen pounds each . . . he fell asleep.

He woke an hour later to hear Dr. Messinger cursing, and to see him sitting astride his hammock working with bandages, iodine and his great toe.

"A vampire bat got it. I must have gone to sleep with my foot against the netting. God knows how long he had been at it, before I woke up. That lamp ought to keep them off but it doesn't seem to."

The black boys were still awake, munching over the fire. "Vampires plenty bad this side, chief," they said. "Dat why for us no leave de fire."

"It's just the way to get sick, blast it," said Dr. Messinger. "I may have lost pints of blood."

Brenda and Jock were dancing together at Anchorage House. It was late, the party was thinning, and now for the first time that evening, it was possible to dance with pleasure. The ballroom was hung with tapestry and lit by candles. Lady Anchorage had lately curtsied her farewell to the last royalty.

"How I hate staying up late," Brenda said, "but it seems a shame to take my Mr. Beaver away. He's so thrilled to be here, bless him, and it was a great effort to get him asked . . . Come to think of it," she added later, "I suppose that this is the last year *I* shall be able to go to this kind of party."

"You're going through with it?"

"I don't know, Jock. It doesn't really depend on me. It's all a matter of holding down Mr. Beaver. He's getting very restive. I have to feed him a bit of high life every week or so, and I suppose that'll all stop if there's a divorce. Any news of Tony?"

"Not for some time now. I got a cable when he landed. He's gone off on some expedition with a crook doctor."

"Is it *absolutely* safe?"

"Oh, I imagine so. The whole world is civilized now isn't it?—charabancs and Cook's offices everywhere."

"Yes, I suppose it is . . . I hope he's not *brooding*. I shouldn't like to think of him being unhappy."

"I expect he's getting used to things."

"I do hope so. I'm very fond of Tony, you know, in spite of the monstrous way he behaved."

There was an Indian village a mile or two distant from the camp. It was here that Tony and Dr. Messinger proposed to recruit porters for the two hundred mile march that lay between them and the Pie-wie country. The Negroes were river men and could not be taken into Indian territory. They would go back with the boat.

At dawn Tony and Dr. Messinger drank a mug each of hot cocoa and ate some biscuits and what was left over from the bully beef opened the night before. Then they set out for the village. One of the blacks went in front with cutlass to clear the trail. Dr. Messinger and Tony followed one behind the other; another black came behind them carrying samples of trade goods—a twenty dollar Belgian gun, some rolls of printed cotton, hand-mirrors in coloured celluloid frames, some bottles of highly scented pomade.

It was a rough, unfrequented trail, encumbered by numerous fallen trunks; they waded knee-deep through two streams that ran to feed the big river; underfoot there was sometimes a hard network of bare root, sometimes damp and slippery leaf mould.

Presently they reached the village. They came into sight of it quite suddenly, emerging from the bush into a wide clearing. There were eight or nine circular huts of mud and palm thatch. No one was visible but two or three columns of smoke, rising straight and thin into the morning air, told them that the place was inhabited.

"Dey people all afeared," said the black boy.

"Go and find someone to speak to us," said Dr. Messinger.

The Negro went to the low door of the nearest house and peered in.

"Dere ain't no one but women dere," he reported. "Dey dressing deirselves. Come on out dere," he shouted into the gloom. "De chief want talk to you."

At last, very shyly, a little old woman emerged, clad in the filthy calico gown that was kept for use in the presence of strangers. She waddled towards them on bandy legs. Her ankles were tightly bound with blue beads. Her hair was lank and ragged; her eyes were fixed on the earthenware bowl of liquid which she carried. When she was a few feet from Tony and Dr. Messinger she set the bowl on the ground, and still with downcast eyes, shook hands with them. Then she stooped, picked up the bowl once more and held it to Dr. Messinger.

"Cassiri," he explained, "the local drink made of fermented cassava."

He drank some and handed the bowl to Tony. It contained a thick, purplish liquid. When Tony had drunk a little, Dr. Messinger explained, "It is made in an interesting way. The women chew the root up and spit it into a hollow tree-trunk."

He then addressed the woman in Wapishiana. She looked at him for the first time. Her brown, Mongol face was perfectly blank, devoid alike of comprehension and curiosity. Dr. Messinger repeated and amplified his question. The woman took the bowl from Tony and set it on the ground.

Meanwhile other faces were appearing at the doors of the huts. Only one woman ventured out. She was very stout and she smiled confidently at the visitors.

"Good morning," she said. "How do you do? I am Rosa. I speak English good. I live bottom-side two years with Mr. Forbes. You give me cigarette."

"Why doesn't this woman answer?"

"She no speak English."

"But I was speaking Wapishiana."

"She Macushi woman. All these people Macushi people."

"Oh. I didn't know. Where are the men?"

"Men all go hunting three days."

"When will they be back?"

"They go after bush pig."

"When will they be back?"

"No, bush pig. Plenty bush pig. Men all go hunting. You give me cigarette."

"Listen, Rosa, I want to go to the Pie-wie country."

"No, this Macushi. All the people Macushi."

"But we want to go Pie-wie."

"No, *all* Macushi. You give me cigarette."

"It's hopeless," said Dr. Messinger. "We shall have to wait till the men come back." He took a packet of cigarettes from his pocket. "Look," he said, "cigarettes."

"Give me."

"When men come back from hunting you come to river and tell me. Understand?"

"No, men hunting bush pig. You give me cigarettes."

Dr. Messinger gave her the cigarettes.

"What else you got?" she said.

Dr. Messinger pointed to the load which the second black had laid on the ground.

"Give me," she said.

"When men come back, I give you plenty things if men come with me to Pie-wies."

"No, *all* Macushi here."

"We aren't doing any good," said Dr. Messinger. "We'd better go back to camp and wait. The men have been away three days. It's not likely they will be much longer . . . I wish I could speak Macushi."

They turned about, the four of them, and left the village. It was ten o'clock by Tony's wrist watch when they reached their camp.

Ten o'clock on the river Waurupang was question time at Westminster. For a long time now Jock had had a question which his constituents wanted him to ask. It came up that afternoon.

"I should like to ask the Minister of Agriculture whether in view of the dumping in this country of Japanese pork pies, the right honourable member is prepared to consider a modification of the eight and a half score basic pig from two and a half inches of thickness round the belly as originally specified, to two inches."

Replying for the Minister, the under-secretary said: "The matter is receiving the closest attention. As the honourable member is no doubt aware the question of the importation of pork pies is a matter for the Board of Trade, not for the Board of Agriculture. With regard to the specifications of the basic pig, I must remind the honourable member that, as he is doubtless aware, the eight and a half score pig is modelled on the requirements of the bacon curers and has no direct relation to pig meat for sale in pies. That is being dealt with by a separate committee who have not yet made their report."

"Would the honourable member consider an increase of the specified maximum of fatness on the shoulders?"

"I must have notice of that question."

Jock left the House that afternoon with the comfortable feeling that he had at last done something tangible in the interest of his constituents.

Two days later the Indians returned from hunting. It was tedious waiting. Dr. Messinger put in some hours daily in checking the stores. Tony went into the bush with his gun but the game had all migrated from that part of the river bank. One of the black boys was badly injured in the foot and calf by a sting-ray; after that they stopped bathing and washed in a zinc pail. When the news of the Indians' return reached camp, Tony and Dr. Messinger went to the village to see them but a feast had already started and everyone in the place was drunk. The men lay in their hammocks and the women trotted between them carrying calabashes of cassiri. Everything reeked of roast pork.

"It will take them a week to get sober," said Dr. Messinger.

All that week the black boys lounged in camp; sometimes they washed their clothes and hung them out on the bulwarks of the boat to dry in the sun; sometimes they went fishing and came back with a massive catch, speared on a stick (the flesh was tasteless and rubbery); usually in the evenings they sang songs round the fire. The fellow who had been stung kept to his hammock, groaning loudly and constantly asking for medicine.

On the sixth day the Indians began to appear. They shook hands all round and then retired to the margin of the bush where they stood gazing at the camp equipment. Tony tried to photograph them but they ran away giggling like schoolgirls. Dr. Messinger spread out on the ground the goods he had brought for barter.

They retired at sundown but on the seventh day they came again, greatly reinforced. The entire population of the village was there. Rosa sat down on Tony's hammock under the thatch roof.

"Give me cigarettes," she said.

"You tell them I want men to go Pie-wie country," said Dr. Messinger.

"Pie-wie bad people. Macushi people no go with Pie-wie people."

"You say I want the men. I give them guns."

"You give me cigarettes . . ."

Negotiations lasted for two days. Eventually twelve men agreed to come; seven of them insisted on bringing their wives with them. One of these was Rosa. When everything was arranged there was a party in the village and all the Indians got drunk again. This time, however, it was a shorter business as the women had not had time to prepare much cassiri. In three days the caravan was able to set out.

One of the men had a long, single-barrelled, muzzle-loading gun; several others carried bows and arrows; they were naked except for red cotton cloths round their loins. The women wore grubby calico dresses—they had been issued to them years back by an itinerant preacher and kept for occasions of this kind; they had wicker panniers on their shoulders, supported by a band across the forehead. All the heaviest luggage was carried by the women in these panniers, including the rations for themselves and their men. Rosa had, in addition, an umbrella with a dented, silver crook, a relic of her association with Mr. Forbes.

The Negroes returned down-stream to the coast. A dump of provisions, in substantial tin casing, was left in the ruinous shelter by the bank.

"There's no one to touch it. We can send back for it in case of emergency from the Pie-wie country," said Dr. Messinger.

Tony and Dr. Messinger walked immediately behind the man with the gun who was acting as guide; behind them the file straggled out for half a mile or more through the forest.

"From now onwards the map is valueless to us," said Dr. Messinger with relish.

(Roll up the map—you will not need it again for how many years, said William Pitt . . . memories of Tony's private school came back to him at Dr. Messinger's words, of inky little desks and a coloured picture of a Viking raid, of Mr. Trotter who had taught him history and wore very vivid ties.)

3

"Mumsey, Brenda wants a job."

"Why?"

"Just like everybody else, short of money and nothing to do. She wondered if she could be any use to you at the shop."

"Well . . . It's hard to say. At any other time she is exactly the kind of saleswoman I am always looking for . . . but I don't know. *As things are* I'm not sure it would be wise."

"I said I'd ask you, that's all."

"John, you never tell me *anything* and I don't like to seem interfering; but what *is* going to happen between you and Brenda."

"I don't know."

"You never tell me *anything*," repeated Mrs. Beaver. "And there are so many rumours going round. Is there going to be a divorce?"

"I don't know."

Mrs. Beaver sighed. "Well I must get back to work. Where are you lunching?"

"Brat's."

"Poor John. By the way, I thought you were joining Brown's."

"I haven't heard anything from them. I don't know whether they've had an election yet."

"Your father was a member."

"I've an idea I shan't get in . . . anyway I couldn't really afford it."

"I'm not happy about you, John. I'm not sure that things are working out as well as I hoped about Christmas time."

"There's my telephone. Perhaps it's Margot. She hasn't asked me to anything for weeks."

But it was only Brenda.

"I'm afraid mother's got nothing for you at the shop," he said.

"Oh well. I expect something will turn up. I could do with a little good luck just at the moment."

"So could I. Have you asked Allan about Brown's?"

"Yes, I did. He says they elected about ten chaps last week."

"Oh, does that mean I've been black balled?"

"I shouldn't know. Gentlemen are so odd about their clubs."

"I thought that you were going to make Allan and Reggie support me."

"I asked them. What does it matter anyway? D'you want to come to Veronica's for the week-end?"

"I'm not sure that I do."

"I'd like it."

"It's a beastly little house—and I don't think Veronica likes me. Who'll be there?"

"I shall be."

"Yes . . . well, I'll let you know."

"Am I seeing you this evening?"

"I'll let you know."

"Oh dear," said Brenda as she rang off. "Now he's taken against me. It isn't my fault he can't get in to Brown's. As a matter of fact I believe Reggie *did* try to help."

Jenny Abdul Akbar was in the room with her. She came across every morning now in her dressing gown and they read the newspaper together. The dressing gown was of striped Berber silk.

"Let's go and have a cosy lunch at the Ritz," she said.

"The Ritz isn't cosy at lunch time and it costs eight and six. I daren't cash a cheque for three weeks, Jenny. The lawyers are so disagreeable. I've never been like this before."

"What wouldn't I do to Tony? Leaving you stranded like this."

"Oh, what's the good of knocking Tony? I don't suppose he's having a packet of fun himself in Brazil or wherever it is."

"I hear they are putting in bathrooms at Hetton—while you are practically starving. And he hasn't even gone to Mrs. Beaver for them."

"Yes, I *do* think that was mean."

Presently Jenny went back to dress. Brenda telephoned to a delicatessen store round the corner for some sandwiches. She would spend that day in bed, as she spent two or three days a week at this time. Perhaps, if Allan was making a speech somewhere, as he usually was, Marjorie would have her to dinner. The Helm-Hubbards had a supper party that night but Beaver had not been asked. "If I went there without him it would be a major bust-up . . . Come to think of it, Marjorie's probably going. Well I can always have sandwiches for dinner here. They make all kinds. Thank God for the little shop round the corner." She was reading a biography of Thiers that had lately appeared; it was very long and would keep her going well into the night.

At one o'clock Jenny came in to say good-bye (she had a latch key of Brenda's) dressed for a cosy lunch. "I got Polly and Souki," she said. "We're going to Daisy's joint. I *wish* you were coming."

"Me? Oh, I'm all right," said Brenda and she thought, "It might occur to her to sock a girl a meal once in a way."

They walked for a fortnight, averaging about fifteen miles a day. Sometimes they would do much more and sometimes much less; the Indian who went in front decided the camping places; they depended on water and evil spirits.

Dr. Messinger made a compass traverse of their route. It gave him something to think about. He took readings every hour from an aneroid. In the evening, if they had halted early enough, he employed the last hours of daylight in elaborating a chart. *"Dry water course, three deserted huts, stony ground . . ."*

"We are now in the Amazon system of rivers," he announced with satisfaction one day. "You see, the water is running South." But almost immediately they crossed a stream flowing in the opposite direction. "Very curious," said Dr. Messinger. "A discovery of genuine scientific value."

Next day they waded through four streams at intervals of two miles, running alternately North and South. The chart began to have a mythical appearance.

"Is there a name for any of these streams," he asked Rosa.

"Macushi people called him Waurupang."

"No, not river where we first camped. *These rivers.*"

"Yes, Waurupang."

"*This river here.*"

"Macushi people call him all Waurupang."

"It's hopeless," said Dr. Messinger.

"Don't you think that possibly we *have* struck the upper waters of the Waurupang?" suggested Tony, "and have crossed and recrossed the stream as it winds down the valley."

"It is a hypothesis," said Dr. Messinger.

When they were near water they forced their way through blind bush; the trail there was grown over and barred by timber; only Indian eyes and Indian memory could trace its course; sometimes they crossed little patches of dry savannah, dun grass growing in tufts from the baked earth; thousands of lizards scampered and darted before their feet and the grass rustled like newspaper; it was burning hot in these enclosed spaces. Sometimes they climbed up into the wind, over loose red pebbles that bruised their feet; after these painful ascents they would lie in the wind till their wet clothes grew cold against their bodies; from these low eminences they could see other hill tops and the belts of bush through which they had travelled, and the file of porters trailing behind them. As each man and woman arrived he sank on to the dry grass and rested against his load; when the last of them came up with the party Dr. Messinger would give the word and they would start off again, descending into the green heart of the forest before them.

Tony and Dr. Messinger seldom spoke to one another, either when they were marching or at the halts for they were constantly strained and exhausted. In the evenings after they had washed and changed into clean shirts and flannel trousers, they talked a little, mostly about the number of miles they had done that day, their probable position and the state of their feet. They drank rum and water after their bath; for supper there was usually bully beef stewed with rice and flour dumplings. The Indians ate farine, smoked hog and occasional delicacies picked up by the way—armadillo, iguana, fat white grubs from the palm trees. The women had some dried fish with them that lasted for eight days; the smell grew stronger every day until the stuff was eaten, then it still hung about them and the stores but grew fainter until it merged into the general indefinable smell of the camp.

There were no Indians living in this country. In the last five days of the march they suffered from lack of water. They had left the Waurupang behind and the streams they came to were mostly dry; they had to reconnoitre up and down their beds in search of tepid, stagnant puddles. But after two weeks they came to a river once more, flowing deep and swift to the Southeast. This was the border of the Pie-wie country and Dr. Messinger marked the place where they stopped, Second Base Camp. The cabouri fly infested this stream in clouds.

"John, I think it's time you had a holiday."

"A holiday what from, mumsey?"

"A change . . . I'm going to California in July. To the Fischbaums —Mrs. Arnold Fischbaum, not the one who lives in Paris. I think it would do you good to come with me."

"Yes, mumsey."

"You *would* like it, wouldn't you?"

"Me? Yes, I'd like it."

"You've picked up that way of talking from Brenda. It sounds ridiculous in a man."

"Sorry, mumsey."

"All right then, that's settled."

At sunset the cabouri fly disappeared. Until then, through the day, it was necessary to keep covered; they settled on any exposed flesh like house-flies upon jam; it was only when they were gorged that their bite was perceptible; they left behind a crimson, smarting circle with a black dot at its centre. Tony and Dr. Messinger wore cotton gloves which they had brought for the purpose, and muslin veils, hanging down under their hats. Later they employed two women to squat beside their hammocks and fan them with leafy boughs; the slightest breeze was enough to disperse the flies, but soon as Tony and Dr. Messinger dozed the women would lay aside their work, and they woke instantly, stung in a hundred places. The Indians bore the insects as cows bear horse-flies; passively with occasional fretful outbursts when they would slap their shoulders and thighs.

After dark there was some relief for there were few mosquitoes at this camp but they could hear the vampire bats all night long nuzzling and flapping against their netting.

The Indians would not go hunting in this forest. They said there was no game, but Dr. Messinger said it was because they were afraid of the evil spirits of the Pie-wie people. Provisions were not lasting as well as Dr. Messinger had calculated. During the march it had been difficult to keep a proper guard over the stores. There was a bag of farine, half a bag of sugar and a bag of rice short. Dr. Messinger instituted careful rationing; he served them himself, measuring everything strictly in an enamel cup; even so the women managed to get to the sugar behind his back. He and Tony had finished the rum except for one bottle which was kept in case of emergency.

"We can't go on breaking into tinned stores," said Dr. Messinger peevishly. "The men must go out and shoot something."

But they received the orders with expressionless, downcast faces and remained in camp.

"No birds, no animals here," explained Rosa. "All gone. May be they get some fish."

But the Indians could not be persuaded to exert themselves. They could see the sacks and bales of food heaped on the bank; it would be plenty of time to start hunting and fishing when that had been exhausted.

Meanwhile there were canoes to be built.

"This is clearly Amazon water," said Dr. Messinger. "It probably flows into the Rio Branco or the Rio Negro. The Pie-wies live along the bank and the City must from all accounts be down-stream of us, up one of the tributaries. When we reach the first Pie-wie village we will be able to get guides."

The canoes were made of woodskin. Three days were spent in finding trees of suitable age and straightness and in felling them. They cut four trees and worked on them where they lay, clearing the brush for a few feet round them. They stripped the bark with their broad-bladed knives; that took another week. They worked patiently but clumsily; one woodskin was split in getting it off the trunk. There was nothing Tony and Dr. Messinger could do to help. They spent that week guarding the sugar from the women. As the men moved about the camp and the surrounding bush, their steps were soundless; their bare feet seemed never to disturb the fallen leaves, their bare shoulders made no rustle in the tangled undergrowth; their speech was brief and scarcely audible, they never joined in the chatter and laughing of their women; sometimes they gave little grunts as they worked; only once they were merry, when one of them let his knife slip as he was working on the tree-trunk and cut deeply into the ball of his thumb. Dr. Messinger dressed the wound with iodine, lint and bandages. After that the women constantly solicited him, showing him little scratches on their arms and legs and asking for iodine.

Two of the trees were finished on one day, then another next day (that was the one which split) and the fourth two days after that; it was a larger tree than the others. When the last fibre was severed four men got round the trunk and lifted the skin clear. It curled up again at once making a hollow cylinder, which the men carried down to the water-side and set afloat, fastening it to a tree with a loop of vine-rope.

When all the woodskins were ready it was an easy matter to make canoes of them. Four men held them open while two others fixed the struts. The ends were left open, and curled up slightly so as to lift them clear (when the craft was fully laden it drew only an inch or two of water). Then the men set about fashioning some single-bladed paddles; that, too, was an easy matter.

Every day Dr. Messinger asked Rosa, "When will the boats be ready? Ask the men," and she replied, "Just now."

"How many days—four?—five?—how many?"

"No, not many. Boats finish just now."

At last when it was clear that the work was nearly complete, Dr. Messinger busied himself with arrangements. He sorted out the stores, dividing the necessary freight into two groups; he and Tony were to sit in separate boats and each had with him a rifle and ammunition, a camera, tinned rations, trade goods and his own luggage. The third canoe which would be manned solely by Indians was to hold the flour and rice, sugar and farine, and the rations for the men. The canoes would not hold all the stores and an "emergency dump" was made a little way up the bank.

"We shall take eight men with us. Four can stay behind with the women to guard the camp. Once we are among the Pie-wies everything will be easy. These Macushis can go home then. I don't think they will rob the stores. There is nothing here that would be much use to them."

"Hadn't we better keep Rosa with us to act as interpreter with the Macushis?"

"Yes, perhaps we had. I will tell her."

That evening everything was finished except the paddles. In the first exhilarating hour of darkness, when Tony and Dr. Messinger were able to discard the gloves and veils that had been irking them all day, they called Rosa across to the part of the camp where they ate and slept.

"Rosa, we have decided to take you down the river with us. We need you to help us talk to the men. Understand?"

Rosa said nothing; her face was perfectly blank, lit from below by the storm lantern that stood on a box between them; the shadow of her high cheek bones hid her eyes; lank, ragged hair, a tenuous straggle of tattooing along forehead and lip, rotund body in its filthy cotton gown, bandy brown legs.

"Understand?"

But still she said nothing; she seemed to be looking over their heads into the dark forest, but her eyes were lost in shadow.

"Listen, Rosa, all women and four men stay here in camp. Six men come in boats to Pie-wie village. You come with boats. When we reach Pie-wie village, you and eight men and boats go back to camp to other women and men. Then back to Macushi country. Understand?"

At last Rosa spoke. "Macushi people no go with Pie-wie people."

"I am not asking you to go *with* Pie-wie people. You and the men take us as far as Pie-wies, then you go back to Macushi people. Understand?"

Rosa raised her arm in an embracing circle which covered the camp and the road they had travelled and the broad savannahs behind them. "Macushi peoples there," she said. Then she raised the other arm and waved it down-stream towards the hidden country. "Pie-wie peoples there," she said. "Macushi peoples no go with Pie-wie peoples."

"Now listen, Rosa. You are sensible woman. You lived two years with black gentleman, Mr. Forbes. You like cigarettes——"

"Yes, give me cigarettes."

"You come with men in boats, I give you plenty, plenty cigarettes."

Rosa looked stolidly ahead of her and said nothing.

"Listen. You will have your man and seven others to protect you. How can we talk with men without you?"

"Men no go," said Rosa.

"Of course the men will go. The only question is, will you come too?"

"Macushi peoples no go with Pie-wie peoples," said Rosa.

"Oh God," said Dr. Messinger wearily. "All right we'll talk about it in the morning."

"You give me cigarette . . ."

"It's going to be awkward if that woman doesn't come."

"It's going to be much more awkward if none of them come," said Tony.

Next day the boats were ready. By noon they were launched and tied in to the bank. The Indians went silently about the business of preparing their dinner. Tony and Dr. Messinger ate tongue, boiled rice and some tinned peaches.

"We're all right for stores," said Dr. Messinger. "There's enough for three weeks at the shortest and we are bound to come across the Pie-wies in a day or two. We will start tomorrow."

The Indians' wages, in rifles, fish-hooks and rolls of cotton, had been left behind for them at their village. There were still half a dozen boxes of "trade" for use during the later stages of the journey. A leg of bush-pig was worth a handful of shot or twenty gun caps in that currency; a fat game bird cost a necklace.

When dinner was over, at about one o'clock, Dr. Messinger called Rosa over to them. "We start tomorrow," he said.

"Yes, just now."

"Tell the men what I told you last night. Eight men to come in boats, others wait here. You come in boats. All these stores stay here. All these stores go in boats. You tell men that."

Rosa said nothing.

"Understand?"

"No peoples go in boats," she said. "All peoples go this way," and she extended her arm towards the trail that they had lately followed. "Tomorrow or next day all people go back to village."

There was a long pause; at last Dr. Messinger said, "You tell the men to come here . . . It's no use threatening them," he remarked to Tony when Rosa had waddled back to the fireside. "They are a queer, timid lot. If you threaten them they take fright and disappear leaving you stranded. Don't worry, I shall be able to persuade them."

They could see Rosa talking at the fireside but none of the group moved. Presently, having delivered her message, she was silent and squatted down among them with the head of one of the women between her knees. She had been searching it for lice when Dr. Messinger's summons had interrupted her.

"We'd better go across and talk to them."

Some of the Indians were in hammocks. The others were squatting on their heels; they had scraped earth over the fire and extinguished it. They gazed at Tony and Dr. Messinger with slit, pig eyes. Only Rosa seemed incurious; her head was averted; all her attention went to her busy fingers as she picked and crunched the lice from her friend's hair.

"What's the matter?" asked Dr. Messinger. "I told you to bring the men here."

Rosa said nothing.

"So Macushi people are cowards. They are afraid of Pie-wie people."

"It's the cassava field," said Rosa. "We must go back to dig the cassava. Otherwise it will be bad."

"Listen. I want the men for one, two weeks. No more. After that, all finish. They can go home."

"It is the time to dig the cassava. Macushi people dig cassava before the big rains. All people go home just now."

"It's pure blackmail," said Dr. Messinger. "Let's get out some trade goods."

He and Tony together prised open one of the cases and began to spread out the contents on a blanket. They had chosen these things together at a cheap store in Oxford Street. The Indians watched the display in unbroken silence. There were bottles of scent and pills, bright celluloid combs set with glass jewels, mirrors, pocket knives with embossed aluminum handles, ribbons and necklaces and barter of more solid worth in the form of axe-heads, brass cartridge cases and flat, red flasks of gunpowder.

"You give me this," said Rosa picking out a pale blue rosette, that had been made as a boat-race favour. "Give me this," she repeated, rubbing some drops of scent into the palm of her hands and inhaling deeply.

"Each man can choose three things from this box if he comes in the boats."

But Rosa replied monotonously, "Macushi people dig cassava field just now."

"It's no good," said Dr. Messinger after half an hour's fruitless negotiation. "We shall have to try with the mice. I wanted to keep them till we reached the Pie-wies. It's a pity. But they'll fall for the mice, you see. I *know* the Indian mind."

These mice were comparatively expensive articles; they had cost three and sixpence each, and Tony remembered vividly the embarrassment with which he had witnessed their demonstration on the floor of the toy department.

They were of German manufacture; the size of large rats but conspicuously painted in spots of green and white; they had large glass eyes, stiff whiskers and green and white ringed tails; they ran on hidden wheels, and inside them were little bells that jingled as they moved. Dr. Messinger took one out of their box, unwrapped the tissue paper and held it up to general scrutiny. There was no doubt that he had captured his audience's interest. Then he wound it up. The Indians stirred apprehensively at the sound.

The ground where they were camping was hard mud, inundated at flood time. Dr. Messinger put the toy down at his feet and set it going; tinkling merrily it ran towards the group of Indians. For a moment Tony was afraid that it would turn over, or become stuck against a root but the mechanism was unimpaired and by good chance there was a clear course. The effect exceeded anything that he had expected. There was a loud intake of breath, a series of horrified, small grunts, a high wail of terror from the women, and a sudden stampede; a faint patter of bare brown feet among the fallen leaves, bare limbs, quiet as bats, pushed through the undergrowth, ragged cotton gowns caught and tore in the thorn bushes. Before the toy had run down, before it had jingled its way to the place where the nearest Indian had been squatting, the camp was empty.

"Well I'm damned," said Dr. Messinger, "that's better than I expected."

"More than you expected anyway."

"Oh it's all right. They'll come back. I know them."

But by sundown there was still no sign. Throughout the hot afternoon Tony and Dr. Messinger, shrouded from cabouri fly, sprawled in their hammocks. The empty canoes lay in the river; the mechanical mouse had been put away. At sundown Dr. Messinger said, "We'd better make a fire. They'll come back when it is dark."

They brushed the earth away from the old embers, brought new wood and made a fire; they lit the storm lantern.

"We'd better get some supper," said Tony.

They boiled water and made some cocoa, opened a tin of salmon and finished the peaches that were left over from midday. They lit their pipes and drew the sheaths of mosquito netting across their hammocks. Most of this time they were silent. Presently they decided to go to sleep.

"Good."

That night the fever came on again. They were camping on a sand bank. Dr. Messinger heated stones and put them under Tony's feet and in the small of his back. He was awake most of the night fuelling the fire and refilling Tony's mug with water. At dawn Tony slept for an hour and woke feeling slightly better; he was taking frequent doses of quinine and his ears were filled with a muffled sound as though he were holding those shells to them in which, he had been told in childhood, one could hear the beat of the sea.

"We've got to go on," said Dr. Messinger. "We can't be far from a village now."

"I feel awful. Wouldn't it be better to wait a day till I am perfectly fit again."

"It's no good waiting. We've got to get on. D'you think you can manage to get into the canoe?"

Dr. Messinger knew that Tony was in for a long bout.

For the first few hours of that day Tony lay limp in the bows. They had shifted the stores so that he could lie full length. Then the fever came on again and his teeth chattered. He sat up and crouched with his head in his knees, shaking all over; only his forehead and cheeks were burning hot under the noon sun. There was still no sign of a village.

It was late in the afternoon when he first saw Brenda. For some time he had been staring intently at the odd shape amidships where the stores had been piled; then he realized that it was a human being.

"So the Indians came back?" he said.

"Yes."

"I knew they would. Silly of them to be scared by a toy. I suppose the others are following."

"Yes, I expect so. Try and sit still."

"Damned fool, being frightened of a toy," Tony said derisively to the woman amidships. Then he saw that it was Brenda. "I'm sorry," he said. "I didn't see it was you. *You* wouldn't be frightened of a toy."

But she did not answer him. She sat as she used often to sit when

"We shall find them all here in the morning," said Dr. Messinger. "They're an odd bunch."

All round them the voices of the bush whistled and croaked, changing with the hours as the night wore on to morning.

Dawn broke in London, clear and sweet, dove-grey and honey, with promise of good weather; the lamps in the streets paled and disappeared; the empty streets ran with water, and the rising sun caught it as it bubbled round the hydrants; the men in overalls swung the nozzles of their hoses from side to side and the water jetted and cascaded in a sparkle of light.

"Let's have the window open," said Brenda. "It's stuffy in here."

The waiter drew back the curtains, opened the windows.

"It's quite light," she added.

"After five. Oughtn't we to go to bed."

"Yes."

"Only another week and then all the parties will be over," said Beaver.

"Yes."

"Well let's go."

"All right. Can you pay? I just haven't any money."

They had come on after the party, for breakfast at a club Daisy had opened. Beaver paid for the kippers and tea. "Eight shillings," he said. "How does Daisy expect to make a success of the place when she charges prices like that?"

"It does seem a lot . . . So you really *are* going to America?"

"I must. Mother has taken the tickets."

"Nothing I've said tonight makes any difference?"

"Darling, don't go on. We've been through all that. You know it's the only thing that *can* happen. Why spoil the last week?"

"You *have* enjoyed the summer, haven't you?"

"Of course . . . well, shall we go?"

"Yes. You needn't bother to see me home."

"Sure you don't mind? It *is* miles out of the way and it's late."

"There's no knowing what I mind."

"Brenda, darling, for heaven's sake . . . It isn't like you to go on like this."

"I never was one for making myself expensive."

The Indians returned during the night, while Tony and Dr. Messinger were asleep; without a word spoken the little people crept out of hiding; the women had removed their clothes and left them at a distance so that no twig should betray their movements; their naked bodies moved soundlessly through the undergrowth; the glowing embers of the fire and the storm lantern twenty yards away were their only light; there was no moon. They collected their wicker baskets and their rations of farine, their bows and arrows, the gun and their broad-bladed knives; they rolled up their hammocks into compact cylinders. They took nothing with them that was not theirs. Then they crept back through the shadows, into the darkness.

When Tony and Dr. Messinger awoke it was clear to them what had happened.

"The situation is grave," said Dr. Messinger. "But not desperate."

4

For four days Tony and Dr. Messinger paddled down-stream. They sat, balancing themselves precariously, at the two ends of the canoe; between them they had piled the most essential of their stores; the remainder, with the other canoes, had been left at the camp, to be called for when they had recruited help from the Pie-wies. Even the minimum which Dr. Messinger had selected overweighted the craft so that it was dangerously low; and movement brought the water to the lip of the gunwale and threatened disaster; it was heavy to steer and they made slow progress, contenting themselves for the most part, with keeping end on, and drifting with the current.

Twice they came to the stretches of cataract, and here they drew in to the bank, unloaded, and waded beside the boat, sometimes plunging waist deep, sometimes clambering over the rocks, guiding it by hand

until they reached clear water again. Then they tied up to the bank and carried their cargo down to it through the bush. For the rest of the way the river was broad and smooth; a dark surface which reflected in fine detail the walls of forest on either side, towering up from the undergrowth to their flowering crown a hundred or more feet above them. Sometimes they came to a stretch of water scattered with fallen petals and floated among them, moving scarcely less slowly than they, as though resting in a blossoming meadow. At night they spread their tarpaulin on stretches of dry beach, and hung their hammocks in the bush. Only the cabouri fly and rare, immobile alligators menaced the peace of their days.

They kept a constant scrutiny of the banks but saw no sign of human life.

Then Tony developed fever. It came on him quite suddenly, during the fourth afternoon. At their midday halt he was in complete health and had shot a small deer that came down to drink on the opposite bank; an hour later he was shivering so violently that he had to lay down his paddle; his head was flaming with heat, his body and limbs frigid; by sunset he was slightly delirious.

Dr. Messinger took his temperature and found that it was a hundred and four degrees, Fahrenheit. He gave him twenty-five grains of quinine and lit a fire so close to his hammock that by morning it was singed and blacked with smoke. He told Tony to keep wrapped up in his blanket, but at intervals throughout that night he woke from sleep to find himself running with sweat; he was consumed with thirst and drank mug after mug of river water. Neither that evening nor next morning was he able to eat anything.

But next morning his temperature was down again. He felt weak and exhausted but he was able to keep steady in his place and paddle a little.

"It was just a passing attack, wasn't it?" he said. "I shall be perfectly fit tomorrow, shan't I?"

"I hope so," said Dr. Messinger.

At midday Tony drank some cocoa and ate a cupful of rice. "I feel grand," he said.

she came back from London, huddled over her bowl of bread and milk.

Dr. Messinger steered the boat in to the side. They nearly capsized as he helped Tony out. Brenda got ashore without assistance. She stepped out in her delicate, competent way, keeping the balance of the boat.

"That's what poise means," said Tony. "D'you know I once saw a questionnaire that people had to fill in when they applied for a job in an American firm, and one of the things they had to answer was 'Have you poise?'"

Brenda was at the top of the bank waiting for him. "What was so absurd about the question was that they only had the applicant's word for it," he explained laboriously. "I mean—is it a sign of poise to think you have it?"

"Just sit quiet here while I sling your hammock."

"Yes, I'll sit here with Brenda. I am so glad she could come. She must have caught the three-eighteen."

She was with him all that night and all the next day. He talked to her ceaselessly but her replies were rare and enigmatic. On the succeeding evening he had another fit of sweating. Dr. Messinger kept a large fire burning by the hammock and wrapped Tony in his own blanket. An hour before dawn Tony fell asleep and when he awoke Brenda had gone.

"You're down to normal again."

"Thank God. I've been pretty ill, haven't I? I can't remember much."

Dr. Messinger had made something of a camp. He had chopped a square clear of undergrowth, the size of a small room. Their two hammocks hung on opposite sides of it. The stores were all ashore, arranged in an orderly pile on the tarpaulin.

"How d'you feel?"

"Grand," said Tony, but when he got out of his hammock he found he could not stand without help. "Of course, I haven't eaten anything. I expect it will be a day or two before I'm really well."

Dr. Messinger said nothing, but strained the tea clear of leaves by pouring it slowly from one mug into another; he stirred into it a large spoonful of condensed milk.

"See if you can drink this."

Tony drank it with pleasure and ate some biscuits.

"Are we going on today?" he asked.

"We'll think about it." He took the mugs down to the bank and washed them in the river. When he came back he said, "I think I'd better explain things. It's no use your thinking you are cured because you are out of fever for one day. That's the way it goes. One day fever and one day normal. It may take a week or it may take much longer. That's a thing we've got to face. I can't risk taking you in the canoe. You nearly upset us several times the day before yesterday."

"I thought there was someone there I knew."

"You thought a lot of things. It'll go on like that. Meanwhile we've provisions for about ten days. There's no immediate anxiety there but it's a thing to remember. Besides what you need is a roof over your head and constant nursing. If only we were at a village . . ."

"I'm afraid I'm being a great nuisance."

"That's not the point. The thing is to find what is best for us to do."

But Tony felt too tired to think; he dozed for an hour or so. When he awoke Dr. Messinger was cutting back the bush further. "I'm going to fix up the tarpaulin as a roof."

(He had marked this place on his map *Temporary Emergency Base Camp.*)

Tony watched him listlessly. Presently he said, "Look here, why don't you leave me here and go down the river for help?"

"I thought of that. It's too big a risk."

That afternoon Brenda was back at Tony's side and he was shivering and tossing in his hammock.

When he was next able to observe things, Tony noted that there was a tarpaulin over his head, slung to the tree-trunks. He asked, "How long have we been here?"

"Only three days."

"What time is it now?"

"Getting on for ten in the morning."

"I feel awful."

Dr. Messinger gave him some soup. "I am going down-stream for the day," he said, "to see if there's any sign of a village. I hate leaving you but it's a chance worth taking. I shall be able to get a long way in the canoe now it's empty. Lie quiet. Don't move from the hammock. I shall be back before night. I hope with some Indians to help."

"All right," said Tony and fell asleep.

Dr. Messinger went down to the river's edge and untied the canoe; he brought with him a rifle, a drinking cup and a day's provisions. He sat in the stern and pushed out from the bank; the current carried the bow down and in a few strokes of the paddle he was in mid-stream.

The sun was high and its reflection in the water dazzled and scorched him; he paddled on with regular, leisurely strokes; he was travelling fast. For a mile's stretch the river narrowed and the water raced so that all he had to do was to trail the blade of the paddle as a rudder; then the walls of forest on either side of him fell back and he drifted into a great open lake, where he had to work heavily to keep in motion; all the time he watched keenly to right and left for the column of smoke, the thatched domes, the sly brown figure in the undergrowth, the drinking cattle, that would disclose the village he sought. But there was no sign. In the open water he took up his field glasses and studied the whole wooded margin. But there was no sign.

Later the river narrowed once more and the canoe shot forward in the swift current. Ahead of him the surface was broken by rapids; the smooth water seethed and eddied; a low monotone warned him that beyond the rapids was a fall. Dr. Messinger began to steer for the bank. The current was running strongly and he exerted his full strength; ten yards from the beginning of his rapids his bow ran in under the bank. There was a dense growth of thorn here, overhanging the river; the canoe slid under them and bit into the beach; very cautiously Dr. Messinger knelt forward in his place and stretched up to a bough over his head. It was at that moment he came to grief; the stern swung out downstream and as he snatched at the paddle the craft was swept broadside into the troubled waters; there it adopted an eccentric course, spinning and tumbling to the falls. Dr. Messinger was tipped into the water; it was quite shallow in places and he caught at the rocks but they were worn smooth as ivory and afforded no hold for his hands; he rolled over twice, found himself in deep water and attempted to swim, found himself among boulders again and attempted to grapple with them. Then he reached the falls.

They were unspectacular as falls in that country go—a drop of ten feet or less—but they were enough for Dr. Messinger. At their foot the foam subsided into a great pool, almost still, and strewn with blossoms from the forest trees that encircled it. Dr. Messinger's hat floated very slowly towards the Amazon and the water closed over his bald head.

Brenda went to see the family solicitors.

"Mr. Graceful," she said, "I've got to have some more money."

Mr. Graceful looked at her sadly. "I should have thought that was really a question for your bank manager. I understand that your securities are in your own name and that the dividends are paid into your account."

"They never seem to pay dividends nowadays. Besides it's really very difficult to live on so little."

"No doubt. No doubt."

"Mr. Last left you with power of attorney, didn't he?"

"With strictly limited powers, Lady Brenda. I am instructed to pay the wage bill at Hetton and all expenses connected with the upkeep of the estate—he is putting in new bathrooms and restoring some decorations in the morning room which had been demolished. But I am afraid that I have no authority to draw on Mr. Last's account for other charges."

"But, Mr. Graceful, I am sure he didn't intend to stay abroad so long. He can't possibly have meant to leave me stranded like this, can he? . . . Can he?"

Mr. Graceful paused and fidgeted a little. "To be quite frank, Lady Brenda, I fear that was his intention. I raised this particular point shortly before his departure. He was quite resolved on the subject."

"But is he *allowed* to do that? I mean haven't I got any rights under the marriage settlement or anything?"

"Nothing which you can claim without application to the Courts. You *might* find solicitors who would advise you to take action. I cannot say that I should be one of them. Mr. Last would oppose any such order to the utmost and I think that, in the present circumstances, the Courts would undoubtedly find for him. In any case it would be a prolonged, costly and slightly undignified proceeding."

"Oh, I see . . . well, that's that, isn't it?"

"It certainly looks as though it were."

Brenda rose to go. It was high summer and through the open windows she could see the sun-bathed gardens of Lincoln's Inn.

"There's one thing. Do you know, I mean, can you tell me whether Mr. Last made another will?"

"I'm afraid that is a thing I cannot discuss."

"No, I suppose not. I'm sorry if it was wrong to ask. I just wanted to know how I am with him."

She still stood between the door and the table looking lost, in her bright summer clothes. "Perhaps I can say as much as this to guide you. The heirs presumptive to Hetton are now his cousins, the Richard Lasts at Princes Risborough. I think that your knowledge of Mr. Last's character and opinions will tell you that he would always wish his fortune to go with the estate, in order that it may be preserved in what he holds to be its right condition."

"Yes," said Brenda, "I ought to have thought of that. Well, goodbye."

And she went out alone into the sunshine.

All that day Tony lay alone, fitfully oblivious of the passage of time. He slept a little; once or twice he left his hammock and found himself weak and dizzy. He tried to eat some of the food which Dr. Messinger had left out for him, but without success. It was not until it grew dark that he realized the day was over. He lit the lantern and began to collect wood for the fire, but the sticks kept slipping from his fingers and each time that he stooped he felt giddy, so that after a few fretful efforts he left them where they had fallen and returned to his hammock. And lying there, wrapped in his blanket, he began to cry.

After some hours of darkness the lamp began to burn low; he leant painfully over, and shook it. It needed refilling. He knew where the oil was kept, crept to it, supporting himself first on the hammock rope and then on a pile of boxes. He found the keg, pulled out the bung and began to refill the lamp, but his hand trembled and the oil spilled over the ground, then his head began to swim again so that he shut his eyes; the keg rolled over on its side and emptied itself with slow gurglings. When he realized what had happened he began to cry again. He lay down in his hammock and in a few minutes the light sank, flickered and went out. There was a reek of kerosene on his hands and on the sodden earth. He lay awake in the darkness crying.

Just before dawn the fever returned and a constant company of phantoms perplexed his senses.

Brenda awoke in the lowest possible spirits. The evening before she had spent alone at a cinema. Afterwards she felt hungry—she had had no proper meal that day—but she had not the strength to go alone into any of the supper restaurants. She bought a meat pie at a coffee stall and took it home. It looked delicious but, when she came to eat she found that she had lost her appetite. The remains of that pie lay on the dressing table when she awoke.

It was August and she was entirely alone. Beaver was that day landing in New York. (He had cabled her from mid-ocean that the crossing was excellent.) It was for her the last of Beaver. Parliament was over and Jock Grant-Menzies was paying his annual visit to his elder brother in Scotland; Marjorie and Allan at the last moment had made Lord Monomark's yacht and were drifting luxuriously down the coast of Spain attending bull-fights (they had even asked her to look after Djinn). Her mother was at the chalet Lady Anchorage always lent her on the lake of Geneva. Polly was everywhere. Even Jenny Abdul Akbar was cruising in the Baltic.

Brenda opened her newspaper and read an article by a young man who said that the London Season was a thing of the past; that everyone was too busy in those days to keep up the pre-war routine; that there were no more formal dances but a constant round of more modest entertaining; that August in London was the gayest time of all (he rewrote this annually in slightly different words). It did not console Brenda to read that article.

For weeks past she had attempted to keep a fair mind towards Tony and his treatment of her; now at last she broke down and turning over buried her face in the pillow, in an agony of resentment and self-pity.

In Brazil she wore a ragged cotton gown of the same pattern as Rosa's. It was not unbecoming. Tony watched her for some time before he spoke. "Why are you dressed like that?"

"Don't you like it? I got it from Polly."

"It looks so dirty."

"Well, Polly travels about a lot. You must get up now to go to the County Council Meeting."

"But it isn't Wednesday?"

"No, but time is different in Brazil, surely you remember."

"I can't get as far as Pigstanton. I've got to stay here until Messinger comes back. I'm ill. He told me to be quiet. He's coming this evening."

"But all the County Council are here. The Shameless Blonde brought them in her aeroplane."

Sure enough they were all there. Reggie St. Cloud was chairman. He said, "I strongly object to Milly being on the committee. She is a woman of low repute."

Tony protested. "She has a daughter. She has as much right here as Lady Cockpurse."

"Order," said the Mayor. "I must ask you gentlemen to confine your remarks to the subject under discussion. We have to decide about the widening of the Bayton-Pigstanton road. There have been several complaints that it's impossible for the Green Line Buses to turn the corner safely at Hetton Cross."

"Green Line *rats.*"

"I said Green Line rats. Mechanical green line rats. Many of the villagers have been scared by them and have evacuated their cottages."

"I evacuated," said Reggie St. Cloud. "I was driven out of my house by mechanical green rats."

"Order," said Lady Cockpurse. "I move that Mr. Last address the meeting."

"Hear, hear."

"Ladies and gentlemen," said Tony. "I beg you to understand that I am ill and must not move from the hammock. Dr. Messinger has given the clearest instructions."

"Winnie wants to bathe."

"No bathing in Brazil. No bathing in Brazil." The meeting took up the cry. "No bathing in Brazil."

"But you had two breakfasts."

"Order," said the Mayor. "Lord St. Cloud, I suggest you put the question to the vote."

"The question is whether the contract for the widening of the corner at Hetton Cross shall be given to Mrs. Beaver. Of the tenders submitted hers was by far the most expensive but I understand that her plans included a chromium plated wall on the south side of the village . . ."

". . . and two breakfasts," prompted Winnie.

". . . and two breakfasts for the men engaged on the work. Those in favour of the motion will make a clucking sound in imitation of hens, those against will say bow-wow."

"A most improper proceeding," said Reggie. "What will the servants think?"

"We have got to do something until Brenda has been told."

". . . Me? I'm all right."

"Then I take it the motion is carried."

"Oh, I *am* glad Mrs. Beaver got the job," said Brenda. "You see I'm in love with John Beaver, I'm in love with John Beaver, I'm in love with John Beaver."

"Is that the decision of the committee?"

"Yes, she is in love with John Beaver."

"Then that is carried unanimously."

"No," said Winnie. "He ate two breakfasts."

". . . by an overwhelming majority."

"Why are you all changing your clothes?" asked Tony for they were putting on hunting coats.

"For the lawn meet. Hounds are meeting here today."

"But you can't hunt in summer."

"Time is different in Brazil and there is no bathing."

"I saw a fox yesterday in Bruton wood. A mechanical green fox with a bell inside him that jingled as he ran. It frightened them so much that they ran away and the whole beach was deserted and there was no bathing except for Beaver. He can bathe every day for the time is different in Brazil."

"I'm in love with John Beaver," said Ambrose.

"Why, I didn't know you were here."

"I came to remind you that you were ill, sir. You must on no account leave your hammock."

"But how can I reach the City if I stay here?"

"I will serve it directly, sir, in the library."

"Yes, in the library. There is no point in using the dining hall now that her ladyship has gone to live in Brazil."

"I will send the order to the stables, sir."

"But I don't want the pony. I told Ben to sell her."

"You will have to ride to the smoking room, sir. Dr. Messinger has taken the canoe."

"Very well, Ambrose."

"Thank you, sir."

The committee had moved off down the avenue; all except Colonel Inch who had taken the other drive and was trotting towards Compton Last. Tony and Mrs. Rattery were all alone.

"Bow-wow," she said, scooping in the cards. "That carries the motion."

Looking up from the card table, Tony saw beyond the trees the ramparts and battlements of the City; it was quite near him. From the turret of the gatehouse a heraldic banner floated in the tropic breeze. He struggled into an upright position and threw aside his blankets. He was stronger and steadier when the fever was on him. He picked his way through the surrounding thorn-scrub; the sound of music rose from the glittering walls; some procession or pageant was passing along them. He lurched into tree-trunks and became caught up in roots and hanging tendrils of bush-vine; but he pressed forward unconscious of pain and fatigue.

At last he came into the open. The gates were open before him and trumpets were sounding along the walls, saluting his arrival; from bastion to bastion the message ran to the four points of the compass; petals of almond and apple blossom were in the air; they carpeted the way, as, after a summer storm, they lay in the orchards at Hetton. Gilded cupolas and spires of alabaster shone in the sunlight.

Ambrose announced, "The City is served."

VI

À CÔTÉ DE CHEZ TODD

ALTHOUGH Mr. Todd had lived in Amazonas for nearly sixty years, no one except a few families of Pie-wie Indians was aware of his existence. His house stood in a small savannah, one of those little patches of sand and grass that crop up occasionally in that neighbourhood, three miles or so across, bounded on all sides by forest.

The stream which watered it was not marked on any map; it ran through rapids, always dangerous and at most seasons of the year impassable, to join the upper waters of the river where Dr. Messinger had come to grief. None of the inhabitants of the district, except Mr. Todd, had ever heard of the governments of Brazil or Dutch Guiana, both of which, from time to time claimed its possession.

Mr. Todd's house was larger than those of his neighbours, but similar in character—a palm thatch roof, breast high walls of mud and wattle, and a mud floor. He owned the dozen or so head of puny cattle which grazed in the savannah, a plantation of cassava, some banana and mango trees, a dog and, unique in the neighbourhood, a single-barrelled breech-loading shot gun. The few commodities which he employed from the outside world came to him through a long succession of traders, passed from hand to hand, bartered for in a dozen languages at the extreme end of one of the longest threads in the web of commerce that spreads from Manáos into the remote fastness of the forest.

One day while Mr. Todd was engaged in filling some cartridges, a Pie-wie came to him with the news that a white man was approaching through the forest, alone and very sick. He closed the cartridge and loaded his gun with it, put those that were finished into his pocket and set out in the direction indicated.

The man was already clear of the bush when Mr. Todd reached him, sitting on the ground, clearly in a very bad way. He was without hat or boots, and his clothes were so torn that it was only by the dampness of his body that they adhered to it; his feet were cut and grossly swollen; every exposed surface of skin was scarred by insect and bat bites; his eyes were wild with fever. He was talking to himself in delirium but stopped when Todd approached and addressed him in English.

"You're the first person who's spoken to me for days," said Tony. "The others won't stop. They keep bicycling by . . . I'm tired . . . Brenda was with me at first but she was frightened by a mechanical mouse, so she took the canoe and went off. She said she would come back that evening but she didn't. I expect she's staying with one of her new friends in Brazil . . . You haven't seen her have you?"

"You are the first stranger I have seen for a very long time."

"She was wearing a top hat when she left. You can't miss her." Then he began talking to someone at Mr. Todd's side, who was not there.

"Do you see that house over there? Do you think you can manage to walk to it? If not I can send some Indians to carry you."

Tony squinted across the savannah at Mr. Todd's hut.

"Architecture harmonizing with local character," he said, "indigenous material employed throughout. Don't let Mrs. Beaver see it or she will cover it with chromium plating."

"Try and walk." Mr. Todd hoisted Tony to his feet and supported him with a stout arm.

"I'll ride your bicycle. It *was* you I passed just now on a bicycle wasn't it? . . . except that your beard is a different colour. His was green . . . green as mice."

Mr. Todd led Tony across the hummocks of grass towards the house.

"It is a very short way. When we get there I will give you something to make you better."

"Very kind of you . . . rotten thing for a man to have his wife go away in a canoe. That was a long time ago. Nothing to eat since." Presently he said, "I say, you're English. I'm English too. My name is Last."

"Well, Mr. Last, you aren't to bother about anything more. You're ill and you've had a rough journey. I'll take care of you."

Tony looked round him. "Are you all English?"

"Yes, all of us."

"That dark girl married a Moor . . . It's very lucky I met you all. I suppose you're some kind of cycling club?"

"Yes."

"Well, I feel too tired for bicycling . . . never liked it much . . . you fellows ought to get motor bicycles you know, much faster and noisier . . . Let's stop here."

"No, you must come as far as the house. It's not very much further."

"All right . . . I suppose you would have some difficulty getting petrol here."

They went very slowly, but at length reached the house.

"Lie there in the hammock."

"That's what Messinger said. He's in love with John Beaver."

"I will get something for you."

"Very good of you. Just my usual morning tray—coffee, toast, fruit. And the morning papers. If her ladyship has been called I will have it with her . . ."

Mr. Todd went into the back room of the house and dragged a tin canister from under a heap of skins. It was full of a mixture of dried leaf and bark. He took a handful and went outside to the fire. When he returned his guest was bolt upright astride the hammock, talking angrily.

". . . You would hear better and it would be more polite if you stood still when I addressed you instead of walking round in a circle. It is for your own good that I am telling you . . . I know you are friends of my wife and that is why you will not listen to me. But be careful. She will say nothing cruel, she will not raise her voice, there will be no hard words. She hopes you will be great friends afterwards as before. But she will leave you. She will go away quietly during the night. She will take her hammock and her rations of farine . . . Listen to me. I know I am not clever but that is no reason why we should forget courtesy. Let us kill in the gentlest manner. I will tell you what I have learned in the forest, where time is different. There is no City. Mrs. Beaver has covered it with chromium plating and converted it into flats. Three guineas a week with a separate bathroom. Very suitable for base love. And Polly will be there. She and Mrs. Beaver under the fallen battlements . . ."

Mr. Todd put a hand behind Tony's head and held up the concoction of herbs in the calabash. Tony sipped and turned away his head. "Nasty medicine," he said, and began to cry.

Mr. Todd stood by him holding the calabash. Presently Tony drank some more, screwing up his face and shuddering slightly at the bitterness. Mr. Todd stood beside him until the draught was finished; then he threw out the dregs on to the mud floor. Tony lay back in the hammock sobbing quietly. Soon he fell into a deep sleep.

Tony's recovery was slow. At first, days of lucidity alternated with delirium; then his temperature dropped and he was conscious even when most ill. The days of fever grew less frequent, finally occurring in the normal system of the tropics, between long periods of comparative health. Mr. Todd dosed him regularly with herbal remedies.

"It's very nasty," said Tony, "but it does do good."

"There is medicine for everything in the forest," said Mr. Todd;

"to make you well and to make you ill. My mother was an Indian and she taught me many of them. I have learned others from time to time from my wives. There are plants to cure you and give you fever, to kill you and send you mad, to keep away snakes, to intoxicate fish so that you can pick them out of the water with your hands like fruit from a tree. There are medicines even I do not know. They say that it is possible to bring dead people to life after they have begun to stink, but I have not seen it done."

"But surely you are English?"

"My father was—at least a Barbadian. He came to Guiana as a missionary. He was married to a white woman but he left her in Guiana to look for gold. Then he took my mother. The Pie-wie women are ugly but very devoted. I have had many. Most of the men and women living in this savannah are my children. That is why they obey—for that reason and because I have the gun. My father lived to a great age. It is not twenty years since he died. He was a man of education. Can you read?"

"Yes, of course."

"It is not everyone who is so fortunate. I cannot."

Tony laughed apologetically. "But I suppose you haven't much opportunity here."

"Oh yes, that is just it. I have a *great* many books. I will show you when you are better. Until five years ago there was an Englishman—at least a black man, but he was well educated in Georgetown. He died. He used to read to me every day until he died. You shall read to me when you are better."

"I shall be delighted to."

"Yes, you shall read to me," Mr. Todd repeated, nodding over the calabash.

During the early days of his convalescence Tony had little conversation with his host; he lay in the hammock staring up at the thatched roof and thinking about Brenda. The days, exactly twelve hours each, passed without distinction. Mr. Todd retired to sleep at sundown, leaving a little lamp burning—a hand-woven wick drooping from a pot of beef fat—to keep away vampire bats.

The first time that Tony left the house Mr. Todd took him for a little stroll around the farm.

"I will show you the black man's grave," he said, leading him to a mound between the mango trees. "He was very kind. Every afternoon until he died, for two hours, he used to read to me. I think I will put up a cross—to commemorate his death and your arrival—a pretty idea. Do you believe in God?"

"I suppose so. I've never really thought about it much."

"I have thought about it a *great* deal and I still do not know . . . Dickens did."

"I suppose so."

"Oh yes, it is apparent in all his books. You will see."

That afternoon Mr. Todd began the construction of a headpiece for the Negro's grave. He worked with a large spokeshave in a wood so hard that it grated and rang like metal.

At last when Tony had passed six or seven consecutive nights without fever, Mr. Todd said, "Now I think you are well enough to see the books."

At one end of the hut there was a kind of loft formed by a rough platform erected in the eaves of the roof. Mr. Todd propped a ladder against it and mounted. Tony followed, still unsteady after his illness. Mr. Todd sat on the platform and Tony stood at the top of the ladder looking over. There was a heap of small bundles there, tied up with rag, palm leaf and raw hide.

"It has been hard to keep out the worms and ants. Two are practically destroyed. But there is an oil the Indians make that is useful."

He unwrapped the nearest parcel and handed down a calf bound book. It was an early American edition of *Bleak House*.

"It does not matter which we take first."

"You are fond of Dickens?"

"Why, yes, of course. More than fond, far more. You see, they are the only books I have ever heard. My father used to read them and then later the black man . . . and now you. I have heard them all several times by now but I never get tired; there is always more to be learned and noticed, so many characters, so many changes of scene, so many words . . . I have all Dickens's books here except those that the ants devoured. It takes a long time to read them all—more than two years."

"Well," said Tony lightly, "they will well last out my visit."

"Oh, I hope not. It is delightful to start again. Each time I think I find more to enjoy and admire."

They took down the first volume of *Bleak House* and that afternoon Tony had his first reading.

He had always rather enjoyed reading aloud and in the first year of marriage had shared several books in this way with Brenda, until one day, in a moment of frankness, she remarked that it was torture to her. He had read to John Andrew, late in the afternoon, in winter, while the child sat before the nursery fender eating his supper. But Mr. Todd was a unique audience.

The old man sat astride his hammock opposite Tony, fixing him throughout with his eyes, and following the words, soundlessly, with his lips. Often when a new character was introduced he would say, "Repeat the name, I have forgotten him," or "Yes, yes, I remember her well. She dies, poor woman." He would frequently interrupt with questions; not as Tony would have imagined about the circumstances of the story—such things as the procedure of the Lord Chancellor's Court or the social conventions of the time, though they must have been unintelligible, did not concern him—but always about the characters. "Now why does she say that? Does she really mean it? Did she feel faint because of the heat of the fire or of something in that paper?" He laughed loudly at all the jokes and at some passages which did not seem humorous to Tony, asking him to repeat them two or three times; and later at the description of the sufferings of the outcasts in "Tom-all-alones" tears ran down his cheeks into his beard. His comments on the story were usually simple. "I think that Dedlock is a very proud man," or, "Mrs. Jellyby does not take enough care of her children."

Tony enjoyed the readings almost as much as he did.

At the end of the first day the old man said, "You read beautifully, with a far better accent than the black man. And you explain better. It is almost as though my father were here again." And always at the end of a session he thanked his guest courteously. "I enjoyed that *very* much. It was an extremely distressing chapter. But, if I remember rightly, it will all turn out well."

By the time that they were in the second volume however, the novelty of the old man's delight had begun to wane, and Tony was feeling strong enough to be restless. He touched more than once on the subject of his departure, asking about canoes and rains and the possibility of finding guides. But Mr. Todd seemed obtuse and paid no attention to these hints.

One day, running his thumb through the pages of *Bleak House* that remained to be read, Tony said, "We still have a lot to get through. I hope I shall be able to finish it before I go."

"Oh yes," said Mr. Todd. "Do not disturb yourself about that. You will have time to finish it, my friend."

For the first time Tony noticed something slightly menacing in his host's manner. That evening at supper, a brief meal of farine and dried beef, eaten just before sundown, Tony renewed the subject.

"You know, Mr. Todd, the time has come when I must be thinking about getting back to civilization. I have already imposed myself on your hospitality for too long."

Mr. Todd bent over the plate, crunching mouthfuls of farine, but made no reply.

"How soon do you think I shall be able to get a boat? . . . I said how soon do you think I shall be able to get a boat? I appreciate all your kindness to me more than I can say but . . ."

"My friend, any kindness I may have shown is amply repaid by your reading of Dickens. Do not let us mention the subject again."

"Well I'm very glad you have enjoyed it. I have, too. But I really must be thinking of getting back . . ."

"Yes," said Mr. Todd. "The black man was like that. He thought of it all the time. But he died here . . ."

Twice during the next day Tony opened the subject but his host was evasive. Finally he said, "Forgive me, Mr. Todd, but I really must press the point. When can I get a boat?"

"There is no boat."

"Well, the Indians can build one."

"You must wait for the rains. There is not enough water in the river now."

"How long will that be?"

"A month . . . two months . . ."

They had finished *Bleak House* and were nearing the end of *Dombey and Son* when the rain came.

"Now it is time to make preparations to go."

"Oh, that is impossible. The Indians will not make a boat during the rainy season—it is one of their superstitions."

"You might have told me."

"Did I not mention it? I forgot."

Next morning Tony went out alone while his host was busy, and, looking as aimless as he could, strolled across the savannah to the group of Indian houses. There were four or five Pie-wies sitting in one of the doorways. They did not look up as he approached them. He addressed them in the few words of Macushi he had acquired during the journey but they made no sign whether they understood him or not. Then he drew a sketch of a canoe in the sand, he went through some vague motions of carpentry, pointed from them to him, then made motions of giving something to them and scratched out the outlines of a gun and a hat and a few other recognizable articles of trade. One of the women giggled but no one gave any sign of comprehension, and he went away unsatisfied.

At their midday meal Mr. Todd said, "Mr. Last, the Indians tell me that you have been trying to speak with them. It is easier that you say anything you wish through me. You realize, do you not, that they would do nothing without my authority. They regard themselves, quite rightly in many cases, as my children."

"Well, as a matter of fact, I was asking them about a canoe."

"So they gave me to understand . . . and now if you have finished your meal perhaps we might have another chapter. I am quite absorbed in the book."

They finished *Dombey and Son;* nearly a year had passed since Tony had left England, and his gloomy foreboding of permanent exile became suddenly acute when, between the pages of *Martin Chuzzlewit,* he found a document written in pencil in irregular characters.

Year 1919.
I James Todd of Brazil do swear to Barnabas Washington of Georgetown that if he finish this book in fact Martin Chuzzlewit I will let him go away back as soon as finished.

There followed a heavy pencil X and after it: *Mr. Todd made this mark signed Barnabas Washington.*

"Mr. Todd," said Tony, "I must speak frankly. You saved my life, and when I get back to civilization I will reward you to the best of my ability. I will give you anything within reason. But at present you are keeping me here against my will. I demand to be released."

"But, my friend, what is keeping you? You are under no restraint. Go when you like."

"You know very well that I can't get away without your help."

"In that case you must humour an old man. Read me another chapter."

"Mr. Todd, I swear by anything you like that when I get to Manáos I will find someone to take my place. I will pay a man to read to you all day."

"But I have no need of another man. You read so well."

"I have read for the last time."

"I hope not," said Mr. Todd politely.

That evening at supper only one plate of dried meat and farine was brought in and Mr. Todd ate alone. Tony lay without speaking, staring at the thatch.

Next day at noon a single plate was put before Mr. Todd but with it lay his gun, cocked, on his knee, as he ate. Tony resumed the reading of *Martin Chuzzlewit* where it had been interrupted.

Weeks passed hopelessly. They read *Nicholas Nickleby* and *Little Dorrit* and *Oliver Twist*. Then a stranger arrived in the savannah, a half-caste prospector, one of that lonely order of men who wander for a lifetime through the forests, tracing the little streams, sifting the gravel and, ounce by ounce, filling the little leather sack of gold dust, more often than not dying of exposure and starvation with five hundred dollars' worth of gold hung around their necks. Mr. Todd was vexed at his arrival, gave him farine and *tasso* and sent him on his journey within an hour of his arrival, but in that hour Tony had time to scribble his name on a slip of paper and put it into the man's hand.

From now on there was hope. The days followed their unvarying routine; coffee at sunrise, a morning of inaction while Mr. Todd pottered about on the business of the farm, farine and *tasso* at noon, Dickens in the afternoon, farine and *tasso* and sometimes some fruit for supper, silence from sunset to dawn with the small wick glowing in the beef fat and the palm thatch overhead dimly discernible; but Tony lived in quiet confidence and expectation.

Sometime, this year or the next, the prospector would arrive at a Brazilian village with news of his discovery. The disasters of the Messinger expedition would not have passed unnoticed. Tony could imagine the headlines that must have appeared in the popular press; even now probably there were search parties working over the country he had crossed; any day English voices must sound over the savannah and a dozen friendly adventurers come crashing through the bush. Even as he was reading, while his lips mechanically followed the printed pages, his mind wandered away from his eager, crazy host opposite, and he began to narrate to himself incidents of his home-coming—the gradual re-encounters with civilization (he shaved and bought new clothes at Manáos, telegraphed for money, received wires of congratulation; he enjoyed the leisurely river journey to Belem, the big liner to Europe; savoured good claret and fresh meat and spring vegetables; he was shy at meeting Brenda and uncertain how to address her . . . *"Darling,* you've been much longer than you said. I quite thought you were lost . . .")

And then Mr. Todd interrupted. "May I trouble you to read that passage again? It is one I particularly enjoy."

The weeks passed; there was no sign of rescue but Tony endured the day for hope of what might happen on the morrow; he even felt a slight stirring of cordiality towards his jailer and was therefore quite willing to join him when, one evening after a long conference with an Indian neighbour, he proposed a celebration.

"It is one of the local feast days," he explained, "and they have been making *piwari*. You may not like it but you should try some. We will go across to this man's home tonight."

Accordingly after supper they joined a party of Indians that were assembled round the fire in one of the huts at the other side of the savannah. They were singing in an apathetic, monotonous manner and passing a large calabash of liquid from mouth to mouth. Separate bowls were brought for Tony and Mr. Todd, and they were given hammocks to sit in.

"You must drink it all without lowering the cup. That is the etiquette."

Tony gulped the dark liquid, trying not to taste it. But it was not unpleasant, hard and muddy on the palate like most of the beverages he had been offered in Brazil, but with a flavour of honey and brown bread. He leant back in the hammock feeling unusually contented. Perhaps at that very moment the search party was in camp a few hours' journey from them. Meanwhile he was warm and drowsy. The cadence of song rose and fell interminably, liturgically. Another calabash of *piwari* was offered him and he handed it back empty. He lay full length watching the play of shadows on the thatch as the Pie-wies began to dance. Then he shut his eyes and thought of England and Hetton and fell asleep.

He awoke, still in the Indian hut, with the impression that he had outslept his usual hour. By the position of the sun he knew it was late afternoon. No one else was about. He looked for his watch and found to his surprise that it was not on his wrist. He had left it in the house, he supposed, before coming to the party.

"I must have been tight last night," he reflected. "Treacherous drink that." He had a headache and feared a recurrence of fever. He found when he set his feet to the ground that he stood with difficulty; his walk was unsteady and his mind confused as it had been during the first weeks of his convalescence. On the way across the savannah he was obliged to stop more than once, shutting his eyes and breathing deeply. When he reached the house he found Mr. Todd sitting there.

"Ah, my friend, you are late for the reading this afternoon. There is scarcely another half hour of light. How do you feel?"

"Rotten. That drink doesn't seem to agree with me."

"I will give you something to make you better. The forest has remedies for everything; to make you awake and to make you sleep."

"You haven't seen my watch anywhere?"

"You have missed it?"

"Yes. I thought I was wearing it. I say, I've never slept so long."

"Not since you were a baby. Do you know how long? Two days."

"Nonsense. I can't have."

"Yes, indeed. It is a long time. It is a pity because you missed our guests."

"Guests?"

"Why, yes. I have been quite gay while you were asleep. Three men from outside. Englishmen. It is a pity you missed them. A pity for them, too, as they particularly wished to see you. But what could I do? You were so sound asleep. They had come all the way to find you, so —I thought you would not mind—as you could not greet them yourself I gave them a little souvenir, your watch. They wanted something to take back to England where a reward is being offered for news of you. They were very pleased with it. And they took some photographs of the little cross I put up to commemorate your coming. They were pleased with that, too. They were very easily pleased. But I do not suppose they will visit us again, our life here is so retired . . . no pleasures except reading . . . I do not suppose we shall ever have visitors again . . . well, well, I will get you some medicine to make you feel better. Your head aches, does it not? . . . We will not have any Dickens today . . . but tomorrow, and the day after that, and the day after that. Let us read *Little Dorrit* again. There are passages in that book I can never hear without the temptation to weep."

V I I

ENGLISH GOTHIC—III

A LIGHT breeze in the dewy orchards; brilliant, cool sunshine over meadows and copses; the elms were all in bud in the avenue; everything was early that year for it had been a mild winter. High overhead among its gargoyles and crockets the clock chimed for the hour and solemnly struck fourteen. It was half past eight. The clock had been irregular lately. It was one of the things that Richard Last intended to see to when death duties were paid and silver foxes began to show a profit.

Molly Last bowled up the drive on her two-stroke motor-cycle; there was bran mash on her breeches and in her hair. She had been feeding the Angora rabbits.

On the gravel in front of the house the new memorial stood, shrouded in a flag. Molly propped the motor-cycle against the wall of the drawbridge and ran in to breakfast.

Life at Hetton was busier but simpler since Richard Last's succession. Ambrose remained but there were no longer any footmen; he and a boy and four women servants did the work of the house. Richard Last called them his "skeleton staff." When things were easier he would extend the household; meanwhile the dining hall and the library were added to the state apartments which were kept locked and shuttered; the family lived in the morning room, the smoking room and what had been Tony's study. Most of the kitchen quarters, too, were out of use; an up-to-date and economical range had been installed in one of the pantries.

The family all appeared downstairs by half past eight, except Agnes who took longer to dress and was usually some minutes late; Teddy and Molly had been out for an hour, she among the rabbits, he to the silver foxes. Teddy was twenty-two and lived at home. Peter was still at Oxford.

They breakfasted together in the morning room. Mrs. Last sat at one end of the table; her husband at the other; there was a constant traffic from hand to hand to and fro between them of cups, plate, honey jars and correspondence.

Mrs. Last said, "Molly, you have rabbit feed on your head again."

"Oh well, I shall have to tidy up anyway before the jamboree."

Mr. Last said, "*Jamboree*. Is nothing sacred to you children?"

Teddy said, "Another casualty at the stinkeries. That little vixen we bought from the people at Oakhampton got her brush bitten off during the night. Must have got it through the wire into the next cage. Tricky birds, foxes."

Agnes came next; she was a neat, circumspect child of twelve, with large, grave eyes behind her goggles. She kissed her father and mother and said, "I'm sorry if I'm late."

"*If* you're late . . ." said Mr. Last tolerantly.

"How long will the show last?" asked Teddy. "I've got to run over to Bayton and get some more rabbits for the foxes. Chivers says he's got about fifty waiting for me. We can't shoot enough here. Greedy little beggars."

"It will be all over by half past eleven. Mr. Tendril isn't going to preach a sermon. It's just as well really. He's got it into his head that cousin Tony died in Afghanistan."

"There's a letter here from Cousin Brenda. She's very sorry but she can't get down for the dedication."

"Oh."

There was a general silence.

"She says that Jock has a three line whip for this afternoon."

"Oh."

"She could have come without him," said Molly.

"She sends her love to us all and to Hetton."

There was another pause.

"Well I think it's a jolly good thing," said Molly. "*She* couldn't show much widowly grief. It didn't take *her* long to get hitched up again."

"*Molly.*"

"And you know you think the same."

"I will not allow you to talk like that about Cousin Brenda, what-ever we think. She had a perfect right to marry again and I hope she and Mr. Grant-Menzies are very happy."

"She was always jolly decent to us when she used to live here," said Agnes.

"Well I should hope so," said Teddy. "After all it's *our* place."

The day was still fine at eleven o'clock, though the wind had got up, fluttering the papers on which the order of the service was printed and once threatening to unveil the memorial prematurely. Several relatives were present, Lady St. Cloud, Aunt Frances, and the family of impoverished Lasts who had not profited by Tony's disappearance. All the household and estate servants were there, several tenants and most of the village; there were also a dozen or so neighbours, among them Colonel Inch—Richard Last and Teddy had hunted regularly that season with the Pigstanton. Mr. Tendril conducted the brief service in his clear, resonant voice that was clearly audible above the blustering wind. When he pulled the cord the flag fell away from the memorial without mishap.

It was a plain monolith of local stone, inscribed:

ANTHONY LAST OF HETTON
EXPLORER

Born at Hetton, 1902
Died in Brazil, 1934

When the local visitors had left and the relatives had gone into the house to be shown the new labour saving arrangements, Richard Last and Lady St. Cloud remained for a short time on the gravel.

"I'm glad we put that up," he said. "You know, I should have never thought of it, if it had not been for a Mrs. Beaver. She wrote to me as soon as the news of Tony's death was published. I didn't know her at the time. Of course we knew very few of Tony's friends."

"It was her suggestion?"

"Yes, she said that as one of Tony's closest friends she knew he would wish to have some monument at Hetton. She was most considerate—even offering to arrange with the contractors for it. Her own plans were more ambitious. She proposed that we should have the Chapel redecorated as a chantry. But I think this is what he would have preferred. The stone comes from one of our own quarries and was cut by the estate workmen."

"Yes, I think he would have preferred this," said Lady St. Cloud.

Teddy had chosen Galahad for his bedroom. He disengaged himself from the family and hurried up to change out of his dark clothes. Within ten minutes he was in his car driving to Chivers' farm. Before luncheon he was back with the rabbits. They were skinned and tied round the feet into four bundles.

"Coming to the stinkeries?" he asked Agnes.

"No, I'm looking after Cousin Frances. She got rather on mother's nerves through crabbing the new boiler."

The silver fox farm was behind the stables; a long double row of wire cages; they had wire floors covered with earth and cinders to prevent the animals digging their way out. They lived in pairs; some were moderately tame but it was unwise to rely upon them. Teddy and Ben Hacket—who helped with them—had been badly bitten more than once that winter. They ran up to the doors when they saw Teddy come with the rabbits. The vixen who had lost her brush seemed little the worse for her accident.

Teddy surveyed his charges with pride and affection. It was, by means of them that he hoped one day to restore Hetton to the glory that it had enjoyed in the days of his Cousin Tony.

AN AFTERWORD ON
"A HANDFUL OF DUST"

TO the new generation of readers this anthology tries to
offer many favorites of yesterday which have become lost
or overlooked in the shuffle. *A Handful of Dust* is a tragic
novel of today which, for extrinsic reasons that mere onlookers
can only guess at, dropped into the bookshops of this country as
unnoticed as a pebble falling into the sea. Place was made for it
in this collection in the belief that at least a distinguished minority of American readers would find it profoundly moving and of
engrossing interest.

Evelyn Waugh, who was born in 1903, is the youngest of the
three Waughs. The father, Arthur Waugh, long the head of
Messrs. Chapman and Hall in London, began his crowded career
as a bookman by serving as office-boy and factotum to Wolcott
Balestier, the astonishing young man from Vermont whose dazzling, comet-like passage through the English publishing world
had many consequences, including the marriage of Rudyard
Kipling and the writing of such works as *The Naulahka* and
Captains Courageous. In 1917 Arthur Waugh's elder son, Alec,
made something of a name for himself with the disturbing school-
story called *The Loom of Youth*. Later, a travel book of his called
Hot Countries reached a considerable American audience. His
brother Evelyn is to my notion the nearest thing to a genius
among the young writers who have arisen in post-war England.
For various reasons, his own school-story, *Decline and Fall,* his

beautiful and terrifying *Vile Bodies,* and his fantastic Abyssinian nightmare, *Black Mischief,* are here recommended. Like them and to a greater degree than any of them, *A Handful of Dust* is a heartsick book and here, too, the very gayety has the desperate jauntiness of an orchestra fiddling away for dear life on a sinking ship.

A. W.

ENVOY

In *Sophomores Abroad,* a forgotten sequel to *The Diary of a Freshman* which after sleeping for a third of a century came suddenly to life again—much as if the lost Dauphin were now to be discovered living quietly in Appleton, Wisconsin—our old friend Flandrau describes Granny Wood packing for his first trip to Europe. On the last morning the milk-carts were already rattling through the damp, quiet streets of Cambridge before he faced the task of getting his hillock of possessions into one steamer trunk. Rather late it dawned on him that in the nine days of the voyage he could scarcely use all the duffel he had thought of as indispensable. Apparently he had been allowing for shipwreck and protracted sojourns on desert islands. At least, when the trunk was stuffed to bursting, there were still unpacked enough things to fill two more.

The compiler of an anthology will be no stranger to his desperation. This paragraph was written the day before this book went to press. And on the floor—left out in the delirium of packing—were such essentials as *All Kneeling* by Anne Parrish, *The History of Mr. Polly* by H. G. Wells, and *Gentle Julia* by Booth Tarkington. General consternation! And too late to do anything about it, unless you as the reader and the undersigned as the editor should work together so congenially that, instead of being ignominiously left down, we might one day be promoted to the Second Reader.

ALEXANDER WOOLLCOTT

"We shall find them all here in the morning," said Dr. Messinger. "They're an odd bunch."

All round them the voices of the bush whistled and croaked, changing with the hours as the night wore on to morning.

Dawn broke in London, clear and sweet, dove-grey and honey, with promise of good weather; the lamps in the streets paled and disappeared; the empty streets ran with water, and the rising sun caught it as it bubbled round the hydrants; the men in overalls swung the nozzles of their hoses from side to side and the water jetted and cascaded in a sparkle of light.

"Let's have the window open," said Brenda. "It's stuffy in here."

The waiter drew back the curtains, opened the windows.

"It's quite light," she added.

"After five. Oughtn't we to go to bed."

"Yes."

"Only another week and then all the parties will be over," said Beaver.

"Yes."

"Well let's go."

"All right. Can you pay? I just haven't any money."

They had come on after the party, for breakfast at a club Daisy had opened. Beaver paid for the kippers and tea. "Eight shillings," he said. "How does Daisy expect to make a success of the place when she charges prices like that?"

"It does seem a lot . . . So you really *are* going to America?"

"I must. Mother has taken the tickets."

"Nothing I've said tonight makes any difference?"

"Darling, don't go on. We've been through all that. You know it's the only thing that *can* happen. Why spoil the last week?"

"You *have* enjoyed the summer, haven't you?"

"Of course . . . well, shall we go?"

"Yes. You needn't bother to see me home."

"Sure you don't mind? It *is* miles out of the way and it's late."

"There's no knowing what I mind."

"Brenda, darling, for heaven's sake . . . It isn't like you to go on like this."

"I never was one for making myself expensive."

The Indians returned during the night, while Tony and Dr. Messinger were asleep; without a word spoken the little people crept out of hiding; the women had removed their clothes and left them at a distance so that no twig should betray their movements; their naked bodies moved soundlessly through the undergrowth; the glowing embers of the fire and the storm lantern twenty yards away were their only light; there was no moon. They collected their wicker baskets and their rations of farine, their bows and arrows, the gun and their broad-bladed knives; they rolled up their hammocks into compact cylinders. They took nothing with them that was not theirs. Then they crept back through the shadows, into the darkness.

When Tony and Dr. Messinger awoke it was clear to them what had happened.

"The situation is grave," said Dr. Messinger. "But not desperate."

4

For four days Tony and Dr. Messinger paddled down-stream. They sat, balancing themselves precariously, at the two ends of the canoe; between them they had piled the most essential of their stores; the remainder, with the other canoes, had been left at the camp, to be called for when they had recruited help from the Pie-wies. Even the minimum which Dr. Messinger had selected overweighted the craft so that it was dangerously low; and movement brought the water to the lip of the gunwale and threatened disaster; it was heavy to steer and they made slow progress, contenting themselves for the most part, with keeping end on, and drifting with the current.

Twice they came to the stretches of cataract, and here they drew in to the bank, unloaded, and waded beside the boat, sometimes plunging waist deep, sometimes clambering over the rocks, guiding it by hand until they reached clear water again. Then they tied up to the bank and carried their cargo down to it through the bush. For the rest of the way the river was broad and smooth; a dark surface which reflected in fine detail the walls of forest on either side, towering up from the undergrowth to their flowering crown a hundred or more feet above them. Sometimes they came to a stretch of water scattered with fallen petals and floated among them, moving scarcely less slowly than they, as though resting in a blossoming meadow. At night they spread their tarpaulin on stretches of dry beach, and hung their hammocks in the bush. Only the cabouri fly and rare, immobile alligators menaced the peace of their days.

They kept a constant scrutiny of the banks but saw no sign of human life.

Then Tony developed fever. It came on him quite suddenly, during the fourth afternoon. At their midday halt he was in complete health and had shot a small deer that came down to drink on the opposite bank; an hour later he was shivering so violently that he had to lay down his paddle; his head was flaming with heat, his body and limbs frigid; by sunset he was slightly delirious.

Dr. Messinger took his temperature and found that it was a hundred and four degrees, Fahrenheit. He gave him twenty-five grains of quinine and lit a fire so close to his hammock that by morning it was singed and blacked with smoke. He told Tony to keep wrapped up in his blanket, but at intervals throughout that night he woke from sleep to find himself running with sweat; he was consumed with thirst and drank mug after mug of river water. Neither that evening nor next morning was he able to eat anything.

But next morning his temperature was down again. He felt weak and exhausted but he was able to keep steady in his place and paddle a little.

"It was just a passing attack, wasn't it?" he said. "I shall be perfectly fit tomorrow, shan't I?"

"I hope so," said Dr. Messinger.

At midday Tony drank some cocoa and ate a cupful of rice. "I feel grand," he said.

"Good."

That night the fever came on again. They were camping on a sand bank. Dr. Messinger heated stones and put them under Tony's feet and in the small of his back. He was awake most of the night fuelling the fire and refilling Tony's mug with water. At dawn Tony slept for an hour and woke feeling slightly better; he was taking frequent doses of quinine and his ears were filled with a muffled sound as though he were holding those shells to them in which, he had been told in childhood, one could hear the beat of the sea.

"We've got to go on," said Dr. Messinger. "We can't be far from a village now."

"I feel awful. Wouldn't it be better to wait a day till I am perfectly fit again."

"It's no good waiting. We've got to get on. D'you think you can manage to get into the canoe?"

Dr. Messinger knew that Tony was in for a long bout.

For the first few hours of that day Tony lay limp in the bows. They had shifted the stores so that he could lie full length. Then the fever came on again and his teeth chattered. He sat up and crouched with his head in his knees, shaking all over; only his forehead and cheeks were burning hot under the noon sun. There was still no sign of a village.

It was late in the afternoon when he first saw Brenda. For some time he had been staring intently at the odd shape amidships where the stores had been piled; then he realized that it was a human being.

"So the Indians came back?" he said.

"Yes."

"I knew they would. Silly of them to be scared by a toy. I suppose the others are following."

"Yes, I expect so. Try and sit still."

"Damned fool, being frightened of a toy," Tony said derisively to the woman amidships. Then he saw that it was Brenda. "I'm sorry," he said. "I didn't see it was you. *You* wouldn't be frightened of a toy."

But she did not answer him. She sat as she used often to sit when but was afraid, and while he hesitated old age came, and then Death, and found him grasping a box-iron.

I hurried home with the mouthful, but neighbours had dropped in, and this was for her ears only, so I drew her to the stair, and said imperiously,

> "What can I do to be for ever known,
> And make the age to come my own?"

It was an odd request for which to draw her from a tea-table, and she must have been surprised, but I think she did not laugh, and in after years she would repeat the lines fondly, with a flush on her soft face. "That is the kind you would like to be yourself!" we would say in jest to her, and she would reply almost passionately, "No, but I would be windy of being his mother." It is possible that she could have been his mother had that other son lived, he might have managed it from sheer love of her, but for my part I can smile at one of those two figures on the stair now, having long given up the dream of being for ever known, and seeing myself more akin to my friend, the tailor, for as he was found at the end on his board, so I hope shall I be found at my handloom, doing honestly the work that suits me best. Who shall know so well as I that it is but a handloom compared to the great guns that reverberate through the age to come? But she who stood with me on the stair that day was a very simple woman, accustomed all her life to making the most of small things, and I weaved sufficiently well to please her, which has been my only steadfast ambition since I was a little boy.

Not less than mine became her desire that I should have my way—but, ah, the iron seats in that Park of horrible repute, and that bare room at the top of many flights of stairs! While I was away at college she drained all available libraries for books about those who go to London to live by the pen, and they all told the same shuddering tale. London, which she never saw, was to her a monster that licked up country youths as they stepped from the train; there were the garrets in which they sat abject, and the park seats where they passed the night. Those park seats were the monster's glaring eyes to her, and as

him; he was one of the most engrossing of mortals to her, she admired him prodigiously, pictured him at the head of his caravan, now attacked by savages, now by wild beasts, and adored him for the uneasy hours he gave her, but she was also afraid that he wanted to take me with him, and then she thought he should be put down by law. Explorers' mothers also interested her very much; the books might tell her nothing about them, but she could create them for herself and wring her hands in sympathy with them when they had got no news of him for six months. Yet there were times when she grudged him to them—as the day when he returned victorious. Then what was before her eyes was not the son coming marching home again but an old woman peering for him round the window curtain and trying not to look uplifted. The newspaper reports would be about the son, but my mother's comment was "She's a proud woman this night."

We read many books together when I was a boy, *Robinson Crusoe* being the first (and the second), and the *Arabian Nights* should have been the next, for we got it out of the library (a penny for three days), but on discovering that they were nights when we had paid for knights we sent that volume packing, and I have curled my lips at it ever since. *The Pilgrim's Progress* we had in the house (it was as common a possession as a dresser-head), and so enamoured of it was I that I turned our garden into sloughs of Despond, with pea-sticks to represent Christian on his travels and a buffet-stool for his burden, but when I dragged my mother out to see my handiwork she was scared, and I felt for days, with a certain elation, that I had been a dark character. Besides reading every book we could hire or borrow I also bought one now and again, and while buying (it was the occupation of weeks) I read, standing at the counter, most of the other books in the shop, which is perhaps the most exquisite way of reading. And I took in a magazine called *Sunshine,* the most delicious periodical, I am sure, of any day. It cost a halfpenny or a penny a month, and always, as I fondly remember, had a continued tale about the dearest girl, who sold water-cress, which is a dainty not grown and I suppose never seen in my native town. This romantic little creature took such hold of my imagination that I cannot eat water-cress even now without emotion. I lay in bed wondering what she would be up to in the next number; I have lost trout because when they nibbled my mind was wandering with her; my early life was embittered by her not arriving regularly on the first of the month. I know not whether it was owing to her loitering on the way one month to an extent flesh and blood could not bear, or because we had exhausted the penny library, but on a day I conceived a glorious idea, or it was put into my head by my mother, then desirous of making progress with her new clouty hearth-rug. The notion was nothing short of this, why should I not write the tales myself? I did write them—in the garret—but they by no means helped her to get on with her work, for when I finished a chapter I bounded downstairs to read it to her, and so short were the chapters, so ready was the pen, that I was back with new manuscript before another clout had been added to the rug. Authorship seemed, like her bannock-baking, to consist of running between two points. They were all tales of adventure (happiest is he who writes of adventure), no characters were allowed within if I knew their like in the flesh, the scene lay in unknown parts, desert islands, enchanted gardens, with knights (none of your nights) on black chargers, and round the first corner a lady selling water-cress.

At twelve or thereabout I put the literary calling to bed for a time, having gone to a school where cricket and football were more esteemed, but during the year before I went to the university, it woke up and I wrote great part of a three-volume novel. The publisher replied that the sum for which he would print it was a hundred and—however, that was not the important point (I had sixpence): where he stabbed us both was in writing that he considered me a "clever lady." I replied stiffly that I was a gentleman, and since then I have kept that manuscript concealed. I looked through it lately, and, oh, but it is dull. I defy anyone to read it.

The malignancy of publishers, however, could not turn me back. From the day on which I first tasted blood in the garret my mind was made up; there could be no hum-dreadful-drum profession for me; literature was my game. It was not highly thought of by those who wished me well. I remember being asked by two maiden ladies, about

the time I left the university, what I was to be, and whe brazenly, "An author," they flung up their hands, and one reproachfully, "And you an M.A.!" My mother's views at not dissimilar; for long she took mine jestingly as something grow out of, and afterwards they hurt her so that I tried them up. To be a minister—that she thought was among the prospects, but she was a very ambitious woman, and sometime would add, half scared at her appetite, that there were mini who had become professors, "but it was not canny to think of s things."

I had one person only on my side, an old tailor, one of the fulle men I have known, and quite the best talker. He was a bachelor (he told me all that is to be known about woman), a lean man, pallid of face, his legs drawn up when he walked as if he was ever carrying something in his lap; his walks were of the shortest, from the tea-pot on the hob to the board on which he stitched, from the board to the hob, and so to bed. He might have gone out had the idea struck him, but in the years I knew him, the last of his brave life, I think he was only in the open twice, when he "flitted"—changed his room for another hard by. I did not see him make these journeys, but I seem to see him now, and he is somewhat dizzy in the odd atmosphere; in one hand he carries a box-iron, he raises the other, wondering what this is on his head, it is a hat; a faint smell of singed cloth goes by with him. This man had heard of my set of photographs of the poets and asked for a sight of them, which led to our first meeting. I remember how he spread them out on his board, and after looking long at them, turned his gaze on me and said solemnly,

> "What can I do to be for ever known,
> And make the age to come my own?"

These lines of Cowley were new to me, but the sentiment was not new, and I marvelled how the old tailor could see through me so well. So it was strange to me to discover presently that he had not been thinking of me at all, but of his own young days, when that couplet sang in his head, and he, too, had thirsted to set off for Grub Street,

I go by them now she is nearer to me than when I am in any other part of London. I daresay that when night comes, this Hyde Park which is so gay by day, is haunted by the ghosts of many mothers, who run, wild-eyed, from seat to seat, looking for their sons.

But if we could dodge those dreary seats she longed to see me try my luck, and I sought to exclude them from the picture by drawing maps of London with Hyde Park left out. London was as strange to me as to her, but long before I was shot upon it I knew it by maps, and drew them more accurately than I could draw them now. Many a time she and I took our jaunt together through the map, and were most gleeful, popping into telegraph offices to wire my father and sister that we should not be home till late, winking to my books in lordly shop-windows, lunching at restaurants (and remembering not to call it dinner), saying, "How do?" to Mr. Alfred Tennyson when we passed him in Regent Street, calling at publishers' offices for a cheque, when "Will you take care of it, or shall I?" I asked gaily, and she would be certain to reply, "I'm thinking we'd better take it to the bank and get the money," for she always felt surer of money than of cheques, so to the bank we went ("Two tens, and the rest in gold"), and thence straightway (by cab) to the place where you buy sealskin coats for middling old ladies. But ere the laugh was done the Park would come through the map like a blot.

"If you could only be sure of as much as would keep body and soul together," my mother would say with a sigh.

"With something over, mother, to send to you."

"You couldna expect that at the start."

The wench I should have been courting now was journalism, that grisette of literature who has a smile and a hand for all beginners, welcoming them at the threshold, teaching them so much that is worth knowing, introducing them to the other lady whom they have worshipped from afar, showing them even how to woo her, and then bidding them a bright God-speed—he were an ingrate who, having had her joyous companionship, no longer flings her a kiss as they pass. But though she bears no ill-will when she is jilted, you must serve faithfully while you are hers, and you must seek her out and make much of her, and, until you can rely on her good-nature (note this), not a word about the other lady. When at last she took me in I grew so fond of her that I called her by the other's name, and even now I think at times that there was more fun in the little sister, but I began by wooing her with contributions that were all misfits. In an old book I find columns of notes about works projected at this time, nearly all to consist of essays on deeply uninteresting subjects; the lightest was to be a volume on the older satirists, beginning with Skelton and Tom Nash—the half of that manuscript still lies in a dusty chest—the only story was about Mary Queen of Scots, who was also the subject of many unwritten papers. Queen Mary seems to have been luring me to my undoing ever since I saw Holyrood, and I have a horrid fear that I may write that novel yet. That anything could be written about my native place never struck me. We had read somewhere that a novelist is better equipped than most of his trade if he knows himself and one woman, and my mother said, "You know yourself, for everybody must know himself" (there never was a woman who knew less about herself than she), and she would add dolefully, "But I doubt I'm the only woman you know well."

"Then I must make you my heroine," I said lightly.

"A gey auld-farrant-like heroine!" she said, and we both laughed at the notion—so little did we read the future.

Thus it is obvious what were my qualifications when I was rashly engaged as a leader-writer (it was my sister who saw the advertisement) on an English provincial paper. At the moment I was as uplifted as the others, for the chance had come at last, with what we all regarded as a prodigious salary, but I was wanted in the beginning of the week, and it suddenly struck me that the leaders were the one thing I had always skipped. Leaders! How were they written? what were they about? My mother was already sitting triumphant among my socks, and I durst not let her see me quaking. I retired to ponder, and presently she came to me with the daily paper. Which were the leaders? she wanted to know, so evidently I could get no help from her. Had she any more newspapers? I asked, and after rummaging, she produced a few with which her boxes had been lined. Others, very dusty, came from beneath carpets, and lastly a sooty bundle was dragged down the chimney. Surrounded by these I sat down, and studied how to become a journalist.

I V

AN EDITOR

A DEVOUT lady, to whom some friend had presented one of my books, used to say when asked how she was getting on with it, "Sal, it's dreary, weary, uphill work, but I've wrastled through with tougher jobs in my time, and, please God, I'll wrastle through with this one." It was in this spirit I fear, though she never told me so, that my mother wrestled for the next year or more with my leaders, and indeed I was always genuinely sorry for the people I saw reading them. In my spare hours I was trying journalism of another kind and sending it to London, but nearly eighteen months elapsed before there came to me, as unlooked for as a telegram, the thought that there was something quaint about my native place. A boy who found that a knife had been put into his pocket in the night could not have been more surprised. A few days afterwards I sent my mother a London evening paper with an article entitled "An Auld Licht Community," and they told me that when she saw the heading she laughed, because there was something droll to her in the sight of the words Auld Licht in print. For her, as for me, that newspaper was soon to have the face of a friend. To this day I never pass its placards in the street without shaking it by the hand, and she used to sew its pages together as lovingly as though they were a child's frock; but let the truth be told, when she read that first article she became alarmed, and fearing the talk of the town, hid the paper from all eyes. For some time afterwards, while I proudly pictured her showing this and similar articles to all who felt an interest in me, she was really concealing them fearfully in a bandbox on the garret stair. And she wanted to know by return of post whether I was paid for these articles just as I was paid for real articles; when she heard that I was paid better, she laughed again and had them out of the bandbox for re-reading, and it cannot be denied that she thought the London editor a fine fellow but slightly soft.

When I sent off that first sketch I thought I had exhausted the subject, but our editor wrote that he would like something more of the same, so I sent him a marriage, and he took it, and then I tried him with a funeral, and he took it, and really it began to look as if we had him. Now my mother might have been discovered, in answer to certain excited letters, flinging the bundle of undarned socks from her lap, and "going in for literature"; she was racking her brains, by request, for memories I might convert into articles, and they came to me in letters which she dictated to my sisters. How well I could hear her saying between the lines: "But the editor-man will never stand that, it's perfect blethers"—"By this post it must go, I tell you; we must take the editor when he's hungry—we canna be blamed for it, can we? he prints them of his free will, so the wite is his"—"But I'm near terrified. —If London folk reads them we're done for." And I was sounded as to the advisability of sending him a present of a lippie of short-bread, which was to be her crafty way of getting round him. By this time, though my mother and I were hundreds of miles apart, you may picture us waving our hands to each other across country, and shouting "Hurrah!" You may also picture the editor in his office thinking he was behaving like a shrewd man of business, and unconscious that up in the north there was an elderly lady chuckling so much at him that she could scarcely scrape the potatoes.

I was now able to see my mother again, and the park seats no longer loomed so prominent in our map of London. Still, there they were, and it was with an effort that she summoned up courage to let me go. She feared changes, and who could tell that the editor would continue to be kind? Perhaps when he saw me——

She seemed to be very much afraid of his seeing me, and this, I would point out, was a reflection on my appearance or my manner.

No, what she meant was that I looked so young, and—and that would take him aback, for had I not written as an aged man?

"But he knows my age, mother."

"I'm glad of that, but maybe he wouldna like you when he saw you."

"Oh, it is my manner, then!"

"I dinna say that, but——"

Here my sister would break in: "The short and the long of it is just this, she thinks nobody has such manners as herself. Can you deny it, you vain woman?"

My mother would deny it vigorously.

"You stand there," my sister would say with affected scorn, "and tell me you don't think you could get the better of that man quicker than any of us?"

"Sal, I'm thinking I could manage him," says my mother, with a chuckle.

"How would you set about it?"

Then my mother would begin to laugh. "I would find out first if he had a family, and then I would say they were the finest family in London."

"Yes, that is just what you would do, you cunning woman! But if he has no family?"

"I would say what great men editors are!"

"He would see through you."

"Not he!"

"You don't understand that what imposes on common folk would never hoodwink an editor."

"That's where you are wrong. Gentle or simple, stupid or clever, the men are all alike in the hands of a woman that flatters them."

"Ah, I'm sure there are better ways of getting round an editor than that."

"I daresay there are," my mother would say with conviction, "but if you try that plan you will never need to try another."

"How artful you are, mother—you with your soft face! Do you not think shame?"

"Pooh!" says my mother brazenly.

"I can see the reason why you are so popular with men."

"Ay, you can see it, but they never will."

"Well, how would you dress yourself if you were going to that editor's office?"

"Of course I would wear my silk and my Sabbath bonnet."

"It is you who are shortsighted now, mother. I tell you, you would manage him better if you just put on your old grey shawl and one of your bonny white mutches, and went in half smiling and half timid and said, 'I am the mother of him that writes about the Auld Lichts, and I want you to promise that he will never have to sleep in the open air.'"

But my mother would shake her head at this, and reply almost hotly, "I tell you if I ever go into that man's office, I go in silk."

I wrote and asked the editor if I should come to London, and he said No, so I went, laden with charges from my mother to walk in the middle of the street (they jump out on you as you are turning a corner), never to venture forth after sunset, and always to lock up everything (I who could never lock up anything, except my heart in company). Thanks to this editor, for the others would have nothing to say to me though I battered on all their doors, she was soon able to sleep at nights without the dread that I should be waking presently with the iron-work of certain seats figured on my person, and what relieved her very much was that I had begun to write as if Auld Lichts were not the only people I knew of. So long as I confined myself to them she had a haunting fear that, even though the editor remained blind to his best interests, something would one day go crack within me (as the mainspring of a watch breaks) and my pen refuse to write for evermore. "Ay, I like the article brawly," she would say timidly, "but I'm doubting it's the last—I always have a sort of terror the new one may be the last," and if many days elapsed before the arrival of another article her face would say mournfully, "The blow has fallen—he can think of nothing more to write about." If I ever shared her fears I never told her so, and the articles that were not Scotch grew in number until there were hundreds of them, all carefully preserved by her: they were the only thing in the house that, having served one purpose, she did not convert into something else, yet they could give her uneasy moments. This was because I nearly always assumed a character when I wrote. I must be a country squire, or an undergraduate, or a butler, or a member of the House of Lords, or a dowager, or a lady called Sweet Seventeen, or an engineer in India, else was my pen clogged, and though this gave my mother certain fearful joys, causing her to laugh unexpectedly (so far as my articles were concerned she nearly always laughed in the wrong place), it also scared her. Much to her amusement the editor continued to prefer the Auld Licht papers, however, as was proved (to those who knew him) by his way of thinking that the others would pass as they were, while he sent these back and asked me to make them better. Here again she came to my aid. I had said that the row of stockings were hung on a string by the fire, which was a recollection of my own, but she could tell me whether they were hung upside down. She became quite skilful at sending or giving me (for now I could be with her half the year) the right details, but still she smiled at the editor, and in her gay moods she would say, "I was fifteen when I got my first pair of elastic-sided boots. Tell him my charge for this important news is two pounds ten."

"Ay, but though we're doing well, it's no the same as if they were a book with your name on it." So the ambitious woman would say with a sigh, and I did my best to turn the Auld Licht sketches into a book with my name on it. Then perhaps we understood most fully how good a friend our editor had been, for just as I had been able to find no well-known magazine—and I think I tried all—which would print any article or story about the poor of my native land, so now the publishers, Scotch and English, refused to accept the book as a gift. I was willing to present it to them, but they would have it in no guise; there seemed to be a blight on everything that was Scotch. I daresay we sighed, but never were collaborators more prepared for rejection, and though my mother might look wistfully at the scorned manuscript at times and murmur, "You poor cold little crittur shut away in a drawer, are you dead or just sleeping?" she had still her editor to say grace over. And at last publishers, sufficiently daring and far more than sufficiently generous, were found for us by a dear friend, who made one woman very "uplifted." He also was an editor, and had as large a part in making me a writer of books as the other in determining what the books should be about.

Now that I was an author I must get into a club. But you should have heard my mother on clubs! She knew of none save those to which you subscribe a pittance weekly in anticipation of rainy days, and the London clubs were her scorn. Often I heard her on them—she raised her voice to make me hear, whichever room I might be in, and it was when she was sarcastic that I skulked the most: "Thirty pounds is what he will have to pay the first year, and ten pounds a year after that. You think it's a lot o' siller? Oh, no, you're mista'en—it's nothing ava. For the third part of thirty pounds you could rent a four-roomed house, but what is a four-roomed house, what is thirty pounds, compared to the glory of being a member of a club! Where does the glory come in? Sal, you needna ask me, I'm just a doited auld stock that never set foot in a club, so it's little I ken about glory. But I may tell you if you bide in London and canna become member of a club, the best you can do is to tie a rope round your neck and slip out of the world. What use are they? Oh, they're terrible useful. You see it doesna do for a man in London to eat his dinner in his lodgings. Other men shake their heads at him. He maun away to his club if he is to be respected. Does he get good dinners at the club? Oh, they cow! You get no common beef at clubs; there is a manzy of different things all sauced up to be unlike themsels. Even the potatoes daurna look like potatoes. If the food in a club looks like what it is, the members run about, flinging up their hands and crying, 'Woe is me!' Then this is another thing, you get your letters sent to the club instead of to your lodgings. You see you would get them sooner at your lodgings, and you may have to trudge weary miles to the club for them, but that's a great advantage, and cheap at thirty pounds, is it no? I wonder they can do it at the price."

My wisest policy was to remain downstairs when these withering blasts were blowing, but probably I went up in self-defence.

"I never saw you so pugnacious before, mother."

"Oh," she would reply promptly, "you canna expect me to be sharp in the uptake when I am no a member of a club."

"But the difficulty is in becoming a member. They are very particular about whom they elect, and I daresay I shall not get in."

"Well, I'm but a poor crittur (not being member of a club), but I think I can tell you to make your mind easy on that head. You'll get in, I'se uphaud—and your thirty pounds will get in, too."

"If I get in it will be because the editor is supporting me."

"It's the first ill thing I ever heard of him."

"You don't think he is to get any of the thirty pounds, do you?"

" 'Deed if I did I should be better pleased, for he has been a good friend to us, but what maddens me is that every penny of it should go to those bare-faced scoundrels."

"What bare-faced scoundrels?"

"Them that have the club."

"But all the members have the club between them."

"Havers! I'm no to be catched with chaff."

"But don't you believe me?"

"I believe they've filled your head with their stories till you swallow whatever they tell you. If the place belongs to the members, why do they have to pay thirty pounds?"

"To keep it going."

"They dinna have to pay for their dinners, then?"

"Oh, yes, they have to pay extra for dinner."

"And a gey black price, I'm thinking."

"Well, five or six shillings."

"Is that all? Losh, it's nothing. I wonder they dinna raise the price."

Nevertheless my mother was of a sex that scorned prejudice, and, dropping sarcasm, she would at times cross-examine me as if her mind was not yet made up. "Tell me this, if you were to fall ill, would you be paid a weekly allowance out of the club?"

No, it was not that kind of club.

"I see. Well, I am just trying to find out what kind of club it is. Do you get anything out of it for accidents?"

Not a penny.

"Anything at New Year's time?"

Not so much as a goose.

"Is there any one mortal thing you get free out of that club?"

There was not one mortal thing.

"And thirty pounds is what you pay for this?"

If the committee elected me.

"How many are in the committee?"

About a dozen I thought.

"A dozen! Ay, ay, that makes two pound ten apiece."

When I was elected I thought it wisdom to send my sister upstairs with the news. My mother was ironing, and made no comment, unless with the iron, which I could hear rattling more violently in its box. Presently I heard her laughing—at me undoubtedly, but she had recovered control over her face before she came downstairs to congratulate me sarcastically. This was grand news, she said without a twinkle, and I must write and thank the committee, the noble critturs. I saw behind her mask, and maintained a dignified silence, but she would have another shot at me. "And tell them," she said from the door, "you were doubtful of being elected, but your auld mother had aye a mighty confidence they would snick you in." I heard her laughing softly as she went up the stair, but though I had provided her with a joke I knew she was burning to tell the committee what she thought of them.

Money, you see, meant so much to her, though even at her poorest she was the most cheerful giver. In the old days, when the article arrived, she did not read it at once, she first counted the lines to discover what we should get for it—she and the daughter who was so dear to her had calculated the payment per line, and I remember once overhearing a discussion between them about whether that sub-title meant another sixpence. Yes, she knew the value of money; she had always in the end got the things she wanted, but now she could get them more easily, and it turned her simple life into a fairy tale. So often in those days she went down suddenly upon her knees; we would come upon her thus, and go away noiselessly. After her death I found that she had preserved in a little box, with a photograph of me as a child, the envelopes which had contained my first cheques. There was a little ribbon round them.

V

A DAY OF HER LIFE

I SHOULD like to call back a day of her life as it was at this time, when her spirit was as bright as ever and her hand as eager, but she was no longer able to do much work. It should not be difficult, for she repeated herself from day to day and yet did it with a quaint unreasonableness that was ever yielding fresh delight. Our love for her was such that we could easily tell what she would do in given circumstances, but she had always a new way of doing it.

Well, with break of day she wakes and sits up in bed and is standing in the middle of the room. So nimble was she in the mornings (one of our troubles with her) that these three actions must be considered as one; she is on the floor before you have time to count them. She has strict orders not to rise until her fire is lit, and having broken them there is a demure elation on her face. The question is what to do before she is caught and hurried to bed again. Her fingers are tingling to prepare the breakfast; she would dearly love to black-lead the grate, but that might rouse her daughter from whose side she has slipped so cunningly. She catches sight of the screen at the foot of the bed, and immediately her soft face becomes very determined. To guard her from draughts the screen had been brought here from the lordly east room, where it was of no use whatever. But in her opinion it was too beautiful for use; it belonged to the east room, where she could take pleasant peeps at it; she had objected to its removal, even become low-spirited. Now is her opportunity. The screen is an unwieldy thing, but still as a mouse she carries it, and they are well under way when it strikes against the gas-bracket in the passage. Next moment a reproachful hand arrests her. She is challenged with being out of bed, she denies it—standing in the passage. Meekly or stubbornly she returns to bed, and it is no satisfaction to you that you can say, "Well, well, of all the women!" and so on, or "Surely you knew that the screen was brought here to protect you," for she will reply scornfully, "Who was touching the screen?"

By this time I have awakened (I am through the wall) and join them anxiously: so often has my mother been taken ill in the night that the slightest sound from her room rouses the house. She is in bed again, looking as if she had never been out of it, but I know her and listen sternly to the tale of her misdoings. She is not contrite. Yes, maybe she did promise not to venture forth on the cold floors of daybreak, but she had risen for a moment only, and we just t'neaded her with our talk about draughts—there were no such things as draughts in her young days—and it is more than she can do (here she again attempts to rise but we hold her down) to lie there and watch that beautiful screen being spoilt. I reply that the beauty of the screen has ever been its miserable defect: ho, there! for a knife with which to spoil its beauty and make the bedroom its fitting home. As there is no knife handy, my foot will do; I raise my foot, and then—she sees that it is bare, she cries to me excitedly to go back to bed lest I catch cold. For though, ever careless of herself, she will wander the house un-shod, and tell us not to talk havers when we chide her, the sight of one of us similarly negligent rouses her anxiety at once. She is willing now to sign any vow if only I will take my bare feet back to bed, but probably she is soon after me in hers to make sure that I am nicely covered up.

It is scarcely six o'clock, and we have all promised to sleep for another hour, but in ten minutes she is sure that eight has struck (house disgraced), or that if it has not, something is wrong with the clock. Next moment she is captured on her way downstairs to wind up the clock. So evidently we must be up and doing, and as we have no servant, my sister disappears into the kitchen, having first asked me to see that "that woman" lies still, and "that woman" calls out that she always does lie still, so what are we blethering about?

She is up now, and dressed in her thick maroon wrapper; over her shoulders (lest she should stray despite our watchfulness) is a shawl, not placed there by her own hands, and on her head a delicious mutch. O, that I could sing the pæan of the white mutch (and the dirge of the elaborate black cap) from the day when she called witchcraft to her aid and made it out of snow-flakes, and the dear worn hands that washed it tenderly in a basin, and the starching of it, and the finger-iron for its exquisite frills that looked like curls of sugar, and the sweet bands with which it tied beneath the chin! The honoured snowy mutch, how I love to see it smiling to me from the doors and windows of the poor; it is always smiling—sometimes may be a wavering wistful smile, as if a tear-drop lay hidden among the frills. A hundred times I have taken the characterless cap from my mother's head and put the mutch in its place and tied the bands beneath her chin, while she protested but was well pleased. For in her heart she knew what suited her best and would admit it, beaming, when I put a mirror into her hands and told her to look; but nevertheless the cap cost no less than so and so, whereas— Was that a knock at the door? She is gone, to put on her cap!

She begins the day by the fireside with the New Testament in her hands, an old volume with its loose pages beautifully refixed, and its covers sewn and resewn by her, so that you would say it can never fall to pieces. It is mine now, and to me the black threads with which she stitched it are as part of the contents. Other books she read in the ordinary manner, but this one differently, her lips moving with each word as if she were reading aloud, and her face very solemn. The Testament lies open on her lap long after she has ceased to read, and the expression of her face has not changed.

I have seen her reading other books early in the day but never without a guilty look on her face, for she thought reading was scarce respectable until night had come. She spends the forenoon in what she calls doing nothing, which may consist in stitching so hard that you would swear she was an over-worked steamstress at it for her life, or you will find her on a table with nails in her mouth, and anon she has to be chased from the garret (she has suddenly decided to change her curtains), or she is under the bed searching for band-boxes and asking sternly where we have put that bonnet. On the whole she is behaving in a most exemplary way today (not once have we caught her trying to go out into the washing-house), and we compliment her at dinner time, partly because she deserves it, and partly to make her think herself so good that she will eat something, just to maintain her new character. I question whether one hour of all her life was given to thoughts of food; in her great days to eat seemed to her to be waste of time, and afterwards she only ate to boast of it, as something she had done to please us. She seldom remembered whether she had dined, but always presumed she had, and while she was telling me in all good faith what the meal consisted of, it might be brought in. When in London I had to hear daily what she was eating, and perhaps she had refused all dishes until they produced the pen and ink. These were flourished before her, and then she would say with a sigh, "Tell him I am to eat an egg." But they were not so easily deceived; they waited, pen in hand, until the egg was eaten. She never "went for a walk" in her life. Many long trudges she had as a girl when she carried her father's dinner in a flagon to the country place where he was at work, but to walk with no end save the good of your health seemed a very droll proceeding to her. In her young days, she was positive, no one had ever gone for a walk, and she never lost the belief that it was an absurdity introduced by a new generation with too much time on their hands. That they enjoyed it she could not believe; it was merely a form of showing off, and as they passed her window she would remark to herself with blasting satire, "Ay, Jeames, are you off for your walk?" and add fervently, "Rather you than me!" I was one of those who walked, and though she smiled, and might drop a sarcastic word when she saw me putting on my boots, it was she who had heated them in preparation for my going. The arrangement between us was that she should lie down until my return, and to ensure its being carried out I saw her in bed before I started, but with the bang of the door she would be at the window to watch me go: there is one spot on the road where a thousand times I have turned to wave my stick to her, while she nodded and smiled and kissed her hand to me. That kissing of the hand was the one English custom she had learned.

In an hour or so I return, and perhaps find her in bed, according to promise, but still I am suspicious. The way to her detection is circuitous.